# ALGEBRA TWO

Mervin L. Keedy

Marvin L. Bittinger

Stanley A. Smith

Addison-Wesley Publishing Company

Menlo Park, California     Reading, Massachusetts     London

Amsterdam     Don Mills, Ontario     Sydney

## AUTHORS

**Mervin L. Keedy** is Professor of Mathematics at Purdue University. He received his Ph.D. degree at the University of Nebraska, and formerly taught at the University of Maryland. He has also taught mathematics and science in junior and senior high schools. Professor Keedy is the author of many books on mathematics, including *A Modern Introduction to Basic Mathematics* (Addison-Wesley, 1969).

**Marvin L. Bittinger** is Professor of Mathematics Education at Indiana University-Purdue University at Indianapolis. He earned his Ph.D. degree at Purdue University. He is the author of *Logic and Proof* (Addison-Wesley, 1970), and is co-author with Professor Keedy of several college textbooks published by Addison-Wesley.

**Stanley A. Smith** is Coordinator, Office of Mathematics (K-12), for Baltimore County Public Schools, Maryland. He has taught junior high school mathematics and science and senior high school mathematics. He earned his M.A. degree at the University of Maryland. He is co-author with Professor Keedy of *Exploring Modern Mathematics,* Books 1 and 2 (Holt, Rinehart & Winston, 1976).

Photographs: Opening photograph for Chapter 1 by NASA; for Chapter 2 © William Rosenthal, Jeroboam, Inc.; for Chapter 3 by M. W. S. Tweedie, National Audubon Society Collection, Photo Researchers, Inc.; for Chapter 12 by Fred J. Maroon, Photo Researchers, Inc.; for Chapter 14 by William Liller. All other photographs by Betty Medsger.*

ISBN 0-201-10310-9
ABCDEFGHIJKL-VH-887654321

*Photographs provided expressly for the publisher. Special thanks to Weatherly Aviation, Hollister, California, for their cooperation.

Cover Photo: Copyright Barrie Rokeach 1981

# To the Students

Why are you studying second-year algebra? You may be planning a career in business, the arts, or the sciences, and you know that a mathematical background can be very useful. Or you may be planning to go to college and you have learned that second-year algebra is important for getting into a good college or university. It may be that you are taking this course because your counselor advised you to or because most of your friends are taking it. Or you may find mathematics interesting and challenging, the way puzzles are interesting.

No matter why you are studying second-year algebra, we want you to have success and we want you to enjoy the course as much as possible. So, we have written this book accordingly. If you will read it carefully and put forth some effort, you will succeed. When you come to exercises marked "Try This," you should stop and work those exercises. They are very much like the examples in the text and very much like the homework exercises. The homework will be relatively easy and your understanding of the material will be good. If you have been leery of math in the past, perhaps you will now find that it is not so bad after all.

We hope that you will attack the subject with an inquiring attitude. This is a subject that can be fun just because it is interesting. Yes, algebra is very useful in many careers, but if you will study it just to see how the ideas are developed and how they fit together, this is enough. The career aspects will take care of themselves.

Enjoy yourself as much as possible as you study. Then, no matter what your career objective, you will be further down the road. Moreover, your life will be more pleasant in the process.

The Authors

# Special Thanks

To Judy Beecher, formerly of Southport High School, Indianapolis, Indiana, for her careful checking of the manuscript and preparation of the answers.

To all the students who participated in learner verification studies.

To all the teachers who aided in reviewing this text:

L. A. Abert
Livermore, California

Flora Berry
Union County Schools
Union, South Carolina

Mildred H. Davis
Kansas City, Missouri

Terry Haug
Sacramento, California

Stephen L. Johnson
Jewell School District
Seaside, Oregon

Gaye P. Lindsey
Greenway, Virginia

Calvin Miller
Midland Public Schools
Midland, Michigan

Donavon Nagel
John Marshall High School
Rochester, Minnesota

Joann E. Roller
Saginaw Public Schools
Saginaw, Michigan

Ed Rykowski
Springfield, Missouri

J. Norman C. Sharp
Borough of Etobicoke
Etobicoke, Ontario

Louise M. Smith
Charleston County School District
Charleston, South Carolina

John Walton
Denver Public Schools
Denver, Colorado

# Contents

**Chapter 19**

## COMBINATORIAL ALGEBRA; PROBABILITY, 565

## ADDITIONAL MATERIAL

# Chapter 1
# Real Numbers and Their Properties

*What is the volume of the earth?*

# 1-1 Real Numbers

After finishing Lesson 1-1, you should be able to
**I** give examples of natural numbers, whole numbers, integers, and rational numbers.
**II** convert fractional to decimal notation for rational numbers.
**III** distinguish between rational and irrational numbers.

## I Some Subsets of Real Numbers

There is only one real number for each point of a line.

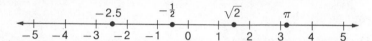

The *positive* real numbers are those shown to the right of 0. The *negative* real numbers are those to the left of 0. Zero is neither negative nor positive. There are various kinds of real numbers. The *natural numbers* are those used for counting.

The *natural numbers* are 1, 2, 3, 4, 5, 6, 7, 8, 9, 10, 11, and so on.

When we include 0, we then have the set of *whole numbers*.

The *whole numbers* are 0, 1, 2, 3, 4, 5, 6, 7, 8, 9, 10, 11, and so on.

**TRY THIS** ➡

> 1. Name four natural numbers.
> 2. Name four whole numbers.

We extend the set of whole numbers to the integers by including some *negative* numbers. The negative integers are those pictured to the left of 0.

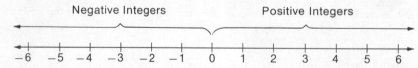

The *integers* are 0, −1, 1, −2, 2, −3, 3, −4, 4, and so on.

**TRY THIS** ➡

> 3. Name four integers.

The set of *rational* numbers includes not only the integers, but all quotients of integers (excluding division by zero).

Any rational number can be named by a fractional symbol having integers for numerator and denominator.

**Example 1.**  The following are rational numbers.

$$\frac{4}{5}, \frac{-4}{7}, \frac{9}{1}, 9, \frac{234}{1}, 234, \frac{-78}{1}, -78, \frac{78}{-4}, -\frac{2}{3}$$

**TRY THIS** ➡️

> 4.  Name six rational numbers.

## ıı Decimal Notation

Rational numbers can also be named using decimal notation.

**Example 2.**  Find decimal notation for $\frac{5}{8}$.

$\frac{5}{8}$ means $5 \div 8$, so we divide:

$$
\begin{array}{r}
0.625 \\
8\overline{)5.000} \\
\underline{4\,8}\phantom{00} \\
20\phantom{0} \\
\underline{16}\phantom{0} \\
40 \\
\underline{40}
\end{array}
$$

Thus $\frac{5}{8} = 0.625$. We call 0.625 a *decimal*. We call it a *terminating decimal* because it ends.

Sometimes we get a repeating decimal when we divide.

**Example 3.**  Find decimal notation for $\frac{6}{11}$.

$\frac{6}{11}$ means $6 \div 11$, so we divide:

$$
\begin{array}{r}
0.5454\ldots \\
11\overline{)6.0000} \\
\underline{5\,5.}\phantom{000} \\
50\phantom{00} \\
\underline{44}\phantom{00} \\
60\phantom{0} \\
\underline{55}\phantom{0} \\
50 \\
\underline{44} \\
6
\end{array}
$$

Such decimals are often abbreviated by putting a bar over the repeating part. Thus $\frac{6}{11} = 0.\overline{54}$. When such repeating decimals occur in problems, we round them.

Decimal notation for rational numbers either ends or repeats.

**TRY THIS** ━━━━━➤

> Find decimal notation for each of the following.
>
> 5. $\frac{7}{8}$
>
> 6. $\frac{7}{11}$
>
> 7. $\frac{17}{15}$

## ⅢIrrationalNumbers

Any rational number can be named by fractional notation, $\frac{a}{b}$, where both numerator and denominator are integers. Rational numbers can be named in other ways, but they can all be named *this* way. Is there a rational number that is a square root of 2; that is, a number $\frac{a}{b}$ for which $\frac{a}{b} \cdot \frac{a}{b} = 2$? We can find rational numbers whose squares are close to 2, but we can never find one whose square is exactly 2. Thus $\sqrt{2}$ is not a rational number. It is *irrational*. There are many irrational numbers. Unless a whole number is a perfect square, its square root is irrational.

**Example 4.** $\sqrt{3}$, $\sqrt{8}$, and $\sqrt{45}$ are irrational numbers.

Decimal notation for rational numbers either terminates or repeats. Thus decimal notation for irrational numbers never terminates or repeats.

### Examples.

**5.** 8.97979797 . . . is rational since the numeral repeats.

**6.** 3.121121112 . . . is irrational since the numeral does not repeat or terminate.

**7.** 0.984 is rational since the numeral terminates.

**TRY THIS** ━━━━━➤

> Which of the following are rational? Which are irrational?
>
> 8. $\frac{-4}{5}$
>
> 9. $\frac{59}{37}$
>
> 10. 7.42
>
> 11. 0.047474747 . . . (numeral repeats
>
> 12. 2.573410756631 . . . (numeral does not repeat)
>
> 13. $\sqrt{7}$

# Exercise Set 1-1

▌(*See page 2.*)

1. Name four natural numbers.
2. Name four whole numbers.
3. Name four positive integers.
4. Name four negative integers.
5. Name four positive rational numbers.
6. Name four negative rational numbers.

▌▌Find decimal notation for each of the following. (*See Examples 2 and 3.*)

7. $\dfrac{5}{8}$

8. $\dfrac{1}{8}$

9. $\dfrac{3}{7}$

10. $\dfrac{4}{7}$

11. $\dfrac{9}{16}$

12. $\dfrac{7}{16}$

13. $\dfrac{5}{12}$

14. $\dfrac{11}{12}$

15. $\dfrac{7}{11}$

16. $\dfrac{5}{11}$

▌▌▌Which of the following are rational? Which are irrational? (*See Examples 4–7.*)

17. $\dfrac{-5}{6}$

18. $\dfrac{-2}{7}$

19. 8.93

20. 7.604

21. 3.579579$\overline{579}$

22. 8.2323$\overline{23}$

23. 2.1010010001 . . . (numeral does not repeat)

24. 5.2121121112 . . . (numeral does not repeat)

25. $\sqrt{6}$

26. $\sqrt{5}$

27. $\sqrt{13}$

28. $\sqrt{15}$

29. $\sqrt{16}$

30. $\sqrt{36}$

---

### Challenge Exercises

31. Find decimal notation for $\frac{1}{13}, \frac{2}{13}, \frac{3}{13}, \ldots, \frac{12}{13}$. Study the repeating portion of the numerals. What pattern do you find?

32. Suppose $n = 0.88\overline{8}$. Find fractional notation for $n$. (*Hint:* Find $10n$ and then $10n - n$.)

33. Make up a name for an irrational number using only the digits 0 and 9.

---

# 1-2 Addition

After finishing Lesson 1-2, you should be able to

  **I**   find the absolute value and additive inverse of a number.

 **II**   add real numbers.

**III**   find the additive inverse of a real number.

## I Absolute Value and Additive Inverses

The absolute value of a number can be thought of as its distance from 0 on the number line. The absolute value of any number $a$ can be named $|a|$.

**Example 1.**   Simplify $|-7|$.

$$
\begin{array}{ccccccccccc}
-7 & -6 & -5 & -4 & -3 & -2 & -1 & 0 & 1 & 2
\end{array}
$$

The distance from $-7$ to 0 is 7. Thus $|-7| = 7$.

**Example 2.**   Simplify $|0|$.

$$
\begin{array}{ccccc}
-2 & -1 & 0 & 1 & 2
\end{array}
$$

The distance from 0 to 0 is 0. Thus $|0| = 0$.

### TRY THIS

Simplify. Think of distance on a number line.

1.   $|-2|$

2.   $|\sqrt{3}|$

3.   $|0|$

4.   $\left|-\dfrac{1}{4}\right|$

Every real number has an *additive inverse*.

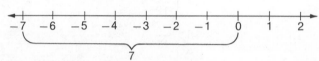

Additive Inverses

### Examples.

**3.**   The additive inverse of $-3$ is 3.

**4.**   The additive inverse of $\dfrac{1}{2}$ is $-\dfrac{1}{2}$.

**5.**   The additive inverse of 0 is 0.

### TRY THIS

Find the additive inverse of each number.

5.   9

6.   $-23$

7.   $-14$

8.   0

The additive inverse of *a* can be named −*a*.

**Examples.** Simplify, if possible.

**6.** −(−8.4) = 8.4 (The additive inverse of −8.4 is 8.4.)

**7.** −0 = 0 (The additive inverse of 0 is 0.)

**8.** −4 *can't be simplified* (This tells us that −4 can be read two ways: as "the additive inverse of 4" or as "negative 4.")

**TRY THIS**

Simplify, if possible.

9. −(−9)
10. −(−7)
11. −0
12. −8.4
13. $-\left(-\dfrac{1}{2}\right)$
14. −(−9.8)

## ▪ Addition of Real Numbers

The number line can help explain addition of real numbers. To find *a* + *b*, we start at *a* and move according to *b*. If *b* is positive, we move to the right. If *b* is negative, we move to the left.

**Examples.** Add, using a number line.

**9.** 6 + (−4) = 2

**10.** −6 + 9 = 3

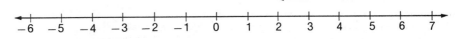

**11.** −3 + (−2) = −5

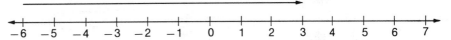

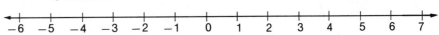

**TRY THIS**

Add, using a number line.

15. 3 + (−5)
16. −3 + 8
17. −5 + 0
18. −9 + (−5)

The sum of two negative real numbers is negative. We add their absolute values and then take the additive inverse. The result is negative.

**Examples.** Add.

**12.** $-5 + (-9) = -14$

**13.** $-10 + (-21) = -31$

**14.** $-9.4 + (-3.2) = -12.6$

**15.** $-\dfrac{9}{6} + \left(-\dfrac{11}{6}\right) = -\dfrac{20}{6}$, or $-\dfrac{10}{3}$

**TRY THIS** ➡

Add.

19.  $-7 + (-11)$
20.  $-8 + (-9)$
21.  $-20 + (-9)$
22.  $-8.9 + (-9.7)$
23.  $-\dfrac{6}{5} + \left(-\dfrac{23}{5}\right)$

To add a positive and a negative number with different absolute values, find the difference of their absolute values. If the negative number has the greater absolute value, the answer is negative. If the positive number has the greater absolute value, the answer is positive.

**Examples.** Add.

**16.** $3 + (-5) = -2$

**17.** $14 + (-9) = 5$

**18.** $-9.2 + 3.1 = -6.1$

**19.** $-\dfrac{5}{4} + \dfrac{1}{7} = -\dfrac{35}{28} + \dfrac{4}{28} = -\dfrac{31}{28}$

When we add 0 and any real number, the result is the number itself. Since 0 has this property, we call it the *additive identity*.

**TRY THIS** ➡

Add.

24.  $4 + (-7)$
25.  $23 + (-11)$
26.  $-7.8 + 4.5$
27.  $-\dfrac{7}{3} + 0$
28.  $\dfrac{3}{8} + \left(-\dfrac{5}{6}\right)$

### ⦙⦙⦙ Additive Inverses

**DEFINITION**

The additive inverse of a number $a$ is the number which when added to $a$ gives 0. The additive inverse of $a$ is $-a$.

Thus for any real number $a$, $a + (-a) = (-a) + a = 0$.

**Examples.**

**20.** $-8 + 8 = 0$

**21.** $0 + 0 = 0$

**22.** $4.2 + (-4.2) = 0$

**TRY THIS** ➡️

> Add.
>
> 29. $-5 + 5$
> 30. $10 + (-10)$
> 31. $-\dfrac{1}{4} + \dfrac{1}{4}$

Note that the symbol $-a$ refers to the number we add to $a$ to get 0. We cannot know whether $-a$ is positive, negative, or 0 unless we know what $a$ stands for.

**Example 23.** Find $-a$ when $a$ stands for $-8$.

$$-a = -(-8) = 8$$

**Example 24.** Find $-a$ when $a$ stands for 0.

$$-a = -0 = 0$$

**Example 25.** Find $-a$ when $a$ stands for 7.

$$-a = -(7) = -7$$

**TRY THIS** ➡️

> Find $-x$ when $x$ stands for
>
> 32. 4
> 33. $-14$
> 34. $-8.6$
> 35. 0

## Exercise Set 1-2

▌Simplify. (*See Examples 1 and 2.*)

1. $|-4|$
2. $|-6|$
3. $|9|$
4. $|11|$
5. $|\sqrt{5}|$
6. $|\sqrt{6}|$
7. $\left|-\dfrac{1}{9}\right|$
8. $\left|-\dfrac{5}{8}\right|$
9. $|0|$
10. $|3|$
11. $|-19|$
12. $|-23|$
13. $|-4.7|$
14. $|-6.3|$

Find the additive inverse of each number. (*See Examples 3–5.*)

15. 12
16. 18
17. $-31$
18. $-43$
19. 5
20. 0

21. $-\dfrac{1}{6}$

22. $-\dfrac{7}{8}$

23. $-7.6$

24. $-8.3$

25. $9.03$

26. $5.72$

Simplify, if possible. (*See Examples 6–8.*)

27. $-(-8)$

28. $-(-7)$

29. $-5$

30. $-9$

31. $-(-7.5)$

32. $-(-6.4)$

33. $-0$

34. $-7$

■■ Add. (*See Examples 9–19.*)

35. $5 + (-4)$

36. $9 + (-6)$

37. $-8 + (-10)$

38. $-4 + (-8)$

39. $-12 + (-16)$

40. $-11 + (-18)$

41. $-8 + (-8)$

42. $-6 + (-6)$

43. $8 + (-3)$

44. $9 + (-4)$

45. $11 + (-7)$

46. $12 + (-8)$

47. $-16 + 9$

48. $-23 + 8$

49. $-24 + 0$

50. $-34 + 0$

51. $-8.4 + 9.6$

52. $-6.3 + 8.2$

53. $-2.62 + (-6.24)$

54. $-5.83 + (-7.43)$

55. $-\dfrac{2}{7} + \dfrac{3}{7}$

56. $-\dfrac{5}{6} + \dfrac{1}{6}$

57. $-\dfrac{11}{12} + \left(-\dfrac{5}{12}\right)$

58. $-\dfrac{3}{8} + \left(-\dfrac{7}{8}\right)$

59. $-\dfrac{8}{3} + \dfrac{3}{4}$

60. $-\dfrac{4}{5} + \dfrac{5}{6}$

■■■ Find $-a$ when $a$ stands for: (*See Examples 23–25.*)

61. $8$

62. $11$

63. $-18$

64. $-19$

65. $-\sqrt{11}$

66. $-\sqrt{7}$

67. $\dfrac{5}{6}$

68. $\dfrac{3}{4}$

**Challenge Exercises**

Simplify.

69. $|-8 - 4|$

70. $|6| + |-8|$

71. $-|-9|$

72. $-|-7 + (-3)|$

73. $|-4| + |-7|$

74. $|-|17| + |-2||$

75. $-|0| + |6|$

76. $|-(-3)|$

# 1-3 *Properties of Addition and Subtraction*

After finishing Lesson 1-3, you should be able to
**I**  simplify expressions involving parentheses.
**II**  tell which laws are illustrated by certain sentences.
**III**  subtract real numbers.

## I Parentheses, Symbols of Grouping

What does $4 + 5 \times 3$ mean? If we add 4 and 5 and then multiply
by 3, we get 27. If we multiply 5 and 3 and add the result to 4,
we get 19. To tell which operation to do first, we use parentheses. Calculations shown in parentheses are to be done first.

**Example 1.**

$(3 \times 7) + 10$ means $21 + 10$, or 31.
$3 \times (7 + 10)$ means $3 \times 17$, or 51.

**TRY THIS**

> Do these calculations.
>
> 1.  $(4 \times 10) + 13$
> 2.  $6(10 + 14)$
> 3.  $(-13 + 9) + 2$
> 4.  $-13 + (9 + 2)$

## II Order and Grouping in Addition

A basic property of real numbers is that they can be added
in any order.

**Examples.**

**2.**  $4 + 7 = 7 + 4 = 11$

**3.**  $-3.2 + 5.6 = 5.6 + (-3.2) = 2.4$

**The Commutative Law of Addition**

For any numbers $a$ and $b$, $a + b = b + a$.

**TRY THIS**

> 5.  Add and compare.
>
> a)  $-9 + 4$; $4 + (-9)$
> b)  $-6 + (-8)$; $-8 + (-6)$
> c)  $-4.7 + (-5.2)$;
>     $-5.2 + (-4.7)$

If we write $10 + 14 + 15$, what does it mean? Does it mean
$(10 + 14) + 15$ or $10 + (14 + 15)$? Either way we get 39. If we
are doing only addition, we can omit parentheses.

**Example 4.**

$-4 + (9 + 8) = -4 + 17$, or 13
$(-4 + 9) + 8 = 5 + 8$, or 13

### The Associative Law of Addition

For any real numbers $a$, $b$, and $c$,
$a + (b + c) = (a + b) + c.$

**TRY THIS** ➡

6. Add and compare.

a) $(5 + 8) + 3;\ 5 + (8 + 3)$
b) $(-9 + 4) + (-6);\ -9 + (4 + (-6))$
c) $(4.3 + 7.2) + 6.8;\ 4.3 + (7.2 + 6.8)$

**Examples.** Tell which property of real numbers is illustrated by each sentence.

**5.** $4.5 + \left(9 + \dfrac{1}{2}\right) = (4.5 + 9) + \dfrac{1}{2}$

Associative law of addition

**6.** $7.8 + \dfrac{1}{4} = \dfrac{1}{4} + 7.8$

Commutative law of addition

**TRY THIS** ➡

Tell which property of real numbers is illustrated by each sentence.

7. $4 + \left(9 + \dfrac{1}{4}\right) = (4 + 9) + \dfrac{1}{4}$

8. $4.5 + 9.67 = 9.67 + 4.5$

9. $\left(9 + \dfrac{1}{2}\right) + \dfrac{1}{2} = 9 + \left(\dfrac{1}{2} + \dfrac{1}{2}\right)$

**Remark.** We have seen that the real numbers with respect to addition are associative. Also, we know that 0 is the additive identity and each real number has an additive inverse. Any mathematical system with one operation which has these properties is called a *group*. Do the integers form a group with respect to addition?

## ▥ Subtraction of Real Numbers

### DEFINITION

The difference $a - b$ is the number which when added to $b$ gives $a$.

**Example 7.** Subtract: $-3 - 5$.

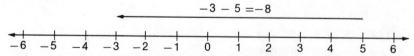

$$-3 - 5 = -8$$

To subtract 5 from $-3$ we find the number which when added to 5 gives $-3$. Thus we start at 5. We move 8 units to the left (negative direction) to get to $-3$. Since adding $-8$ to 5 gives $-3$, we know that $-3 - 5 = -8$.

**TRY THIS**

Draw a number line. Then do these subtractions. Check by adding.

10. $-2 - 3$
11. $5 - 8$
12. $-2 - (-5)$

To see how to subtract without a number line compare column A and column B and look for a pattern.

| Column A | Column B |
|---|---|
| a) $3 - 8 = -5$ | a) $3 + (-8) = -5$ |
| b) $-2 - (-9) = 7$ | b) $-2 + 9 = 7$ |
| c) $-6 - 4 = -10$ | c) $-6 + (-4) = -10$ |
| d) $0 - (-3) = 3$ | d) $0 + 3 = 3$ |
| e) $-11 - (-4) = -7$ | e) $-11 + 4 = -7$ |

The pattern suggests that we can always subtract by adding an additive inverse. This can be proved, so we call it a *theorem*. Anything that can be proved is called a theorem. In this book, we will prove theorems occasionally. We will not prove all of them because there isn't room, and because we don't have the necessary mathematics to prove some of them.

**THEOREM 1-1**
For any real numbers $a$ and $b$, $a - b = a + (-b)$. (We can subtract by adding the additive inverse of the subtrahend.)

**Examples.** Subtract.

8. $5 - (-4) = 5 + 4 = 9$

9. $-7 - 4 = -7 + (-4) = -11$

10. $-19.4 - 5.6 = -19.4 + (-5.6) = -25$

11. $-\frac{4}{3} - \left(-\frac{2}{5}\right) = -\frac{4}{3} + \frac{2}{5} = -\frac{20}{15} + \frac{6}{15} = -\frac{14}{15}$

**TRY THIS**

Subtract by adding an inverse.

13. $8 - (-9)$
14. $-10 - 6$
15. $-23.7 - 5.9$
16. $-\frac{11}{16} - \left(-\frac{23}{12}\right)$

## A Proof of Theorem 1-1

We have seen that $a - b = a + (-b)$. Let us prove this, where $a$ and $b$ are real numbers.

By the definition of subtraction, $a - b$ is the number which, when added to $b$, gives $a$. If we can show that $a + (-b)$ is the number which when added to $b$ gives $a$, then we will have proved that $a - b = a + (-b)$. Consider what happens when we add $a + (-b)$ to $b$.

$$[a + (-b)] + b = a + [(-b) + b] \qquad \textit{Adding a + (-b) to b and}$$
$$\textit{using the associative property}$$
$$= a + 0 \qquad \textit{Property of additive inverses}$$
$$= a$$

We have shown that $a + (-b)$ is a number which when added to $b$ gives $a$. Thus $a + (-b) = a - b$ by the definition of subtraction.

## Exercise Set 1-3

▌ Do these calculations. (*See Example 1.*)

1. $(5 \times 8) + 9$
2. $(6 \times 3) + 11$
3. $(8 \times 12) + (-3)$
4. $(7 \times 13) + (-4)$
5. $(9 \times 9) + (9 \times 6)$
6. $(10 \times 12) + (7 \times 9)$
7. $(2 - 8) + (8 - 2)$
8. $(7 - 11) + (11 - 7)$

▌▌ Tell which property of real numbers is illustrated by each sentence. (*See Examples 5 and 6.*)

9. $1.9 + 7.3 = 7.3 + 1.9$
10. $1.23 + 3.21 = 3.21 + 1.23$
11. $8 + (2 + 5) = (8 + 2) + 5$
12. $14 + (9 + 16) = (14 + 9) + 16$
13. $(2.6 + 5.2) + 3.4 =$ $2.6 + (5.2 + 3.4)$
14. $(6.8 + 9.6) + 3.1 =$ $6.8 + (9.6 + 3.1)$
15. $-8 + (-4) = -4 + (-8)$
16. $-16 + (-2) = -2 + (-16)$

▌▌▌ Subtract by adding an inverse. (*See Examples 8–11.*)

17. $5 - 7$
18. $9 - 12$
19. $-5 - 7$
20. $-9 - 12$
21. $-6 - (-11)$
22. $-7 - (-12)$
23. $10 - (-5)$
24. $28 - (-16)$
25. $15.8 - 27.4$
26. $17.2 - 34.9$
27. $-18.01 - 11.24$
28. $-19.04 - 15.76$
29. $-\dfrac{21}{4} - \left(-\dfrac{7}{2}\right)$
30. $-\dfrac{16}{5} - \left(-\dfrac{5}{3}\right)$

# 1-4 Multiplication and Division

After finishing Lesson 1-4, you should be able to
▮ multiply real numbers.
▮▮ tell which laws are illustrated by certain sentences.
▮▮▮ divide real numbers.
▮▮▮▮ divide by multiplying by a reciprocal.
▮▮▮▮▮ recognize impossible divisions (divisions by 0).

## ▮Multiplication of Real Numbers

When we multiply a positive and negative number we multiply their absolute values. The answer is negative.

**Examples.** Multiply.

**1.** $-3 \cdot 5 = -15$

**2.** $6 \cdot (-7) = -42$

**3.** $-5.2 \times 10 = -52$

**4.** $4 \cdot \left(-\dfrac{1}{5}\right) = -\dfrac{4}{5}$

**TRY THIS** ➡

> Multiply.
> 1.  $-4 \cdot 6$
> 2.  $8(-9)$
> 3.  $-7.4 \cdot (10)$
> 4.  $8\left(-\dfrac{1}{4}\right)$

When we multiply two negative numbers we multiply their absolute values. The answer is positive.

**Examples.** Multiply.

**5.** $-3 \cdot (-5) = 15$

**6.** $-6 \cdot (-7) = 42$

**7.** $-5.2 \cdot (-10) = 52$

**8.** $-7 \cdot \left(-\dfrac{2}{3}\right) = \dfrac{14}{3}$

When we multiply 1 and any real number the result is the number itself. Since 1 has this property, we call it the *multiplicative identity*.

**TRY THIS** ➡

> Multiply.
> 5.  $-8 \cdot (-9)$
> 6.  $-1 \cdot (-5)$
> 7.  $-20 \cdot (-6.4)$
> 8.  $-5\left(-\dfrac{2}{3}\right)$

## ıı **Properties of Multiplication**

Our experience with real numbers tells us that multiplication is both commutative and associative.

For any real numbers $a$, $b$, $c$,
$a \cdot b = b \cdot a$,      Commutative law of multiplication
$a \cdot (b \cdot c) = (a \cdot b) \cdot c$.      Associative law of multiplication

**Examples.** Which laws are illustrated by these sentences?

**9.** $3 \times 9 = 9 \times 3$      Commutative law of multiplication

**10.** $-4 + 4.2 = 4.2 + (-4)$      Commutative law of addition

**11.** $-9 + (10 + 5) = (-9 + 10) + 5$      Associative law of addition

**12.** $\frac{1}{2} \times \left( \frac{1}{4} \times 58 \right) = \left( \frac{1}{2} \times \frac{1}{4} \right) \times 58$      Associative law of multiplication

**TRY THIS**

Which laws are illustrated by these sentences?

9.  $4 + 9 = 9 + 4$
10.  $67 \times (9 \times 11) = (67 \times 9) \times 11$
11.  $-6.7 \times 89 = 89 \times (-6.7)$
12.  $5.6 + (89 + 4) = (5.6 + 89) + 4$

## ııı **Division of Real Numbers**

### DEFINITION

The quotient $\frac{p}{q}$ is the number which when multiplied by $q$ gives $p$.

**Examples.**

**13.** $\frac{10}{-2} = -5$ because $-5 \cdot (-2) = 10$.

**14.** $\frac{-32}{4} = -8$ because $-8 \cdot (4) = -32$.

**15.** $\frac{-56}{-7} = 8$ because $8 \cdot (-7) = -56$.

When we divide a positive number by a negative or a negative by a positive, the answer is negative. When we divide a negative number by a negative number, the answer is positive.

**TRY THIS**

Divide.

13.  $\frac{24}{-8}$

14.  $\frac{-125}{5}$

15.  $\frac{-75}{-25}$

16.  $\frac{-42}{-21}$

## IIII Reciprocals and Division

### DEFINITION
Two numbers whose product is 1 are called *reciprocals* of each other. They are also called *multiplicative inverses* of each other.

### Examples.

**16.** The reciprocal of $\frac{4}{5}$ is $\frac{5}{4}$ because $\frac{4}{5} \cdot \frac{5}{4} = \frac{20}{20} = 1$.

**17.** The reciprocal of 8 is $\frac{1}{8}$ because $8 \cdot \frac{1}{8} = \frac{8}{8} = 1$.

**18.** The reciprocal of $-\frac{2}{3}$ is $-\frac{3}{2}$ because $-\frac{2}{3} \cdot \left(-\frac{3}{2}\right) = \frac{6}{6} = 1$.

Any nonzero real number $a$ has a reciprocal $\frac{1}{a}$. The reciprocal of a negative number is negative. The reciprocal of a positive number is positive.

**TRY THIS** ➡

Name the reciprocal of each number.

17. $\frac{3}{8}$

18. 18

19. $-\frac{112}{234}$

20. $-43$

To subtract we can add an inverse. To divide we can multiply by a reciprocal.

### THEOREM 1-2
To do the division $\frac{a}{b} \div \frac{c}{d}$, we can do the multiplication $\frac{a}{b} \times \frac{d}{c}$.
(We can multiply by the reciprocal of the divisor.)

**Examples.** Divide by multiplying by the reciprocal of the divisor.

**19.** $\frac{1}{4} \div \frac{3}{5} = \frac{1}{4} \times \frac{5}{3} = \frac{5}{12}$

**20.** $-\frac{5}{6} \div \frac{4}{3} = -\frac{5}{6} \times \frac{3}{4} = -\frac{15}{24}$, or $-\frac{5}{8}$

**21.** $\frac{2}{3} \div \left(-\frac{4}{9}\right) = \frac{2}{3} \times \left(-\frac{9}{4}\right) = -\frac{18}{12}$, or $-\frac{3}{2}$

**TRY THIS** ➡

Divide by multiplying by a reciprocal.

21. $\left(-\frac{3}{4}\right) \div \frac{7}{5}$

22. $\left(-\frac{11}{5}\right) \div \left(-\frac{7}{8}\right)$

## ⅠⅠⅠⅠⅠ Division by Zero

Why do we not divide by zero? Recall the definition of division.

$\frac{n}{0}$ would be some number $c$ such that $c \cdot 0 = n$. But $c \cdot 0 = 0$, so

the only possible number $n$ which could be divided by 0 is 0.

Let's consider what $\frac{0}{0}$ might be.

a) $\frac{0}{0} = 5$ because $0 = 0 \cdot 5$.

b) $\frac{0}{0} = 567$ because $0 = 0 \cdot 567$.

c) $\frac{0}{0} = -8$ because $0 = 0 \cdot (-8)$.

d) $\frac{0}{0} = \frac{1}{4}$ because $0 = 0 \cdot \frac{1}{4}$.

It looks as if $\frac{0}{0}$ could be any number at all. Thus we

agree to exclude division by zero.

Division by 0 is not defined. We never divide by 0.

We cannot divide by 0, but we can divide 0 by any

nonzero number $a$. The result is 0. That is, $\frac{0}{a} = 0$,

because $a \cdot 0 = 0$.

**TRY THIS** ⟹

Which of these divisions are possible?

23. $\frac{7}{0}$

24. $\frac{0}{7}$

25. $\frac{4}{x - x}$

26. $\frac{-9}{15 - (3 \cdot 4)}$

## Exercise Set 1-4

Ⅰ Multiply. (*See Examples 1–8.*)

1. $3(-7)$
2. $5(-8)$
3. $-2 \cdot 4$
4. $-5 \cdot 9$
5. $(-8)(-2)$
6. $(-7)(-3)$
7. $(-9)(-14)$
8. $(-8)(-17)$
9. $(-6)(-5.7)$
10. $(-7)(-6.1)$
11. $-4.2(-6.3)$
12. $-7.4(-9.6)$
13. $-3\left(-\frac{2}{3}\right)$
14. $-5\left(-\frac{3}{5}\right)$
15. $-3(-4)(5)$
16. $-6(-8)(9)$
17. $4(-3) \cdot (-2)(1)$
18. $-3 \cdot (-6)(8)(0)$

▮▮ Which laws are illustrated by these sentences? (*See Examples 9–12.*)

19. $5 + (4 + 23) = (5 + 4) + 23$

20. $5.2 \times 3.6 = 3.6 \times 5.2$

21. $-6 + 5 = 5 + (-6)$

22. $\left(\dfrac{2}{3} \times \dfrac{3}{8}\right) \times \dfrac{5}{6} = \dfrac{2}{3} \times \left(\dfrac{3}{8} \times \dfrac{5}{6}\right)$

▮▮▮ Divide. (*See Examples 13–15.*)

23. $\dfrac{-8}{4}$

24. $\dfrac{-16}{2}$

25. $\dfrac{56}{-8}$

26. $\dfrac{63}{-7}$

27. $\dfrac{-77}{-11}$

28. $\dfrac{-48}{-6}$

29. $\dfrac{-5.4}{-18}$

30. $\dfrac{-8.4}{-12}$

▮▮▮▮ Name the reciprocal of each. (*See Examples 16–18.*)

31. $\dfrac{3}{4}$

32. $\dfrac{9}{10}$

33. $-\dfrac{7}{8}$

34. $-\dfrac{5}{6}$

35. $26$

36. $38$

37. $-56$

38. $-97$

Divide by multiplying by a reciprocal. (*See Examples 19–21.*)

39. $\dfrac{2}{7} \div \left(-\dfrac{11}{3}\right)$

40. $\dfrac{3}{5} \div \left(-\dfrac{6}{7}\right)$

41. $-\dfrac{10}{3} \div \left(-\dfrac{2}{15}\right)$

42. $-\dfrac{12}{5} \div \left(-\dfrac{3}{10}\right)$

▮▮▮▮▮ Which of these divisions are possible? (*See page 18.*)

43. $\dfrac{9}{0}$

44. $\dfrac{8}{0}$

45. $\dfrac{0}{16}$

46. $\dfrac{0}{28}$

47. $\dfrac{9}{y - y}$

48. $\dfrac{3}{2x - 2x}$

---

**Calculator Exercises**

Compute.

49. $-80{,}397 \times (-583)$

50. $-14{,}773 \times (-27)$

51. $-0.56004 \times 0.003$

52. $-0.00431 \times 0.005$

# 1-5 The Distributive Laws and Their Use

After finishing Lesson 1-5, you should be able to

**I**    evaluate expressions when numbers are specified for the letters.

**II**    evaluate expressions involving the distributive law.

**III**    use the distributive law to factor and multiply expressions.

**IIII**    collect like terms.

## ▪ Some Agreements

When a letter can represent various numbers, we call it a *varia-ble*. When we write two or more variables together we agree that this means multiplication. We have the same agreement when variables and numerals occur.

**Examples.** What does each of the following mean?

**1.** *pqr* means $p \cdot q \cdot r$

**2.** *mmm* means $m \cdot m \cdot m$

**3.** *5xy* means $5 \cdot x \cdot y$

**TRY THIS** ➡

> What does each of the following mean?
>
> 1. *abc*
> 2. *bbb*
> 3. *8ab*

We also agree that in an expression like $(4 \cdot 10) + (9 \cdot 2)$, we can omit the parentheses. Thus $4 \cdot 10 + 9 \cdot 2$ means $(4 \cdot 10) + (9 \cdot 2)$. In other words, do the multiplications first. We have a similar agreement for subtraction. That is, $4 \cdot 10 - 9 \cdot 2$ means $(4 \cdot 10) - (9 \cdot 2)$. The multiplications are still to be done first.

**Example 4.** Evaluate and simplify.

$$8 \cdot 4 + 3 \cdot 6 = 32 + 18 \quad \textit{Multiplying first}$$
$$= 50 \quad \textit{Adding}$$

**TRY THIS** ➡

> Evaluate and simplify.
>
> 4. $10 \cdot 5 + 4 \cdot 2$
> 5. $-4 \cdot 7 - 8 \cdot 9$

In expressions like $ab + cd$ and $ab - cd$ it is understood that parentheses belong around *ab* and *cd*. In other words, the multiplications are to be done first.

**Example 5.** Evaluate $xy + z$ when $x = 2$, $y = -3$, and $z = -4$.

$$xy + z = 2 \cdot (-3) + (-4)$$
$$= -6 + (-4)$$
$$= -10$$

**TRY THIS**

Evaluate each expression when $a = 5$, $b = -2$, $c = 4$, and $d = 10$.

6. $ab + cd$
7. $ab - cd$

## ‖ The Distributive Laws

Compare.

a)  $5(4 + 8) = 5 \cdot 12$
$\qquad = 60$
$\quad 5 \cdot 4 + 5 \cdot 8 = 20 + 40$
$\qquad\qquad = 60$

b)  $-4(9 + 5) = -4 \cdot 14$
$\qquad\qquad = -56$
$\quad -4 \cdot 9 + (-4)5 = -36 + (-20)$
$\qquad\qquad\qquad = -56$

We can either add and then multiply, or we can multiply and then add. The results are the same.

**The Distributive Law of Multiplication over Addition**

For any numbers $a$, $b$, and $c$, $a(b + c) = ab + ac$.

Note that we cannot omit the parentheses in $a(b + c)$. If we did, we would have $ab + c$, which by our agreement means $(ab) + c$. Compare.

a)  $5(4 - 8) = 5(-4)$
$\qquad = -20$
$\quad 5 \cdot 4 - 5 \cdot 8 = 20 - 40$
$\qquad\qquad = -20$

b)  $10(7 - 4) = 10 \cdot 3$
$\qquad\qquad = 30$
$\quad 10 \cdot 7 - 10 \cdot 4 = 70 - 40$
$\qquad\qquad\qquad = 30$

When we multiply a number by a difference, we can either subtract and then multiply, or multiply and then subtract.

**The Distributive Law of Multiplication over Subtraction**

For any numbers $a$, $b$, and $c$, $a(b - c) = ab - ac$.

Note again that we cannot omit the parentheses on the left. If we did, we would have $ab - c$, which would mean $(ab) - c$.

**Examples.** Evaluate each expression when $x = 2$, $y = 3$, and $z = 8$.

**6.** $x(y + z) = 2(3 + 8)$
$= 2 \cdot 11$
$= 22$

**7.** $xy + xz = 2 \cdot 3 + 2 \cdot 8$
$= 6 + 16$
$= 22$

**8.** $x(y - z) = 2(3 - 8)$
$= 2(-5)$
$= -10$

**9.** $xy - xz = 2 \cdot 3 - 2 \cdot 8$
$= 6 - 16$
$= -10$

**TRY THIS**

Evaluate each expression when $a = -4$, $b = -10$, and $c = 5$.

8. $a(b + c)$
9. $ab + ac$

Evaluate each expression when $a = 6$, $b = 10$, and $c = -2$.

10. $a(b - c)$
11. $ab - ac$

---

**Remark** We have seen that the real numbers have the following properties.

**Addition**
1. Commutative
2. Associative
3. Additive Identity (0)
4. Each number has an additive inverse.

**Multiplication**
1. Commutative
2. Associative
3. Multiplicative Identity (1)
4. Each number except 0 has a reciprocal (multiplicative inverse).

Multiplication is distributive over addition.

Any system with two operations having these properties is called a *field*.

---

## ⅲ Factoring and Multiplying

Any equation can be reversed without changing its meaning. Thus the distributive laws could be written as follows.

$ab + ac = a(b + c)$ and
$ab - ac = a(b - c)$

When we write the distributive laws like this, they show more clearly the basis of *factoring*.

**Examples.** Factor.

**10.** $8x + 8y = 8(x + y)$    *By a distributive law*

**11.** $cx - cy = c(x - y)$    *By a distributive law*

The parts of an expression, such as $3x$, $+ 4y$, $-2z$, are called *terms*. Notice that we take the $+$ or the $-$ as part of the term. When all the terms of an expression contain a common factor, we can "remove" it, using the distributive laws.

**Examples.** Factor.

**12.** $4x + 8 = 4x + 4 \cdot 2$
$\qquad\quad = 4(x + 2)$

**13.** $5x - 10 = 5x - 5 \cdot 2$
$\qquad\qquad = 5(x - 2)$

**14.** $P + Prt = P(1 + rt)$

**15.** $9x + 27y - 9 = 9x + 9(3y) - 9 \cdot 1$
$\qquad\qquad\qquad = 9(x + 3y - 1)$

**TRY THIS** ⟹

Factor.

12. $9x + 9y$
13. $ac - ay$
14. $6x + 12$
15. $4y - 16$
16. $bs + bt - bw$
17. $35x - 25y + 15$

One kind of multiplying is the reverse of the factoring process above.

**Examples.** Multiply.

**16.** $4(x - 2) = 4x - 4 \cdot 2$
$\qquad\qquad = 4x - 8$

**17.** $3(x + 10) = 3x + 3 \cdot 10$
$\qquad\qquad\; = 3x + 30$

**18.** $b(s - t + f) = bs - bt + bf$

In Examples 16, 17, and 18, we used the distributive laws. We multiplied each term inside the parentheses by the factor outside.

**TRY THIS** ⟹

Multiply.

18. $5(x - 9)$
19. $8(y + 10)$
20. $a(x + y - z)$

## IIII **Collecting Like Terms**

If two terms have the same variable, we say they are *like* terms, or *similar* terms. We can often simplify expressions by a process called *collecting like terms* or *combining like terms*. This also depends on the distributive laws.

**Examples.** Collect like terms.

**19.** $4x - 7x = (4 - 7)x$
$$= -3x$$

**20.** $y - 3y = 1 \cdot y - 3 \cdot y$
$$= (1 - 3)y$$
$$= -2y$$

**21.** $2x + 3y - 5x - 2y = 2x + 3y + (-5x) + (-2y)$      *Using Theorem 1-1*
$$= 2x + (-5x) + 3y + (-2y)$$
$$= (2 - 5)x + (3 - 2)y$$
$$= -3x + y$$

It is not necessry to write all the steps.

**Example 22.**  $5t - 8x - 10t + 11x = -5t + 3x$

**TRY THIS** ⬛➡

> Collect like terms.
>
> 21.  $9x - 11x$
> 22.  $5x + 12x$
> 23.  $5y + y$
> 24.  $t - 7t$
> 25.  $22x - 25y + 14x + 6y$

## **Exercise Set 1-5**

❙ What does each of the following mean? (*See Examples 1–3.*)

1.  $xyz$                               2.  $rst$
3.  $xxx$                               4.  $yyy$
5.  $9xy$                               6.  $12ab$

Evaluate and simplify. (*See Example 4.*)

7.  $7 \cdot 3 + 4 \cdot 6$             8.  $2 \cdot 5 + 6 \cdot 3$
9.  $-8 \cdot 7 + 7 \cdot 4$            10.  $-5 \cdot 9 + 8 \cdot 2$
11.  $-6 \cdot 9 - 5 \cdot (-7)$        12.  $-3 \cdot 8 - 4 \cdot (-7)$

Evaluate each expression when $x = -2$, $y = 3$, and $z = -4$. (*See Example 5.*)

13.  $xy + x$                           14.  $xy - y$
15.  $xz + yz$                          16.  $xy - xz$
17.  $yz + xy$                          18.  $xz + xy$

▌▌Evaluate each expression when $r = 8$, $s = 7$, and $t = -5$. *(See Examples 6–9.)*

19. $rs + rt$
20. $r(s + t)$
21. $rs - rt$
22. $r(s - t)$

▌▌▌Factor. *(See Examples 10–15.)*

23. $8x + 8y$
24. $7a + 7b$
25. $9p - 9q$
26. $12x - 12y$
27. $7x - 21$
28. $6y - 36$
29. $xy + xz$
30. $ab + ac$
31. $2x - 2y + 2z$
32. $3x + 3y - 3z$
33. $3x + 6y - 9z$
34. $4a + 8b - 16c$
35. $ab + ac - ad$
36. $xy - xz + xw$
37. $P + Prt$
38. $2\pi rh + 2\pi rr$
39. $\pi rr + \pi rs$
40. $\frac{1}{2}ah + \frac{1}{2}bh$

Multiply. *(See Examples 16–18.)*

41. $3(a + 2)$
42. $8(x + 5)$
43. $4(x - y)$
44. $9(a - b)$
45. $-5(2a + 3b)$
46. $-2(3c + 5d)$
47. $2a(b - c + d)$
48. $5x(y - z + w)$
49. $2\pi r(h + r)$
50. $P(1 + rt)$
51. $\frac{1}{2}h(a + b)$
52. $\pi r(r + s)$

▌▌▌▌Collect like terms. *(See Examples 19–21.)*

53. $4a + 5a$
54. $9x + 3x$
55. $8b - 11b$
56. $9c - 12c$
57. $14y + y$
58. $13x + x$
59. $12a - a$
60. $15x - x$
61. $t - 9t$
62. $x - 6x$
63. $5x - 3x + 8x$
64. $3x - 11x + 2x$
65. $5x - 8y + 3x$
66. $9a - 10b + 4a$
67. $7c + 8d - 5c + 2d$
68. $12a + 3b - 5a + 6b$

---

## Calculator Exercises

Collect like terms.

69. $830{,}979x + 15{,}007y - 947{,}864x + 833{,}609y$
70. $438{,}909a + 76{,}503b - 880{,}479a + 606{,}422b$
71. $0.00897x - 0.109743y + 0.00042x - 0.001048y$
72. $0.994107x - 0.001349y + 0.008049x - 0.001005y$

# 1-6 Multiplying by −1 and Simplifying

After finishing Lesson 1-6, you should be able to
  **I**    rename an additive inverse without parentheses.
  **II**   identify the terms of an expression.
  **III**  simplify expressions by removing parentheses.
  **IIII** simplify expressions by removing parentheses within parentheses.

## I Multiplying by −1

What happens when we multiply a number by −1?

**Examples.**

  **1.**  $-1 \cdot 9 = -9$

  **2.**  $-1 \cdot 0 = 0$

  **3.**  $-1 \cdot (-6) = 6$

**TRY THIS**

> Multiply.
>
> 1.   $-1 \cdot 24$
> 2.   $-1 \cdot 0$
> 3.   $-1 \cdot (-10)$

**THEOREM 1-3**

For any number $a$, $-1 \cdot a = -a$. Negative 1 times $a$ is the additive inverse of $a$.

Whenever we see something like −( ) in an expression, we can replace the "−" by "−1·" if we wish. Whenever we see −1·( ), we can replace "−1·" by "−".
We can use Theorem 1-3 to rename additive inverses.

**Examples.**   Rename each additive inverse without parentheses.

  **4.**  $\begin{aligned} -(3x) &= -1(3x) \\ &= (-1 \cdot 3)x \\ &= -3x \end{aligned}$

  **5.**  $\begin{aligned} -(-9y) &= -1(-9y) \\ &= -1 \cdot (-9)y \\ &= 9y \end{aligned}$

**TRY THIS**

> Rename each additive inverse without parentheses.
>
> 4.   $-(9x)$
> 5.   $-(-24t)$

**Examples.** Rename each additive inverse without parentheses.

**6.**  $-(4 + x) = -1 \cdot (4 + x)$    *Replacing — by —1 · (Theorem 1-3)*
$\qquad\qquad = -1 \cdot 4 + (-1) \cdot x$    *Using a distributive law*
$\qquad\qquad = -4 + (-x)$    *Replacing —1 · x by —x (Theorem 1-3)*
$\qquad\qquad = -4 - x$    *Adding an inverse is the same as subtracting (Theorem 1-1)*

**7.**  $-(a - b) = -1(a - b)$
$\qquad\qquad = (-1)a - (-1)b$
$\qquad\qquad = -a + [-(-1)b]$
$\qquad\qquad = -a + b$
$\qquad\qquad = b - a$

Note that $-(a - b)$, or $-1(a - b)$, is just $b - a$.

**TRY THIS**

> Rename each additive inverse without parentheses.
>
> 6.  $-(7 - y)$
> 7.  $-(x - y)$
> 8.  $-(9x + 6y + 11)$
> 9.  $-(23x - 7y - 2)$

We can rename an additive inverse by multiplying every term by $-1$. We could also say that we "change the sign" of every term inside the parentheses.

**Examples.**

**8.**  $-(-9t + 7z - \frac{1}{4}w) = 9t - 7z + \frac{1}{4}w$    *Changing the sign of every term*

**9.**  $-(-x) = x$

**TRY THIS**

> Rename each additive inverse without parentheses.
>
> 10.  $-(-2x - 5z + 24)$
> 11.  $-(-t)$

## ıı Terms

We have already said what we mean by the terms of an expression. When there are only addition signs, the terms are easy to identify. They are the parts separated by addition signs. If there are subtraction signs, we can rename using addition signs.

**Example 10.**  What are the terms of $3x - 4y + 2z$?

$3x - 4y + 2z = 3x + (-4y) + 2z$

Thus the terms are: $3x$, $-4y$, and $2z$.

**TRY THIS**

> What are the terms of
>
> 12.  $-5x - 7y + 67t - \frac{4}{5}$?
> 13.  $-9a - 4b + 17c - 24$?

## ⅢⅠ Removing Certain Parentheses

In some expressions there are parentheses preceded by subtraction signs. These parentheses can be removed.

**Examples.** Remove parentheses and simplify.

**11.** $6x - (4x + 2) = 6x + [-(4x + 2)]$      *Subtracting is adding the additive inverse (Theorem 1-1)*

$$= 6x + (-4x) + (-2)$$
$$= 6x - 4x - 2$$
$$= 2x - 2$$

**12.** $3y - 4 - (9y - 7) = 3y - 4 - 9y + 7$
$$= -6y + 3$$

When removing parentheses preceded by a subtraction sign, or additive inverse sign, the sign of each term inside the parentheses is changed. If parentheses are preceded by an addition sign, no signs are changed.

**TRY THIS** ➡

> Remove parentheses and simplify.
>
> 14.  $6x - (3x + 8)$
> 15.  $6y - 4 - (2y - 5)$
> 16.  $6x - (9y - 4) - (8x + 10)$

## ⅢⅡ Parentheses Within Parentheses

When parentheses occur within parentheses, we may use parentheses of different shapes, such as [ ] (also called "brackets") and { } (usually called "braces"). In mathematics, these all have the same meaning. The computations in the innermost parentheses are to be done first.

**Example 13.** Simplify.

$$\{3(2 - 5) - 4(2 + 3)\} - \{6 - [3 - (7 + 3)]\} = \{3(-3) - 4 \cdot 5\} - \{6 - [3 - 10]\}$$
$$= \{-9 - 20\} - \{6 - (-7)\}$$
$$= -29 - 13$$
$$= -42$$

**TRY THIS** ━━━▶

Simplify.

17.  $\{4(5 - 6) - 3(4 + 5)\}$
18.  $-\{7 - [9 - (7 + 8)]\}$
19.  $\{\frac{3}{2}(8 - 4) - \frac{2}{3}(8 + 4)\}$
20.  $-\{-7 - [-6 - (5 - 12)]\}$

When expressions within parentheses contain variables we may simplify by removing parentheses. We still work from the inside out.

**Example 14.**  Simplify.

$[5(x + 2) - 3x] - \{4[3(y - 2) - 4(y + 2)] - 3\}$
$= [5x + 10 - 3x] - \{4[3y - 6 - 4y - 8] - 3\}$
$= 2x + 10 - \{4[-y - 14] - 3\}$  *Collecting like terms*
$= 2x + 10 - \{-4y - 56 - 3\}$
$= 2x + 10 - \{-4y - 59\}$
$= 2x + 10 + 4y + 59$
$= 2x + 4y + 69$

**TRY THIS** ━━━▶

Simplify.

21.  $[4(x - 3) + 4x]$
22.  $-\{8[2(3y - 4) - (9y + 4)] + 7\}$
23.  $2(x + 4) - 7[4(x - 5) + 3y]$

## Exercise Set 1-6

▌ Rename each additive inverse without parentheses. (*See Examples 4–9.*)

1.  $-(5)$
2.  $-(9)$
3.  $-(-19)$
4.  $-(-34)$
5.  $-(-4b)$
6.  $-(-5x)$
7.  $-(a + 2)$
8.  $-(b + 9)$
9.  $-(b - 3)$
10.  $-(x - 8)$
11.  $-(t - y)$
12.  $-(r - s)$
13.  $-(a + b + c)$
14.  $-(x + y + z)$
15.  $-(8x - 6y + 13)$
16.  $-(9a - 7b + 24)$
17.  $-(m - n - s)$
18.  $-(x - y - z)$
19.  $-(-2c + 5d - 3e + 4f)$
20.  $-(-4x + 8y - 5w + 9z)$

▌▌ What are the terms of the following? (*See Example 10.*)

21.  $4a - 5b + 6$
22.  $5x - 9y + 12$
23.  $8m - 5n + \frac{1}{2}p$
24.  $4a - 21b + \frac{3}{4}c$
25.  $\sqrt{2}x - \sqrt{3}y - 2z$
26.  $\sqrt{5}a - \sqrt{7}b - 9c$

**▮▮▮** Remove parentheses and simplify. (*See Examples 11 and 12.*)

27. $a + (2a + 5)$        28. $x + (5x + 9)$

29. $b - (b + 2)$        30. $x - (x + 7)$

31. $4m - (3m - 1)$        32. $5a - (4a - 3)$

33. $3d - 7 - (5 - 2d)$        34. $8x - 9 - (7 - 5x)$

35. $-(p - q) + (p - q)$        36. $-(x - y) + (x - y)$

37. $(2a - 3b) + (-3a + 4b)$        38. $(3x - 5y) + (-8x + 7y)$

39. $-2(x + 3) - 5(x - 4)$        40. $-9(y + 7) - 6(y - 3)$

**▮▮▮▮** Remove parentheses and simplify. (*See Examples 13 and 14.*)

41. $2x + [4 - 3(4x - 5)]$        42. $5y + [8 - 9(3y - 7)]$

43. $9a - [7 - 5(7a - 3)]$        44. $12b - [9 - 7(5b - 6)]$

45. $5\{-2 + 3[4 - 2(3 + 5)] - (8 - 3)\}$        46. $7\{-7 + 8[5 - 3(4 + 6)] - (9 - 4)\}$

47. $[8(x - 2) + 9x] -$
$\{7[3(2y - 5) - (8y + 7)] + 9\}$        48. $[11(a - 3) + 12a] -$
$\{6[4(3b - 7) - (9b + 10)] + 11\}$

49. $-3[9(x - 4) + 5x] -$
$8\{3[5(3y + 4)] - 12\}$        50. $-6[8(y - 7) + 9y] -$
$7\{5[7(4z + 3)] - 14\}$

### Calculator Exercises

Remove parentheses and simplify.

51. $(87,573a - 47,924b) + (-578,563a + 903,408b)$

52. $-348(107,324x + 57,820) - 927(33,429x - 88,007)$

53. $(0.00079x - 0.000843y) - (-0.007943x - 0.000059y)$

### Challenge Exercises

Simplify.

54. $-[-(-(-9))]$      55. $-\{-[-(-(-10))]\}$      56. $-\{-[-(-(-(-8)))]\}$

### COMPUTER NOTE: Software and Hardware

Hardware in a computer system is the solid part of the system. It includes all the electronic and mechanical parts. Software is organized information. It includes programs telling the computer what to do and data for the computer to work on. Software information is usually kept on punched paper tape or magnetic tape.

# 1-7 Exponential Notation

After finishing Lesson 1-7, you should be able to
▪  rewrite expressions with and without exponents.
▪▪ rewrite expressions involving negative exponents.

## ▪ Whole Number Exponents

Exponential notation is like shorthand. For $3 \cdot 3 \cdot 3 \cdot 3$ we can write $3^4$. The latter is called *exponential notation*. In $3^4$ the number 3 is called a *base* and the number 4 is called an *exponent*.

**DEFINITION**

Exponential notation $a^n$, where *n* is an integer greater than 1, means

$$\underbrace{a \cdot a \cdot \cdots \cdot a \cdot a}_{n \; factors}$$

**Examples.** Write exponential notation for the following.

**1.** $7 \cdot 7 \cdot 7$ $\qquad$ $7^3$

**2.** $xxx$ $\qquad$ $x^3$

**3.** $2x \cdot 2x \cdot 2x$ $\qquad$ $(2x)^3$

**TRY THIS** ⟹

> Write exponential notation.
>
> 1.  $8 \cdot 8 \cdot 8 \cdot 8$
> 2.  $mmm$
> 3.  $4y \cdot 4y \cdot 4y \cdot 4y \cdot 4y$

**Examples.** Rewrite without exponents.

**4.** $5^2$ $\qquad$ $5 \cdot 5$, or 25

**5.** $(4y)^3$ $\qquad$ $4y \cdot 4y \cdot 4y$

**TRY THIS** ⟹

> Rewrite without exponents.
>
> 4.  $3^4$ $\qquad$ 5.  $y^2$ $\qquad$ 6.  $(5x)^4$

**Example 6.** Simplify.

$$
\begin{aligned}
(4x)^2 &= 4x \cdot 4x \\
&= 4 \cdot 4 \cdot x \cdot x \qquad \text{\textit{Using associative and commutative laws}} \\
&= 16x^2
\end{aligned}
$$

**TRY THIS** ⟹

> Simplify.
>
> 7.  $(5y)^2$
> 8.  $(-2x)^3$

In general, the exponent tells how many times the base occurs as a factor. What happens when the exponent is 1? Look for a pattern.

$$10^3 = 10 \cdot 10 \cdot 10 = 1000$$
$$10^2 = 10 \cdot 10 \quad\quad = 100$$
$$10^1 = ? \quad\quad\quad = ?$$

For the pattern to continue, $10^1$ would have to be 10. We shall make a definition (agreement) accordingly. An exponent of 1 makes no change in the meaning of an expression.

**DEFINITION**
For any number $a$, $a^1 = a$.

**Examples.** Rename each of the following without an exponent.

**7.** $4^1 = 4$

**8.** $(-5)^1 = -5$

**9.** $(-9y)^1 = -9y$

**TRY THIS** ➡

How should we define an exponent of 0? Look for a pattern.

$$10^3 = 10 \cdot 10 \cdot 10 = 1000$$
$$10^2 = 10 \cdot 10 \quad\quad = 100$$
$$10^1 = 10 \quad\quad\quad = 10$$
$$10^0 = ? \quad\quad\quad = ?$$

Rename each without an exponent.

9. $8^1$
10. $(31)^1$
11. $(-7.89)^1$
12. $(23\frac{1}{4})^1$

For the pattern to continue, $10^0$ would have to be 1. We shall make a definition (agreement) accordingly. When 0 occurs as the exponent of a nonzero base $a$, we agree that $a^0$ means 1.

**DEFINITION**
For any nonzero $a$, $a^0 = 1$.

**Examples.** Rename each of the following without exponents.

**10.** $6^0 = 1$

**11.** $6789^0 = 1$

**12.** $(-34.7)^0 = 1$

**13.** $(-9zt)^0 = 1$, when $z$ and $t$ stand for nonzero numbers

**TRY THIS**

## ▮ Negative Exponents

How should we define negative exponents? Look for a pattern.

$$10^3 = 1000$$
$$10^2 = 100$$
$$10^1 = 10$$
$$10^0 = 1$$
$$10^{-1} = ?$$
$$10^{-2} = ?$$

Rename without exponents.

13. $3^0$
14. $(-7)^0$
15. $y^0$, $y$ stands for a nonzero number.
16. $(\frac{1}{4}xy)^0$, $x$ and $y$ stand for nonzero numbers.

For the pattern to continue, $10^{-1}$ would have to be $\frac{1}{10}$ and $10^{-2}$

would have to be $\frac{1}{100}$. This leads us to make the definition.

**DEFINITION**

If $n$ is any integer and $a$ is not zero, $a^{-n}$ means $\frac{1}{a^n}$.

In other words $a^n$ and $a^{-n}$ are reciprocals.

**Examples.** Rename without using a negative exponent.

**14.** $7^{-3} = \frac{1}{7^3}$

**15.** $8^{-5} = \frac{1}{8^5}$

**TRY THIS**

Rename without using a negative exponent.

17. $10^{-4}$
18. $12^{-7}$

**Examples.** Rename using a negative exponent.

**16.** $\frac{1}{5^2} = 5^{-2}$

**17.** $\frac{1}{9^6} = 9^{-6}$

**TRY THIS**

Rename using a negative exponent.

19. $\frac{1}{4^3}$   20. $\frac{1}{9^8}$

**Example 18.** Write three other symbols for $5^{-4}$.

$$5^{-4} = \frac{1}{5^4} = \frac{1}{5 \cdot 5 \cdot 5 \cdot 5} = \frac{1}{625}$$

**TRY THIS** ➡

> 21. Write three other symbols for $4^{-3}$.

## Exercise Set 1-7

▌Write exponential notation. (*See Examples 1–3.*)

1. $4 \cdot 4 \cdot 4 \cdot 4 \cdot 4$
2. $6 \cdot 6 \cdot 6$
3. $5 \cdot 5 \cdot 5 \cdot 5 \cdot 5 \cdot 5$
4. $x \cdot x \cdot x \cdot x$
5. $mmmm$
6. $ttttt$
7. $3a \cdot 3a \cdot 3a \cdot 3a$
8. $5x \cdot 5x \cdot 5x \cdot 5x \cdot 5x$
9. $5 \cdot 5 \cdot c \cdot c \cdot c \cdot d \cdot d \cdot d \cdot d$
10. $2 \cdot 2 \cdot 2 \cdot r \cdot r \cdot r \cdot r \cdot t \cdot t$

Rename without exponents. (*See Examples 4–6.*)

11. $2^5$
12. $3^4$
13. $(-3)^4$
14. $(-8)^2$
15. $x^4$
16. $y^6$
17. $(4b)^3$
18. $(3x)^4$
19. $(ab)^4$
20. $(xyz)^3$

Rename each without an exponent. (*See Examples 7–13.*)

21. $5^1$
22. $(\sqrt{6})^1$
23. $\left(\frac{7}{8}\right)^1$
24. $\left(\frac{9}{7}\right)^1$
25. $(\sqrt{8})^0$
26. $(-4)^0$
27. $(3z)^0$
28. $(5xy)^0$

▌▌Rename without using a negative exponent. (*See Examples 14 and 15.*)

29. $6^{-3}$
30. $8^{-4}$
31. $9^{-5}$
32. $16^{-2}$
33. $11^{-1}$
34. $40^{-4}$

Rename using a negative exponent. (*See Examples 16 and 17.*)

35. $\dfrac{1}{3^4}$
36. $\dfrac{1}{9^2}$
37. $\dfrac{1}{10^3}$
38. $\dfrac{1}{12^5}$
39. $\dfrac{1}{16^2}$
40. $\dfrac{1}{8^6}$

# 1-8 Properties of Exponents

After finishing Lesson 1-8, you should be able to
  **I**   use exponential notation in multiplication and division.
**II**   use exponential notation in raising a power to a power.

## I Multiplication and Division

Consider an expression like $a^3 \cdot a^2$. To see how to simplify, recall the definition of exponents.

**DEFINITION**

$$\overset{\overset{\textstyle n\ \textit{factors}}{\frown}}{a^n = a \cdot a \cdot \,\cdots\, \cdot a}, \text{ if } n > 1$$
$$a^n = a, \text{ if } n = 1$$
$$a^n = 1, \text{ if } n = 0, a \neq 0$$
$$a^{-n} = \frac{1}{a^n} \text{ if } a \neq 0$$

$a^3 \cdot a^2$ means $(a \cdot a \cdot a)(a \cdot a)$ and $(a \cdot a \cdot a)(a \cdot a) = a^5$. The exponent in $a^5$ is the sum of the exponents in $a^3 \cdot a^2$. In general, when we multiply like this, the exponents are added. The base must be the same in both parts. Let's consider a case where one exponent is positive and one is negative.

$$b^5 \cdot b^{-2} = (b \cdot b \cdot b \cdot b \cdot b) \cdot \frac{1}{b \cdot b} \qquad \textit{Definition of exponents}$$
$$= \frac{b \cdot b}{b \cdot b} \cdot b \cdot b \cdot b$$
$$= b \cdot b \cdot b, \text{ or } b^3 \qquad \textit{Simplifying}$$

If we add exponents, we again get the correct result. Now let's consider a case where both exponents are negative.

$$c^{-3} \cdot c^{-2} = \frac{1}{c \cdot c \cdot c} \cdot \frac{1}{c \cdot c} \qquad \textit{Definition of exponents}$$
$$= \frac{1}{c \cdot c \cdot c \cdot c \cdot c} \qquad \textit{Multiplying}$$
$$= \frac{1}{c^5}, \text{ or } c^{-5} \qquad \textit{Simplifying}$$

Again, adding the exponents gives the correct result.

**THEOREM 1-4**

In multiplication with exponential notation, we can add exponents if the bases are the same.

$a^m a^n = a^{m+n}$

**Examples.** Multiply and simplify.

**1.** $x^4 \cdot x^3 = x^{4+3} = x^7$

**2.** $4^5 \cdot 4^{-3} = 4^{5+(-3)} = 4^2$

**3.** $(8x^4 y^{-2})(3x^{-3}y) = 8 \cdot 3 \cdot x^4 \cdot x^{-3} \cdot y^{-2} \cdot y^1 = 24x^{4+(-3)}y^{-2+1} = 24xy^{-1}$

**TRY THIS**

Multiply and simplify.

1. $8^9 \cdot 8^4$
2. $7^{-3} \cdot 7^5$
3. $y^7 \cdot y^{-2}$
4. $x^{-7} \cdot x^{-3}$
5. $(5x^{-3}y^4)(2x^{-9}y^{-2})$
6. $(-4x^{-2}y^4)(15x^2y^{-3})$

Consider division with exponential notation.

$\dfrac{8^5}{8^3}$ means $\dfrac{8 \cdot 8 \cdot 8 \cdot 8 \cdot 8}{8 \cdot 8 \cdot 8}$, which simplifies to $8 \cdot 8$, or $8^2$.

The results can be obtained by subtracting exponents. This holds in general.

**THEOREM 1-5**

In division with exponential notation, we can subtract exponents if the bases are the same.

$\dfrac{a^m}{a^n} = a^{m-n}$

**Examples.** Divide.

**4.** $\dfrac{5^7}{5^3} = 5^{7-3} = 5^4$

**5.** $\dfrac{5^7}{5^{-3}} = 5^{7-(-3)} = 5^{10}$

**6.** $\dfrac{9^{-2}}{9^5} = 9^{-2-5} = 9^{-7}$

**7.** $\dfrac{7^{-4}}{7^{-5}} = 7^{-4-(-5)} = 7^1 = 7$

Divide and simplify.

7. $\dfrac{4^8}{4^5}$

8. $\dfrac{5^4}{5^{-2}}$

9. $\dfrac{10^{-5}}{10^9}$

10. $\dfrac{9^{-8}}{9^{-2}}$

**TRY THIS**

**Examples.** Divide and simplify.

**8.** $\dfrac{x^3}{x^5} = x^{3-5} = x^{-2}$

**9.** $\dfrac{16x^4y^7}{-8x^3y^9} = \dfrac{16}{-8} \cdot \dfrac{x^4}{x^3} \cdot \dfrac{y^7}{y^9}$

$\qquad\qquad = -2x^{4-3} \cdot y^{7-9}$

$\qquad\qquad = -2xy^{-2}$

**TRY THIS** $\longrightarrow$

Divide and simplify.

11. $\dfrac{y^6}{y^{-5}}$

12. $\dfrac{10y^2}{2y^3}$

13. $\dfrac{42y^7x^6}{-21y^{-3}x^{10}}$

---

**Remark.** We said that $0^0$ was not defined. To see why, consider the following: $0^0 = 0^{1-1} = \dfrac{0^1}{0^1} = \dfrac{0}{0}$. But we cannot divide by 0. To avoid this difficulty, we leave $0^0$ undefined.

---

## ‖ Raising Powers to Powers

Consider an expression like $(5^2)^4$.

$\qquad (5^2)^4$ means $5^2 \cdot 5^2 \cdot 5^2 \cdot 5^2$, and this is equal to $5^8$.

In this case we could have multiplied the exponents in $(5^2)^4$. Suppose the exponents are not both positive, as in the following example.

$(8^{-2})^3$ means $\dfrac{1}{8^2} \cdot \dfrac{1}{8^2} \cdot \dfrac{1}{8^2}$, which is $\dfrac{1}{8^6}$, or $8^{-6}$.

Again we could have multiplied exponents.

**THEOREM 1-6**

To raise a power to a power we can multiply exponents.
$(a^m)^n = a^{mn}$

**Examples.** Simplify.

**10.** $(3^5)^7 = 3^{5 \cdot 7} = 3^{35}$

**11.** $(x^{-5})^4 = x^{-5 \cdot 4} = x^{-20}$

**TRY THIS** $\longrightarrow$

Simplify.

14. $(5^6)^4$

15. $(8^2)^{-4}$

16. $(9^{-3})^{-5}$

There may be several factors inside parentheses as in the following.

**Examples.**  Simplify.

**12.**  $(3x^2y^{-2})^3 = 3^3(x^2)^3(y^{-2})^3$
$= 3^3x^6y^{-6}$, or $27x^6y^{-6}$

**13.**  $(5x^3y^{-5}z^2)^4 = 5^4(x^3)^4(y^{-5})^4(z^2)^4$
$= 5^4x^{12}y^{-20}z^8$, or $625x^{12}y^{-20}z^8$

**TRY THIS** ➡

Simplify.

17. $(2xy)^3$
18. $(4x^{-2}y^7)^2$
19. $(-3x^4y^2)^5$
20. $(10x^{-4}y^7z^{-2})^3$

## Exercise Set 1-8

❚ Multiply and simplify. (*See Examples 1–3.*)

1. $5^6 \cdot 5^3$
2. $6^2 \cdot 6^6$
3. $8^{-6} \cdot 8^2$
4. $9^{-5} \cdot 9^3$
5. $8^{-2} \cdot 8^{-4}$
6. $9^{-1} \cdot 9^{-6}$
7. $b^2 \cdot b^{-5}$
8. $a^4 \cdot a^{-3}$
9. $a^{-3} \cdot a^4 \cdot a^2$
10. $x^{-8} \cdot x^5 \cdot x^3$
11. $(2x)^3(3x)^2$
12. $(9y)^2(2y)^3$
13. $(14m^2n^3)(-2m^3n^2)$
14. $(6x^5y^{-2})(-3x^2y^3)$

Divide and simplify. (*See Examples 4–9.*)

15. $\dfrac{6^8}{6^3}$
16. $\dfrac{7^9}{7^4}$

17. $\dfrac{4^3}{4^{-2}}$
18. $\dfrac{5^8}{5^{-3}}$

19. $\dfrac{10^{-3}}{10^6}$
20. $\dfrac{12^{-4}}{12^8}$

21. $\dfrac{9^{-4}}{9^{-6}}$
22. $\dfrac{2^{-7}}{2^{-5}}$

23. $\dfrac{a^3}{a^{-2}}$
24. $\dfrac{y^4}{y^{-5}}$

25. $\dfrac{9a^2}{(-3a)^2}$
26. $\dfrac{24a^5b^3}{-8a^4b}$

❚❚ Simplify. (*See Examples 10–13.*)

27. $(4^3)^2$
28. $(5^4)^5$
29. $(8^4)^{-3}$
30. $(9^3)^{-4}$
31. $(6^{-4})^{-3}$
32. $(7^{-8})^{-5}$
33. $(3x^2y^2)^3$
34. $(2a^3b^4)^5$
35. $(-2x^3y^{-4})^{-2}$
36. $(-3a^2b^{-5})^{-3}$
37. $(-6a^{-2}b^3c)^{-2}$
38. $(-8x^{-4}y^5z^2)^{-4}$

# 1-9 Order and Properties of Absolute Value

After finishing Lesson 1-9, you should be able to
- **I** determine whether an inequality is true or false.
- **II** simplify expressions with absolute values.

## I Inequalities

Sentences like those in the following definition are called *inequalities*.

**DEFINITION**

$a \neq b$ means $a$ is not equal to $b$.
$a < b$ means $a$ is less than $b$.
$a \leq b$ means $a$ is less than or equal to $b$.
$a > b$ means $a$ is greater than $b$.
$a \geq b$ means $a$ is greater than or equal to $b$.

**Examples.** Determine whether each sentence is true or false.

**1.** $3 < -4$    This sentence says that 3 is less than $-4$. It is false.

**2.** $-3 \leq 5$    This sentence says that $-3 < 5$ is true or $-3 = 5$ is true. It is true since $-3 < 5$ is true.

**3.** $5 \leq 5$    True, since $5 = 5$ is true.

**4.** $9 \leq 5$    False, since both $9 < 5$ and $9 = 5$ are false.

**TRY THIS** ➤

> Determine whether each sentence is true or false.
>
> 1.  $-3 \geq -1$
> 2.  $-8 \leq -2$
> 3.  $-4 > 7$

A sentence like

$$-4 \leq 5 < 8 \quad \textbf{(1)}$$

is an abbreviation for

$$-4 \leq 5 \text{ and } 5 < 8 \quad \textbf{(2)}$$

For the sentence **(1)** to be true, both parts of **(2)** must be true. Both parts are true, so **(1)** is true.

**Examples.** Determine whether each sentence is true or false.

**5.** $-3 < 5 < 0$          False, since $5 < 0$ is false.

**6.** $-3 < -4 \leq 0$          False, since $-3 < -4$ is false.

**7.** $-10 < -5 < 0$          True, since $-10 < -5$ and $-5 < 0$ are
                                                     both true.

**TRY THIS**

Determine whether each sentence is true or false.

4. $2 \leq 5 < 7$
5. $-4 < 0 \leq 8$
6. $5 \leq 2 < -3$

## ▪▪ Properties of Absolute Value

The absolute value of a nonnegative number is that number itself. The absolute value of a negative number is its additive inverse. We can formalize this definition as follows.

**DEFINITION**
For any number $x$,
$|x| = x$ if $x \geq 0$;
$|x| = -x$ if $x < 0$.

**Examples.** Simplify.

**8.** $|8| = 8$

**9.** $|-3| = -(-3) = 3$

**10.** $|0| = 0$

**TRY THIS**

Simplify.

7. $|19|$
8. $|-9|$
9. $|-15|$

Certain properties of absolute value notation follow at once. For
example, the absolute value of a product is the product of the
absolute values.

**Example 11.** $|-2 \cdot 5| = |-10| = 10$, and
                              $|-2| \cdot |5| = 2 \cdot 5 = 10$, so
                              $|-2 \cdot 5| = |-2| \cdot |5|$.

Similarly, the absolute value of a quotient is the quotient of the absolute values.

**Example 12.** $\left|\dfrac{-42}{7}\right| = |-6| = 6$, and

$$\dfrac{|-42|}{|7|} = \dfrac{42}{7} = 6, \text{ so}$$

$$\left|\dfrac{-42}{7}\right| = \dfrac{|-42|}{|7|}.$$

The absolute value of an even power can be simplified by leaving off the absolute value signs, because no even power can be negative.

**Example 13.** $|(-5)^2| = |25| = 25$, and

$$(-5)^2 = 25, \text{ so}$$

$$|(-5)^2| = (-5)^2.$$

**THEOREM 1-7**

For any real numbers $a$ and $b$,

a) $|ab| = |a| \cdot |b|$

b) $\left|\dfrac{a}{b}\right| = \dfrac{|a|}{|b|}$, assuming $b \neq 0$

c) $|a^n| = a^n$ if $n$ is an even integer.

**Examples.** Simplify, leaving as little as possible inside absolute value signs.

**14.** $|5x| = |5| \cdot |x| = 5|x|$

**15.** $|x^2| = x^2$

**16.** $|x^2 y^3| = |x^2 \cdot y^2 \cdot y| = |x^2| \cdot |y^2| \cdot |y| = x^2 y^2 |y|$

**17.** $\left|\dfrac{x^2}{y}\right| = \dfrac{|x^2|}{|y|} = \dfrac{x^2}{|y|}$

**18.** $|-5x| = |-5| \cdot |x| = 5|x|$

**TRY THIS** ⟹

> Simplify, leaving as little as possible inside absolute value signs.
>
> 10. $|7x|$
> 11. $|x^8|$
> 12. $|5a^2 b|$
> 13. $\left|\dfrac{7a}{b^2}\right|$
> 14. $|-9x|$

## Exercise Set 1-9

▎Determine whether each sentence is true or false. (*See Examples 1–7.*)

1. $-9 \geq -2$
2. $-11 \geq -7$
3. $-6 \leq -5$
4. $-5 \leq -2$
5. $11 > 12$
6. $9 > 11$
7. $6 + 3 \neq 5 - 13$
8. $9 + 4 \neq 6 - 10$
9. $-2 < -1 \leq 0$
10. $6 \leq 9 < 11$
11. $-2 \leq 2 \leq 8$
12. $6 \leq 6 < 5$
13. $-3 < -5 \leq 0$
14. $9 \leq 8 < 10$

▎▎Simplify, leaving as little as possible inside absolute value signs. (*See Examples 14–18.*)

15. $|3x|$
16. $|4x|$
17. $|x^6|$
18. $|x^8|$
19. $|7x^2y^3|$
20. $|9a^4b^5|$
21. $\left| \dfrac{a^2}{b} \right|$
22. $\left| \dfrac{x^4}{y} \right|$
23. $|-4t|$
24. $|-8b|$
25. $|-5a^4b|$
26. $|-10x^6y|$
27. $|t^3|$
28. $|p^5|$
29. $|a^8|$
30. $|y^6|$

### Challenge Exercises

31. We have seen that $|a \cdot b| = |a| \cdot |b|$. Experiment and determine the relationship between $|a + b|$ and $|a| + |b|$.

### SCIENCE NOTE: Photographing Distant Stars

Some telescopes can turn to keep pointed at a certain star for hours at a time. The light from these telescopes is directed to photographic film. The light accumulates on the film. That is, the telescope provides a time exposure of the star. Using such a telescope, astronomers have recorded light from stars more than 1,000,000,000 light-years away. That means the film image shows how these stars looked 1,000,000,000 years ago.

# COMPUTER ACTIVITY

## Finding the Absolute Value of Any Number

**PROBLEM:** Find the absolute value of N.

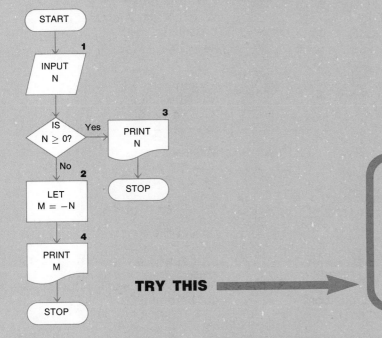

**Examples using the flowchart:**

| 1 | 2 | 3,4 |
|---|---|---|
| N | M | \|N\| |
| 5.6 | | 5.6 |
| $-3\frac{1}{5}$ | $-(-3\frac{1}{5})$ | $3\frac{1}{5}$ |

**TRY THIS**

1. Suppose the number is 95.6. What is |95.6|?
2. Suppose the number is 0. What is |0|?
3. Suppose the number is $-89\frac{1}{3}$. What is $|-89\frac{1}{3}|$?

**Note:** A flowchart will be used in many activities to follow. Flowchart symbols are defined below:

1. ▱ Input operation—brings data from keyboard, punched cards, magnetic tape, disc memory

2. ◇ Decision operation—indicates which alternative path to follow

3. ▭ Processing operation— "M = −N" means that M takes on the value of −N

4. ▱ Output operation—sends data to printer, video display, punched cards, magnetic tape, disc memory

## CHAPTER 1 REVIEW

Review the material in the chapter. Then see how you have done by trying these review exercises. If you miss an exercise, restudy the indicated lesson.

1-1  1. Find decimal notation for $\frac{5}{8}$.

1-1  Which of the following are rational and which are irrational?
  2. $\sqrt{7}$
  3. $\frac{-5}{7}$
  4. 2.113111311113... (numeral does not repeat)

1-2  Simplify.
  5. $|4|$
  6. $\left|-\frac{3}{4}\right|$
  7. $|0|$

1-2  Find the additive inverse of each.
  8. 7     9. $-\frac{9}{10}$     10. 0

1-2  Add.
  11. $7 + (-9)$
  12. $-11 + 4$
  13. $-16 + (-9)$

1-3, Tell which property of real numbers
1-4, is illustrated by each sentence.
1-5  14. $5 + 6 = 6 + 5$
  15. $(3 + 2) + 6 = 3 + (2 + 6)$
  16. $(5 \cdot 6) \cdot 7 = 5 \cdot (6 \cdot 7)$
  17. $-9(3 + 5) = (-9)(3) + (-9)(5)$

1-3  Subtract.
  18. $8 - (-3)$
  19. $-6 - (-5)$
  20. $-17 - 8$

1-4  Multiply.
  21. $-4(8)$
  22. $(-7)(-3)$
  23. $9(-6)$

1-4  Divide.
  24. $\frac{-18}{3}$
  25. $\frac{-24}{-6}$
  26. $\frac{2}{3} \div \left(-\frac{8}{5}\right)$

1-4  Which of these divisions are possible?
  27. $\frac{10}{0}$     28. $\frac{0}{56}$     29. $\frac{10}{x - x}$

1-5  Factor.
  30. $3m + 6n$
  31. $5a - 15$
  32. $2ab + 6ac - 8ad$

1-5  Multiply.
  33. $6(x - 5)$
  34. $-3(s - 2t)$
  35. $12\left(\frac{a}{2} - \frac{b}{3} + \frac{c}{4}\right)$

1-5  Collect like terms.
  36. $6y - 8y - 4y + 3y$
  37. $2.3y - 8 - 4y + 7.6x - 5.8x$

1-6  Rename each additive inverse without parentheses.
  38. $-(-6x)$
  39. $-(r - s)$

1-6  Remove parentheses and simplify.
  40. $2a - (3a - 4)$
  41. $5x - [2x + (3x - 2)]$

1-7, Simplify.
1-8  42. $8^{-3}$
  43. $7^2 \cdot 7^{-3} \cdot 7^{-1}$
  44. $(10^2)^3$
  45. $\frac{a^4}{a^{-2}}$
  46. $(4r^2)(-8r^6)$
  47. $\frac{54x^5y^4}{18x^3y^{-1}}$

1-9  Simplify, leaving as little as possible inside absolute value signs.
  48. $|-8t|$
  49. $|20t^2m^3|$

## CHAPTER 1 TEST

1. Find decimal notation for $\frac{3}{8}$.

Which of the following are rational and which are irrational?

2. $\sqrt{5}$
3. $-\frac{8}{9}$
4. 3.221222122221... (numeral does not repeat)

Simplify.

5. $|5|$
6. $\left|-\frac{2}{3}\right|$
7. $|0|$

Find the additive inverse of each.

8. 19    9. $-\frac{3}{10}$    10. 0

Add.

11. $9 + (-11)$
12. $-14 + 6$
13. $-18 + (-6)$

Tell which property of real numbers is illustrated by each sentence.

14. $9 + 7 = 7 + 9$
15. $(8 + 6) + 9 = 8 + (6 + 9)$
16. $(4 \cdot 3) \cdot 9 = 4 \cdot (3 \cdot 9)$
17. $-6(8 + 9) = (-6)(8) + (-6)(9)$

Subtract.

18. $9 - (-4)$
19. $-7 - (-6)$
20. $-14 - 6$

Multiply.

21. $-9(7)$
22. $(-6)(-8)$
23. $4(-3)$

Divide.

24. $\dfrac{-27}{3}$

25. $\dfrac{-16}{-4}$

26. $\dfrac{3}{5} \div \left(-\dfrac{6}{5}\right)$

Which of these divisions are possible?

27. $\dfrac{19}{0}$    28. $\dfrac{0}{53}$    29. $\dfrac{11}{y - y}$

Factor.

30. $8x + 16y$
31. $6b - 18$
32. $3xy + 12xz - 15xw$

Multiply.

33. $9(y - 4)$
34. $-8(a - 4b)$
35. $12\left(\dfrac{x}{6} - \dfrac{y}{2} + \dfrac{z}{4}\right)$

Collect like terms.

36. $9x - 5x - 6x + 7x$
37. $3.2y - 9 - 5y + 4.8x - 5.7x$

Rename each additive inverse without parentheses.

38. $-(-9y)$
39. $-(x - t)$

Remove parentheses and simplify.

40. $3t - (5t - 6)$
41. $9y - [4y - (2y - 5)]$

Simplify.

42. $9^{-4}$
43. $8^3 \cdot 8^{-5} \cdot 8^{-2}$
44. $(11^4)^3$
45. $\dfrac{x^5}{x^{-3}}$
46. $(5x^3)(-6x^5)$
47. $\dfrac{63y^4z^9}{9y^2z^{-3}}$

Simplify, leaving as little as possible inside absolute value signs.

48. $|-7y|$
49. $|36x^2y^5|$

## Ready for Solving Equations?

1-2    Add.

1. $5 + (-3)$            2. $-8 + (-4)$
3. $-6 + 0$             4. $-8.2 + 3.6$
5. $-\frac{4}{5} + \frac{1}{2}$          6. $3.8 + (-3.8)$

1-2    Find $-a$ when $a$ stands for

7. $-7$
8. $0$
9. $8$

1-3    Subtract.

10. $8 - (-5)$
11. $-11 - 9$
12. $-18.2 - 4.7$
13. $-\frac{2}{3} - \left(-\frac{4}{7}\right)$

1-4    Multiply.

14. $-5 \cdot 2$           15. $3 \cdot (-8)$
16. $-4.7 \cdot 10$       17. $3 \cdot \left(-\frac{1}{4}\right)$
18. $-2.3 \cdot -20$     19. $-8 \cdot \left(-\frac{3}{4}\right)$

1-4    Find the reciprocal of

20. $\frac{2}{3}$
21. $5$
22. $-\frac{4}{5}$

1-5    23.   Factor:   $5x - 10y + 15$.

1-5    Multiply.

24. $5(y - 4)$
25. $c(x + y - z)$

1-5    26.   Collect like terms:   $x + 3x - 5x$.

# Chapter 2
# Solving Equations

*We can solve equations to predict future running
records.*

# 2-1 Solving Equations

After finishing Lesson 2-1, you should be able to
**I**   tell what an equation means.
**II**  solve equations using the addition principle.
**III** solve equations using the multiplication principle.

## I Equations

The most common kind of sentence we use in algebra is an equation. An equation is a number sentence with $=$ for its verb. Some equations are true. Some are false. Some are neither true nor false.

**Examples.**

**1.** The equation $1 + 10 = 11$ is true.

**2.** The equation $7 - 8 = 9 - 13$ is false.

**3.** The equation $x - 9 = 3$ is neither true nor false because we do not know what $x$ represents.

**TRY THIS**

> 1. Write three true equations.
> 2. Write three false equations.
> 3. Write three equations that are neither true nor false.

An equation says that the symbols on either side of the equals sign name the same number. For example, $7 - 8 = 9 - 13$ says that $7 - 8$ and $9 - 13$ name the same number. In this case, the equation is false.

**TRY THIS**

**Answers.**   4. The equation $89 + 2 = 3 + 4$ says that $89 + 2$ and $3 + 4$ name the same number.   5. The equation $6 - 7 + \frac{1}{2} = 14$ says that $6 - 7 + \frac{1}{2}$ and $14$ name the same number.

> Tell what each equation means.
> 4. $89 + 2 = 3 + 4$
> 5. $6 - 7 + \frac{1}{2} = 14$

If an equation contains a variable it may be neither true nor false. Some replacements for the variable may make it true. Some may make it false. When we find the solution we say that we have *solved* the equation.

## DEFINITION

The replacements that make an equation true are called its *solutions*.

**Example 4.**

**a)** Find three replacements that make $3x + 6 = 12$ false.

0, 1, and 8, because
$3 \cdot 0 + 6 = 12$ is false;
$3 \cdot 1 + 6 = 12$ is false; and
$3 \cdot 8 + 6 = 12$ is false.

**b)** Find the replacement that makes $3x + 6 = 12$ true.

2, because $3 \cdot 2 + 6 = 12$ is true.

**TRY THIS**

> 6. Find three replacements that make $2x + 3 = 11$ false.
> 7. Find the replacement that makes $2x + 3 = 11$ true.

## ıı The Addition Principle

The equation $a = b$ says that $a$ and $b$ represent the same number. Suppose this is true. Then add a number $c$ to the number $a$. We will get the same answer as if we add $c$ to $b$, because $a$ and $b$ are the same number.

**THEOREM 2-1 (The Addition Principle)**

If an equation $a = b$ is true, then $a + c = b + c$ is true for any number $c$.

When we use the addition principle we sometimes say that we "add the same number on both sides of an equation." Let's use this principle to solve an equation.

**Example 5.** Solve: $x + 6 = -15$.

$$x + 6 + (-6) = -15 + (-6) \quad \text{\textit{Using the addition principle;}}$$
$$x + 0 = -15 + (-6) \quad \text{\textit{adding} $-6$ \textit{on both sides}}$$
$$x = -21 \quad \text{\textit{Simplifying}}$$

Check:

$$\begin{array}{c|c} x + 6 = -15 \\ \hline -21 + 6 & -15 \\ -15 & \end{array}$$

The solution is $-21$.

In Example 5, to get $x$ alone, we added the inverse of 6. This "got rid of" the 6 on the left.

**TRY THIS**

> Solve, using the addition principle.
>
> 8. $x + 9 = 2$
> 9. $13 = -25 + y$
> 10. $x + \frac{1}{4} = -\frac{3}{4}$
> 11. $y - 61.4 = 78.9$

**Remark.** When we solve an equation such as $x + 6 = -15$ using the addition principle we have really proved "If $x + 6 = -15$, then $x = -21$." Such an if-then sentence is called a *conditional sentence*. The conditional sentence is made up of two sentences. The sentence following the *if*, in this case "$x + 6 = -15$," is called the *antecedent* of the conditional. The sentence following the *then*, in this case "$x = -21$," is called the *consequent* of the conditional. To prove "if $x + 6 = -15$, then $x = -21$" we assume the antecedent is true. We then use theorems to try to get the consequent. Any solution of the antecedent (the *if* sentence) must be a solution of the consequent (the *then* sentence).

## ⅢⅠ The Multiplication Principle

Suppose the equation $a = b$ is true and we multiply the number $a$ by some number $c$. We will get the same answer as if we multiply $b$ by $c$. This must be so because $a$ and $b$ are the same number.

**THEOREM 2-2 (The Multiplication Principle)**

If an equation $a = b$ is true, then $a \cdot c = b \cdot c$ is true for any number $c$.

**Example 6.** Solve: $4x = 9$.

$$\frac{1}{4} \cdot 4x = \frac{1}{4} \cdot 9 \qquad \text{\textit{Using the multiplication principle;}}$$
$$\text{\textit{multiplying by} } \tfrac{1}{4}$$
$$1 \cdot x = \frac{9}{4}$$
$$\text{\textit{Simplifying}}$$
$$x = \frac{9}{4}$$

Check:
$$\begin{array}{c|c} \multicolumn{2}{c}{4x = 9} \\ \hline 4 \cdot \dfrac{9}{4} & 9 \\ 9 & \end{array}$$

The solution is $\dfrac{9}{4}$.

Checking by substituting in the original equation is an important part of solving.

In Example 6 we multiplied by the reciprocal of 4. When we multiplied we got $1 \cdot x$, which simplified to $x$. This enabled us to "get rid of" the 4 on the left.

**Example 7.** Solve: $-\dfrac{4}{5}x = 22$.

$$\left(-\frac{5}{4}\right)\left(-\frac{4}{5}x\right) = \left(-\frac{5}{4}\right) \cdot 22$$

$$1 \cdot x = -\frac{55}{2}$$

$$x = -\frac{55}{2}$$

This checks, so the solution is $-\dfrac{55}{2}$.

**TRY THIS**

Solve, using the multiplication principle.

12. $8x = 10$
13. $-4x = 64$
14. $-3x = -\dfrac{6}{7}$
15. $-12.6 = 4.2y$

**Remark.** When we solve an equation such as that of Example 7 we have proved "If $-\frac{4}{5}x = 22$, then $x = -\frac{55}{2}$." This means that whenever $-\frac{4}{5}x = 22$ is true, $x = -\frac{55}{2}$ is also true. Thus *if* there is a solution, it is $-\frac{55}{2}$. The *converse* of this conditional sentence is formed by interchanging the antecedent and consequent: "If $x = -\frac{55}{2}$, then $-\frac{4}{5}x = 22$." The converse of a conditional sentence is not necessarily true. If the converse is true, this will tell us that $-\frac{55}{2}$ is a solution. The check shows that the converse is true. Thus, $-\frac{55}{2}$ is a solution.

# Exercise Set 2-1

▌ Tell what each equation means. (*See Examples 1–4.*)

1. $91 + 4 = 7 - 9$
2. $18 \times 4 = 144 \div 2$
3. Find three replacements that make $5x + 4 = 19$ false.
4. Find three replacements that make $7x - 3 = 11$ false.
5. Find the replacement that makes $3x + 4 = 22$ true.
6. Find the replacement that makes $8x - 2 = 62$ true.

▌▌Solve using the addition principle. Check. (*See Example 5.*)

7. $x + 5 = 14$

8. $y + 7 = 19$

9. $y + 11 = 8$

10. $t + 13 = 4$

11. $x - 18 = 22$

12. $y - 19 = 26$

13. $t - 12 = 9$

14. $p - 15 = 11$

15. $x + 9 = -6$

16. $x + 11 = -8$

17. $t + 11 = -30$

18. $p + 14 = -42$

19. $x - 6 = -4$

20. $y - 7 = -3$

21. $t - 9 = -23$

22. $r - 8 = -19$

23. $-8 + y = 15$

24. $-9 + t = 17$

25. $r + \dfrac{2}{5} = \dfrac{8}{5}$

26. $x + \dfrac{5}{9} = \dfrac{8}{9}$

27. $t + \dfrac{5}{6} = -\dfrac{7}{12}$

28. $p + \dfrac{1}{3} = -\dfrac{5}{6}$

29. $-\dfrac{1}{6} + z = -\dfrac{1}{4}$

30. $-\dfrac{3}{4} + x = -\dfrac{7}{16}$

31. $x + 14.2 = 7.14$

32. $y + 62.8 = 37.3$

33. $p - 29.6 = 83.9$

34. $z - 14.9 = 57.3$

▌▌▌Solve using the multiplication principle. Check. (*See Examples 6 and 7.*)

35. $5x = 20$

36. $3x = 21$

37. $56 = 7x$

38. $48 = 8y$

39. $8y = -72$

40. $9t = -81$

41. $-24x = -192$

42. $-13y = -117$

43. $\dfrac{1}{5}y = 8$

44. $\dfrac{1}{4}x = 9$

45. $\dfrac{2}{3}x = 27$

46. $\dfrac{4}{5}x = 35$

47. $\dfrac{1}{6} = \dfrac{1}{4}t$

48. $\dfrac{1}{8} = \dfrac{1}{5}y$

49. $-\dfrac{3}{4}x = -\dfrac{3}{10}$

50. $-\dfrac{2}{3}y = -\dfrac{3}{8}$

51. $0.5x = 1.5$

52. $0.4x = 2.8$

53. $26.2y = 209.6$

54. $34.7t = 312.3$

---

**Calculator Exercises**

Solve. Remember that you must check.

55. $0.0008x = 0.0000056$

56. $-0.015y = -0.0001821$

57. $-34.324y = -0.07756$

58. $43.008z = 1.201135$

---

# 2-2 More on Solving Equations

After finishing Lesson 2-2, you should be able to
**I**   solve equations using both the addition and multiplication principles.
**II**   solve equations containing parentheses.
**III**   use the principle of zero products to solve equations (already factored).

## I Using the Principles Together

Let's see how to use the addition and multiplication principles together.

**Example 1.**   Solve: $3x - 4 = 13$.

$$3x - 4 + 4 = 13 + 4 \qquad \textit{Using the addition principle, adding 4}$$

$$3x + (-4) + 4 = 13 + 4$$
$$\textit{Simplifying}$$

$$3x = 17$$

$$\frac{1}{3} \cdot 3x = \frac{1}{3} \cdot 17 \qquad \textit{Using the multiplication principle,}$$
$$\textit{multiplying by } \tfrac{1}{3}$$

$$x = \frac{17}{3} \qquad \textit{Simplifying}$$

This checks, so the solution is $\frac{17}{3}$, or $5\frac{2}{3}$.

**TRY THIS** ➡

Solve.
1. $9x - 4 = 8$
2. $-\dfrac{1}{4}y + \dfrac{3}{2} = \dfrac{1}{2}$

In Example 1, we used the addition principle first. This is usually best.

If there are like terms in an equation, they should be collected first.

**Example 2.**   Solve: $7x - 3x = 32$.

$$4x = 32 \qquad \textit{Collecting like terms}$$

$$\frac{1}{4} \cdot 4x = \frac{1}{4} \cdot 32 \qquad \textit{Using the multiplication principle}$$

$$x = 8$$

This checks, so the solution is 8.

**TRY THIS** ➡

Solve.
3. $5x + 9x = 42$
4. $14x - 9x + 7 = -22$

If there are like terms on opposite sides of an equation, we can get them on the same side using the addition principle, and then "combine" them.

**Example 3.** Solve: $8x + 6 - 2x = -12 - 4x + 5$.

$$8x - 2x = -12 - 4x + 5 - 6 \qquad \textit{Adding } -6 \textit{ and simplifying}$$

$$8x - 2x + 4x = -12 + 5 - 6 \qquad \textit{Adding 4x and simplifying}$$

$$10x = -13 \qquad \textit{Collecting like terms and simplifying}$$

$$\frac{1}{10} \cdot 10x = \frac{1}{10} \cdot (-13) \qquad \textit{Multiplying by } \tfrac{1}{10}$$

$$x = \frac{-13}{10}, \text{ or } -1.3 \qquad \textit{Simplifying}$$

Check:

$$8x + 6 - 2x = -12 - 4x + 5$$

| $8\left(\dfrac{-13}{10}\right) + 6 - 2\left(\dfrac{-13}{10}\right)$ | $-12 - 4\left(\dfrac{-13}{10}\right) + 5$ |
|---|---|
| $\dfrac{-52}{5} + 6 - \dfrac{-13}{5}$ | $-12 - \dfrac{-26}{5} + 5$ |
| $\dfrac{-39}{5} + 6$ | $-7 + \dfrac{26}{5}$ |
| $\dfrac{-9}{5}$ | $\dfrac{-9}{5}$ |

In Example 3 we used the addition principle to get all terms with the variable on one side of the equation and all other terms on the other side. Then we combined like terms and proceeded as before.

**TRY THIS**

Solve.

5. $30 + 7(x - 1) = 3(2x + 7)$

## ▪ Equations with Parentheses

Certain equations with parentheses can be solved by first removing the parentheses and then proceeding as before.

**Example 4.** Solve: $3(7 - 2x) = 14 - 8(x - 1)$.

$$21 - 6x = 14 - 8x + 8 \qquad \textit{Removing parentheses}$$

$$21 - 6x = 22 - 8x \qquad \textit{Simplifying}$$

$$8x - 6x = 22 + (-21) \qquad \textit{Using the addition principle}$$

$$2x = 1 \qquad \textit{Collecting like terms and simplifying}$$

$$x = \frac{1}{2} \qquad \textit{Using the multiplication principle}$$

This checks, so the solution is $\frac{1}{2}$.

**TRY THIS** ➡

Solve.

6. $3(y - 1) - 1 = 2 - 5(y + 5)$

## ▪▪▪ The Principle of Zero Products

When we multiply two numbers, the product will be zero if one of the factors is zero. Furthermore, if a product is zero, then at least one of the factors must be zero.

**THEOREM 2-3   (The Principle of Zero Products)**
For any numbers $a$ and $b$,
if $ab = 0$, then $a = 0$ or $b = 0$, and
if $a = 0$ or $b = 0$, then $ab = 0$.

**Example 5.**  Solve: $(x + 4)(x - 2) = 0$.

Here we have a product which is zero. This equation will become true when either factor is zero. Hence it is true when $x + 4 = 0$ or $x - 2 = 0$. We have applied the principle of zero products. Solving each equation separately we get:

$x = -4$ or $x = 2$.

There are two solutions, $-4$ and $2$.

The check is not necessary when we use the principle of zero products, except to detect errors.

**Example 6.**  Solve: $7x(4x + 2) = 0$.

$7x = 0$  or  $4x + 2 = 0$    *Using the principle of zero products*
$x = 0$  or    $4x = -2$
$x = 0$        $x = -\frac{1}{2}$    *Solving each equation separately*

The solutions are $0$ and $-\frac{1}{2}$.

**TRY THIS** ➡

Solve.

7. $(x - 19)(x + 5) = 0$
8. $x(3x - 17) = 0$
9. $(9x + 2)(-6x + 3) = 0$

## Exercise Set 2-2

▌Solve. (*See Example 1.*)

1. $4x - 12 = 60$
2. $4x - 6 = 70$
3. $5y + 3 = 28$
4. $7t + 11 = 74$
5. $2y - 11 = 37$
6. $3x - 13 = 29$
7. $5x - 10 = 45$
8. $6z - 7 = 11$
9. $9t + 4 = -104$
10. $5x + 7 = -108$
11. $-7x + 2 = -54$
12. $-9y + 8 = -91$
13. $-4x - 7 = -35$
14. $-8y - 83 = -5$

Solve. (*See Examples 2 and 3.*)

15. $6x + 2x = 16$
16. $9y + 2y = 33$
17. $5x + 2x = 56$
18. $3x + 7x = 120$
19. $9y - 7y = 42$
20. $8t - 3t = 65$
21. $-8x - 4x = 60$
22. $-9y - 5y = 28$
23. $-6y - 10y = -32$
24. $-8t - 12t = -80$
25. $8x + 48 = 3x - 12$
26. $15x + 20 = 8x - 22$
27. $7y - 1 = 23 - 5y$
28. $3z - 15 = 15 - 3z$
29. $4x - 3 = 5 + 12x$
30. $9t - 4 = 14 + 15t$
31. $5 - 4a = a - 13$
32. $8 - 5x = x - 16$
33. $3m - 7 = -7 - 4m - m$
34. $5x - 8 = -8 + 3x - x$
35. $5r - 2 + 3r = 2r + 6 - 4r$
36. $5m - 17 - 2m = 6m - 1 - m$

▌▌Solve. (*See Example 4.*)

37. $2(x + 6) = 8x$
38. $3(y + 5) = 8y$
39. $80 = 10(3t + 2)$
40. $27 = 9(5y - 2)$
41. $180(n - 2) = 900$
42. $210(x - 3) = 840$
43. $5y - (2y - 10) = 25$
44. $8x - (3x - 5) = 40$
45. $7(3x + 6) = 11 - (x + 2)$
46. $9(2x + 8) = 20 - (x + 5)$
47. $\frac{1}{8}(16y + 8) - 17 = -\frac{1}{4}(8y - 16)$
48. $\frac{1}{6}(12t + 48) - 20 = -\frac{1}{8}(24t - 144)$
49. $a + (a - 3) = (a + 2) - (a + 1)$
50. $8 - 4(b - 1) = 2 + 3(4 - b)$

▌▌▌Solve. (*See Examples 5 and 6.*)

51. $(x + 2)(x - 5) = 0$
52. $(x + 4)(x - 8) = 0$
53. $(y - 8)(y - 9) = 0$
54. $(t - 3)(t - 7) = 0$
55. $(2x - 3)(3x - 2) = 0$
56. $(3y - 4)(4y - 1) = 0$
57. $m(m - 8) = 0$
58. $p(p - 5) = 0$
59. $0 = (2x + 8)(3x - 9)$
60. $0 = (4x + 16)(5x - 10)$
61. $x(x - 1)(x + 2) = 0$
62. $y(y - 4)(y + 2) = 0$

# 2-3 Solving Problems

After finishing Lesson 2-3, you should be able to
▮  solve problems by translating to equations.

▮ The first step in solving a problem is to translate to mathematical
language. Very often this means translating to an equation.
Drawing a picture sometimes helps. We solve the equation. Then
we check to see if we have a solution to the problem.

**Example 1.**  A 8-meter rope is cut into two pieces. One piece is
3 meters longer than the other. How long are the pieces?

One way to translate is this:

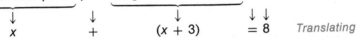

Length of one piece plus  length of other piece $= 8$

$$x \qquad + \qquad (x + 3) \qquad = 8 \qquad \textit{Translating}$$

(We use $x$ for the length of one piece and $x + 3$ for the length of
the other because we know one is 3 m longer than the other.)
Now we solve: $x + (x + 3) = 8$

$$2x + 3 = 8 \qquad \textit{Combining like terms}$$
$$2x = 5$$
$$x = \tfrac{5}{2}, \text{ or } 2\tfrac{1}{2}$$

Do we have an answer to the problem itself? If one piece is $2\tfrac{1}{2}$ m
long and the other is 3 m longer, it must be $5\tfrac{1}{2}$ m long. Then the
lengths of the pieces add up to 8 m. This checks, so the answer
is that the pieces are $2\tfrac{1}{2}$ m and $5\tfrac{1}{2}$ m long.

**TRY THIS**

> 1.  A 12-cm rod is cut into two
>    pieces, one three times as
>    long as the other. How
>    long are the pieces?

**Example 2.**  It has been found that the world record for the
10,000-meter run has been decreasing steadily since 1940. The
record is 30.18 minutes minus 0.12 times the number of years
since 1940. If the record continues to decrease this way, what
will the record be in 1980?

Record is $\underbrace{30.18 \text{ minutes}}$ minus 0.12 times $\underbrace{\text{the number of years since 1940}}$

$$\begin{array}{ccccccc} \downarrow & \downarrow & \downarrow & \downarrow & \downarrow & \downarrow & & \downarrow \\ R & = & 30.18 & - & 0.12 & \cdot & & t \end{array}$$ *Translating*

$$\begin{aligned} R &= 30.18 - 0.12t \\ &= 30.18 - 0.12(40) \quad \textit{1980 is 40 years from} \\ &= 30.18 - 4.8 \qquad\qquad \textit{1940} \\ &= 25.38 \end{aligned}$$

The number 25.38 checks in the problem, so the world record in the 10,000-meter run in 1980 will be 25.38 minutes (a prediction).

**TRY THIS** ➡

---

**Example 3.** On December 17, 1974 the pilots of Pan American Airlines shocked the business world by taking a pay *cut* of 11% to a new salary of $48,950 per year. What was their former salary?

$\underbrace{\text{(Former salary)}}$ $-$ $11\%\underbrace{\text{(Former salary)}}$ $=$ $\underbrace{\text{New salary}}$

$$\begin{array}{ccccccc} \downarrow & & \downarrow & \downarrow & & \downarrow & & \downarrow & & \downarrow \\ x & & - & 11\% & \cdot & x & & = & & 48{,}950 \end{array}$$ *Translating*

We have used $x$ to represent the former salary.

$$\begin{aligned} x - 11\%x &= 48{,}950 \quad \textit{Solving} \\ 1x - 0.11x &= 48{,}950 \\ (1 - 0.11)x &= 48{,}950 \\ 0.89x &= 48{,}950 \\ x &= \frac{48{,}950}{0.89} \\ x &= 55{,}000 \end{aligned}$$

Check: 11% of 55,000 is 6050. Subtracting from 55,000 we get 48,950. This checks, so the former salary was $55,000

**TRY THIS** ➡

---

2. It has been found that the world record for the 800-meter run has been decreasing steadily since 1930. The record is 1.82 minutes minus 0.0035 times the number of years since 1930. Predict what the record will be in 1980.

3. The County Cab Company charges sixty cents plus eleven cents per km as the fare. What will be the total cost of a 12 km ride?

4. A clothing store drops the price of suits 25% to a sale price of $93. What was the former price?

5. An investment is made at 8% simple interest. It grows to $783 at the end of 1 year. How much was invested originally? (*Hint:* Recall the expression $P + Prt$ regarding the return on a principal of $P$ dollars.)

## Exercise Set 2-3

▌Solve. (*See Examples 1–3.*)

1. A 12-cm piece of tubing is cut into two pieces. One piece is 4 cm longer than the other. How long are the pieces?

2. A 10 meter piece of wire is cut into two pieces. One piece is 2 meters longer than the other. How long are the pieces?

3. A piece of wire four meters long is cut into two pieces so that one piece is two-thirds as long as the other. Find the length of each piece.

4. A piece of rope five meters long is cut into two pieces so that one piece is three-fifths as long as the other. Find the length of each piece.

5. Tony's baby-sitting service charges $2.50 per day plus $1.75 per hour. What is the cost of a seven hour baby-sitting job?

6. The cost of renting a rug shampooer is $3.25 per hour plus $2.75 for the shampoo. Find the cost of shampooing if the time involved is 3.5 hours.

7. The Klunker car rental charges $16 per day plus 15¢ per kilometer. Find the cost of renting a car for a one day trip of 290 kilometers.

8. A phone company charges 30¢ per long distance call plus 20¢ per minute. Find the cost of an 18-minute long distance call.

9. Eight plus five times a number is seven times the number. What is the number?

10. Six plus three times a number is four times the number. What is the number?

11. Five more than three times a number is the same as ten less than six times the number. What is the number?

12. Six more than nine times a number is the same as two less than ten times the number. What is the number?

13. A pro shop in a bowling alley drops the price of bowling balls 24% to a sale price of $34.20. What was the former price?

14. An appliance store drops the price of a certain type of TV 18% to a sale price of $410. What was the former price?

15. Money is borrowed at 9% simple interest. After 1 year $708.50 pays off the loan. How much was originally borrowed?

16. Money is borrowed at 7% simple interest. After 1 year $856 pays off the loan. How much was originally borrowed?

17. The second angle of a triangle is three times the first and the third is 12° less than twice the first. Find the measures of the angles.

18. The second angle of a triangle is four times the first and the third is 5° more than twice the first. Find the measures of the angles.

19. The perimeter of a college basketball court is 96 m and the length is 14 m more than the width. What are the dimensions?

20. The perimeter of a certain soccer field is 310 m. The length is 65 m more than the width. What are the dimensions?

# 2-4 Formulas

After finishing Lesson 2-4, you should be able to
▮ solve a formula for a specified letter.

▮ A formula is a kind of recipe for doing a certain kind of calculation. Formulas are often given by equations. Here is a formula
we have considered.

$$A = P + Prt$$

This formula tells us the amount $A$ we will have if we invest principal $P$ at simple interest, at rate $r$ for $t$ years. Suppose we know
$A$, $r$, and $t$, and want to find $P$. To do this, we get $P$ alone on one
side, or "solve" the formula for $P$.

**Example 1.** Solve for $P$.

$$A = P + Prt$$
$$A = P(1 + rt) \qquad \textit{Factoring}$$
$$\frac{1}{1 + rt} \cdot A = P(1 + rt) \cdot \frac{1}{1 + rt} \qquad \textit{Multiplying by } \frac{1}{1 + rt}, \textit{ to get P}$$
$$\textit{alone on one side}$$
$$\frac{A}{1 + rt} = P$$

**TRY THIS** ➡

> 1. Solve for $Q$.
> $$T = Q + Qiy$$

**Example 2.** Solve for $D$.

$$C = \pi D$$
$$\frac{1}{\pi} \cdot C = \frac{1}{\pi} \cdot \pi D \qquad \textit{Multiplying by } \frac{1}{\pi}$$
$$\frac{C}{\pi} = D \qquad \textit{Simplifying}$$

**TRY THIS** ➡

> 2. A formula for the area of a
> triangle is $A = \frac{1}{2}bh$. Solve
> for $b$.

**Example 3.** Solve for $r$.

$$H = 2r + 3m$$
$$H - 3m = 2r \qquad \text{Adding } -3m$$
$$\tfrac{1}{2}(H - 3m) = r \qquad \text{Multiplying by } \tfrac{1}{2}$$

**TRY THIS** ➡️

3. Solve for $m$.
$$H = 2r + 3m$$

## Exercise Set 2-4

▌ Solve for the indicated letter. (*See Examples 1–3.*)

1. $A = \ell w$, for $\ell$
2. $A = \ell w$, for $w$
3. $W = EI$, for $I$
4. $W = EI$, for $E$
5. $F = ma$, for $m$
6. $F = ma$, for $a$
7. $I = Prt$, for $t$
8. $I = Prt$, for $P$
9. $E = mc^2$, for $m$
10. $E = mc^2$, for $c^2$
11. $P = 2\ell + 2w$, for $\ell$
12. $P = 2\ell + 2w$, for $w$
13. $C^2 = a^2 + b^2$, for $a^2$
14. $C^2 = a^2 + b^2$, for $b^2$
15. $A = \pi r^2$, for $r^2$
16. $A = \pi r^2$, for $\pi$
17. $W = \frac{11}{2}(h - 40)$, for $h$
18. $C = \frac{5}{9}(F - 32)$, for $F$
19. $V = \frac{4}{3}\pi r^3$, for $r^3$
20. $V = \frac{4}{3}\pi r^3$, for $\pi$
21. $A = \frac{1}{2}h(a + b)$, for $h$
22. $A = \frac{1}{2}h(a + b)$, for $b$
23. $\dfrac{P_1 V_1}{T_1} = \dfrac{P_2 V_2}{T_2}$, for $V_1$
24. $\dfrac{P_1 V_1}{T_1} = \dfrac{P_2 V_2}{T_2}$, for $T_2$
25. $F = \dfrac{Wr^2}{gr}$, for $r$
26. $F = \dfrac{Wr^2}{gr}$, for $W$

**CONSUMER NOTE: Balloon Payments**

Installment buying usually requires monthly payments that are all about the same. Sometimes, though, an installment contract calls for a "balloon" payment at the end. This is a final payment much larger than any of the others. If the buyer cannot pay it, the item being bought can be repossessed—taken away by the credit company. All the buyer has left is some hard-won knowledge about installment contracts.

Installment buyers should watch out for balloon payments. They can be a trap.

## CHAPTER 2 REVIEW

Review the material in the chapter. Then see how you have done by trying these review exercises. If you miss an exercise, restudy the indicated lesson.

2-1   Solve using the addition principle.
1. $x + 13 = 27$
2. $p - 17 = 9$

2-1   Solve using the multiplication principle.
3. $7y = -56$
4. $-14y = -126$

2-2   Solve.
5. $8x - 19 = 53$
6. $-9t - 74 = -2$
7. $3(x + 7) = 63$
8. $9y - (4y - 7) = -33$
9. $(x + 4)(x - 3) = 0$
10. $(2x - 5)(3x - 4) = 0$

2-3   Solve.
11. A 12-meter piece of wire is cut into two pieces. One piece is 3 meters longer than the other. How long are the pieces?
12. The cost of renting a lawn thatcher is $4.75 per hour plus $1.50 for gasoline. Find the cost of thatching a lawn if the time involved is 3.5 hours.

2-4   Solve for the indicated letter.
13. $A = \frac{1}{2}bh$, for $b$
14. $V = ah + at$, for $a$

## CHAPTER 2 TEST

Solve using the addition principle.
1.  $x + 18 = 32$
2.  $t - 19 = 6$

Solve using the multiplication principle.
3.  $-8y = 72$
4.  $15y = -225$

Solve.
5.  $9x + 14 = -67$
6.  $-3p - 75 = -3$
7.  $8(x + 9) = 112$
8.  $8y - (5y - 9) = -160$
9.  $(x + 7)(x - 8) = 0$
10.  $(3x + 5)(2x - 6) = 0$

Solve.
11.  A 14-meter piece of cable is cut into two pieces. One piece is 4 meters longer than the other. How long are the pieces?
12.  The cost of renting a floor sander is $5.25 per hour plus $2 for sandpaper. Find the cost of sanding a floor if the time involved is 4.5 hours.

Solve for the indicated letter.
13.  $E = \dfrac{I}{R}$, for $I$
14.  $Q = P - Prt$, for $P$

**Ready for Linear Equations?**

1-5    1.   Evaluate $y - xz$ when $x = -2$, $y = 3$, $z = -4$.

1-2    Add.
      2.   $-4 + 0$
      3.   $-2 + (-7)$
      4.   $-2.7 + (-3.5)$
      5.   $15 + (-8)$
      6.   $-8.1 + 2.4$
      7.   $\frac{2}{3} + (-\frac{3}{5})$

1-2    Find $-a$ when $a$ stands for
      8.   $-10$
      9.   $0$
    10.   $\frac{1}{2}$

      Solve.
2-1   11.   $x + 8 = -12$
2-1   12.   $3x = 21$
2-2   13.   $4x - 5 = 11$
2-2   14.   $9x - 2x = 21$
2-2   15.   $7x - 4 + 2x = -8 - 3x + 6$

# Chapter 3
# Linear Equations

*Temperature is related to cricket chirps by a linear equation.*

# 3-1 Graphs and Equations

After finishing Lesson 3-1, you should be able to
**I** plot points given their coordinates.
**II** decide whether a given point is a solution of an equation.
**III** draw graphs of simple equations.

On a number line each point is the graph of a number. On a plane each point is the graph of a number pair. Two perpendicular number lines called *axes* are used. The point where they cross is called the *origin* and is labeled 0. The arrows show the positive directions.

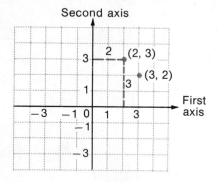

## I Plotting Points

Notice that (2, 3) and (3, 2) give different points. They are called *ordered pairs* of numbers since it makes a difference which number comes first.

**Example 1.** Plot the point (−4, 3).

The first number, −4, tells us the distance in the first direction.
We go 4 units *left*. The second number, 3, tells us the distance in the second direction. We go 3 units *up*.
The numbers in an ordered pair are called *coordinates*. In (−4, 3), −4 is the *first coordinate* and 3 is the *second coordinate*.

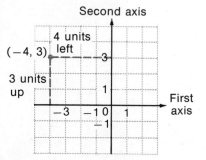

**TRY THIS**

Use graph paper. Draw and label the first and second axes. Then plot these points.

1. (6, 4)
2. (−3, 5)
3. (4, 6)
4. (−4, −3)
5. (0, 2)

When plotting a point, the first coordinate of the ordered pair tells us the distance in the first direction. The second coordinate tells us the distance in the second direction.

When finding the coordinates of a point, we see how far to the right or left it is located and how far up or down.

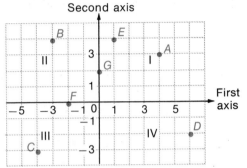

**Example 2.**  Find the coordinates of point *A*.

Point *A* is 4 units to the right and 3 units up. Its coordinates are (4, 3).

**TRY THIS**

> 6.  Find the coordinates of points *B*, *C*, *D*, *E*, *F*, and *G* in the drawing of Example 2.

Note that in region I (called the first *quadrant*) both coordinates of a point are positive. In region II (second quadrant) the first coordinate is negative and the second is positive.

**TRY THIS**

> 7.  What can you say about the coordinates of a point in the third quadrant?
> 8.  What can you say about the coordinates of a point in the fourth quadrant?

## ❚❚ Solutions of Equations

If an equation has two variables, its solutions must be pairs of numbers. We usually take the variables in alphabetical order. We get ordered pairs of numbers for solutions.

**Example 3.**  Determine whether $(-1, -4)$ is a solution of $y = 3x - 1$.

We replace *x* by $-1$ and *y* by $-4$.

$$
\begin{array}{c|l}
 & y = 3x - 1 \\
\hline
-4 & 3 \cdot (-1) - 1 \\
 & -3 - 1 \\
 & -4
\end{array}
$$

$(-1, -4)$ is a solution.

**Example 4.** Determine whether (7, 5) is a solution of $q = 3p - 1$.

We take the variables in alphabetical order, so $p = 7$ and $q = 5$.

$$
\begin{array}{c|l}
\multicolumn{2}{l}{q = 3p - 1} \\
\hline
5 & 3 \cdot 7 - 1 \\
  & 21 - 1 \\
  & 20
\end{array}
$$

(7, 5) is not a solution.

**TRY THIS**

> 9. Determine whether $(9, -2)$ is a solution of $y = 4x + 17$.
> 10. Determine whether $(0, 23)$ is a solution of $q = 4p + 17$.
> 11. Determine whether $(2, -2)$ is a solution of $2s + 6r = 8$.

## Ⅲ Graphs of Equations

To *graph an equation* we plot enough points to see a pattern and then draw a line or curve.

**Example 5.** Graph the equation $y - 2x = 1$.

We use alphabetical order for the variables. The first axis will be the *x*-axis and the second axis will be the *y*-axis.
First solve the equation for *y*.

$$y = 2x + 1$$

Next, find some solutions (ordered pairs), keeping the results in a table. To find an ordered pair we choose *any* number for *x*, substitute it in the equation, and then find *y*. Suppose we choose 0 for *x*. Then

$$
\begin{aligned}
y &= 2x + 1 \\
  &= 2 \cdot 0 + 1 \\
  &= 0 + 1 \\
  &= 1
\end{aligned}
$$

When $x = 0$, $y = 1$. This gives us an ordered pair (0, 1). We continue to find ordered pairs, filling in the table.

| $x$ | $y$ |
|:---:|:---:|
| 0 | 1 |
| −1 | −1 |
| −2 | −3 |
| 1 | 3 |
| 2 | 5 |

*We choose these numbers.*          *We find these numbers by substituting in the equation.*

Now we plot these points. (See the graph to the left below.)

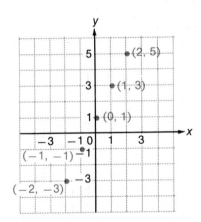
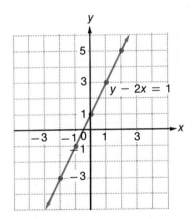

In this case the points seem to lie on a straight line. In fact, they do. If we take all the solutions of the equation we get the entire line, so the graph of this equation is a straight line containing the points we plotted. We can draw the line with a ruler. The graph is shown above to the right.

**TRY THIS**

12. Graph $y = 2x - 1$.
13. Graph $y = -x + 1$.

## Exercise Set 3-1

▮ Use graph paper. Draw a first and a second axis. Then plot these points.
You may plot several points on the same piece of paper. (*See Example 1.*)

1. (3, 4)
3. (−2, 3)
5. (2, −4)
7. (−3, −5)
9. (0, 3)
11. (0, −2)
13. (6, 0)
15. (−6, 0)

2. (6, 3)
4. (−3, 5)
6. (3, −4)
8. (−7, −4)
10. (0, 7)
12. (0, −5)
14. (4, 0)
16. (−7, 0)

(*See Example 2.*)

17. Find the coordinates of points *A*, *B*, *C*, *D*, and *E*.

18. Find the coordinates of points *A*, *B*, *C*, *D*, and *E*.

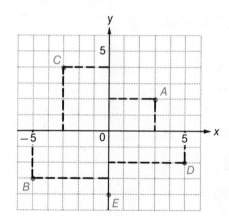

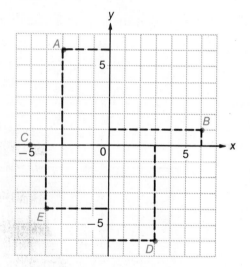

▮▮ Decide whether the given point is a solution of the indicated equation. (*See Examples 3 and 4.*)

19. (1, −1); $y = 2x − 3$
21. (3, 4); $3s + t = 4$
23. (3, 5); $4x − y = 7$
25. (0, $\frac{3}{5}$); $2a + 5b = 3$
27. (2, −1); $4r + 3s = 5$
29. (3, 2); $3x − 2y = −4$

20. (2, 5); $y = 3x − 1$
22. (2, 3); $2p + q = 5$
24. (2, 7); $5x − y = 3$
26. (0, $\frac{3}{2}$); $3f + 4g = 6$
28. (2, −4); $5w + 2z = 2$
30. (1, 2); $2x − 5y = −6$

▪▪▪ Graph the following equations. (*See Example 5.*)

31. $y = x$

32. $y = -x$

33. $y = -3x$

34. $y = 3x$

35. $q = p + 2$

36. $q = p - 2$

37. $y = 3x + 1$

38. $y = 2x - 1$

39. $t = -4s + 1$

40. $t = -3s + 2$

41. $3x = 2y + 1$

42. $2x = 3y + 1$

43. $2x + 5y = 10$

44. $3x + 9y = 12$

45. $3p - 2q = 6$

46. $4r - 3s = 12$

47. $y = \frac{1}{2}x + 2$

48. $y = \frac{1}{3}x - 2$

## Calculator Exercises

Decide whether the given point is a solution of the indicated equation.

49. $(3.721, -3.058)$; $4x - 2y = 21$

50. $(-1.072, 1.592)$; $2x + 7y = 9$

## Challenge Exercises

Devise a coordinate system in which the axes are not perpendicular. Graph the following equations using your coordinate system.

51. $y = x$    52. $y = x + 2$

### HISTORICAL NOTE: Let a Machine Do It

Anyone who has done a difficult calculation experiences two feelings. One is impatience. The work seems to take a long time. The other feeling is worry. An error in any part of the calculation will mean an error in the result. These two feelings prompted the invention of calculating machines.

Blaise Pascal invented a calculating machine in France in 1642. Gottfried Wilhelm von Leibniz, a great German mathematician, invented one in 1671. Charles Babbage of England designed several calculating machines in the 1800s. None of these inventions was produced for public sale, but their principles of operation led to modern calculating machines.

# 3-2 Linear Equations

After finishing Lesson 3-2, you should be able to
**I** identify linear equations.
**II** find the standard form of a linear equation.
**III** graph linear equations.
**IIII** graph linear equations using intercepts.
**IIIII** graph linear equations with a missing variable (single variable).

## I Recognizing Linear Equations

Equations which have straight lines for their graphs are called *linear* equations. An equation is linear if the variables occur to the first power only. There must be no products of variables or variables in denominators.

**Example 1.** Which of the following equations are linear?

a) $xy = 9$  b) $2r + 7 = 4s$  c) $4x^3 = 7y$

d) $8x - 17y = y$  e) $q = \dfrac{3}{p}$  f) $4x = -3$

Equations b), d), and f) are linear equations.

Since in linear equations the variables occur to the first power only, they are also called *first degree equations*.

**TRY THIS** ➡️

> Which of these equations are linear (first degree)?
>
> 1. $5y + 8x = 9$
> 2. $7y = 11$
> 3. $5y^2x = 13$
> 4. $x = 4 + \dfrac{7}{y}$
> 5. $xy = 0$
> 6. $3x - 2y + 5 = 0$

## II Finding the Standard Form

### DEFINITION

The *standard form* for a linear equation is $Ax + By + C = 0$, where $A$ and $B$ are not both zero.

**Example 2.** Find standard form for the equation $4x + y = 2$.

$4x + y - 2 = 0$  *Using the addition principle, adding* $-2$

This equation is of the form $Ax + By + C = 0$, where $A = 4$, $B = 1$, and $C = -2$.

**Example 3.**  Find standard form for the equation $7x = \frac{1}{4} - 5x$.

$$7x = \frac{1}{4} - 5x$$
$$7x + 5x - \frac{1}{4} = 0 \qquad \textit{Using the addition principle, adding } 5x - \frac{1}{4}$$
$$12x + 0y - \frac{1}{4} = 0$$

This equation is of the form $Ax + By + C = 0$, where $A = 12$, $B = 0$, and $C = -\frac{1}{4}$.

**TRY THIS**

Find standard form for each equation.

7.  $5y = \frac{1}{2} + 5x$
8.  $8y = 10 + 5y$

## III Graphing Linear Equations

### THEOREM 3-1

The graph of any linear equation is a straight line.

From Theorem 3-1, we know that the graph of a first degree equation will be a straight line. Plotting two points is sufficient, but we usually use at least one more point, as a check.

**Example 4.**  Graph the equation $3y + 3 = 2x$.

We solve for $y$.

$$y = \frac{2}{3}x - 1.$$

We find two points.

If $x = 0$, $y = \frac{2}{3} \cdot 0 - 1$
$$= -1$$

If $x = -2$, $y = \frac{2}{3} \cdot (-2) - 1$
$$= -\frac{7}{3}$$

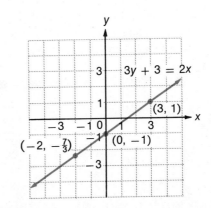

We plot the points $(0, -1)$ and $(-2, -\frac{7}{3})$ and draw the line.
We find a third point as a check.

If $x = 3$, $y = \frac{2}{3} \cdot 3 - 1$
$$= 2 - 1$$
$$= 1$$

We plot the point $(3, 1)$ as a check. It lies on the line, so our graph is probably correct.

**TRY THIS**

9.  Graph $2x - 6y = -2$
10.  Graph $3y = 2x - 6$

#### IIII **Graphing Using Intercepts**

### DEFINITION

The points where a line crosses the axes are called the *intercepts*.

We can usually find intercepts easily, so we often use them in graphing. To find an intercept, we give one variable the value 0.

**Example 5.**  Graph $4x + 5y = 20$.

To find the *y*-intercept, we let $x = 0$.

Then     $4 \cdot 0 + 5y = 20$
$5y = 20$
$y = 4$

Thus $(0, 4)$ is the *y*-intercept.

To find the *x*-intercept, we let $y = 0$.

Then     $4x + 5 \cdot 0 = 20$
$4x = 20$
$x = 5$

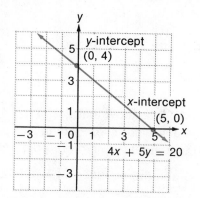

Thus $(5, 0)$ is the *x*-intercept.

We plot the points $(0, 4)$ and $(5, 0)$ and draw the graph. If a line goes through the origin $(0, 0)$, we must use another point. A third point should be used as a check.

**TRY THIS**

Graph using intercepts.

11.  $3y = 2x - 6$
12.  $4x + 7y = 28$
13.  $9x + 2y = 18$

#### IIIII **Equations with a Missing Variable**

Consider the equation $y = 4$. We can think of it as $y = 0 \cdot x + 4$. No matter what number we choose for *x*, we find *y* is 4. Thus $(x, 4)$ is a solution no matter what *x* is.

### THEOREM 3-2

If *x* is missing in a linear equation the graph is a line parallel to the *x*-axis. If *y* is missing the graph is a line parallel to the *y*-axis.

**Example 6.** Graph $y = 4$.

Any ordered pair $(x, 4)$ is a solution.
So the line is parallel to the $x$-axis
with $y$-intercept $(0, 4)$.

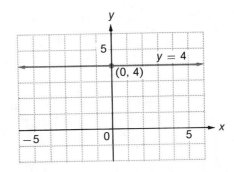

**Example 7.** Graph $x = -2$.

Any ordered pair $(-2, y)$
is a solution. So the line
is parallel to the $y$-axis
with $x$-intercept $(-2, 0)$.

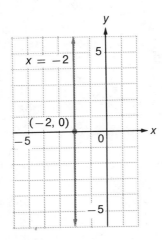

**TRY THIS** ➡

Graph these equations, using
the same axes.

14. $x = 4$
15. $y = -3$
16. $y = 0$

## Exercise Set 3-2

▌ Which of the following equations are linear? If an equation is not linear,
give the reason. (*See Example 1.*)

1. $3x - 4 = y$
2. $x = 9$
3. $4r^2 = 2r + 1$
4. $2 + 3pq = -9$
5. $y = 7$
6. $3x^2 + 4y^2 = 16$
7. $4x - 5y = 20$
8. $5 = \dfrac{1}{x}$
9. $3p - 4 = q - 1$
10. $5 = r + 4t$

**▮▮** Find standard form. (*See Examples 2 and 3.*)

11. $4x - 8 = y$

12. $x = 2y - 1$

13. $y = 2x + 3$

14. $y = 6x - 2$

15. $y + 4 = 4x + 8$

16. $3x - 8 = x - 2$

17. $x = 6$

18. $y = 9$

19. $\sqrt{2}y = 3x$

20. $\sqrt{3}x = 5y$

**▮▮▮** Use graph paper. Graph these linear equations. Use a different set of axes for each. (*See Example 4.*)

21. $x + 2y = 4$

22. $x + 3y = 9$

23. $-x + 4y = 8$

24. $-x + 2y = 6$

25. $4x + y = 8$

26. $3x + y = 6$

27. $3y - 3 = 6x$

28. $2y - 6 = 4x$

29. $y = 3x$

30. $y = 4x$

31. $3x + 6y = 18$

32. $4x + 5y = 20$

**▮▮▮▮** Find the intercepts of each equation. (*See Example 5.*)

33. $x - 2 = y$

34. $x - 4 = y$

35. $3a - 1 = b$

36. $3a - 4 = b$

37. $5x - 4y = 20$

38. $3x - 5y = 15$

39. $y = -5 - 5x$

40. $y = -2 - 2x$

41. $2p + 7q = 14$

42. $3p + 6q = 12$

Use graph paper and different axes for each equation. Label the intercepts and a third point used as a check. (*See Example 5.*)

43. Graph the equation in Exercise 33.

44. Graph the equation in Exercise 34.

45. Graph the equation in Exercise 35.

46. Graph the equation in Exercise 36.

47. Graph the equation in Exercise 37.

48. Graph the equation in Exercise 38.

49. Graph the equation in Exercise 39.

50. Graph the equation in Exercise 40.

51. Graph the equation in Exercise 41.

52. Graph the equation in Exercise 42.

**▮▮▮▮▮** Graph the following equations. (*See Examples 6 and 7.*)

53. $x = 2$

54. $x = 4$

55. $y = -6$

56. $y = -3$

57. $x = -5$

58. $x = -3$

59. $y = 7$

60. $y = 5$

---

**Calculator Exercises**

Find the intercepts of each equation.

61. $4.92x - 3.07 = y$

62. $1.706x - 3.481y = 7.283$

# 3-3 Slope

After finishing Lesson 3-3, you should be able to
**I** find the slope of a line containing a given pair of points.
**II** find the slope, if it exists, of lines such as $y = 6$ or $x = 5$.
**III** given a point on a line and its slope, use the point-slope equation of a line to find an equation for the line.

## I Finding the Slope of a Line

Graphs of some linear equations slant upward from left to right. Others slant downward. Some slant more steeply than others. Here is a line with two points marked. As we go from $P_1$ to $P_2$ the change in $x$ is $x_2 - x_1$. The change in $y$ is $y_2 - y_1$.

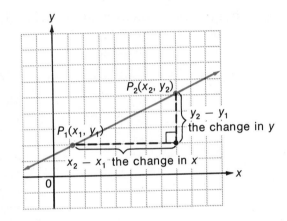

### DEFINITION

The slope $m$ of a line is $\dfrac{y_2 - y_1}{x_2 - x_1}\left(\dfrac{\text{change in } y}{\text{change in } x}\right)$, where $(x_1, y_1)$ and $(x_2, y_2)$ are any two points on the line.

To find the slope of a line, we find two points on it. We find the change in $y$ and the change in $x$ and divide.

**Example 1.** The points $(1, 2)$ and $(3, 6)$ are on a line. Find its slope.

The slope, $m = \dfrac{y_2 - y_1}{x_2 - x_1}, \dfrac{\text{change in } y}{\text{change in } x}$

$$= \frac{6 - 2}{3 - 1}$$

$$= \frac{4}{2}, \text{ or } 2.$$

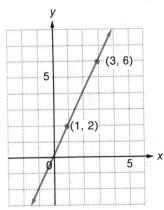

If we use the points $(1, 2)$ and $(3, 6)$ in opposite order, we find that the change in $y$ is negative and the change in $x$ is negative. We get the same number for the slope.

$$m = \frac{2 - 6}{1 - 3} = \frac{-4}{-2}, \text{ or } 2$$

To compute slope the order of the points does not matter as long as we take the same order for finding the differences.

**TRY THIS** ━━━▶

Find the slope of the line containing these points.

1. (1, 1) and (12, 14)
2. (3, 9) and (4, 10)

If a line slants up from left to right, it has positive slope. See Example 1. The line in the example below has negative slope. It slants down from left to right.

**Example 2.** Graph the line containing the points (1, −1) and (3, −4) and find its slope.

$$m = \frac{-4 - (-1)}{3 - 1}$$

$$= \frac{-4 + 1}{2}$$

$$= -\frac{3}{2}$$

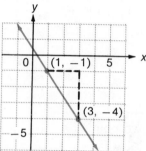

**TRY THIS** ━━━▶

Graph the lines containing these points and find their slopes.

3. (−1, −1) and (2, −4)
4. (0, 2) and (3, 1)

## ‖ Horizontal and Vertical Lines

What about the slopes of vertical and horizontal lines?

**Example 3.** Find the slope of the line $y = 3$.

$$y_2 - y_1 = 3 - 3$$
$$= 0$$
$$x_2 - x_1 = -2 - 4$$
$$= -6$$
$$\text{slope} = \frac{0}{-6} = 0$$

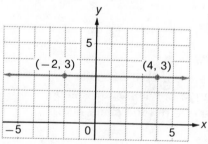

Any two points on a horizontal line have the same second coordinate. Thus the change in $y$ is 0, so the slope is 0.

**Example 4.** Find the slope of the line $x = -4$.

$$y_2 - y_1 = -2 - 3$$
$$= -5$$
$$x_2 - x_1 = -4 - (-4)$$
$$= 0$$
$$\text{slope} = \frac{-5}{0}$$

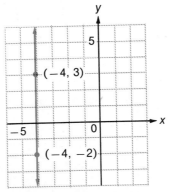

(−4, 3)

(−4, −2)

Since division by 0 is not defined, we say that this line has no slope.

Any two points on a vertical line have the same first coordinates. Thus the change in $x$ is 0, so the denominator in the formula for slope would be 0. Since we cannot divide by 0, the line has no slope.

**THEOREM 3-3**

A horizontal line has slope 0. A vertical line has *no* slope.

**TRY THIS**

Find the slopes, if they exist, of the lines containing these points.

5. (4, 6) and (−2, 6)
6. (−7, 3) and (−7, 2)

## ⊪ Point-Slope Equations of Lines

If we know the slope of a line and the coordinates of a point on the line, we can find an equation of the line.

**THEOREM 3-4** **(The Point-Slope Equation)**

A line containing a point $(x_1, y_1)$ with slope $m$ has an equation $(y - y_1) = m(x - x_1)$.

**Example 5.** Find an equation of the line containing the point $(\frac{1}{2}, -1)$ with slope 5.

$$(y - y_1) = m(x - x_1)$$
$$y - (-1) = 5(x - \tfrac{1}{2}) \quad \textit{Substituting}$$
$$y + 1 = 5(x - \tfrac{1}{2})$$
$$y = 5x - \tfrac{7}{2} \quad \textit{Simplifying}$$

**Example 6.** Find an equation of the line with *y*-intercept (0, 4) and slope $\frac{3}{5}$.

$$(y - y_1) = m(x - x_1)$$
$$y - 4 = \tfrac{3}{5}(x - 0) \qquad \textit{Substituting}$$
$$y = \tfrac{3}{5}x + 4 \qquad \textit{Simplifying}$$

**TRY THIS**

7. Find an equation of the line containing the point (−2, 4) with slope −3.
8. Find an equation of the line containing the point (−4, −10) with slope $\frac{1}{4}$.
9. Find an equation of the line with *x*-intercept (5, 0) and slope $-\frac{1}{2}$.

**A Proof of Theorem 3-4**

We have seen that a line containing a point $(x_1, y_1)$ with slope *m* has an equation $(y - y_1) = m(x - x_1)$. Let us prove this.

Think of a fixed point *P*, with coordinates $(x_1, y_1)$, on a nonvertical line. Suppose we have a movable point *P* on the line with coordinates $(x, y)$. The slope *m* is

$$\frac{y - y_1}{x - x_1}.$$

This is true only when $(x, y)$ is a point different from $(x_1, y_1)$. Now we can use the multiplication principle.

$$\frac{y - y_1}{x - x_1} = m \qquad \textit{Definition of slope}$$

$$\frac{(y - y_1)}{(x - x_1)} \cdot (x - x_1) = m(x - x_1) \qquad \textit{Multiplication principle}$$

$$(y - y_1) \cdot \frac{(x - x_1)}{(x - x_1)} = m(x - x_1) \qquad \textit{Simplifying}$$

$$(y - y_1) = m(x - x_1)$$

This equation holds even when $(x, y) = (x_1, y_1)$.

# Exercise Set 3-3

**I** Find the slopes of the lines containing these points. (*See Examples 1 and 2.*)

1. (5, 0) and (6, 8)
3. (0, 7) and (−2, 9)
5. (4, −3) and (6, −4)
7. (0, 0) and (−4, −8)
9. (−2, −4) and (−9, −7)
11. ($\frac{1}{2}$, $\frac{1}{4}$) and ($\frac{3}{2}$, $\frac{3}{4}$)
13. ($\frac{1}{8}$, $\frac{1}{4}$) and ($\frac{3}{4}$, $\frac{1}{2}$)

2. (4, 0) and (7, 3)
4. (0, 8) and (3, 8)
6. (5, −7) and (8, −3)
8. (0, 0) and (−5, −6)
10. (−3, −7) and (−8, −5)
12. ($\frac{3}{5}$, $\frac{1}{2}$) and ($\frac{1}{5}$, −$\frac{1}{2}$)
14. ($\frac{1}{3}$, −$\frac{1}{8}$) and ($\frac{5}{6}$, −$\frac{1}{4}$)

**II** Find the slope, if it exists, of each of these lines. (*See Examples 3 and 4.*)

15. $x = 7$
17. $y = -3$
19. $x = 6$
21. $y = 20$

16. $x = -4$
18. $y = 18$
20. $x = -17$
22. $y = -31$

**III** Find equations of the lines containing the given points with the indicated slopes. (*See Examples 5 and 6.*)

23. (3, 2); $m = 4$
25. (−5, −2); $m = -1$
27. (−6, 4); $m = \frac{1}{2}$
29. (0, −7); $m = 0$

24. (4, 7); $m = -2$
26. (−2, −4); $m = 3$
28. (3, −1); $m = -\frac{4}{3}$
30. (3, 0); $m = 0$

## Calculator Exercises

Find the slopes of the lines containing these points.

31. (0.04, 0.08) and (0.47, 0.83)
32. (0.02, 0.8) and (−0.2, −0.04)
33. (46,592, 86,874) and (−56,729, −83,497)
34. (54,706, −73,082) and (−93,349, −75,876)

## Challenge Exercises

35. Use graph paper. Plot the points $A$(0, 0), $B$(8, 2), $C$(11, 6) and $D$(3, 4). Draw $\overline{AB}$, $\overline{BC}$, $\overline{CD}$, and $\overline{DA}$. Find the slopes of each of these four segments. Compare the slopes of $\overline{AB}$ and $\overline{CD}$. Compare the slopes of $\overline{BC}$ and $\overline{DA}$.
36. Use graph paper. Plot the points $E$(−2, −5), $F$(2, −2), $G$(7, −2) and $H$(3, −5). Draw $\overline{EF}$, $\overline{FG}$, $\overline{GH}$, $\overline{HE}$, $\overline{EG}$, and $\overline{FH}$. Compare the slopes of $\overline{EG}$ and $\overline{FH}$.

# 3-4 More Equations of Lines

After finishing Lesson 3-4, you should be able to
**I** given two points, find the two-point equation of the line.
**II** given the slope-intercept equation for a line, find the slope and y-intercept.

## I Two-Point Equations of Lines

Given two points, we can find an equation of the line containing them.

**THEOREM 3-5 (The Two-Point Equation)**

Any nonvertical line containing the points $(x_1, y_1)$ and $(x_2, y_2)$ has

an equation $y - y_1 = \dfrac{y_2 - y_1}{x_2 - x_1}(x - x_1)$.

**Example 1.** Find an equation of the line containing the points (2, 3) and (1, −4).

a) We take (2, 3) as $P_1$ and (1, −4) as $P_2$. Then substitute in the two-point equation.

$y - 3 = \dfrac{-4 - 3}{1 - 2}(x - 2)$

$y - 3 = \dfrac{-7}{-1}(x - 2)$

$y - 3 = 7(x - 2)$     *Simplifying*
$y - 3 = 7x - 14$     *Removing parentheses*
$\quad\;\; y = 7x - 11$     *Using the addition principle*

b) It doesn't matter which point we take as $P_1$ and which we take as $P_2$. If we take (1, −4) as $P_1$ and (2, 3) as $P_2$, we get the same equation.

$y - (-4) = \dfrac{3 - (-4)}{2 - 1}(x - 1)$

$\quad\quad\;\; y = 7x - 11$     *Simplifying*

**TRY THIS** ⟶

Find an equation of the line containing the points

1. (1, 4) and (3, −2)
2. (3, −6) and (0, 4)

## ıı Slope-Intercept Equations of Lines

Given the slope and $y$-intercept of a line, we can find an equation of the line.

### THEOREM 3-6 (The Slope-Intercept Equation)

A nonvertical line with slope $m$ and $y$-intercept $(0, b)$ has an equation $y = mx + b$.

For brevity, we often refer to the number $b$ as the intercept.

**Example 2.** Find the slope and $y$-intercept of $y = 5x - \frac{1}{4}$.

We can read the numbers from the equation directly.

$$y = 5x - \tfrac{1}{4}$$

slope 5     intercept $-\frac{1}{4}$

**Example 3.** Find the slope and $y$-intercept of $y = 8$.

We can first write this equation as

$$y = 0x + 8.$$

Then   slope 0     intercept 8

**TRY THIS**

> 3. Find the slope and $y$-intercept of $y = -7x + 11$.
> 4. Find the slope and $y$-intercept of $y = -4$.

From any equation for a nonvertical line we can find the slope-intercept equation by solving for $y$.

**Example 4.** Find the slope and $y$-intercept of the line whose equation is $3x - 6y - 7 = 0$.

First solve for $y$.

$$-6y = -3x + 7$$
$$-\tfrac{1}{6} \cdot (-6y) = -\tfrac{1}{6} \cdot (-3x) + \left(-\tfrac{1}{6}\right) \cdot 7$$
$$y = \tfrac{1}{2}x - \tfrac{7}{6}$$

slope $\frac{1}{2}$     $y$-intercept $-\frac{7}{6}$

There is no slope-intercept equation for a vertical line because such a line has no slope.

**TRY THIS**

> 5. a) Find the slope-intercept equation of the line whose equation is $-2x + 3y - 6 = 0$.
>     b) Find the slope and $y$-intercept of this line.

## Exercise Set 3-4

▌Find an equation of the line containing each of the following pairs of points. (*See Example 1.*)

1. $(1, 4)$ and $(5, 6)$
2. $(2, 6)$ and $(4, 1)$
3. $(-1, -1)$ and $(2, 2)$
4. $(-3, -3)$ and $(6, 6)$
5. $(-2, 0)$ and $(0, 5)$
6. $(6, 0)$ and $(0, -3)$
7. $(3, 5)$ and $(-5, 3)$
8. $(4, 6)$ and $(-6, 4)$
9. $(0, 0)$ and $(5, 2)$
10. $(0, 0)$ and $(7, 3)$
11. $(-4, -7)$ and $(-2, -1)$
12. $(-2, -3)$ and $(-4, -6)$

▌▌Find the slope and *y*-intercept of each of the following lines. (*See Examples 2–4.*)

13. $y = 2x + 3$
14. $y = 3x + 4$
15. $y = -4x + 9$
16. $y = -5x - 7$
17. $y = 6 - x$
18. $y = 7 - x$
19. $2y = -6x + 10$
20. $-3y = -12x + 6$
21. $3x - 4y = 12$
22. $5x + 2y = -7$
23. $6x + 2y - 8 = 0$
24. $3y - 2x + 5 = 0$
25. $-7x - 3y - 9 = 0$
26. $-8x - 5y - 7 = 0$
27. $y = 7$
28. $y = 9$
29. $3y + 10 = 0$
30. $4y + 11 = 0$

---

### Calculator Exercises

Find the slope and *y*-intercept of each of the following lines.

31. $2.735x - 1.379y - 6.084 = 0$
32. $-4.005x + 2.057y + 8.316 = 0$

### Challenge Exercises

33. Find an equation of the line containing $(2, -3)$ and having the same slope as the line $3x + 4y = 10$.
34. Find an equation of the line containing $(3, -4)$ and having slope $-2$. If this line contains the points $(a, 8)$ and $(5, b)$, find $a$ and $b$.

# 3-5 Parallel and Perpendicular Lines

After finishing Lesson 3-5, you should be able to
**I**   tell, without graphing, whether the graphs of a pair of equations are parallel.
**II**  given an equation of a line and a point, write an equation of the line parallel to the given line through the given point.
**III** given an equation of a line and a point, write an equation of the line perpendicular to the given line through the given point.

## I Parallel Lines

When we graph a pair of linear equations, there are three possibilities.

1.  The equations have the same graph.
2.  The graphs intersect at exactly one point.
3.  The graphs are parallel lines.

**THEOREM 3-7**

If nonvertical lines have the same slope but different $y$-intercepts, they are parallel. Also, if nonvertical lines are parallel they have the same slope and different $y$-intercepts.

**Example 1.** Determine whether the graphs of $y = -3x + 5$ and $4y = -12x + 20$ are parallel.

These equations have the same graph, so the lines are not parallel. We can determine this without looking at the graphs. We find the slope-intercept equations by solving for $y$.

$$y = -3x + 5$$
$$y = -3x + 5$$

The slope-intercept equations are the same. This tells us that the graphs are the same line.

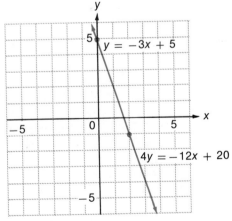

**Example 2.** Determine whether the graphs of $y - 3x = 1$ and $-2y = 3x + 2$ are parallel.

These graphs intersect. We can determine this without looking at the graphs. We find the slope-intercept equations by solving for $y$.

$$y = 3x + 1$$
$$y = -\tfrac{3}{2}x - 1$$

The slopes are different, so the lines are not parallel.

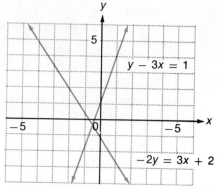

**Example 3.** Determine whether the graphs of $3x - y = -5$ and $y - 3x = -2$ are parallel.

We can determine this without looking at the graphs. We find the slope-intercept equations by solving for $y$.

$$y = 3x + 5$$
$$y = 3x - 2$$

The slopes are the same, but the $y$-intercepts are different, so the lines are parallel.

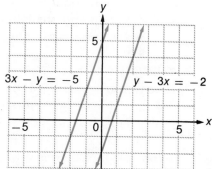

**TRY THIS**

Without graphing, tell whether the graphs of each pair of equations are parallel. (*Hint:* First find the slope-intercept equation.)

1. $x + 4 = y$
   $y - x = -3$
2. $y + 4 = 3x$
   $4x - y = -7$
3. $y = 4x + 5$
   $2y = 8x + 10$

## ▪▪ Finding Equations of Parallel Lines

**Example 4.** Write an equation of the line parallel to the line $2x + y - 10 = 0$ and containing the point $(-1, 3)$.

a)  We first find the slope-intercept equation. It is

$$y = -2x + 10.$$

Now we see that the parallel line must have slope $-2$.

b)  We find the point-slope equation of the line with slope $-2$ and containing the point $(-1, 3)$.

$$y - y_1 = m(x - x_1) \qquad \textit{Theorem 3-4}$$
$$y - 3 = -2[x - (-1)] \qquad \textit{Substituting}$$
$$y = -2x + 1 \qquad \textit{Simplifying}$$

The equations $y = -2x + 10$ and $y = -2x + 1$ have the same slope and different $y$-intercepts. Hence their graphs are parallel.

**TRY THIS**

4.  Write an equation of the line parallel to the line $2y + 8x = 6$ and containing the point $(-2, -4)$.

## ▪▪▪ Perpendicular Lines

If two lines meet at right angles, they are called perpendicular.

**THEOREM 3-8**

If for two nonvertical lines, the product of the slopes is $-1$, the lines are perpendicular. Also, if two lines are perpendicular, the product of the slopes is $-1$.

**Example 5.** Determine whether the lines $5y = 4x + 10$ and $4y = -5x + 4$ are perpendicular.

We find the slope-intercept equations by solving for $y$.

$$y = \tfrac{4}{5}x + 2$$
$$y = -\tfrac{5}{4}x + 1$$

The product of the slopes is $-1$; that is,

$$\tfrac{4}{5} \cdot \left(-\tfrac{5}{4}\right) = -1.$$

The lines are perpendicular.

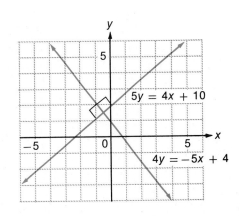

**TRY THIS**

5. Complete.

| Slope of a line | Slope of any perpendicular |
|---|---|
| a) 2 | |
| b) $-\frac{1}{4}$ | |
| c) $\frac{7}{6}$ | |
| d) $-\frac{2}{5}$ | |

6. Without graphing, tell whether the graphs of each pair of equations are perpendicular.

   a) $2y - x = 2$
      $y + 2x = 4$
   b) $3y = 2x + 15$
      $2y = 3x + 10$

**Example 6.** Write an equation of the line perpendicular to $4y - x = 20$ and containing the point $(2, -3)$.

a) We find the slope-intercept equation for $4y - x = 20$.

$$y = \tfrac{1}{4}x + 5$$

We know that the slope of the perpendicular line is $-4$, because

$$\tfrac{1}{4} \cdot (-4) = -1.$$

b) We find the point-slope equation of the line having slope $-4$ and containing the point $(2, -3)$.

$$\begin{array}{ll} y - y_1 = m(x - x_1) & \textit{Theorem 3-4} \\ y - (-3) = -4(x - 2) & \textit{Substituting} \\ y = -4x + 5 & \textit{Simplifying} \end{array}$$

7. Write an equation of the line perpendicular to the line $y = \tfrac{7}{8}x - 3$ and containing the point $(-1, 2)$.
8. Write an equation of the line perpendicular to the line $4 - y = 2x$ and containing the point $(3, 4)$.

**TRY THIS**

## Exercise Set 3-5

▌Without graphing, tell whether the graphs of each pair of equations are parallel. (*See Examples 1–3.*)

1.  $x + 6 = y$
    $y - x = -2$

2.  $2x - 7 = y$
    $y - 2x = 8$

3.  $y + 3 = 5x$
    $3x - y = -2$

4.  $y + 8 = -6x$
    $-2x + y = 5$

5.  $y = 3x + 9$
    $2y = 6x - 2$

6.  $y = -7x - 9$
    $-3y = 21x + 7$

▌▌Write an equation of the line containing the given point and parallel to the given line. (*See Example 4.*)

7.  $(3, 7), x + 2y = 6$

8.  $(0, 3), 3x - y = 7$

9.  $(2, -1), 5x - 7y = 8$

10.  $(-4, -5), 2x + y = -3$

11.  $(-6, 2), 3x - 9y = 2$

12.  $(-7, 0), 5x + 2y = 6$

▌▌▌Write an equation of the line containing the given point and perpendicular to the given line. (*See Example 6.*)

13.  $(2, 5), 2x + y = -3$

14.  $(4, 0), x - 3y = 0$

15.  $(3, -2), 3x + 4y = 5$

16.  $(-3, -5), 5x - 2y = 4$

17.  $(0, 9), 2x + 5y = 7$

18.  $(-3, -4), -3x + 6y = 2$

---

### Challenge Exercises

19.  Find an equation of the line containing $(4, -2)$ and parallel to the line containing $(-1, 4)$ and $(2, -3)$.

20.  Find an equation of the line containing $(-1, 3)$ and perpendicular to the line containing $(3, -5)$ and $(-2, -7)$.

21.  Use the slope relationship to show that the triangle with vertices $(-2, 7)$, $(6, 9)$, and $(3, 4)$ is a right triangle.

---

**CONSUMER NOTE: Inflation**

During inflation, earnings go up, and people have more money to spend. But prices go up, also. If prices rise faster than earnings, people lose buying power. If earnings rise faster than prices, peoples' buying power increases.

# 3-6 *Applications of Linear Equations*

After finishing Lesson 3-6, you should be able to
▮ find a linear equation which fits two data points and use the equation to make predictions.

▮Mathematics is often constructed to fit certain situations. Suppose some experience indicates that a linear equation would fit the situation. In the following diagram, data have been plotted on a graph. It looks as if the points lie more or less on a straight line.

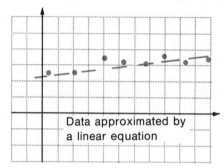

Data approximated by
a linear equation

We can find an equation that fits the situation and use it to make predictions.

**Example.** (*Temperature and Cricket Chirps*). It has been shown experimentally that the temperature in degrees Celsius is related to the number of cricket chirps per minute by a linear equation. When crickets chirp 40 times per minute, the temperature is 10° and when they chirp 112 times per minute, the temperature is 20°.

a) Find a linear equation which fits the data.
b) From your equation, find the temperature when there are 76 chirps per minute; 100 chirps per minute.

a) To find a linear equation which fits the data we use the two-point equation. Let us use $T$ for temperature and $N$ for the number of chirps per minute. We know two ordered pairs that the equation must fit. They are (40, 10°) and (112, 20°). We call these *data points*. The equation is

$$T - T_1 = \frac{T_2 - T_1}{N_2 - N_1}(N - N_1).$$

We substitute and simplify.

$$T - 10 = \frac{20 - 10}{112 - 40}(N - 40)$$

$$T - 10 = \frac{10}{72}(N - 40)$$

$$T - 10 = \frac{10}{72}N - \frac{10}{72} \cdot 40$$

$$T = \frac{5}{36}N - \frac{400}{72} + 10$$

$$T = \frac{5}{36}N + \frac{40}{9}, \text{ or } \frac{5N + 160}{36}$$

b)  Using this formula, we find that when $N = 76$,

$$T = \frac{5(76) + 160}{36}$$

$$= 15°$$

When $N = 100$,

$$T = \frac{5(100) + 160}{36}$$

$$\approx 18.3° \quad (\approx \text{ means approximately equal})$$

**TRY THIS** ➡

1.  (*Records in the 100-meter dash*). It has been found experimentally that running records follow linear equations. In 1920 the record for the 100-meter dash was 10.43 seconds. In 1970 it was 9.93 seconds. Let $R$ represent the record in the 100-meter dash and $t$ the number of years since 1920.
    a)  Fit a linear equation to the data points.
    b)  Use the equation of a) to predict the record in 1980; in 1990.
    c)  In what year will the record be 9.0 seconds?

## Exercise Set 3-6

▌Solve. (*See the Example.*)

1. (*Life expectancy of females in the United States*). In 1950, the life expectancy of females was 72 years. In 1970, it was 75 years. Let *E* represent the life expectancy and *t* the number of years since 1950. ($t = 0$ gives 1950 and $t = 20$ gives 1970).
   a) Fit a linear equation to the data points. [They are (0, 72) and (20, 75).]
   b) Use the equation of a) to predict the life expectancy of females in 1980; in 1985.

2. (*Life expectancy of males in the United States*). In 1950, the life expectancy of males was 65 years. In 1970, it was 68 years. Let *E* represent life expectancy and *t* the number of years since 1950.
   a) Fit a linear equation to the data points.
   b) Use the equation of a) to predict the life expectancy of males in 1980; in 1985.

3. (*Weight versus Height*). It has been shown experimentally that the height *H* of a person is related to that person's weight *W* by a linear equation. A person 180 cm tall weighs 76.4 kg, and a person 170 cm tall weighs 66.6 kg.
   a) Fit a linear equation to the data points.
   b) Use the equation of a) to estimate the weight of a person 160 cm tall. (This equation is valid only for heights above 102 cm.)

4. (*Natural gas demand*). In 1950, natural gas demand in the United States was 20 quadrillion joules. In 1960, the demand was 22 quadrillion joules. Let *D* represent the demand for natural gas *t* years after 1950.
   a) Fit a linear equation to the data points.
   b) Use the equation of a) to predict the natural gas demand in 1980; in 2000.

5. (*Records in the 1500-meter Run*). In 1930, the record for the 1500-meter run was 3.85 minutes. In 1950, it was 3.70 minutes. Let *R* represent the record in the 1500-meter run and *t* the number of years since 1930.
   a) Fit a linear equation to the data points.
   b) Use the equation of a) to predict the record in 1980; in 1984.
   c) When will the record be 3.3 minutes?

6. (*Records in the 400-meter Run*). In 1930, the record for the 400-meter run was 46.8 seconds. In 1970, it was 43.8 seconds. Let *R* represent the record in the 400-meter run and *t* the number of years since 1930.
   a) Fit a linear equation to the data points.
   b) Use the equation of a) to predict the record in 1980; in 1990.
   c) When will the record be 40 seconds?

## COMPUTER ACTIVITY

## Finding the Slope and Y-Intercept of Linear Equations

**PROBLEM:** Find the slope and Y-intercept of AX + BY + C = 0.

**Examples using the flowchart:**

| | 1 | | | 2 | 3 |
| --- | --- | --- | --- | --- | --- |
| | | | | SLOPE M | Y-INTERCEPT (0,K) |
| A | B | C | | | |
| 4 | 5 | −2 | | −0.8 | (0, 0.4) |
| 2.21 | −3.14 | 3 | | 0.70382 | (0, 0.95541) |
| −0.7 | 4.2 | 0.25 | | 0.16667 | (0, −0.05952) |
| 2 | 6 | −3 | | | |
| 1.5 | −3 | −4 | | | |

**Flowchart:**

START

**1** INPUT A,B,C

DOES B = 0?   Yes

No

**2** LET M = −A/B

**3** LET K = −C/B

PRINT M

PRINT (0,K)

STOP

**TRY THIS** ⟹ Find the numbers to complete the examples.

BASIC PROGRAM (Optional)

```
10   INPUT A,B,C
20   IF B = 0 THEN 70
30   LET M = −A/B
40   PRINT K = −C/B
50   PRINT "THE SLOPE ="M
60   PRINT "THE Y-INTERCEPT =
        (0,";K;")"
70   STOP
```

## CHAPTER 3 REVIEW

Review the material in the chapter. Then see how you have done by trying these review exercises. If you miss an exercise, restudy the indicated lesson.

3-1  1. Decide whether (2, 4) is a solution to $2x + 3y = 16$.

3-1  2. Graph $-8x + 4y = -4$. Use a table of values.

3-2  3. Which of these are linear equations?
   a) $x - 5y = 8$
   b) $3xy + y^2 = 0$
   c) $2x = 5y - 9$
   d) $x^2 - 7 = 9y$

3-2  4. Find standard form for $2x = 9y - 7$.

3-2  5. Graph $-5x + 2y = 10$ using intercepts.

3-2  6. Graph $x = 9$.

3-2  7. Graph $y = -2$.

3-3  8. Find the slope of the line containing (8, 2) and $(-4, -3)$.

3-3  9. Find an equation for the line with slope of $-3$ and containing (2, 1).

3-4  10. Find an equation of the line containing (3, 5) and $(-2, -4)$.

3-4  11. Find the slope and $y$-intercept of the equation $-5x + 2y = -4$.

3-5  12. Determine, without graphing, whether the graphs of the following pairs of equations are parallel.
   a) $y + 3 = x$     b) $7x + 3y = 11$     c) $2x - y = 8$
      $x - 5 = y$        $3x + 7y = 12$          $2y = 6 + 4x$

3-5  13. Find an equation of the line containing $(-3, 7)$ which is
   a) parallel to the line $5x + 3y = 8$.
   b) perpendicular to the line $5x + 3y = 8$.

3-6  14. (*Records in the 200-meter Dash*). In 1920 the record for the 200-meter dash was 20.8 seconds. In 1945 it was 20.1 seconds. Let $R$ represent the record in the 200-meter dash and $t$ the number of years since 1920.
   a) Fit a linear equation to the data points.
   b) Use the equation of a) to predict the record in 1980; in 1984.
   c) When will the record be 19.0?

## CHAPTER 3 TEST

1. Determine whether (3, 2) is a solution to $x + 3y = 10$.
2. Graph $-4x + 2y = 2$. Use a table of values.
3. Which of these are linear equations?
   a) $xy + 3y^2 = 0$
   b) $2x - 4y + 9 = 0$
   c) $y = 3x + 2$
   d) $x^2 - y^2 = 16$
4. Find standard form for $8y = 42x - 9$.
5. Graph $-3x + 4y = 12$ using intercepts.
6. Graph $x = -3$.
7. Graph $y = 4$.
8. Find the slope of the line containing (9, 1) and (−5, −6).
9. Find an equation for the line with slope of −4 and containing (3, 2).
10. Find an equation of the line containing (2, 8) and (−3, −6).
11. Determine the slope and $y$-intercept of the equation $-3x + 5y = 10$.
12. Tell, without graphing, whether the graphs of the following pairs of equations are parallel.
    a) $18x + 3y = 16$      b) $x - 3 = y$      c) $3x - y = 9$
       $y = -9x + 2$           $y + 9 = x$           $4y - 8 = 12x$
13. Find an equation of the line containing (−5, 8) which is
    a) parallel to the line $3x + 5y = 15$.
    b) perpendicular to the line $3x + 5y = 15$.
14. (*Records in the 1000-meter Run*). In 1920 the record for the 1000-meter run was 2.47 minutes. In 1940 it was 2.38 minutes. Let $R$ represent the record in the 1000-meter run and $t$ the number of years since 1920.
    a) Fit a linear equation to the data points.
    b) Use the equation of a) to predict the record in 1980; in 1990.
    c) When will the record be 2.20 minutes?

Television and radio service technicians fix communication equipment. This equipment may include stereo components and tape recorders as well as other products.

Advertising copywriters prepare slogans and text used in ads. Copywriters try to describe a product in a way that appeals to a certain group of buyers.

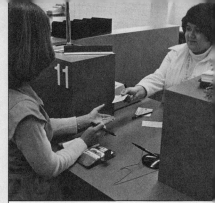

Bank tellers receive and pay out money. During banking hours tellers deal directly with customers. Afterward, tellers count cash and keep records.

Cooks or chefs meet the cooking needs of a dining place. Coffee shops need simple meals prepared quickly. Fine restaurants need a variety of excellent dishes.

# CAREERS IN VARIOUS SERVICES

Careers in various services can be divided into two main groups. One includes careers in finance, insurance, and real estate services. The other includes careers in health, repair, advertising, and hotel services.

The line graph below shows the projected growth of both groups of careers. The graph is based on data gathered by the United States Bureau of Labor Statistics. Note that careers in health, repair, advertising, hotel, and other services are likely to increase more rapidly than careers in the other group. Some of the people who follow careers in various services are pictured here, and their work is described briefly.

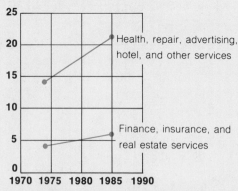

Workers (in millions)

Health, repair, advertising, hotel, and other services

Finance, insurance, and real estate services

1970 1975 1980 1985 1990

**Numbers of Workers Producing Various Services**

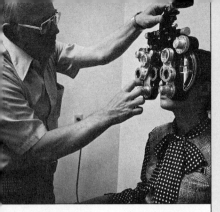

Optometrists measure vision and prescribe lenses or treatments, if needed. Optometrists' prescriptions for glasses or contact lenses are filled by opticians.

Veterinarians provide health care for animals. In cities, veterinarians usually treat pets. In rural areas, veterinarians usually provide health care for farm animals.

Systems analysts decide how to handle information for an entire operation. In business, analysts try to make the operation more efficient and profitable.

Insurance underwriters decide what policies a company should issue. Underwriters judge insurance applications in relation to customer payments and company risks.

Altogether, careers in various services are likely to increase more rapidly than other sorts of service careers, such as trade, government, and transportation. And service careers in general are likely to increase more rapidly than goods-producing careers such as manufacturing and construction.

The growth of service careers in general follows a long trend. These careers have increased steadily since 1947. Goods-producing careers have not increased in that time. Analysts at the Bureau of Labor Statistics expect the long-term trend to continue. They project that the United States labor force in the mid-1980s will have the proportions shown in the circle graph. The graph shows that in the mid-1980s careers in various services are likely to be greater in number than careers in trade or in government (including state and local governments) or in manufacturing.

The black shading around the graph indicates service careers, and the color shading indicates goods-producing careers. The gap between the black and color represents unemployment. (Two kinds of goods-producing careers, mining and agriculture, are part of the "Other" area in the graph.)

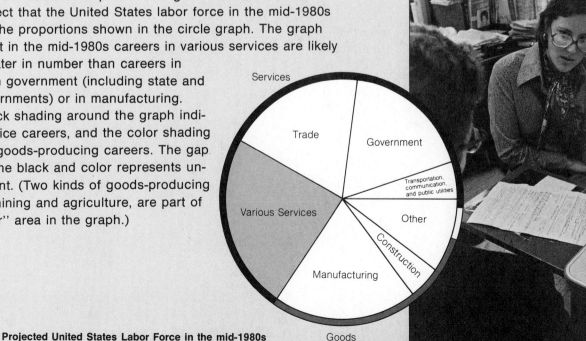

Services

Trade

Government

Transportation, communication, and public utilities

Various Services

Other

Manufacturing

Construction

**Projected United States Labor Force in the mid-1980s**

Goods

## Ready for Systems of Equations?

1-2 Find the additive inverse of each number.
   1. $-8$
   2. $7$
   3. $\frac{3}{4}$
   4. $0$

1-2 Add.
   5. $-\frac{3}{4} + \frac{1}{6}$
   6. $9.7 + (-2.8)$
   7. $\frac{4}{5} + (-\frac{4}{5})$
   8. $-8.6 + (-3.4)$
   9. $-8 + 10$
   10. $-\frac{1}{4} + (-\frac{2}{5})$

1-3 Subtract.
   11. $8 - (-2)$
   12. $-4 - 8$
   13. $-\frac{2}{3} - \frac{4}{5}$
   14. $-3.2 - (-8.1)$

3-1   15. Determine whether $(1, -3)$ is a solution of $y = 2x - 5$.
3-1   16. Determine whether $(2, -1)$ is a solution of $4r + 3s = 7$.

Graph.
3-1   17. $y - 4x = 3$
3-2   18. $4y - 4 = 2x$
3-2   19. $y = 2$

# Chapter 4
# Systems of Equations

*Chemists use systems of equations in mixing solutions.*

# 4-1 Systems of Equations in Two Variables

After finishing Lesson 4-1, you should be able to
▮  identify solutions of a system of two equations.
▮▮ solve systems of two equations graphically.

## ▮ Identifying Solutions

A pair of linear equations is called a *system* of equations. A solution of a system of two equations is an ordered pair that makes both equations true.

**Example 1.** Determine whether $(4, 7)$ is a solution of this system: $x + y = 11$
$3x - y = 5$

We use alphabetical order of the variables. Thus we replace $x$ by 4 and $y$ by 7, and check:

$$\frac{x + y = 11}{\begin{array}{c|c} 4 + 7 & 11 \\ 11 & \end{array}} \qquad \frac{3x - y = 5}{\begin{array}{c|c} 3 \cdot 4 - 7 & 5 \\ 12 - 7 & \\ 5 & \end{array}}$$

The pair $(4, 7)$ checks, so it is a solution of the system. We could describe such a solution by saying that $x = 4$ and $y = 7$.

**Example 2.** Determine whether $(4, 2)$ is a solution of this system: $y - x = -2$
$y + 5x = -1$

$$\frac{y - x = -2}{\begin{array}{c|c} 2 - 4 & -2 \\ -2 & \end{array}} \qquad \frac{y + 5x = -1}{\begin{array}{c|c} 2 + 5 \cdot 4 & -1 \\ 2 + 20 & \\ 22 & \end{array}}$$

$(4, 2)$ is not a solution of $y + 5x = -1$, so it is not a solution of the system.

**TRY THIS**

1.  Determine whether $(20, 40)$ is a solution of this system:
    $x = \frac{1}{2}y$
    $y + \frac{1}{4}x = 45$
2.  Determine whether $(-2, 3)$ is a solution of this system:
    $2a - 5b = 7$
    $5b + 3a = -4$

## ◼ Solving Systems of Equations by Graphing

We can solve some systems of two equations by graphing.

**Example 3.**   Solve this system graphically: $y - x = 1$
$$y + x = 3$$

We graph the two equations using the same axes.
The point of intersection has coordinates which
satisfy both equations. The solution seems to be
(1, 2). Because graphing can be inaccurate, we
should always check.

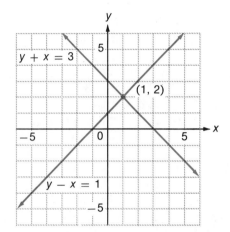

Check:   $\dfrac{y - x = 1}{\begin{array}{c|c} 2 - 1 & 1 \\ 1 & \end{array}}$   $\dfrac{y + x = 3}{\begin{array}{c|c} 2 + 1 & 3 \\ 3 & \end{array}}$

(1, 2) checks, so it is the solution.

**TRY THIS**

Solve graphically.

3.   $-2x + y = 1$
$3x + y = 1$

4.   $x = y$
$3x + y = 12$

## Exercise Set 4-1

◼ Determine whether the given ordered pair is a solution of the system of
equations. Remember to use alphabetical order of variables. (*See Examples 1 and 2.*)

1.   (1, 2); $-4x - y = 2$
$10x - 3y = 4$

2.   (-1, -2); $2x + y = -4$
$x - y = 1$

3.   (2, 5); $y = 3x - 1$
$2x + y = 4$

4.   (-1, -2); $3x - 2y = 12$
$x + 3y = -7$

5.   (1, 5); $x + y = 6$
$y = 2x + 3$

6.   (5, 2); $a + b = 7$
$2a - 8 = b$

7.   (2, -7); $3a + b = -1$
$2a - 3b = -8$

8.   (2, 1); $3p + 2q = 5$
$4p + 5q = 2$

❚❚ Use graph paper. Solve each system graphically and check. (*See Example 3.*)

9. $x + y = 4$
   $x - y = 2$

10. $x - y = 3$
    $x + y = 5$

11. $2x - y = 4$
    $5x - y = 13$

12. $3x + y = 5$
    $x - 2y = 4$

13. $4x - y = 9$
    $x - 3y = 16$

14. $2y = 6 - x$
    $3x - 2y = 6$

15. $a = 1 + b$
    $b = -2a + 5$

16. $x = y - 1$
    $2x = 3y$

17. $2u + v = 3$
    $2u = v + 7$

18. $2b + a = 11$
    $a - b = 5$

19. $y = -\frac{1}{3}x - 1$
    $4x - 3y = 18$

20. $y = -\frac{1}{4}x + 1$
    $2y = x - 4$

## HISTORICAL NOTE: Mathematical Problems in Ancient Egypt

In Egypt 4000 years ago, students of mathematics solved problems written entirely in words. At that time, all mathematical problems were written like this. Symbols for quantities were mixed with symbols that we would call words.

Most problems of ancient Egypt involved fractions. We could translate these problems to first degree equations with one variable. A papyrus from about 2000 B.C. has a quadratic problem. We could translate it to a system of equations.

$$x^2 + y^2 = 100$$
$$y = \frac{3}{4}x$$

The papyrus has the correct answer: one quantity is 8, the other is 6.

# 4-2 Other Methods for Solving

After finishing Lesson 4-2, you should be able to
**I**   solve systems of equations using the substitution method.
**II**   solve systems of equations using the addition method.

We can solve systems of equations without graphing. One method is called the *substitution method*.

## I The Substitution Method

**Example 1.**   Solve this system: $x + y = 5$
$$x = y + 1$$

The second equation says that $x$ and $y + 1$ name the same thing. In the first equation we can substitute $y + 1$ for $x$.

$$x + y = 5$$
$$(y + 1) + y = 5 \quad \textit{Substituting } y + 1 \textit{ for } x$$

Solve this last equation.

$$(y + 1) + y = 5$$
$$2y + 1 = 5$$
$$2y = 4$$
$$y = 2$$

We return to the original pair of equations. Substitute 2 for $y$ in either of them. We use the first equation.

$$x + y = 5$$
$$x + 2 = 5$$
$$x = 3$$

The ordered pair (3, 2) may be a solution.

Check:

| $x + y = 5$ | | $x = y + 1$ | |
|---|---|---|---|
| $3 + 2$ | 5 | 3 | $2 + 1$ |
| | 5 | | 3 |

Since (3, 2) checks, it is the solution.

**TRY THIS** ━━▶

Solve by the substitution method.

1.   $x + y = 6$
     $y = x + 2$
2.   $y = 7 - x$
     $2x - y = 8$

Suppose neither equation of a pair has a variable alone on one side. We then solve one equation for one of the variables.

**Example 2.** Solve this system: $2x + y = 6$

$$3x + 4y = 4$$

First solve one equation for one variable. We solve the first equation for $y$.

$$y = 6 - 2x$$

Then substitute $6 - 2x$ for $y$ in the second equation and solve for $x$.

$3x + 4(6 - 2x) = 4$    *Substituting $6 - 2x$ for $y$*

$3x + 24 - 8x = 4$    *Solving*

$3x - 8x = 4 - 24$

$-5x = -20$

$x = 4$

Now substitute 4 for $x$ in either equation and solve for $y$. We use the first equation.

$2 \cdot 4 + y = 6$

$y = -2$

We obtain $(4, -2)$. This checks, so it is the solution.

**TRY THIS** ➡️

> Solve. Use the substitution method.
>
> 3.   $2y + x = 1$
>      $y = 2x + 8$
> 4.   $8x + 5y = 184$
>      $x - y = -3$

## ▪ The Addition Method

The *addition method* for solving systems of equations makes use of the *addition principle*.

Consider this system: $x + y = 2$

$$3x = 2y$$

The first equation says that $x + y$ and 2 represent the same number. We use the addition principle with the second equation. We add the "same thing" on both sides. On the left we call it $x + y$. On the right we call it 2.

$$3x + (x + y) = 2y + 2.$$

Using this method we try to get an equation with only one variable. We often say that we have eliminated a variable.

**Example 3.** Solve this system: $2x - 3y = 0$
$$-4x + 3y = -1$$

$$2x - 3y = 0$$
$$\underline{-4x + 3y = -1}$$
$$-2x + \phantom{0}0 = -1 \quad \text{\textit{Adding}}$$

We have made one variable "disappear."

$$-2x = -1$$
$$x = \tfrac{1}{2} \quad \text{\textit{Solving for x}}$$
$$2 \cdot \tfrac{1}{2} - 3y = 0 \quad \text{\textit{Substituting } } \tfrac{1}{2} \text{ \textit{for x in the first equation}}$$
$$1 - 3y = 0$$
$$y = \tfrac{1}{3}$$

We obtain $(\tfrac{1}{2}, \tfrac{1}{3})$. This checks, so it is the solution.

**TRY THIS** ➡

Solve. Use the addition method.

5. $5x + 3y = 17$
   $-5x + 2y = 3$
6. $-3a + 2b = 0$
   $3a - 4b = -1$

Note in Example 3 that a term in one equation and a term in the other were additive inverses of each other. Thus their sum was 0. This enabled us to eliminate a variable.

In order to eliminate a variable we sometimes have to multiply one or both of the equations by something before adding.

**Example 4.** Solve this system: $3x + 3y = 15$
$$2x + 6y = 22$$

If we add, we do not eliminate a variable. However, if the $3y$ in the first equation were $-6y$, we could. So, we multiply by $-2$ in the first equation.

$$-6x - 6y = -30 \quad \text{\textit{Multiplying by } } -2$$
$$\underline{2x + 6y = 22}$$
$$-4x + \phantom{0}0 = -8 \quad \text{\textit{Adding}}$$
$$x = 2 \quad \text{\textit{Solving for x}}$$

$$2 \cdot 2 + 6y = 22 \quad \text{\textit{Substituting 2 for x in second equation}}$$
$$4 + 6y = 22$$
$$y = 3 \quad \text{\textit{Solving for y}}$$

We obtain $(2, 3)$. This checks, so it is the solution.

**TRY THIS** ➡

Solve. Use the addition method.

7. $2y + 3x = 12$
   $-4y + 5x = -2$

Sometimes we have to multiply twice.

**Example 5.**  Solve this system: $2x + 3y = 12$
$$5x + 7y = 29$$

From first equation:  $\qquad 10x + 15y = 60$  *Multiplying by 5*
From second equation:  $\underline{-10x - 14y = -58}$  *Multiplying by −2*
$$0 + \quad y = 2 \quad \textit{Adding}$$
$$y = 2 \quad \textit{Solving for y}$$

$2x + 3 \cdot 2 = 12$  *Substituting 2 for y in first equation*
$$2x = 6$$
$$x = 3 \quad \textit{Solving for x}$$

We obtain (3, 2). This checks, so it is the solution.

**TRY THIS**

Solve. Use the addition
method.

8.  $3x + 5y = 30$
$\phantom{8. \ \ }5x + 3y = 34$

# Exercise Set 4-2

▮ Solve using the substitution method. (*See Examples 1 and 2.*)

1.  $3x + 5y = 3$
$\phantom{1. \ \ }x = 8 - 4y$

2.  $2x - 3y = 13$
$\phantom{2. \ \ }y = 5 - 4x$

3.  $9x - 2y = 3$
$\phantom{3. \ \ }3x - 6 = y$

4.  $x = 3y - 3$
$\phantom{4. \ \ }x + 2y = 9$

5.  $5m + n = 8$
$\phantom{5. \ \ }3m - 4n = 14$

6.  $4x + y = 1$
$\phantom{6. \ \ }x - 2y = 16$

7.  $4x + 12y = 4$
$\phantom{7. \ \ }5x - y = -11$

8.  $3b - a = -7$
$\phantom{8. \ \ }5a + 6b = 14$

▮▮ Solve using the addition method. (*See Examples 3–5.*)

9.  $x + 3y = 7$
$\phantom{9. \ \ }-x + 4y = y$

10.  $x + y = 9$
$\phantom{10. \ \ }2x - y = -3$

11.  $2x + y = 6$
$\phantom{11. \ \ }x - y = 3$

12.  $x - 2y = 6$
$\phantom{12. \ \ }-x + 3y = -4$

13.  $9x + 3y = -3$
$\phantom{13. \ \ }2x - 3y = -8$

14.  $6x - 3y = 18$
$\phantom{14. \ \ }6x + 3y = -12$

15.  $5x + 3y = 19$
$\phantom{15. \ \ }2x - 5y = 11$

16.  $3x + 2y = 3$
$\phantom{16. \ \ }9x - 8y = -2$

17.  $5r - 3s = 24$
$\phantom{17. \ \ }3r + 5s = 28$

18.  $5x - 7y = -16$
$\phantom{18. \ \ }2x + 8y = 26$

19.  $0.3x - 0.2y = 4$
$\phantom{19. \ \ }0.2x + 0.3y = 1$

20.  $0.7x - 0.3y = 0.5$
$\phantom{20. \ \ }-0.4x + 0.7y = 1.3$

21.  $\frac{1}{2}x + \frac{1}{3}y = 4$
$\phantom{21. \ \ }\frac{1}{4}x + \frac{1}{3}y = 3$

22.  $\frac{2}{3}x + \frac{1}{7}y = -11$
$\phantom{22. \ \ }\frac{1}{7}x - \frac{1}{3}y = -10$

# 4-3 Inconsistent and Dependent Equations

After finishing Lesson 4-3, you should be able to
▮ determine whether a system of equations is inconsistent or dependent.

▮ Some systems of equations have no solution.

### DEFINITION

A system of equations that has no solution is called *inconsistent*.
If a system has one or more solutions it is called *consistent*.

For a system of two linear equations to be inconsistent, their
graphs must be parallel lines.

**Example 1.** Determine whether this system is inconsistent: $x - 3y = 1$
$$-2x + 6y = 5$$

We multiply on both sides of the first equation by 2 and then
add. This gives us

$$2x - 6y = 2$$
$$0 = 7$$

The second equation says that $0 \cdot x + 0 \cdot y = 7$. There are no
numbers $x$ and $y$ for which this is true, so there is no solution.
The system of equations is inconsistent.

Whenever we obtain a statement such as $0 = 7$,
which is clearly false, we know that the system we
are trying to solve is inconsistent.

**TRY THIS**

1. Determine whether this system of equations is inconsistent.

   $3y - 9x = 12$
   $y - 3x = 9$

Consider this system: $3x + 4y = 1$
$$6x + 8y = 2$$

If we multiply on both sides of the first equation by 2 we get the
second equation. Thus, the two equations are *equivalent,* meaning that they have exactly the same solution set.

### DEFINITION

If a system of $n$ linear equations is equivalent to a system of
fewer than $n$ of them, then the system is called *dependent*.

**Example 2.**    Determine whether this system is dependent: $2x + 3y = 1$
$$4x + 6y = 2$$

Multiplying on both sides of the first equation by 2, we get

$$4x + 6y = 2$$
$$4x + 6y = 2$$

The two equations are equivalent to just one of them, so the system is dependent.

In Example 2, suppose we had multiplied the first equation by $-2$ and then added.

$$-4x - 6y = -2 \qquad \textit{Multiplying by } -2$$
$$\underline{\phantom{-}4x + 6y = 2}$$
$$0 + 0 = 0 \qquad \textit{Adding}$$

The last equation says that $0 \cdot x + 0 \cdot y = 0$. This is true for all numbers $x$ and $y$. Whenever we get an obviously true sentence like this, we know that the system we are trying to solve is dependent.

**TRY THIS**

> 2.  Determine whether this system of equations is dependent.
>
> $$y = 5x + 2$$
> $$2y = 10x + 4$$

## Exercise Set 4-3

▌ Determine which systems are inconsistent and which are dependent. (*See Examples 1 and 2.*)

1.  $y - x = 4$
    $-2x + 2y = 5$

2.  $y + x = 5$
    $-y = x - 3$

3.  $x - 3 = y$
    $2x - 2y = 6$

4.  $3y = x - 2$
    $3x = 6 + 9y$

5.  $x + 2y = 6$
    $2x = 8 - 4y$

6.  $y - 2x = 1$
    $2x - 3 = y$

7.  $y = x$
    $x = y - 1$

8.  $y = 2x$
    $2x = y + 3$

9.  $2x + 3y = 1$
    $x + 1.5y = 0.5$

10.  $15x + 6y = 20$
     $7.5x - 10 = -3y$

# 4-4 Systems of Equations in Three Variables

After finishing Lesson 4-4, you should be able to
- **▮** identify solutions of systems of three equations in three variables.
- **▮▮** solve systems of three equations in three variables.

## ▮ Identifying Solutions

A solution of a system of equations in three variables is an ordered triple which makes all three sentences true.

**Example 1.** Determine whether $(\frac{3}{2}, -4, 3)$ is a solution of this system: $4x - 2y - 3z = 5$
$$-8x - y + z = -5$$
$$2x + y + 2z = 5$$

$$
\begin{array}{c|c}
4x - 2y - 3z = 5 & \\
\hline
4 \cdot \frac{3}{2} - 2 \cdot (-4) - 3 \cdot 3 & 5 \\
6 + 8 - 9 & \\
5 &
\end{array}
\qquad
\begin{array}{c|c}
-8x - y + z = -5 & \\
\hline
-8 \cdot \frac{3}{2} - (-4) + 3 & -5 \\
-12 + 4 + 3 & \\
-5 &
\end{array}
\qquad
\begin{array}{c|c}
2x + y + 2z = 5 & \\
\hline
2 \cdot \frac{3}{2} + (-4) + 2 \cdot 3 & 5 \\
3 - 4 + 6 & \\
5 &
\end{array}
$$

The triple $(\frac{3}{2}, -4, 3)$ checks, so it is a solution of the system.

**TRY THIS** ➡

> 1. Consider this system:
> $4x + 2y + 5z = 6$
> $2x - y + z = 5$
> $x + 2y - z = 0$
> a) Determine whether $(1, 2, 3)$ is a solution of this system.
> b) Determine whether $(2, -1, 0)$ is a solution of this system.

## ▮▮ The Addition Method

The substitution method is not convenient for solving systems with three variables. We will consider only the addition method.

The procedure for using the addition method is as follows.
a) Use *any* two of the three equations to get an equation in two variables.
b) Use a different pair of equations and get another equation in the same two variables. That is, eliminate the same variable as in a).
c) Solve the resulting system (pair) of equations. This will give two of the numbers.
d) Use any of the original three equations to find the third number.

**Example 2.**   Solve: $x + y + z = 4$     **(1)**

$\qquad\qquad\quad x - 2y - z = 1$     **(2)**

$\qquad\qquad\quad 2x - y - 2z = -1$     **(3)**

a)  We first use *any* two of the three equations to get an equation in two variables. Using equations **(1)** and **(2),** we add to eliminate z.

$$\begin{array}{rl} x + \ y + z = 4 & \textbf{(1)} \\ \underline{x - 2y - z = 1} & \textbf{(2)} \\ 2x - \ y \quad\ \ = 5 & \textbf{(4)} \end{array}$$

b)  Using a different pair of equations we get another equation in the same two variables. We eliminate the same variable as in a). Using equations **(1)** and **(3)** we can eliminate z.

$$x + y + z = 4 \quad \textbf{(1)}$$
$$2x - y - 2z = -1 \quad \textbf{(3)}$$

$$\begin{array}{ll} 2x + 2y + 2z = 8 & \textit{Multiplying equation } \textbf{(1)} \textit{ by 2} \\ \underline{2x - \ y - 2z = -1} & \\ 4x + \ y \quad\ \ = 7 \quad \textbf{(5)} & \textit{Adding} \end{array}$$

c)  We solve the resulting system of equations **(4)** and **(5).** This will give us two of the numbers.

$$\begin{array}{ll} 2x - y = 5 & \textbf{(4)} \\ \underline{4x + y = 7} & \textbf{(5)} \\ 6x \quad\ \ = 12 & \textit{Adding} \\ \ x = 2 & \end{array}$$

We use either equation **(4)** or **(5)** to find y. From **(5)** we get

$$4x + y = 7$$
$$4 \cdot 2 + y = 7$$
$$8 + y = 7$$
$$y = -1$$

d)  Using any of the original three equations we substitute to find the third number, z. Let us use equation **(1).**

$$\begin{array}{ll} x + y + z = 4 & \\ 2 + (-1) + z = 4 & \textit{Substituting 2 for x and } -1 \textit{ for y} \\ 1 + z = 4 & \\ z = 3 & \end{array}$$

We obtain $(2, -1, 3)$.

Check:

$$\begin{array}{c|c} x + y + z = 4 \\ \hline 2 + (-1) + 3 & 4 \\ 4 & \end{array} \qquad \begin{array}{c|c} x - 2y - z = 1 \\ \hline 2 - 2(-1) - 3 & 1 \\ 1 & \end{array} \qquad \begin{array}{c|c} 2x - y - 2z = -1 \\ \hline 2 \cdot 2 - (-1) - 2 \cdot 3 & -1 \\ -1 & \end{array}$$

The solution is $(2, -1, 3)$.

**TRY THIS** ⮕

> 2.  Solve: $4x - y + z = 6$
>     $-3x + 2y - z = -3$
>     $2x + y + 2z = 3$
>     Don't forget to check.
> 3.  Solve: $2x + y - 4z = 0$
>     $x - y + 2z = 5$
>     $3x + 2y + 2z = 3$

**Example 3.**  Solve: $\begin{aligned} x + \ y + z &= 180 \qquad \textbf{(1)} \\ x \qquad - z &= -70 \qquad \textbf{(2)} \\ 2y - z &= 0 \qquad \textbf{(3)} \end{aligned}$

a)  There is no $y$ in equation **(2)**, so
b)  we use equations **(1)** and **(3)** and eliminate $y$.

$$\begin{aligned} x + \ y + z &= 180 \qquad \textbf{(1)} \\ 2y - z &= 0 \qquad \textbf{(3)} \end{aligned}$$

$$\begin{array}{ll} -2x - 2y - 2z = -360 & \textit{Multiplying by } -2 \\ \underline{\qquad 2y - \ z = 0} \\ -2x \qquad - 3z = -360 & \textbf{(4)} \end{array}$$

c)  We use equations **(2)** and **(4)**.

$$\begin{aligned} x - \ z &= -70 \qquad \textbf{(2)} \\ -2x - 3z &= -360 \qquad \textbf{(4)} \end{aligned}$$

$$\begin{array}{ll} 2x - 2z = -140 & \textit{Multiplying by } 2 \\ \underline{-2x - 3z = -360} \\ \qquad -5z = -500 \\ \qquad z = 100 \end{array}$$

We use equation **(2)** to find $x$.

$$\begin{aligned} x - 100 &= -70 \\ x &= 30 \end{aligned}$$

d)  Using any of the original equations, we substitute to find the third number, $y$. From equation **(3)** we get

$$\begin{aligned} 2y - 100 &= 0 \\ 2y &= 100 \\ y &= 50 \end{aligned}$$

We obtain $(30, 50, 100)$. This checks so it is the solution.

**TRY THIS** ➡

4. Solve: $x + y + z = 100$
$x - y \qquad = -10$
$x \qquad - z = -30$

## Exercise Set 4-4

▌(*See Example 1.*)

1. Determine whether $(1, -2, 3)$ is a solution of the system
$x + y + z = 2$
$x - 2y - z = 2$
$3x + 2y + z = 2$

2. Determine whether $(2, -1, -2)$ is a solution of the system
$x + y - 2z = 5$
$2x - y - z = 7$
$-x - 2y + 3z = 6$

▌▌Solve. (*See Examples 2 and 3.*)

3. $x + y + z = 6$
$2x - y + 3z = 9$
$-x + 2y + 2z = 9$

4. $2x - y + z = 10$
$4x + 2y - 3z = 10$
$x - 3y + 2z = 8$

5. $2x - y - 3z = -1$
$2x - y + z = -9$
$x + 2y - 4z = 17$

6. $x - y + z = 6$
$2x + 3y + 2z = 2$
$3x + 5y + 4z = 4$

7. $2x - 3y + z = 5$
$x + 3y + 8z = 22$
$3x - y + 2z = 12$

8. $6x - 4y + 5z = 31$
$5x + 2y + 2z = 13$
$x + y + z = 2$

9. $3a - 2b + 7c = 13$
$a + 8b - 6c = -47$
$7a - 9b - 9c = -3$

10. $x + y + z = 0$
$2x + 3y + 2z = -3$
$-x + 2y - 3z = -1$

11. $2x + 3y + z = 17$
$x - 3y + 2z = -8$
$5x - 2y + 3z = 5$

12. $2x + y - 3z = -4$
$4x - 2y + z = 9$
$3x + 5y - 2z = 5$

13. $2x + y + z = -2$
$2x - y + 3z = 6$
$3x - 5y + 4z = 7$

14. $2x + y + 2z = 11$
$3x + 2y + 2z = 8$
$x + 4y + 3z = 0$

15. $x - y + z = 4$
$5x + 2y - 3z = 2$
$3x - 7y + 4z = 8$

16. $2x + y + 2z = 3$
$x + 6y + 3z = 4$
$3x - 2y + z = 0$

17. $4x - y - z = 4$
$2x + y + z = -1$
$6x - 3y - 2z = 3$

18. $a + 2b + c = 1$
$7a + 3b - c = -2$
$a + 5b + 3c = 2$

19. $2r + 3s + 12t = 4$
$4r - 6s + 6t = 1$
$r + s + t = 1$

20. $10x + 6y + z = 7$
$5x - 9y - 2z = 3$
$15x - 12y + 2z = -5$

## Challenge Exercises

Solve.

21. $\dfrac{x}{5} - \dfrac{y}{2} + \dfrac{z}{3} = -1$

$\dfrac{x}{3} + \dfrac{y}{4} + \dfrac{z}{4} = 6$

$\dfrac{x}{5} - \dfrac{y}{8} + \dfrac{z}{6} = 3$

$\left(\text{Hint: } \dfrac{x}{5} = \dfrac{1}{5} \cdot x.\right)$

22. $L + m = 7$
$3m + 2n = 9$
$4L + n = 5$

23. $x + y + z + w = 2$
$2x + 2y + 4z + w = 1$
$x - y - z - w = -6$
$3x + y - z - w = -2$

24. $x - y + z + w = 0$
$2x + 2y + z - w = 5$
$3x + y - z - w = -4$
$x + y - 3z - 2w = -7$

Determine whether each system is inconsistent or dependent.

25. $-2x + 8y + 12z = -8$
$3x + 2y + z = 2$
$x - 4y - 6z = 4$

26. $-2x - y - z = 1$
$6x + 5y + 3z = 2$
$8x + y + 4z = -4$

## BIOGRAPHICAL NOTE: Sonya Kovalesky

When Sonya Kovalesky was a young woman, in the 1860s, Russian universities were closed to women. Her father did not want her to go to a foreign university. By marrying, she was able to travel to Germany. There she distinguished herself as a student of advanced mathematics. She gained a doctoral degree in 1874, but she could not find a teaching position in a university in Germany or in Russia.

Eventually she was accepted as a member of the faculty at the University of Stockholm, Sweden. Even there she faced opposition from scholars who did not think a woman should be a university professor. In time her researches in mathematics earned her honors in France, Russia, Sweden, and other countries.

# 4-5 Solving Problems

After finishing Lesson 4-5, you should be able to
▍ solve problems by translating them to systems of two equations in two variables.

▍To solve problems we often translate to a system of two equations in two variables.

**Example 1.** 8 times a certain number added to 5 times a second number is 184. The first number minus the second number is −3. Find the numbers.

There are two statements in the problem. We translate the first one.

Here x represents the first number and y represents the second. Now we translate the second statement, remembering to use x and y.

We have the system of equations

$$8x + 5y = 184$$
$$x - y = -3$$

The solution of this system is $x = 13$ and $y = 16$.

We check in the original problem. Since $8 \cdot 13 = 104$ and $5 \cdot 16 = 80$, the sum is 184. The difference of 13 and 16 is −3, so the answer checks.

**TRY THIS**

1.  One number is 4 times another number. The sum of the numbers is 175. Find the numbers.

**Example 2.** One day Glovers, Inc., sold 20 pairs of gloves. Cloth gloves sold for $4.95 a pair and pigskin gloves sold for $7.50 a pair. They sold $137.25 worth of gloves. How many pairs of each were sold?

We let $x =$ the number of cloth gloves sold and $y =$ the number of pigskin gloves.

a)  We first consider the number of pairs sold. The total is 20 pairs, so $x + y = 20$.

b)  Second, we consider the amount of money. The amount taken in for cloth gloves was $4.95x$, since each pair sold for $4.95. This amount is *in dollars*. In cents the amount is $495x$. The amount taken in for pigskin gloves is $7.50y$ in dollars, or $750y$ in cents. Then we have the equation $495x + 750y = 13725$.

c)  We solve the system of equations

$$x + y = 20$$
$$495x + 750y = 13725$$

The solution is $x = 5$ and $y = 15$. This checks in the original problem, so the company sold 5 pairs of cloth gloves and 15 pairs of pigskin gloves.

**TRY THIS**

> 2.  One day a store sold 30 sweatshirts. White ones cost $8.95 and red ones cost $9.50. They sold $272.90 worth of sweatshirts. How many of each color were sold?

**Example 3.**  *Mixture Problem.* Solution A is 2% alcohol. Solution B is 6% alcohol. A service station attendant wants to mix the two to get 60 liters of a solution which is 3.2% alcohol. How many liters of each should he use?

Let us assume he uses $x$ liters of A and $y$ liters of B.

a)  First, consider the amount of liquid.
    He wants 60 liters in all, so we have the equation
    $x + y = 60$.

b) Second, consider the amount of alcohol.
The amount of alcohol in the new mixture is to be 3.2% of 60 liters, or 1.92 liters. This is to be made up of the alcohol in the two solutions to be mixed. These amounts are 2%$x$ and 6%$y$. Thus we have another equation.

$$2\%x + 6\%y = 1.92, \text{ or } 0.02x + 0.06y = 1.92$$

We can eliminate decimals by multiplying on both sides by 100.

$$100(0.02x + 0.06y) = 100(1.92)$$
$$2x + 6y = 192$$

c) Now we solve the system

$$x + y = 60$$
$$2x + 6y = 192$$

and get $x = 42$ and $y = 18$. Thus the attendant should use 42 liters of A and 18 liters of B.

**TRY THIS**

3. A gardener has two kinds of solutions containing weedkiller and water. One is 5% weedkiller and the other is 15% weedkiller. She needs 100 liters of 12% solution and wants to make it from the solutions she has by mixing the two. How much should she use of each?

**Example 4.** *Interest Problem.* Two investments are made which total $4800. For a certain year these investments yield $412 in simple interest. Part of the $4800 is invested at 8% and the rest at 9%. Find the amount invested at each rate.

Recall the formula for simple interest.

$$I = Prt$$

Interest $I$ is the principal $P$ times rate $r$ times time $t$.

a) Let $x$ represent the amount invested at 8% and $y$ the amount invested at 9%. Then the interest from $x$ is 8%$x$, and the interest from $y$ is 9%$y$. Thus the $412 total interest is given by

$$8\%x + 9\%y = 412,$$
$$\text{or } 0.08x + 0.09y = 412.$$

b) Considering the total amount invested we have

$$x + y = 4800.$$

c) We now have a system of equations

$$0.08x + 0.09y = 412$$
$$x + y = 4800$$

Multiplying the first equation by 100 to clear of decimals, we get

$$8x + 9y = 41{,}200$$
$$x + y = 4800$$

Solving we get $x = 2000$ and $y = 2800$. This checks, so $2000 is invested at 8% and $2800 is invested at 9%.

**TRY THIS**

4. Two investments are made which total $3700. For a certain year these investments yield $297 in simple interest. Part of the $3700 is invested at 7% and the other part at 9%. Find the amount invested at each rate.

## Exercise Set 4-5

▌Solve. (*See Examples 1–4.*)

1. The sum of a certain number and a second number is −42. The first number minus the second is 52. Find the numbers.

2. The sum of two numbers is −63. The first number minus the second is −41. Find the numbers.

3. The difference between two numbers is 16. Three times the larger number is nine times the smaller. What are the numbers?

4. The difference between two numbers is 11. Twice the smaller number plus three times the larger is 123. What are the numbers?

5. The perimeter of a rectangular field is 628 m. The length of the field exceeds its width by 6 m. Find the dimensions.

6. The perimeter of a rectangular lot is 190 m. The width is one-fourth the length. Find the dimensions.

7. One day a store sold 30 sweatshirts. White ones cost $9.95 and yellow ones cost $10.50. In dollars, $310.60 worth of sweatshirts were sold. How many of each color were sold?

8. One week a business sold 40 scarves. White ones cost $4.95 and printed ones cost $7.95. In dollars, $282 worth of scarves were sold. How many of each kind were sold?

9. Soybean meal is 16% protein; corn meal is 9% protein. How many pounds of each should be mixed together to get a 350 pound mixture which is 12% protein?

10. A chemist has one solution of acid and water which is 25% acid and a second which is 50% acid. How many liters of each should be mixed together to get 10 liters of a solution which is 40% acid?

11. Two investments are made which total $8800. For a certain year these investments yield $663 in simple interest. Part of the $8800 is invested at 7% and part at 8%. Find the amount invested at each rate.

12. Two investments are made which total $15,000. For a certain year these investments yield $1432 in simple interest. Part of the $15,000 is invested at 9% and part at 10%. Find the amount invested at each rate.

13. For a certain year $3900 is received in interest from two investments. A certain amount is invested at 5%, and $10,000 more than this is invested at 6%. Find the amount invested at each rate. (*Hint:* Express each equation in standard form $ax + by = c$.)

14. For a certain year $876 is received from two investments. A certain amount is invested at 7%, and $1200 more than this is invested at 8%. Find the amount invested at each rate.

15. Ann Teak is twice as old as her son. Ten years ago Ann was three times as old as her son. What are their present ages?

16. Gerry Atric is twice as old as his youngest daughter. In eight years Gerry's age will be three times what his daughter's age was six years ago. How old is each at present?

17. The Melody Mart music store averages monthly expenses of $3800 and pays the sales people a 5% commission. The store begins to make a profit when costs equal sales. Find the amount of sales at which the store begins to profit.

18. The Hobby House averages monthly expenses of $4200 and pays the sales people a 4% commission. The store begins to make a profit when costs equal sales. Find the amount of sales at which the store begins to profit.

**Calculator Exercises**

19. The perimeter of a rectangle is 86.21 cm. The length is 19.31 cm greater than the width. Find the length and the width.

20. The perimeter of a rectangle is 385.9 m. The length is 82.46 m greater than the width. Find the length and the width.

**Challenge Exercises**

21. An automobile radiator contains 16 liters of antifreeze and water. This mixture is 30% antifreeze. How much of this mixture should be drained and replaced with pure antifreeze so there will be 50% antifreeze?

# 4-6 Motion Problems

After finishing Lesson 4-6, you should be able to
▌ solve motion problems.

▌Many problems deal with distance, time, and speed. To translate such problems we usually use the definition of speed.

**DEFINITION**

$$\text{Speed} = \frac{\text{distance}}{\text{time}}$$

$$r = \frac{d}{t}$$

From the equation $r = \frac{d}{t}$ we can easily obtain $d = rt$ or $t = \frac{d}{r}$.

**Example 1.** A train leaves Soul City traveling east at 30 km/h. Two hours later another train leaves Soul City traveling east on a parallel track at 45 km/h. How far from Soul City will the trains meet?

We first make a drawing.

From the drawing we see that the distances are the same,

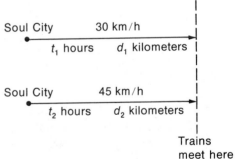

$$d_1 = d_2.$$

Now the slow train travels 2 hours longer than the other, so

$$t_1 = t_2 + 2.$$

We can summarize in a chart.

|            | $r$ | $t$       | $d$   |
|------------|-----|-----------|-------|
| Slow train | 30  | $t_2 + 2$ | $d_1$ |
| Fast train | 45  | $t_2$     | $d_1$ |

Using $d = rt$ in each row of the chart, we get an equation. We have the system of equations

$$30(t_2 + 2) = d_1 \qquad \text{or} \qquad 30t_2 + 60 = d_1$$
$$45t_2 = d_1 \qquad\qquad\qquad\quad 45t_2 = d_1$$

We find that $t_1 = 6$ hours and $t_2 = 4$ hours. The problem asks for distance, however. We find it using $d = rt$. So $d = 30 \cdot 6$ or $45 \cdot 4$. The distance is 180 km. This checks in the original problem.

**TRY THIS**

1. A train leaves Gigville traveling east at 35 km/h. An hour later another train leaves Gigville traveling east on a parallel track at 40 km/h. How far from Gigville will the trains meet?

**Example 2.** A canoeist paddled for 4 hours with a 5 km/h current to reach a campsite. The return trip, against the current, took 9 hours. Find the speed of the canoe in still water.

Make a drawing.

The drawing shows that the distances are the same, $d_1 = d_2$. The rates are $r + 5$ and $r - 5$ where $r$ is the speed in still water.

Downstream $r + 5$
4 hours    $d_1$ kilometers

Upstream $r - 5$
9 hours    $d_2$ kilometers

We can summarize in a chart.

|  | $r$ | $t$ | $d$ |
|---|---|---|---|
| Downstream | $r + 5$ | 4 | $d_1$ |
| Upstream | $r - 5$ | 9 | $d_1$ |

Using $d = rt$ in each row of the chart we get an equation. This gives us a system of equations.

$$
\begin{array}{lll}
(r + 5) \cdot 4 = d_1 & \text{or} & 4r + 20 = d_1 \\
(r - 5) \cdot 9 = d_1 & & 9r - 45 = d_1
\end{array}
$$

We find that $d = 72$ and $r = 13$. The speed in still water is 13 km/h. This checks in the problem.

**TRY THIS**

2. An airplane flew for 3 hours with an 18 km/h tailwind. The return flight against the same wind took 4 hours. Find the speed of the plane in still air.

**Example 3.** Two bicycles leave town traveling in opposite directions. One travels 20 km/h and the other 28 km/h. In how many hours will they be 120 kilometers apart?

Make a drawing.

The time is the same, $t_1 = t_2$. The sum of the distances is 120, so $d_1 + d_2 = 120$ and $d_2 = 120 - d_1$.

We summarize in a chart.

20 km/h
$t_1$ hours   $d_1$ km

28 km/h
$d_2$ km   $t_2$ hours

| | $r$ | $t$ | $d$ |
|---|---|---|---|
| First bicycle | 20 | $t_1$ | $d_1$ |
| Second bicycle | 28 | $t_1$ | $120 - d_1$ |

Using $d = rt$ in each row of the chart we get an equation. This gives us a system of equations.

$$20t_1 = d_1$$
$$28t_1 = 120 - d_1$$

We find that $t_1 = 2\frac{1}{2}$. In $2\frac{1}{2}$ hours, the bicycles will be 120 km apart. This checks in the problem.

**TRY THIS**

3. Two cars leave the center of town at the same time. One travels north at 64 km/h and the other travels south at 56 km/h. In how many hours will they be 480 km apart?

## Exercise Set 4-6

▮ Solve. (*See Examples 1–3.*)

1. A train leaves a station and travels north at 75 km/h. Two hours later a second train leaves on a parallel track and travels north at 125 km/h. How far from the station will they meet?

2. A private plane leaves an airport and flies due east at 180 km/h. Two hours later a jet leaves the same airport and flies due east at 900 km/h. How far from the airport will they meet?

3. Two cars leave town traveling in opposite directions. One travels 80 km/h and the other 96 km/h. In how many hours will they be 528 kilometers apart?

4. A passenger train and a freight train leave Union Station at the same time. The passenger train travels west at 55 km/h, and the freight train travels east at 45 km/h. In how many hours will they be 350 kilometers apart?

5. Two motorcycles travel toward each other from Chicago and Indianapolis, which are about 350 km apart, at rates of 110 and 90 km/h. They started at the same time. In how many hours will they meet?

6. Two planes travel toward each other from cities which are 780 km apart at rates of 190 and 200 km/h. They started at the same time. In how many hours will they meet?

7. Fly High Airlines flies from Podunk to Swampville in 5 hours with a tailwind. The return trip, against the same wind, takes 6 hours. Podunk is about 5550 km from Swampville. Find the speed of the plane and the velocity of the wind.

8. Hopeweland Airlines flies from Plunketville to Seedytown in 4 hours with a tailwind. The return trip, against the same wind, takes 5 hours. Plunketville is about 4000 km from Seedytown. Find the speed of the plane and the velocity of the wind.

9. G. Otrotrot jogs and walks to school each day. He averages 4 km/h walking and 8 km/h jogging. The distance from home to school is 6 km and he makes the trip in 1 hour. How far does he jog in a trip?

10. R. U. Fastre rides a motorbike to work. She had to walk part of the way because of a flat tire. The motorbike averages 40 km/h and she walks 5 km/h. The distance from home to work is 30 km and she made the trip in 3 hours. How far did she ride on the motorbike?

## Calculator Exercises

11. A boat travels 3.15 hours downstream, where the current is 5.82 km/h. It returns in 9.97 hours. Find the speed of the boat in still water.

12. An airplane flies for 4.18 hours with a 28.6 km/h tailwind. The return trip against the same wind takes 4.93 hours. Find the speed of the plane in still air.

## Challenge Exercises

13. A train leaves Koolsville for Groovetown, 216 km away, at 9 A.M. One hour later, a train leaves Groovetown for Koolsville. They meet at noon. If the second train had started at 9 A.M. and the first train at 10:30 A.M., they would still have met at noon. Find the speed of each train.

14. When Jupiter and Mars are on the same side of the sun and in line with it, the distance between them is 549,908,000 km. When they are on opposite sides of the sun and in line with it, the distance between them is 1,005,393,000 km. How far is each planet from the sun?

## COMPUTER ACTIVITY

## Solving Simultaneous Equations by Cramer's Rule

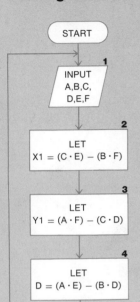

**PROBLEM:** Find the solution (X, Y) of a system of two equations in two unknowns.

Equations:

$$AX + BY = C$$
$$DX + EY = F$$

Solutions:

$$X = \dfrac{\begin{pmatrix} C & B \\ F & E \end{pmatrix}}{\begin{pmatrix} A & B \\ D & E \end{pmatrix}} = \dfrac{X1}{D} \qquad Y = \dfrac{\begin{pmatrix} A & C \\ D & F \end{pmatrix}}{\begin{pmatrix} A & B \\ D & E \end{pmatrix}} = \dfrac{Y1}{D}$$

### Examples using the flowchart:

| 1 | | | 2 | 3 | 4 | 5 | 6 |
|---|---|---|---|---|---|---|---|
| ABC DEF | | | X1 | Y1 | D | X | Y |
| 2 | 1 | 4 | | | | | |
| 3 | 1 | 7 | −3 | 2 | −1 | 3 | −2 |
| 4 | 3 | 7 | | | | | |
| 2 | −7 | 5 | −64 | 6 | −34 | 1.882353 | −0.176471 |
| 3 | 4 | 2 | | | | | |
| −1 | 6 | 3 | | | | | |
| 5 | −2 | .5 | | | | | |
| 6 | 9 | 1 | | | | | |

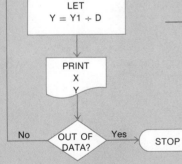

**TRY THIS** ➡ Find the numbers to complete the examples.

BASIC PROGRAM (Optional)

```
10  READ A,B,C,D,E,F          60  LET Y = Y1/D
20  LET X1 = (C*E) − (B*F)    70  PRINT "X="X, "Y="Y
30  LET Y1 = (A*F) − (C*D)    80  GO TO 10
40  LET D = (A*E) − (B*D)     90  DATA 2,1,4,3,1,7
50  LET X = X1/D             100  DATA 4,3,7,2,−7,5
```

## CHAPTER 4 REVIEW

Review the material in the chapter. Then see how you have done by trying these review exercises. If you miss an exercise, restudy the indicated lesson.

4-1     Solve graphically.

    1.  $x + y = 3$    2.  $x + 2y = 5$
         $x - y = 5$         $3x - y = -6$

4-2     3.  Solve, using the substitution method: $2x - y = -9$
                                                 $3x - 8y = -7$

4-2     4.  Solve, using the addition method: $2x + 7y = 2$
                                              $3x + 5y = -8$

4-3     Which of the following systems of equations are inconsistent and which are dependent?

    5.  $2x - y = 4$    6.  $2x - y = 4$    7.  $x - 2y = 3$
         $2x - y = 6$        $4x = 2y - 5$       $4x - 8y = 12$

4-4     8.  Solve: $2a - b + c = 7$
                   $a + 2b + 2c = 3$
                   $7a - 3b - 3c = 4$

4-5     Solve.

    9.  The perimeter of a rectangular lot is 504 meters. The length is 36 meters more than twice the width. Find the dimensions.

4-6     10.  On a recent trip Allie Gator drove 372 km in the same length of time that Crockie Dial required to drive 270 km. Gator's speed was 17 km/h greater than Dial's speed. Find the rate of each.

## CHAPTER 4 TEST

Solve graphically.

1.  $x + y = 2$
    $x - y = 4$

2.  $7x - 4y = 2$
    $5x + y = 13$

3.  Solve, using the substitution method: $x + y = 7$
    $\qquad\qquad\qquad\qquad\qquad\qquad\qquad\quad 2x - y = 8$

4.  Solve, using the addition method: $3x + 2y = 5$
    $\qquad\qquad\qquad\qquad\qquad\qquad\quad 4x + 5y = 2$

Which of the following systems are inconsistent and which are dependent?

5.  $x - 3y = 2$
    $5x - 15y = 10$

6.  $3x - y = 8$
    $3x - y = 10$

7.  $-3x + 2y = 7$
    $4y = 6x - 3$

8.  Solve: $x + y - 3z = 8$
    $\qquad\quad 2x - 3y + z = -6$
    $\qquad\quad 3x + 4y - 2z = 20$

Solve.

9.  The perimeter of a rectangular field is 608 meters. The length is 42 meters more than twice the width. Find the dimensions.

10. Rocky drove his trail bike into the country at the rate of 50 km/h. He returned over the same route at 40 km/h. The total trip took 9 hours. How far did he drive into the country?

## CUMULATIVE REVIEW FOR CHAPTERS 1–4

1-1    1. Find decimal notation for $\frac{11}{20}$.

1-1    Which of the following are rational and which are irrational?
2. $5.1343\overline{434}$    3. $\sqrt{19}$    4. $-\frac{5}{6}$

1-2    5. Simplify: $|-20|$.

1-2    6. Find the additive inverse of $-4.21$.

1-2    7. Add: $-18 + (-2)$.

1-3, 1-4    Tell which property of real numbers is illustrated by each sentence.
8. $14 + 2 = 2 + 14$
9. $(3 \cdot 4) \cdot 6 = 3 \cdot (4 \cdot 6)$

1-3    10. Subtract: $15 - (-4)$.

1-4    11. Multiply: $6(-5)$.

1-4    12. Divide: $\dfrac{-40}{-5}$.

1-4    Which of these divisions are possible?
13. $\frac{0}{11}$      14. $\frac{23}{0}$

1-5    15. Factor: $10x - 14y$.

1-5    16. Multiply: $-2(-x + 7)$.

1-5    17. Collect like terms: $-2w + 7 - 3 - 10w$.

1-6    Remove parentheses and simplify.
18. $-(-14y)$      19. $-(7x + 2) - x$
20. $3w - [w - (3w + 6)]$

1-7, 1-8    Simplify.

21. $3^{-2}$    22. $5^3 \cdot 5^{-6}$    23. $\dfrac{x^{-3}}{x^5}$    24. $(3^{-4})^{-2}$

1-9    25. Simplify: $|-4w^2z^5|$.

Solve.

2-1    26. $5 - y = 10$      27. $-3w = 54$

2-2    28. $-7t + 23 = -33$      29. $-2(4 - y) = 18$
30. $(x - 7)(2x + 1) = 0$

2-3    31. Solve: An 8-meter plank is cut into two pieces. One piece is 3 times as long as the other. How long are the pieces?

2-4    32. Solve for $s$: $Fs = wh$.

3-1    33.   Determine whether $(7, -2)$ is a solution of $2x - 3y = -20$.

3-1    34.   Graph $-x + 2y = 1$.

3-2    35.   Is $3y - x^2 = x - x^2$ a linear equation?

3-2    36.   Find standard form for $3y = -2x + 9$.

3-2    37.   Graph $5x - 3y = 15$ using intercepts.

3-2    38.   Graph $-y = 7$.

3-3    39.   Find the slope of the line containing $(-3, 5)$ and $(2, -1)$.

3-3    40.   Find an equation for the line with slope of $-\frac{1}{2}$ and containing $(-8, 0)$.

3-4    41.   Find an equation for the line containing $(-2, -1)$ and $(-3, 7)$.

3-4    42.   Find the slope and y-intercept of the equation $-2x + 1 = 2y$.

3-5    43.   Without graphing, tell whether the graphs of $x + 8 = y$ and $-y - 3 = x$ are parallel.

3-5    Find an equation of the line containing $(-5, -1)$ which is

        44.   parallel to the line $-2x - y = 10$.

        45.   perpendicular to the line $-2x - y = 10$.

4-1    46.   Solve this system graphically:   $2x - y = 8$
$$-x + 3y = 1$$

4-2    47.   Solve, using the substitution method:   $x - 3y = 2$
$$2x + 3y = -23$$

4-2    48.   Solve, using the addition method:   $-4x + y = -8$
$$2x + 3y = 18$$

4-3    49.   Is this system inconsistent or dependent:   $3x + y = 2$
$$y = -3x + 1$$

4-4    50.   Solve:   $2x - y - z = -11$
$$x + 2y - 3z = -13$$
$$-x - y + 4z = 22$$

Solve.

4-5    51.   One canned juice drink is 15% orange juice; another is 5% orange juice. How many liters of each should be mixed together to get 10 liters which is 10% orange juice?

4-6    52.   Two trucks leave town traveling in opposite directions. One travels 75 km/h and the other 60 km/h. In how many hours will they be 324 km apart?

**?** **Ready for Inequalities?**

1-2    Simplify.
1. $|-8|$
2. $|0|$
3. $|\sqrt{4}|$

1-2    Add.
4. $-8 + (-1.2)$
5. $\frac{3}{4} + \left(-\frac{2}{5}\right)$
6. $-4.8 + 1.2$

Solve.
2-1    7. $r + \frac{5}{6} = -\frac{3}{12}$
2-1    8. $5t = -12$
2-1    9. $\frac{2}{3}x = 16$
2-2    10. $-4y - 3y = 28$
2-2    11. $8 - 5x = x - 14$
2-2    12. $8a = 3(a + 5)$

Graph.
3-1    13. $y - 3x = 6$
3-2    14. $5y + 2 = x$

3-2    15. Find the intercepts of $3x - 4y = 15$.

3-2    Graph.
16. $y = -2$
17. $x = 4$

4-1    18. Solve graphically:  $2x - y = 4$
$x - y = 3$

How can the minimum daily requirements of calcium and protein be obtained at the least cost by eating certain foods?

# 5-1 Solving Inequalities

After finishing Lesson 5-1, you should be able to
**I** graph inequalities in one variable on a line.
**II** solve inequalities using the addition principle.

Sentences containing $<$, $>$, $\leq$, or $\geq$ are called inequalities.
$a < b$ read "a is less than b." The formal definition is as follows.

**DEFINITION**
$a < b$ means that $b - a$ is a positive number.

$a \leq b$ means that $a$ is less than or equal to $b$.
$a > b$ means the same as $b < a$, and $a \geq b$ means the same as $b \leq a$.

## I Solutions and Graphs of Inequalities

A *solution* of an inequality such as

$$-3 \leq x$$

is a replacement for the variable which makes the sentence true.

**Example 1.** Consider $-3 \leq x$. Determine whether each number is a solution.

a) $-2$ is a solution because $-3 \leq -2$ is true.
b) $-3$ is a solution because $-3 \leq -3$ is true.
c) $-5$ is not a solution because $-3 \leq -5$ is false.

**TRY THIS** ➡️

1. Consider $x > -7$. Determine whether each number is a solution.

   a) $-5$    b) $-7$
   c) $4$    d) $0$

2. Consider $x \geq -7$. Determine whether each number is a solution.

   a) $-8$    b) $-6$
   c) $-7$    d) $0$

The *graph* of an inequality shows all its solutions on a number line.

**Example 2.** Graph $x < 2$ on a number line.

The solutions consist of all numbers less than 2, so we shade all numbers less than 2. Note that 2 is not a solution. We indicate this by using an open circle at 2.

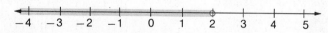

**Example 3.** Graph $x \leq 2$ on a number line.

This time 2 and all numbers less than 2 are solutions. We shade all numbers less than 2 and use a solid circle at 2 to indicate that it is a solution.

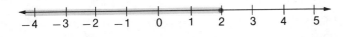

**TRY THIS**

> Graph on a number line.
>
> 3. $x < -2$
> 4. $x \leq -2$

## ◾ The Addition Principle

Consider the true inequality

$$4 < 9.$$

If we add 3 to both numbers we get another true inequality,

$$7 < 12.$$

Similarly if we add $-6$ to both numbers we get another true inequality,

$$-2 < 3.$$

**THEOREM 5-1 (The Addition Principle for Inequalities)**
If any number is added to both members of a true inequality, another true inequality is obtained. For example, for any numbers $a$, $b$, and $c$, if $a < b$, then $a + c < b + c$.

**Example 4.** Solve $x + 3 > 6$. Then graph.

Using Theorem 5-1, we add $-3$.

$$x + 3 + (-3) > 6 + (-3)$$
$$x > 3$$

Any number greater than 3 makes the last sentence true, and hence is a solution of that sentence. Any such number is also a solution of the original sentence.

> Solve and graph.
>
> 5. $x + 6 > 9$
> 6. $x + 4 \leq 7$

**TRY THIS**

**Remark.** We cannot check all the solutions of an inequality by substitution as we can check solutions of equations. There are too many. However, we really do not need to check. Let us see why. Consider the first and last inequalities, $x + 3 > 6$ and $x > 3$.

We have proved "If $x + 3 > 6$, then $x > 3$." The solution set of the antecedent of a conditional sentence is always a subset of the solution set of the consequent.

Thus any number that makes the first inequality true must make the last inequality true. Now the question is, will any number that makes the last one true also be a solution of the first one? Let us use the addition principle again, adding 3:

$$x > 3$$
$$x + 3 > 6$$

This proves the converse, that is, "If $x > 3$, then $x + 3 > 6$."

Now we know that any number that makes $x > 3$ true also makes $x + 3 > 6$ true. Thus the sentences $x > 3$ and $x + 3 > 6$ have the same solutions. Now we know that when we use Theorem 5-1, the first and last sentences will have the same solutions.

**Example 5.** Solve $5x - 2 \leq 4x - 1$.

$$5x - 2 + 2 \leq 4x - 1 + 2 \qquad \textit{Adding 2}$$
$$5x \leq 4x + 1 \qquad \textit{Simplifying}$$
$$5x - 4x \leq 4x + 1 - 4x \qquad \textit{Adding } -4x$$
$$x \leq 1$$

Now we know that any number less than or equal to 1 is a solution.

**TRY THIS**

Solve. You need not graph.

7. $3x + 1 > 2x - 5$
8. $1 + 4y \leq 5y + 2$

**Example 6.** Solve $x + \dfrac{3}{4} > \dfrac{3}{8}$.

$$x + \frac{3}{4} - \frac{3}{4} > \frac{3}{8} - \frac{3}{4} \qquad \textit{Adding } -\frac{3}{4}$$
$$x > \frac{3}{8} - \frac{3}{4}$$
$$x > \frac{3}{8} - \frac{3}{4} \cdot \frac{2}{2} \qquad \textit{Simplifying}$$

$$x > \frac{3}{8} - \frac{6}{8}$$

$$x > -\frac{3}{8}$$

**TRY THIS** ➡️

Solve. You need not graph.

9. $x - \frac{1}{3} > \frac{5}{4}$

## Exercise Set 5-1

▌Graph on a number line. (*See Examples 2 and 3.*)

1. $x \leq 4$
3. $x > 5$
5. $y < 10$
7. $x \geq -5$
9. $x < 0$

2. $y \leq -1$
4. $x > 3$
6. $x < -4$
8. $y \geq -1$
10. $y < -8$

▌▌Solve using the addition principle. (*See Examples 4–6.*)

11. $x + 8 > 3$
13. $y + 3 < 9$
15. $a + 9 \leq -12$
17. $t + 14 \geq 9$
19. $x - 9 \leq 10$
21. $y - 8 > -14$
23. $x - 11 \leq -2$
25. $y - \frac{1}{8} \leq \frac{1}{4}$
27. $x - \frac{1}{4} \geq -\frac{1}{3}$
29. $x + 2.6 \leq 5.3$
31. $5x - 1 > 4x + 7$
33. $1 + 2x < 3x + 5$
35. $11 - 3x \geq -4x - 3$
37. $8x + \frac{2}{3} \leq 7x - \frac{7}{8}$
39. $9x + 2.7 > 8x - 9.7$

12. $x + 5 > 2$
14. $y + 4 < 10$
16. $a + 7 \leq -13$
18. $t + 16 \geq 6$
20. $x - 4 \leq 15$
22. $y - 9 > -18$
24. $y - 18 \leq -4$
26. $y - \frac{1}{4} \leq \frac{1}{2}$
28. $x + \frac{1}{3} \leq -\frac{1}{6}$
30. $x + 3.9 \leq 8.2$
32. $6x - 3 > 5x + 9$
34. $2 + 5x < 6x + 7$
36. $12 - 2x \geq -3x - 7$
38. $5x + \frac{1}{4} \leq 4x - \frac{1}{5}$
40. $10x + 3.8 > 9x - 7.8$

## Calculator Exercises

41. $x + 0.000894 \leq -0.009764$
43. $8x - 0.00962 \leq 7x + 0.00843$

42. $y + 0.001096 \geq -0.005792$
44. $6y - 0.000834 < 5y - 0.000948$

# 5-2 More About Solving Inequalities

After finishing Lesson 5-2, you should be able to
- **❙** solve and graph conjunctions of inequalities in one variable.
- **❙❙** solve and graph disjunctions of inequalities in one variable.
- **❙❙❙** solve inequalities using the multiplication principle.
- **❙❙❙❙** solve inequalities using both the addition and multiplication principles.

## ❙ Conjunctions

Consider the sentence $-2 \le x < 3$. This is an abbreviation for the conjunction $-2 \le x$ *and* $x < 3$. Thus any solution of $-2 \le x < 3$ must be a solution of *both* $-2 \le x$ and $x < 3$.

**Example 1.** Graph $-2 \le x < 3$.

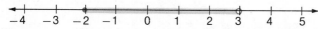

**Example 2.** Graph $-7 < x \le 5$.

**Example 3.** Graph $-4 \le x \le 2$.

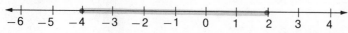

**TRY THIS** ➤

Graph.

1. $-1 \le x < 4$
2. $-1 < x \le 4$
3. $-1 \le x \le 4$

**Example 4.** Solve $-3 < x + 5 < 7$.

*Method 1.* We first express this conjunction with the word *and*. Then we solve the inequalities separately.

$$
\begin{array}{lcl}
-3 < x + 5 & and & x + 5 < 7 \\
-3 + (-5) < x + 5 + (-5) & and & x + 5 + (-5) < 7 + (-5) \\
-8 < x & and & x < 2
\end{array}
$$

Now we translate back.

$$-8 < x < 2$$

*Method 2.* In Method 1 we did the same thing to both inequalities. We can abbreviate as follows.

$$-3 + (-5) < x + 5 + (-5) < 7 + (-5) \quad \textit{Adding } -5$$
$$-8 < x < 2$$

Method 2 is more efficient.

**TRY THIS** ➡

> 4. Consider $-2 < x + 4 < 7$.
>    a) Solve using *Method 1*.
>    b) Solve using *Method 2*.
> 5. Solve $-4 < x - 6 < 9$.

## ‖ Disjunctions

Consider the disjunction $x < -3$ *or* $x > 3$. A disjunction is true when one or both parts are true. There is no number that is both less than $-3$ and greater than 3. Thus the solutions are those numbers which are either less than $-3$ *or* greater than 3.

**Examples.** Graph these disjunctions of inequalities.

**5.** $x < -3$ *or* $x > 3$

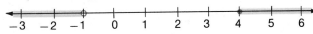

**6.** $x < -1$ *or* $x \geq 4$

**7.** $x \leq 2$ *or* $x \geq 5$

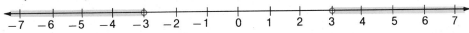

**TRY THIS** ➡

> Graph.
>
> 6. $x \leq -2$ or $x > 2$
> 7. $x < -2$ or $x \geq 2$
> 8. $x \leq -2$ or $x \geq 2$

**Example 8.** Solve: $x - 5 < -2$ *or* $x - 5 > 2$.

We solve the inequalities separately, but we keep writing the word *or*.

$$x - 5 + 5 < -2 + 5 \quad \text{or} \quad x - 5 + 5 > 2 + 5$$
$$x < 3 \quad \text{or} \quad x > 7$$

**TRY THIS** ➡

> Solve.
>
> 9. $x - 4 < -3$
>    or $x - 4 > 3$
> 10. $x + 4 < -3$
>    or $x + 4 > 3$

### ꟼꟼꟼThe Multiplication Principle

Consider the true inequality

$$4 < 9.$$

If we multiply both numbers by 2 we get another true inequality,

$$8 < 18.$$

If we multiply both numbers by $-3$ we get a false inequality,

$$-12 < -27.$$

However, if we reverse the inequality symbol we get a true inequality,

$$-12 > -27.$$

**THEOREM 5-2 (The Multiplication Principle for Inequalities)**

If both members of a true inequality are multiplied by a positive number, another true inequality is obtained.

If both members are multiplied by a *negative* number and the inequality sign is reversed, another true inequality is obtained.

When we solve an inequality using the multiplication principle, we do not need to check, provided that we do not multiply by an expression containing a variable.

**Examples.**  Solve these inequalities.

**9.**  $3y < \dfrac{3}{4}$

$\dfrac{1}{3} \cdot 3y < \dfrac{1}{3} \cdot \dfrac{3}{4}$      *Using Theorem 5-2, multiplying by $\frac{1}{3}$*

$y < \dfrac{1}{4}$

Any number less than $\dfrac{1}{4}$ is a solution.

**10.**  $-4x < \dfrac{4}{5}$

$-\dfrac{1}{4} \cdot -4x > -\dfrac{1}{4} \cdot \dfrac{4}{5}$      *Multiplying by $-\frac{1}{4}$ and reversing the inequality sign*

$x > -\dfrac{1}{5}$

Any number greater than $-\dfrac{1}{5}$ is a solution.

**TRY THIS**

Solve.

11.  $5y \le \dfrac{3}{2}$

12.  $-2y > \dfrac{5}{6}$

## Using the Principles Together

We use the addition and multiplication principles together in solving inequalities in much the same way as for equations.

**Example 11.** Solve: $7 - 4y > 8$.

$$-7 + 7 - 4y > -7 + 8 \qquad \text{\textit{Adding} } -7$$
$$-4y > 1 \qquad \text{\textit{Simplifying}}$$
$$-\frac{1}{4} \cdot -4y < -\frac{1}{4} \cdot 1 \qquad \text{\textit{Multiplying by} } -\frac{1}{4} \text{ \textit{and}}$$
$$\text{\textit{reversing the inequality sign}}$$
$$y < -\frac{1}{4} \qquad \text{\textit{Simplifying}}$$

**TRY THIS**

Solve.

13.  $6 - 5y \ge 7$
14.  $3x + 5x < 4$

**Example 12.** Solve: $16 - 7y \ge 10y - 4$.

$$-16 + 16 - 7y \ge -16 + 10y - 4 \qquad \text{\textit{Adding} } -16$$
$$-7y \ge 10y - 20 \qquad \text{\textit{Simplifying}}$$
$$-10y - 7y \ge -10y + 10y - 20 \qquad \text{\textit{Adding} } -10y$$
$$-17y \ge -20 \qquad \text{\textit{Simplifying}}$$
$$-\frac{1}{17} \cdot (-17y) \le -\frac{1}{17} \cdot (-20) \qquad \text{\textit{Multiplying by} } -\frac{1}{17} \text{ \textit{and}}$$
$$\text{\textit{reversing the inequality sign}}$$
$$y \le \frac{20}{17}$$

**Example 13.** Solve this conjunction of inequalities.

$$-1 < 2x + 3 \le 11$$
$$-1 + (-3) < 2x + 3 + (-3) \le 11 + (-3) \qquad \text{\textit{Adding} } -3$$
$$-4 < 2x \le 8 \qquad \text{\textit{Simplifying}}$$
$$\frac{1}{2} \cdot (-4) < \frac{1}{2} \cdot 2x \le \frac{1}{2} \cdot 8 \qquad \text{\textit{Multiplying by} } \frac{1}{2}$$
$$-2 < x \le 4 \qquad \text{\textit{Simplifying}}$$

Solve.

15.  $17 - 5y \le 8y - 5$
16.  $7 \le 4x - 5 < 11$

**TRY THIS**

## Exercise Set 5-2

▮ Graph. (*See Examples 1–3.*)

1. $-2 < x < 4$
2. $-2 < x \leq 4$
3. $-2 \leq x < 4$
4. $-2 \leq x \leq 4$
5. $1 < x < 6$
6. $0 \leq y \leq 3$
7. $-7 \leq y \leq -3$
8. $-9 \leq x < -5$

Solve. (*See Example 4.*)

9. $-2 < x + 2 < 8$
10. $-1 < x + 1 \leq 6$
11. $2 \leq y + 5 \leq 9$
12. $3 \leq x + 3 \leq 8$
13. $-5 < x + 8 < 12$
14. $-6 < x + 6 \leq 2$
15. $-10 \leq x - 5 \leq -1$
16. $-18 \leq x - 7 < 0$

▮▮ Graph. (*See Examples 5–7.*)

17. $x < -1$ or $x > 2$
18. $x < -2$ or $x > 0$
19. $x \leq -3$ or $x > 1$
20. $x \leq -1$ or $x > 3$
21. $x < -8$ or $x > -2$
22. $t \leq -10$ or $t \geq -5$
23. $t < 1$ or $t \geq 5$
24. $p \leq 3$ or $p \geq 9$

Solve. (*See Example 8.*)

25. $x + 7 < -2$ or $x + 7 > 2$
26. $x + 9 < -4$ or $x + 9 > 4$
27. $x - 8 \leq -3$ or $x - 8 \geq 3$
28. $x - 7 \leq -2$ or $x - 7 \geq 2$
29. $x - 9 < -5$ or $x - 9 > 6$
30. $x - 4 < -8$ or $x - 4 > 12$

▮▮▮ Solve. (*See Examples 9 and 10.*)

31. $3x < 18$
32. $5x < 25$
33. $-5x \geq 10$
34. $-6y \geq 30$
35. $-9x \geq -81$
36. $-8y \leq -32$
37. $-5y \leq 3$
38. $-9x < 7$
39. $-8y < -\dfrac{1}{9}$
40. $-7x \leq -\dfrac{1}{4}$
41. $-\dfrac{3}{4}x \geq -\dfrac{5}{8}$
42. $-\dfrac{5}{6}y \leq -\dfrac{3}{4}$

▮▮▮▮ Solve. (*See Examples 11–13.*)

43. $8 + 5x \leq 38$
44. $7 + 4y \geq 39$
45. $2x - 6 > 8$
46. $5y - 9 > 16$
47. $5y + 2y \leq -21$
48. $9x + 3x \geq -24$
49. $2y - 7 < 5y - 9$
50. $8x - 9 < 3x - 11$
51. $11x - 2 \geq 15x - 7$
52. $10y - 3 \geq 13y - 8$
53. $8 < 3x + 2 < 14$
54. $9 \leq 5x + 3 < 19$
55. $3 \leq 4x - 3 \leq 19$
56. $2 < 5x - 8 \leq 12$
57. $-7 \leq 5x - 2 \leq 12$
58. $-11 \leq 2x - 1 < -5$

# 5-3 Absolute Value

After finishing Lesson 5-3, you should be able to
**I**  find the distance between a pair of numbers on a number line.
**II**  solve inequalities involving absolute value.

## I Distance

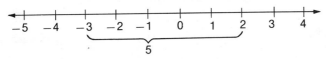

The number line above shows that the distance between −3 and
2 is 5. Another way to find the distance between two numbers
on a number line is to subtract and take the absolute value.

$$|-3 - 2| = |-5| = 5, \text{ or } |2 - (-3)| = |5| = 5$$

Note that the order in which we subtract does not matter.

For any numbers $a$ and $b$, $|a - b|$ is the
distance between the two numbers $a$ and $b$.

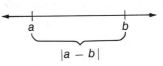

**Example 1.**  Find the distance between −8 and −92.

$$|-8 - (-92)| = |84| = 84$$

**Example 2.**  Find the distance between $x$ and 0.

$$|x - 0| = |x|$$

**TRY THIS** ➤

> Find the distance
> between each
> pair of numbers.
>
> 1.  −7, −35
> 2.  19, 14
> 3.  $a$, 0

## II Equations and Inequalities with Absolute Value

**Example 3.**  Solve $|x| = 4$.

Note that $|x| = |x - 0|$. So $|x - 0|$ is the distance from $x$ to 0.
Thus the solutions of the equation are those numbers $x$ whose
distance from 0 is 4. The solutions are −4 and 4.

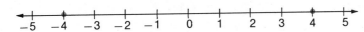

**TRY THIS**

**Example 4.** Solve $|x| < 4$.

Again, note that $|x| = |x - 0|$. So $|x - 0|$ is the distance from $x$ to 0. Thus the solutions of $|x - 0| < 4$ are those numbers $x$ whose distance from 0 is less than 4. The solutions are those numbers $x$ such that $-4 < x < 4$.

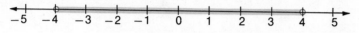

**TRY THIS**

**Example 5.** Solve $|x| \geq 4$.

Since $|x| = |x - 0|$, the solutions of $|x - 0| \geq 4$ are those numbers $x$ whose distance from 0 is greater than or equal to 4. In other words, those numbers $x$ such that $x \leq -4$ or $x \geq 4$.

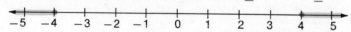

**TRY THIS**

Examples 4 and 5 illustrate solving inequalities involving absolute value. We can prove that they work for any inequalities, so we state the following theorem.

**THEOREM 5-3**

For any number $b > 0$ and any expression $X$,
1. The solutions of $|X| = b$ are those numbers that satisfy $X = -b$ or $X = b$.
2. The solutions of $|X| < b$ are those numbers that satisfy $-b < X < b$.
3. The solutions of $|X| > b$ are those numbers that satisfy $X < -b$ or $X > b$.

Parts 1 and 2 of Theorem 5-3 show that the solutions of $|X| \leq b$ are those numbers that satisfy $-b \leq X \leq b$. Parts 1 and 3 together tell us that the solutions of $|X| \geq b$ are those numbers that satisfy $X \leq -b$ or $X \geq b$.

---

Solve, using a number line.

4. $|x| = 6$
5. $|x| = \dfrac{1}{2}$

---

Solve, using a number line.

6. $|x| < 6$
7. $|x| \leq \dfrac{1}{2}$

---

Solve. Use a number line.

8. $|x| \geq 6$
9. $|x| > \dfrac{1}{2}$

To solve inequalities with absolute value, we can use graphing or Theorem 5-3.

**Example 6.** Solve $|x - 2| < 4$.

(Using Theorem 5-3). We use part 2, replacing $b$ by 4 and $X$ by $x - 2$.

$$|X| < b$$
$$|x - 2| < 4$$
$$-4 < x - 2 < 4$$
$$-2 < x < 6 \quad \textit{Adding 2}$$

**TRY THIS**

10. Solve $|x - 3| < 7$ using Theorem 5-3.

**Example 7.** Solve $|x + 2| \geq 5$.

(Graphing). We can rewrite this as $|x - (-2)| \geq 5$, and then think of distance. The solutions are those numbers $x$ whose distance from $-2$ is greater than or equal to 5. Thus the solutions are those numbers $x$ such that $x \leq -7$ *or* $x \geq 3$.

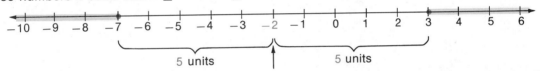

5 units ↑ 5 units

**TRY THIS**

Solve.

11. $|x + 3| \geq 4$
12. $|2x + 5| \leq 11$

**Example 8.** Solve $\left|\dfrac{3x - 1}{5}\right| > 2$.

We use Theorem 5-3, part 3, replacing $b$ by 2 and $X$ by $\dfrac{3x - 1}{5}$.

$$\left|\frac{3x - 1}{5}\right| > 2$$

$$\frac{3x - 1}{5} < -2 \quad \textit{or} \quad \frac{3x - 1}{5} > 2$$

$$3x - 1 < -10 \quad \textit{or} \quad 3x - 1 > 10 \quad \textit{Multiplying by 5}$$

$$3x < -9 \quad \textit{or} \quad 3x > 11 \quad \textit{Adding 1}$$

$$x < -3 \quad \textit{or} \quad x > \frac{11}{3} \quad \textit{Multiplying by } \tfrac{1}{3}$$

**TRY THIS** ➡️

13. Solve $\left|\dfrac{4x + 2}{3}\right| > 1$.

## Exercise Set 5-3

▍Find the distance between each pair of numbers. (*See Examples 1 and 2.*)

1. $-8, -42$
2. $-9, -36$
3. $26, 15$
4. $54, 18$
5. $-26, -35$
6. $-58, -96$
7. $-9, 24$
8. $-18, 37$
9. $-\dfrac{1}{2}, -\dfrac{1}{4}$
10. $-\dfrac{1}{3}, -\dfrac{1}{6}$
11. $h, 0$
12. $b, 0$

▍▍Solve. (*See Examples 3–8.*)

13. $|x| = 3$
14. $|x| = 5$
15. $|y| = 9$
16. $|y| = 12$
17. $|x| < 3$
18. $|x| \leq 5$
19. $|y| \leq 6$
20. $|y| < 10$
21. $|x| > 2$
22. $|x| > 5$
23. $|y| \geq 4$
24. $|y| \geq 8$
25. $|x - 3| < 12$
26. $|x - 2| < 6$
27. $|x + 5| \leq 19$
28. $|x + 3| \leq 12$
29. $|2x + 3| \leq 4$
30. $|5x + 2| \leq 3$
31. $|4x - 9| < 8$
32. $|5x - 8| < 7$
33. $|2y - 7| > 5$
34. $|3y - 4| > 8$
35. $|4x - 9| \geq 14$
36. $|9y - 2| \geq 17$
37. $\left|\dfrac{2x - 1}{3}\right| \leq 1$
38. $\left|\dfrac{5x - 2}{6}\right| \leq 2$
39. $\left|\dfrac{3x - 1}{4}\right| \geq 2$
40. $\left|\dfrac{3x - 2}{5}\right| \geq 1$

## Calculator Exercises

Solve.

41. $\left|\dfrac{0.005x - 0.004}{0.0059}\right| \leq 0.0043$

42. $\left|\dfrac{0.006y - 0.0009}{0.0023}\right| \geq 0.0089$

# 5-4 Inequalities in Two Variables

After finishing Lesson 5-4, you should be able to
▌ graph inequalities in two variables on a plane.

▌ The solutions of inequalities in two variables are ordered pairs.

**Example 1.** Determine whether $(-3, 2)$ is a solution of
$5x - 4y > 13$.

We replace $x$ by $-3$ and $y$ by 2.

$$
\begin{array}{c|c}
5x - 4y > 13 & \\
\hline
5(-3) - 4 \cdot 2 & 13 \\
-15 - 8 & \\
-23 & 
\end{array}
$$

Since $-23 > 13$ is false, $(-3, 2)$ is not a solution.

**TRY THIS** ➡

> 1. Determine whether $(4, -3)$ is a solution of
> $-2x + 3y \leq 6$.

Inequalities in two variables are graphed on a plane.

**Example 2.** Graph $y < x$.

For comparison we first graph the line $y = x$ as shown below. We draw it dashed. Every solution of $y = x$ is an ordered pair having the same first and second coordinates.

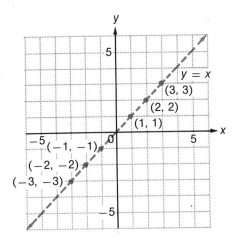

Now look at the vertical line through (2, 2) and some ordered pairs on it as shown below on the left.

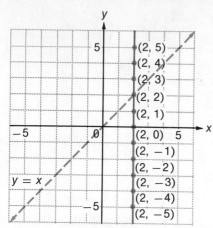
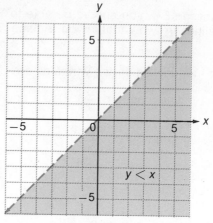

For all points below $y = x$, the second coordinate is less than the first ($y < x$). For all points above the line, $y > x$. The same thing happens for any vertical line. Then for all points below $y = x$ the ordered pairs are solutions. We shade the half-plane below $y = x$. The graph of $y < x$ is shown above on the right. The points on the line $y = x$ are not in the graph; that is why we drew it dashed.

**TRY THIS** ➤

In general,

> the graph of $y < mx + b$ consists of all pairs below the line $y = mx + b$.
>
> the graph of $y > mx + b$ consists of all pairs above the line $y = mx + b$.
>
> for $y < mx + b$, or $y > mx + b$, we draw a *dashed* line for $y = mx + b$.
>
> for $y \leq mx + b$, or $y \geq mx + b$, we draw a *solid* line for $y = mx + b$.

2. Graph $y > x$.

**Example 3.** Graph $6x - 2y < 10$.

a) We first solve for $y$.

$$6x - 2y < 10$$
$$-2y < -6x + 10 \qquad \textit{Adding } -6x$$
$$y > -\tfrac{1}{2}(-6x + 10) \qquad \textit{Multiplying by } -\tfrac{1}{2} \textit{ and reversing inequality sign}$$
$$y > 3x - 5 \qquad \textit{Simplifying}$$

b) We graph $y = 3x - 5$ using a dashed line, and shade the region above the line.

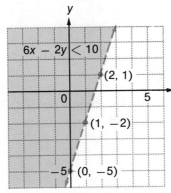

| x | y |
|---|---|
| 0 | −5 |
| 1 | −2 |
| 2 | 1 |

**TRY THIS**

Graph.

3. $6x - 2y \leq 10$
4. $5y - 2x > -10$

Here is an example of a method in which we do not need to solve for $y$.

**Example 4.** Graph $3x - 2y \geq 6$.

a) Graph $3x - 2y = 6$ using a solid line. The $y$-intercept is $(0, -3)$ and the $x$-intercept is $(2, 0)$.

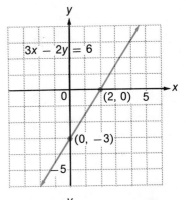

b) We try a checkpoint off the line to see which side of the line to shade. The origin $(0, 0)$ is usually an easy one to try. $3 \cdot 0 - 2 \cdot 0 \geq 6$ is false, so the origin is not in the graph. We shade the other half-plane.

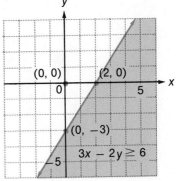

If the line contains the origin then we try another point not on the line. The point (1, 1) is often a good one to try.

**TRY THIS** ➡

> Graph.
>
> 5. $3x - 2y > 6$
> 6. $2x + 3y \leq 6$

**Example 5.** Graph $x \leq 3$.

We can think of this as $x + 0y \leq 3$. The graph consists of all pairs whose first coordinate $x$ is less than or equal to 3.

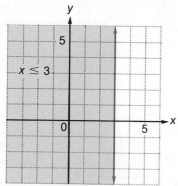

**TRY THIS** ➡

> Graph.
>
> 7. $x \leq -1$
> 8. $x > 2$
> 9. $y > -2$

**Example 6.** Graph $-1 < y \leq 2$.

The graph consists of all pairs whose second coordinate $y$ is greater than $-1$ and less than or equal to 2.

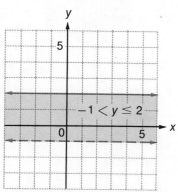

**TRY THIS** ➡

> Graph.
>
> 10. $1 \leq y \leq 3$
> 11. $-4 \leq x < 1$

## Exercise Set 5-4

❚ Use graph paper. Graph these inequalities. (*See Examples 2–6.*)

1. $y > 2x$
2. $y > 3x$
3. $y \leq x + 1$
4. $y \leq x + 3$
5. $y > x + 2$
6. $y > x + 4$
7. $y \leq x - 2$
8. $y < x - 3$
9. $y > x - 1$
10. $y \geq x - 2$
11. $x + y < 4$
12. $x + y \leq 5$
13. $x - y > 8$
14. $x - y \geq 3$
15. $3x + 4y \leq 12$
16. $2x + 3y < 6$
17. $7x + 3y < 21$
18. $5x + 4y \geq 20$
19. $2y - 3x > 6$
20. $2y - x \leq 4$
21. $x < -4$
22. $x \geq 1$
23. $y \geq 5$
24. $y < 2$
25. $x \geq 0$
26. $y \geq 0$
27. $-4 < y < -1$
28. $-2 < y < 3$
29. $-3 \leq x \leq 3$
30. $-4 \leq x \leq 4$

## Challenge Exercises

Graph.

31. $y > |x|$
32. $y \leq |x|$
33. $y > |x| + 3$
34. $|x| + |y| = 2$
35. $|x| + |y| > 2$
36. $|x| + |y| < 2$

## COMPUTER NOTE: Number Crunching

Computers can solve problems that require many thousands or millions of calculations. Dealing with so many calculations is called number crunching. A classic number-crunching problem is the relation of three bodies in space. How do their gravitational fields interact? About 300 years ago, Sir Issac Newton solved the problem for two bodies such as the earth and the moon. It was not until 1950 that the three-body problem was solved. It was done by mathematicians and a number-crunching computer.

# 5-5 Systems of Linear Inequalities

After finishing Lesson 5-5, you should be able to
▪ graph systems of linear inequalities in two variables.
▪▪ graph systems of linear inequalities in two variables and find vertices if a polygon is formed.

## ▪ Graphs

A pair of linear inequalities is called a *system* of inequalities. The solutions of the system are the ordered pairs that make both inequalities true.

**Example 1.** Graph this system: $y < x$
$$y < -2x - 1$$

The graphs of the separate inequalities are shown below on the left. The intersection of these graphs is shown on the right. This is the graph of the system.

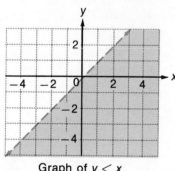

Graph of $y < x$

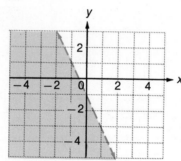

Graph of $y < -2x - 1$

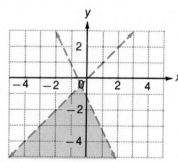

This is the graph of the system.

**Example 2.** Graph this system: $y \leq -2$
$$x \leq -1$$

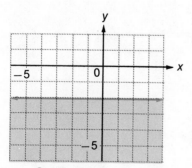

Graph of $y \leq -2$

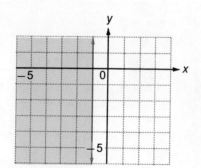

Graph of $x \leq -1$

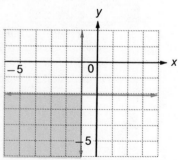

This is the graph of the system.

**TRY THIS** ➤

Graph these systems.

1. $y > x$
   $y < -2x + 1$
2. $y \geq 2$
   $x > -3$

## ‖ Graphs and Vertices

**Example 3.** Graph this system. If a polygon is formed, find the vertices.

$2x + y \geq 2$
$4x + 3y \leq 12$
$\frac{1}{2} \leq x \leq 2$
$y \geq 0$

The separate graphs are shown at the left and the graph of the intersection, which is the graph of the system, is shown at the right.

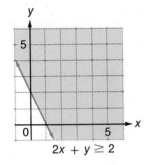

$2x + y \geq 2$

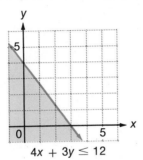

$4x + 3y \leq 12$

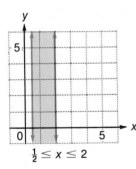

$\frac{1}{2} \leq x \leq 2$

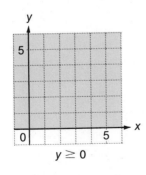

$y \geq 0$

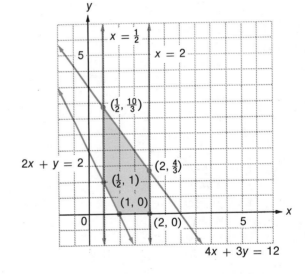

We find the vertex $(\frac{1}{2}, 1)$ by solving the system

$2x + y = 2$
$x = \frac{1}{2}$

We find the vertex $(1, 0)$ by solving the system

$2x + y = 2$
$y = 0$

We find the vertex (2, 0) from the system

$$x = 2$$
$$y = 0$$

The vertices $(2, \frac{4}{3})$ and $(\frac{1}{2}, \frac{10}{3})$ were found by solving, respectively, the systems

| $x = 2$ | and | $x = \frac{1}{2}$ |
|---------|-----|-------------------|
| $4x + 3y = 12$ | | $4x + 3y = 12$ |

**TRY THIS** ━━━▶

Graph. If a polygon is formed, find the vertices.

3. $y \leq 2x + 2$
   $y \geq -\frac{1}{3}x + 2$
   $1 \leq y \leq 3$
   $x \leq 5$

## Exercise Set 5-5

▍Graph (*See Examples 1 and 2.*)

1. $y < x$
   $y > -x + 3$
2. $y > x$
   $y < -x + 1$
3. $y \geq x$
   $y < -x + 4$
4. $y \geq x$
   $y < -x + 2$
5. $y \geq -2$
   $x > 1$
6. $y \leq -2$
   $x > 2$
7. $x < 3$
   $y \geq -3x + 2$
8. $x > -2$
   $y \leq -2x + 3$
9. $y \geq -2$
   $y \geq x + 3$
10. $y \leq 4$
    $y \geq -x + 2$
11. $x + y \leq 1$
    $x - y \leq 2$
12. $x + y \leq 3$
    $x - y \leq 4$
13. $y - 2x > 1$
    $y - 2x < 3$
14. $y + 3x > 0$
    $y + 3x < 2$
15. $2y - x \leq 2$
    $y - 3x \geq -1$
16. $x + 3y \geq 9$
    $3x - 2y \leq 5$

▍▍Graph. If a polygon is formed, find the vertices. (*See Example 3.*)

17. $x + 2y \leq 12$
    $2x + y \leq 12$
    $x \geq 0$
    $y \geq 0$
18. $8x + 5y \leq 40$
    $x + 2y \leq 8$
    $x \geq 0$
    $y \geq 0$
19. $3x + 4y \geq 12$
    $5x + 6y \leq 30$
    $1 \leq x \leq 3$
20. $y - 2x \geq 3$
    $y - 2x \leq 5$
    $6 \leq y \leq 8$

# 5-6 *Linear Programming*

After finishing Lesson 5-6, you should be able to
■ find the maximum and minimum values, if they exist, of a linear function subject to a system of constraints.
■■ solve linear programming problems.

## ▎Linear Programming

You are taking a test in which items of type A are worth 10 points and items of type B are worth 15 points. It takes 3 minutes for each item of type A and 6 minutes for each item of type B. Total time allowed is 60 minutes and you may not answer more than 16 questions. Assuming all of your answers are correct, how many items of each type should you answer to get the best score?

A kind of mathematics called *linear programming* provides the answer.

Let    $x$ = the number of items of type A, and
        $y$ = the number of items of type B.

The total score $T$ is given by $T = 10x + 15y$. The set of ordered pairs $(x, y)$ for which this equation makes sense is determined by the following inequalities, called *constraints*.

| | |
|---|---|
| Total number of questions allowed, not more than 16: | $x + y \leq 16$ |
| Time, not more than 60 minutes: | $3x + 6y \leq 60$ |
| Number of items of type A, not negative: | $x \geq 0$ |
| Number of items of type B, not negative: | $y \geq 0$ |

We now graph the system of inequalities and determine the vertices, if any are formed.

The graph consists of a polygon and its interior. Under this condition, $T$ does have a maximum value and a minimum value. Moreover, the maximum and minimum values occur at the vertices of the polygon. All we need do is find the vertices and substitute the coordinates in $T = 10x + 15y$.

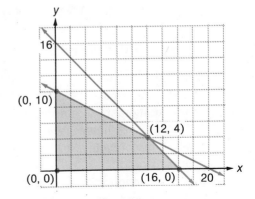

| Vertices: ($x$, $y$) | Score: $T = 10x + 15y$ | |
|---|---|---|
| (0, 0) | 0 | *Minimum* |
| (16, 0) | 160 | |
| (12, 4) | 180 | *Maximum* |
| (0, 10) | 150 | |

Thus the maximum score is 180. To get this you would answer 12 items of type A and 4 items of type B.

The following is the main theorem used to solve linear programming problems.

**THEOREM 5-4**

Suppose a quantity $F$ is given by a linear equation $F = ax + by + c$, and that the set of ordered pairs $(x, y)$ for which the equation makes sense can be described by a system of linear inequalities (called *constraints*). If the graph of this system consists of a polygon and its interior, then $F$ has a maximum and a minimum value, and they occur at the vertices.

**Example 1.** Find the maximum and minimum values of $F = 9x + 40y$, subject to the constraints

$$y - x \geq 1$$
$$y - x \leq 3$$
$$2 \leq x \leq 5$$

We graph the system of inequalities, determine the vertices, and find the function value for those ordered pairs.

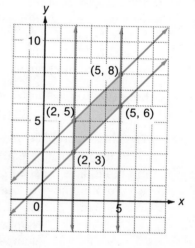

| Vertices: $(x, y)$ | $F = 9x + 40y$ | |
|---|---|---|
| (2, 3) | 138 | *Minimum* |
| (2, 5) | 218 | |
| (5, 6) | 285 | |
| (5, 8) | 365 | *Maximum* |

The maximum value of $F$ occurs when $x = 5$ and $y = 8$.
The minimum value of $F$ occurs when $x = 2$ and $y = 3$.

**TRY THIS**

## ▪ Solving Problems

**Example 2.** A company manufactures motorcycles and bicycles. To stay in business it must produce at least 10 motorcycles each month, but it does not have facilities to produce more than 60 motorcycles. It also does not have facilities to produce more than 120 bicycles. The total production of motorcycles and bicycles cannot exceed 160. The profit on a motorcycle is $134 and on a bicycle is $20. Find the number of each that should be manufactured to maximize profit.

Find maximum and minimum values of the following.

1. $F = 34x + 6y$ subject to:
$$x + y \leq 6$$
$$x + y \geq 1$$
$$1 \leq x \leq 3$$

2. $G = 3x - 5y + 27$ subject to:
$$x + 2y \leq 8$$
$$0 \leq y \leq 3$$
$$0 \leq x \leq 6$$

Let $x$ = the number of motorcycles to be produced,
and $y$ = the number of bicycles to be produced.

The profit $P$ is given by $P = 134x + 20y$, subject to the constraints

$10 \leq x \leq 60$
$0 \leq y \leq 120$
$x + y \leq 160$

| Vertices: $(x, y)$ | Profit $P = 134x + 20y$ | |
|---|---|---|
| $(10, 0)$ | 1340 | |
| $(60, 0)$ | 8040 | |
| $(60, 100)$ | 10,040 | *Maximum* |
| $(40, 120)$ | 7760 | |
| $(10, 120)$ | 3740 | |

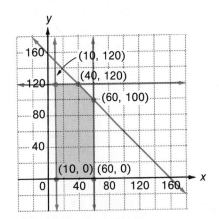

Thus the company will make a maximum profit of $10,040
by producing 60 motorcycles and 100 bicycles.

**TRY THIS**

3. A college snack bar cooks and sells hamburgers and hot dogs during the lunch hour. To stay in business it must sell at least 10 hamburgers but cannot cook more than 40. It must also sell at least 30 hot dogs but cannot cook more than 70. It cannot cook more than 90 sandwiches all together. The profit on a hamburger is $0.33 and on a hot dog it is $0.21. How many of each kind of sandwich should the snack bar sell to make the maximum profit?

## Exercise Set 5-6

▌ Find the maximum and minimum values, and where they occur. (*See Example 1.*)

1. $F = 4x + 28y$ subject to:
   $5x + 9 \leq 34$
   $3x + 5y \leq 30$
   $x \geq 0$
   $y \geq 0$

2. $G = 14x + 16y$ subject to:
   $2y + 9 \leq 16$
   $7x + 4y \leq 28$
   $x \geq 0$
   $y \geq 0$

3. $P = 16x - 2y + 40$ subject to:
   $6x + 8y \leq 48$
   $0 \leq y \leq 4$
   $0 \leq x \leq 7$

4. $Q = 24x - 3y + 52$ subject to:
   $5x + 4y \geq 20$
   $0 \leq y \leq 4$
   $0 \leq x \leq 3$

▮▮ Solve. (*See Example 2.*)

5. You are about to take a test that contains questions of type A worth 4 points and questions of type B worth 7 points. You must do at least 5 questions of type A but time restricts doing more than 10. You must do at least 3 questions of type B but time restricts doing more than 10. In total, you can do no more than 18 questions. How many of each type of question must you do to maximize your score? What is this maximum score?

6. You are about to take a test that contains questions of type A worth 10 points and questions of type B worth 25 points. You must do at least 3 questions of type A but time restricts doing more than 12. You must do at least 4 questions of type B but time restricts doing more than 15. In total you can do no more than 20 questions. How many of each type of question must you do to maximize your score? What is this maximum score?

7. A man is planning to invest up to $22,000 in bank X or bank Y or both. He wants to invest at least $2000 but no more than $14,000 in bank X. Bank Y does not insure more than a $15,000 investment so he will invest no more than that in bank Y. The interest in bank X is 6% and in bank Y it is $6\frac{1}{2}$% and this will be simple interest for one year. How much should he invest in each bank to maximize his income? What is the maximum income?

8. A woman is planning to invest up to $40,000 in corporate or municipal bonds or both. The least she is allowed to invest in corporate bonds is $6000 and she does not want to invest more than $22,000 in corporate bonds. She also does not want to invest more than $30,000 in municipal bonds. The interest on corporate bonds is 8% and on municipal bonds it is $7\frac{1}{2}$%. This is simple interest for one year. How much should she invest in each type of bond to maximize her income? What is the maximum income?

**Challenge Exercises**

9. The minimal daily nutritional requirement of protein is 50 g. For calcium it is 0.75 g. Every gram of beef contains 0.007 g of calcium and 0.186 g of protein, and costs 0.36¢. Every gram of cheddar cheese contains 0.57 g of calcium and 0.205 g of protein, and costs 0.32¢. To avoid gaining weight one should eat no more than 2000 g of beef and 1100 g of cheddar cheese. Assuming only beef and cheddar cheese are eaten, how many grams of each should be eaten to minimize the cost of obtaining the minimal daily requirements?

# COMPUTER ACTIVITY

## Linear Programming

**PROBLEM:** Maximize Q = 24X − 3Y + 52 subject to the constraints that X and Y are integers,

$0 \leq X \leq 3$,
$0 \leq Y \leq 4$,
$5X + 4Y \geq 20$.

**Example using the flowchart:**

| 1 | 2 | 3 | 4 | | |
|---|---|---|---|---|---|
| X | Y | Q | A | X1 | Y1 |
| 0 | 0 | 0 | | | |
| ⋮ | ⋮ | ⋮ | | | |
| 1 | 4 | 64 | 64 | 1 | 4 |
| 2 | 0 | 64 | 64 | 1 | 4 |
| ⋮ | ⋮ | ⋮ | ⋮ | ⋮ | ⋮ |
| 2 | 3 | 91 | 91 | 2 | 3 |
| 2 | 4 | 88 | 91 | 2 | 3 |

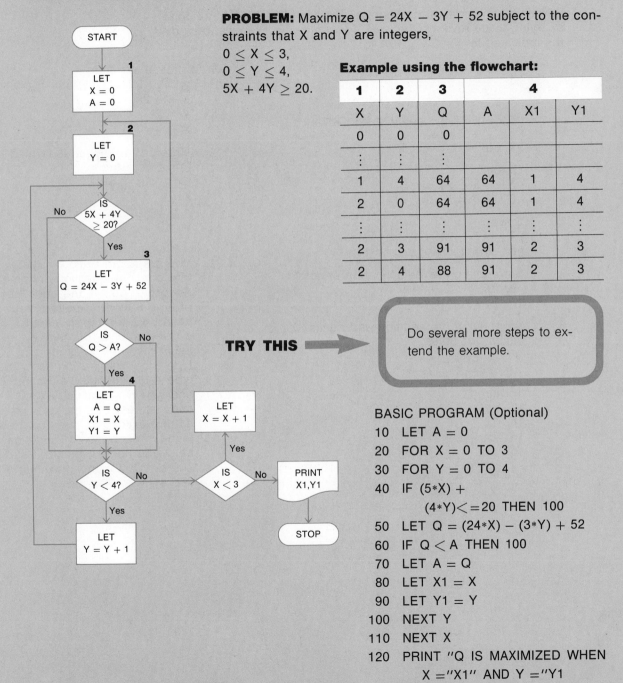

**TRY THIS** ➡ Do several more steps to extend the example.

BASIC PROGRAM (Optional)
```
10   LET A = 0
20   FOR X = 0 TO 3
30   FOR Y = 0 TO 4
40   IF (5*X) +
        (4*Y)<=20 THEN 100
50   LET Q = (24*X) − (3*Y) + 52
60   IF Q < A THEN 100
70   LET A = Q
80   LET X1 = X
90   LET Y1 = Y
100  NEXT Y
110  NEXT X
120  PRINT "Q IS MAXIMIZED WHEN
        X ="X1" AND Y ="Y1
```

## CHAPTER 5 REVIEW

Review the material in the chapter. Then see how you have done by trying these review exercises. If you miss an exercise, restudy the indicated lesson.

5-1     Graph on a line.
1. $x > -1$
2. $x \leq 4$

5-1     Solve using the addition principle.
3. $y + 3 \geq 4$
4. $2x + 7 > x - 9$

5-2     Graph.
5. $-3 < x < 2$
6. $x < -2$ or $x > 5$

5-2     Solve.
7. $-7 < 2x - 1 < 9$
8. $x + 1 < -4$ or $x + 1 > 4$

5-2     Solve using the multiplication principle.
9. $3x \geq 27$
10. $-9y \geq -45$

5-2     Solve using the addition and multiplication principles.
11. $3 + 8y \leq 27$
12. $3x - 8 \leq 7x + 5$

5-3     Solve.
13. $|y| < 4$
14. $|x| \geq 10$
15. $|x - 3| \leq 5$
16. $|3x + 5| < 7$

5-4     Graph on a plane.
17. $y > x + 2$
18. $3x - 5y \geq 15$

5-5     Graph these systems.
19. $y > x$
$y \leq -2x - 2$
20. $y \geq 2$
$x \leq -4$

5-5     21. Graph. If a polygon is formed, find the vertices.
$5x + 10y \leq 50$
$x + y \leq 8$
$x \geq 0$
$y \geq 0$

5-6     Solve.
22. You are about to take a test that contains questions of type A worth 4 points and questions of type B worth 8 points. You must do a total of at least 8 questions, and you must do at least 5 type A questions and 3 type B questions. You know that type A questions take 3 minutes and type B questions take 5 minutes, and that the total time cannot exceed 45 minutes. How many of each type of question must you do to maximize your score? What is this maximum score?

## CHAPTER 5 TEST

Graph on a line.
1. $x > -2$
2. $x \leq 5$

Solve using the addition principle.
3. $y + 5 \geq 8$
4. $3x + 5 > 2x - 7$

Graph.
5. $-2 < x < 4$
6. $x < -3$ or $x > 4$

Solve.
7. $-6 < 3x - 1 < 10$
8. $x + 2 < -3$ or $x + 4 > 8$

Solve using the multiplication principle.
9. $4x \geq 28$
10. $-8y \leq -40$

Solve using the addition and multiplication principles.
11. $4 + 7y \leq 39$
12. $2x - 9 \leq 9x + 4$

Solve.
13. $|x| < 3$
14. $|y| \geq 8$
15. $|x - 2| \leq 6$
16. $|2x + 7| < 9$

Graph on a plane.
17. $y < -x + 3$
18. $3x + 2y \leq 18$

Graph these systems.
19. $y \geq 2x$
    $y < -x + 3$
20. $y \leq 3$
    $x \geq -5$

21. Graph. If a polygon is formed, find the vertices.
    $5x + 10y \leq 50$
    $x + y \leq 8$
    $x \geq 2$
    $y \geq 0$

Solve.
22. You are about to take a test which contains questions of type A worth 7 points and questions of type B worth 12 points. The total number of questions worked must be at least 8. You know that type A questions take 10 minutes and type B questions take 8 minutes, and that the maximum time for the test is 80 minutes. How many of each type of question must you do to maximize your score? What is this maximum score?

## Ready for Polynomials?

1-2    Find the additive inverse of each number.

1.   6         2.   $-8.3$        3.   $-\frac{7}{8}$       4.   0

1-2    Add.

5.   $10 + (-4)$             6.   $-6.3 + 8.2$

7.   $-\frac{3}{8} + (-\frac{3}{24})$          8.   $0 + (-2.2)$

1-3    Subtract.

9.   $4 - 8$              10.   $-4 - 8$

11.   $\frac{21}{5} - (-\frac{5}{2})$         12.   $17.9 - 32.4$

1-4    Multiply.

13.   $-2 \cdot 6$            14.   $3 \cdot (-4)$

15.   $-3.4 \cdot (-10)$      16.   $-7 \cdot (-\frac{4}{5})$

1-5    17.   Factor:   $10x + 15y - 5$.

1-5    Multiply.

18.   $3(y - 2)$      19.   $4(x + 12)$      20.   $c(t + s - f)$

1-5    Collect like terms.

21.   $3y + 2y$      22.   $a + 4a$      23.   $b - 4b + 3b$

1-6    Rename each additive inverse without parentheses.

24.   $-(4x)$      25.   $-(-3a)$      26.   $-(-1)y$

1-6    27.   What are the terms of $-5y + 4x - t - 4$?

1-6    Remove parentheses and simplify.

28.   $3x - (2x + 4)$      29.   $7y - 2 - (8y - 4)$

1-7    30.   Simplify:   $(-2y)^3$.

1-8    Multiply and simplify.

31.   $y^2 \cdot y^5$      32.   $3^{-2} \cdot 3^5$      33.   $(4a^7b^{-2})(2a^2b^3)$

1-8    Simplify.

34.   $(4^3)^4$                     35.   $(y^{-3})^3$

# Chapter 6
# Polynomials

*The $8.00, $8.16, $8.24, and $8.30 are the amounts of interest received on $100.00 at 8% compounded annually, semiannually, quarterly, and monthly. How can we find them?*

# 6-1 Some Properties of Polynomials

After finishing Lesson 6-1, you should be able to
 ▌ rewrite a polynomial with plus signs.
 ▌▌ identify the terms and coefficients of a polynomial.
 ▌▌▌ determine the degree of each term of a polynomial and the degree of the polynomial.
 ▌▌▌▌ collect like terms.
 ▌▌▌▌▌ arrange a polynomial in ascending or descending powers of a given variable.
 ▌▌▌▌▌▌ tell whether a polynomial is a monomial, binomial, trinomial, or none of these.

## ▌Polynomials

Expressions like these are called *polynomials in one variable*.

$$2x + 3, \qquad -7x + 5, \qquad 2y^2 + 5y - 3,$$
$$5a^4 - 3a^2 + \tfrac{1}{4}a - 8, \qquad b^6 + 3b^5 - 8b + 7b^4 + \tfrac{1}{2}$$

They show additions and subtractions. Each part to be added or subtracted is a number or a number times a variable to some whole number power. A polynomial can also consist of just one of the parts. Thus the following are also polynomials in one variable.

$$5x^2, \qquad -8a, \qquad \tfrac{1}{4}y^5, \qquad 8t^4, \qquad x, \qquad a, \qquad t, \qquad 5, \qquad -2, \qquad \tfrac{1}{4}, \qquad 0$$

Expressions like these are called *polynomials in several variables*.

$$5x - xy^2 + 7y + 2, \qquad 9xy^2z - 4x^3z + (-14x^4y^2) + 9, \qquad 15x^3y^2$$

Recall that we can subtract by adding an additive inverse. So any polynomial can be rewritten with plus signs.

### Examples.

**1.** $4x - 3 = 4x + (-3)$
**2.** $7xy - 4x^2 = 7xy + (-4x^2)$
**3.** $-9x^3z - 7xyz^2 + y - 6x^4y^2$
$\qquad = -9x^3z + (-7xyz^2) + y + (-6x^4y^2)$

**TRY THIS** ➡

Rewrite each polynomial with plus signs.

1. $9xy - 5x^3 - y + 4$
2. $8pq - 7pqr^2 - 34xyz^6$

## ⅠⅠ Terms and Coefficients

When a polynomial is written with plus signs, the parts separated by the plus signs are its *terms,* and the numbers in the terms (other than exponents) are the *coefficients.*

**Example 4.** Identify the terms and the coefficients in $-3x^2 - 4x^3z + 14x^4y^3 - 9$.

We rewrite with only plus signs between the parts.

$$-3x^2 + (-4x^3z) + 14x^4y^3 + (-9)$$

The terms are $-3x^2$, $-4x^3z$, $14x^4y^3$, and $-9$. The coefficients are $-3$, $-4$, $14$, and $-9$.

**TRY THIS** ➡

> Identify the terms.
>
> 3. $9xy - 5x^3 - y + 10$
> 4. $-92x^5 - 8x^4 + x^2 + \frac{1}{4}$
> 5. What is the coefficient of each term? $5x^2y - 4xy^2 - 2y^3 + xy - y - 7$

If a coefficient is 0, we usually do not write the term. We say that we have a *missing* term.

**Example 5.** In $9x^5 - 2x^3 + 5x - 9$ there is no term with $x^4$. We say "the $x^4$ term is missing."

**TRY THIS** ➡

> Identify the missing terms in each polynomial.
>
> 6. $-2x^4 + 7$
> 7. $x^3 - 1$
> 8. $-2y^4$

## ⅠⅠⅠ Degrees

The *degree* of a term is the sum of the exponents of the variables. The degree of a polynomial is the same as its term of highest degree.

**Example 6.** Determine the degree of each term and the degree of the polynomial: $6x^2 + 8x^2y^3 - 17xy - 24xy^2z^4 + 2y + 3$.

| Term | Degree |
|------|--------|
| $6x^2$ | 2 |
| $8x^2y^3$ | 5 |
| $-17xy$ | 2 |
| $-24xy^2z^4$ | 7 |
| $2y$ | 1 |
| $3$ | 0 |

The degree of the polynomial is 7.

**TRY THIS** ➡

> 9. Determine the degree of each term and the degree of the polynomial.
> $2y + 4 - 5x + 7x^2y^3z^2 + 5xy^2$

## ⅢⅢ Collecting Like Terms

Terms that have the same variables with the same exponents are called *like* terms.

**Example 7.**    **Like Terms**        **Unlike Terms**

$4x^2$ and $-2x^2$        $4x^2$ and $4x$

$7y^6z^9$ and $23y^6z^9$      $5xyz^2$ and $-5xy$

We can often simplify expressions by collecting like terms. The process is based on the distributive laws. Thus we know that the simplified expression and the original expression will name the same number for all replacements. That is, they are *equivalent*.

**Examples.**  Collect like terms.

**8.**  $4x - 5x = (4 - 5)x$
$$= -1 \cdot x$$
$$= -x$$

**9.**  $4x^3 + 5x - 4x^2 - 2x^3 + 5x^2$
$$= (4 - 2)x^3 + (-4 + 5)x^2 + 5x$$
$$= 2x^3 + x^2 + 5x$$

**TRY THIS**

Collect like terms.

10.  $5x^2 - 2x^2$
11.  $5x^3 - 6x^3 + x^4$
12.  $5x^2 + 3x^4 - 2x^2 - x^4$

**Example 10.**  Collect like terms.

$3x^2y + 5xy^2 - 3x^2y - xy^2 = (3 - 3)x^2y + (5 - 1)xy^2$
$$= 4xy^2$$

**TRY THIS**

Collect like terms.

13.  $5x^2y + 6xy^2 - 7x^2y + 2xy$
14.  $-9pq + 8pqr^3 + 4pq + 3pqr^3 - 1$

## ⅢⅢ Ascending and Descending Order

We usually arrange polynomials in one variable so that the exponents decrease (descending order) or so that they increase (ascending order).

**Examples.**

**11.**  Arrange $-2x + x^2 + 5x^7 + 6x^5$ in descending order.

$5x^7 + 6x^5 + x^2 - 2x$

**12.** Arrange $9x^{10} - 2 + 4x - 8x^2$ in ascending order.

$$-2 + 4x - 8x^2 + 9x^{10}$$

We will usually write polynomials in one variable in descending order although it is not incorrect to use ascending or any other order.

**TRY THIS** ➡

> **15.** Arrange $3x^5 + x + 6x^3 - 5x^2 - 6x^7 - 7x^4$ in descending order.
> **16.** Arrange $4y^2 + 9 - 7y^5 - 2y^3 - 5y^4$ in ascending order.

For polynomials in several variables we choose one of the variables and arrange the terms with respect to it.

**Examples.**

**13.** Arrange $y^4 + 2 - 5x^3 + 3x^3y + 7xy$ in descending powers of $x$.

$$3x^3y - 5x^3 + 7xy + y^4 + 2$$

**14.** Arrange $-17x^3y^2 + 4xy^3 + 13xy + 8$ in ascending powers of $y$.

$$8 + 13xy - 17x^3y^2 + 4xy^3$$

**TRY THIS** ➡

> **17.** Arrange $-8xy^2 + 3xy + 7xy^4 - 2xy^3$ in descending powers of $y$.
> **18.** Arrange $4x^2yz + 5xy^2 + 5x^3yz^2 - 4$ in ascending powers of $x$.

We now give a precise definition of polynomials in one variable.

**DEFINITION**

A polynomial in $x$ is any expression equivalent to one of this form,

$$a_nx^n + a_{n-1}x^{n-1} + a_{n-2}x^{n-2} + \cdots + a_1x + a_0,$$

where $n$ is a natural number and the $a$'s are taken from some number system.

In the standard form of a polynomial used in the definition, we have used descending order. The degree of the polynomial is of course $n$. The $a$'s are the coefficients. Some or all of them can be 0.

In this chapter and the next we consider mainly polynomials with integer coefficients. Later we consider polynomials with rational coefficients. In some situations, polynomials with real number coefficients are important.

### ▪▪▪▪▪▪ Monomials, Binomials, and Trinomials

Polynomials with just one term are called *monomials*. Polynomials with just two terms are called *binomials*. Those with just three terms are called *trinomials*.

**Example 15.**

| Monomials | Binomials | Trinomials |
|---|---|---|
| $5x^2$ | $3x - 5$ | $5x^2 - 6x + \frac{1}{4}$ |
| $-1$ | $-2x^5 + 8x$ | $3xy - 4x^2 - 10$ |
| $-23xyz^3$ | $7x^3y^4 + 91z^4$ | $6x^2y^2 + \frac{1}{2}x^3 - 3$ |

**TRY THIS**

Tell whether each polynomial is a monomial, binomial, trinomial, or none of these.

19. $9y^4 - 8y^3 - 10y + 8$
20. $-8x^5$
21. $4x^3y - 5x^2y^2 + 8xy^3$
22. $P + Prt$

## Exercise Set 6-1

▌Rewrite each polynomial with plus signs. (*See Examples 1–3.*)

1. $8x^2 - 2x - 5$
2. $9y^3 - 3y^2 + 6$
3. $18xy - 8x^3 - y + 50$
4. $24y^3 - 9y^2 - y - 21$
5. $4xy - 5xy^2 + 6x^2y - 7x^2y^2$
6. $8ab - 9ab^3 + 11a^3b - 12a^2b^2$
7. $2x^5 - 7x^4 - 6x^3 + 3x^2 - 8x - 9$
8. $5y^5 - 9y^4 - 8y^3 - 3y^2 + 9y - 11$

▌▌Identify the terms and coefficients. (*See Example 4.*)

9. $5x^3 + 7x^2 - 3x - 9$
10. $8y^3 - 9y^2 + 12y + 11$
11. $-3xyz + 7x^2y^2 - 5xy^2z + 4xyz^2$
12. $-9abc + 19a^2bc - 8ab^2c + 12abc^2$

Identify the missing terms in each polynomial. (*See Example 5.*)

13. $x^3 + 1$
14. $y^3 - 2$
15. $-3y^4 + 8$
16. $-5x^4$

▌▌▌Determine the degree of each term and the degree of the polynomial. (*See Example 6.*)

17. $x^2 + 3y^5 - x^3y^4 - 7$
18. $y^3 + 2y^6 + x^2y - 9$
19. $x^5 + 3x^2y^4 - 5xy + 4x - 3$
20. $9y^6 + 2x^4y^4 - 8x^3y + 5x^2 - 9$

▮▮▮▮ Collect like terms. (*See Examples 8–10.*)

21. $6x^2 - 7x^2 + 3x^2$

22. $-2y^2 - 7y^2 + 5y^2$

23. $5x - 4y - 2x + 5y$

24. $4a - 9b - 6a + 3b$

25. $5a + 7 - 4 + 2a - 6a + 3$

26. $9x + 12 - 8 - 7x + 5x + 10$

27. $x + y - z - 3x + 4z - 7y$

28. $a + b + c - 5a - 4b + 8c$

29. $3a^2b + 4b^2 - 9a^2b - 6b^2$

30. $5x^2y^2 + 4x^3 - 8x^2y^2 - 12x^3$

31. $8x^2 - 3xy + 12y^2 + x^2 - y^2 + 5xy + 4y^2$

32. $a^2 - 2ab + b^2 - 9a^2 + 5ab - 4b^2 + a^2$

33. $3y^2 - 2yz - 2z^2 + 5y^2 + 2z^2 - 3yz - 4y^2 + 5yz - z^2$

34. $x^4 - 5x^2 + 2x - 4 + 2x^3 + 3x + 5 - 4x^4 + x^3 - 7x$

▮▮▮▮▮ Arrange in descending order. (*See Example 11.*)

35. $x - 3x^2 + 1 + x^3$

36. $x^2 - 8x^4 + 9 - x^3$

37. $a - a^3 + 5a^5 - 9 + 6a^2$

38. $y^2 - 9y^4 + 18 - y + 7y^5$

Arrange in ascending order. (*See Example 12.*)

39. $2y^3 - y + y^4 - 7 + 3y^2$

40. $5y^4 - 4y^3 + 8y - 11 - 2y^2$

41. $x^2 - x + 5x^5 - 9x^3 + 18x^4$

42. $-6x^3 + 9x - 42 - 3x^2 + 5x^4$

Arrange in descending powers of $y$. (*See Example 13.*)

43. $x^2y^2 + x^3y - xy^3 + 1$

44. $x^3y - x^2y^2 + xy^3 + 6$

Arrange in ascending powers of $x$. (*See Example 14.*)

45. $-9x^3y + 3xy^3 + x^2y^2 + 2x^4$

46. $5x^2y^2 - 9xy + 8x^3y^2 - 5x^4$

▮▮▮▮▮▮ Tell whether each polynomial is a monomial, binomial, trinomial, or none of these. (*See Example 15.*)

47. $y^3 - 8y$

48. $-9y^4 - 3y^3 + 5y^2 + 2$

49. $5x^2 - 9xy + 8$

50. $-11x^2$

51. $50x^2$

52. $-12x^2 - xy + y^2$

53. $8x^3 - 9x^2y + 15x^3y^2 - 9$

54. $x^2 - 81$

---

## Calculator Exercises

Collect like terms.

55. $0.00976x^2y^2 - 0.08054x^3y + 0.80149x^2y^2 + 0.00943x^3y$

56. $8{,}592{,}429xy^2z - 42.004x^2y^2 + 5{,}976.006x^2y^2 - 4{,}008{,}793xy^2z$

# 6-2 *Calculations with Polynomials*

After finishing Lesson 6-2, you should be able to
ı add polynomials.
ıı rename the additive inverse of a polynomial without using parentheses.
ııı subtract polynomials.

## ı Addition

The sum of two polynomials is a polynomial. To add polynomials
we can write a plus sign between them and then collect like terms.

**Example 1.** Add $-5x^3 + 3x - 5$ and $8x^3 + 4x^2 + 7$.

$$(-5x^3 + 3x - 5) + (8x^3 + 4x^2 + 7) = (-5 + 8)x^3 + 4x^2 + 3x + (-5 + 7)$$
$$= 3x^3 + 4x^2 + 3x + 2$$

We still arrange the terms in descending order.

**TRY THIS** ➡️

Add.

1. $3x^3 + 4x^2 - 7x - 2$ and
   $-7x^3 - 2x^2 + 3x + 4$

The use of columns is often helpful. To do this we
write the polynomials one under the other, writing
like terms under one another and leaving spaces for
missing terms. Let us do the addition in Example 1
using columns.

$$
\begin{array}{r}
-5x^3 \qquad\; + 3x - 5 \\
\underline{8x^3 + 4x^2 \qquad\; + 7} \\
3x^3 + 4x^2 + 3x + 2
\end{array}
$$

**Example 2.** Add $4ax^2 + 4bx - 5$ and $3ax^2 + 5bx + 8$.

$$
\begin{array}{r}
4ax^2 + 4bx - 5 \\
\underline{3ax^2 + 5bx + 8} \\
7ax^2 + 9bx + 3
\end{array}
$$

Although the use of columns is helpful for complicated examples,
you should attempt to write only the answer when you can.

**Example 3.** Add.

$$(13x^3y + 3x^2y - 5y) + (x^3y + 4x^2y - 3xy + 3y) = 14x^3y + 7x^2y - 3xy - 2y$$

**TRY THIS** ━━━▶

## ∎ Additive Inverses

If the sum of two polynomials is 0, they are called *additive inverses* of each other. For example, $(3x - 2) + (-3x + 2) = 0$, so the additive inverse of $(3x - 2)$ is $(-3x + 2)$. In symbols, $-(3x - 2) = -3x + 2$.

Add.

2. $7y^5 - 5$ and
   $3y^5 - 4y^4 + 10$
3. $5p^2q^4 - 2p^2q^2 - 3q$ and
   $-6pq^2 + 3p^2q + 5$

### THEOREM 6-1

The additive inverse of a polynomial can be found by multiplying each term by $-1$.

**Examples.** Rewrite each additive inverse without parentheses.

**4.** $-(5x^3 + 2) = -1(5x^3) + (-1)2$   *Multiplying each term by $-1$ (Theorem 6-1)*
$\qquad\qquad = -5x^3 - 2$

**5.** $-(9xy^2 - 4x^3y - 8x^4 + 7) = -1(9xy^2) + (-1)(-4x^3y) + (-1)(-8x^4) + (-1)7$
$\qquad\qquad\qquad\qquad\qquad\quad = -9xy^2 + 4x^3y + 8x^4 - 7$

Renaming an additive inverse amounts to "changing the sign" of every term inside the parentheses.

**Example 6.** $-(5xy^2 - 7x^3y - 8x + 4) = -5xy^2 + 7x^3y + 8x - 4$

**TRY THIS** ━━━▶

## ∎∎ Subtraction

Subtraction of polynomials is defined like subtraction of numbers.

### DEFINITION

For polynomials $P$ and $Q$, the difference $P - Q$ is the polynomial which when added to $Q$ gives $P$.

Rename each additive inverse without parentheses.

4. $-(4x^3 - 5x^2 + \frac{1}{4}x - 10)$
5. $-(8xy^2 - 4x^3y^2 - 9x - \frac{1}{5})$
6. $-(-9y^5 - 8y^4 + \frac{1}{2}y^3 - y^2 + y - 1)$

We can subtract polynomials the way we subtract numbers.

### THEOREM 6-2

For any polynomials $P$ and $Q$,
$P - Q = P + (-Q)$.
(We can subtract by adding the inverse of the subtrahend.)

**Example 7.** Subtract.

$(-9x^5 - x^3 + 2x^2 + 4) - (2x^5 - x^4 + 4x^3 - 3x^2)$
$= (-9x^5 - x^3 + 2x^2 + 4) + [-(2x^5 - x^4 + 4x^3 - 3x^2)]$     *Adding the inverse (Theorem 6-2)*
$= (-9x^5 - x^3 + 2x^2 + 4) + (-2x^5 + x^4 - 4x^3 + 3x^2)$     *Multiplying each term by $-1$ (Theorem 6-1)*

$= -11x^5 + x^4 - 5x^3 + 5x^2 + 4$

You should try to skip some steps by mentally "changing the sign of each term" and adding like terms. Try to write only the answer.

**TRY THIS** ➡️

Subtract.

7. $(6x^2 + 4) - (3x^2 - 1)$
8. $(9y^3 - 2y - 4) - (-5y^3 - 8)$
9. $(-3p^2 + 5p - 4) - (-4p^2 + 11p - 2)$

We can also use columns for subtraction. We mentally change signs in the subtrahend and then add.

**Example 8.** Subtract: $(4x^2y - 6x^3y^2 + x^2y^2 - 5y) - (4x^2y + x^3y^2 + 3x^2y^3 + 6y)$.

$$\begin{array}{l} 4x^2y - 6x^3y^2 \quad\quad\quad + x^2y^2 - 5y \\ \underline{4x^2y + \quad x^3y^2 + 3x^2y^3 \quad\quad\quad + 6y} \\ \quad - 7x^3y^2 - 3x^2y^3 + x^2y^2 - 11y \end{array}$$

As with addition, you should avoid the use of columns as much as possible. Try to write only the answer when subtracting.

**TRY THIS** ➡️

Subtract.

10. $(2y^5 - y^4 + 3y^3 - y^2 - y - 7) - (-y^5 + 2y^4 - 2y^3 + y^2 - y - 4)$
11. $(4p^4q - 5p^3q^2 + p^2q^3 + 2q^4) - (-5p^4q + 5p^3q^2 - 3p^2q^3 - 7q^4)$
12. $(\frac{3}{2}y^3 - \frac{1}{2}y^2 + 0.3) - (\frac{1}{2}y^3 + \frac{1}{2}y^2 - \frac{4}{3}y + 0.2)$

## Exercise Set 6-2

▌Add. (*See Examples 1–3.*)

1. $3x^2 + 5y^2 + 6$ and $2x^2 - 3y^2 - 1$
3. $2a + 3b - c$ and $4a - 2b + 2c$
5. $a^2 - 3b^2 + 4c^2$ and $-5a^2 + 2b^2 - c^2$
7. $x^2 + 2x - 3xy - 7$ and $-3x^2 - x + 2xy + 6$

2. $9y^2 + 8y - 4$ and $12y^2 - 5y + 8$
4. $5x - 4y + 2z$ and $9x + 12y - 8z$
6. $x^2 - 5y^2 - 9z^2$ and $-6x^2 + 9y^2 - 2z^2$
8. $3a^2 - 2b + ab + 6$ and $-a^2 + 5b - 5ab - 2$

9. $7x^2y - 3xy^2 + 4xy$ and
$-2x^2y - xy^2 + xy$

10. $7ab - 3ac + 5bc$ and
$13ab - 15ac - 8bc$

11. $2r^2 + 12r - 11$ and
$6r^2 - 2r + 4$ and
$r^2 - r - 2$

12. $5x^2 + 19x - 23$ and
$-7x^2 - 11x + 12$ and
$-x^2 - 9x + 8$

13. $2x + 3y + z - 7$ and
$5x - 2y - z + 8$ and
$-3x + y - 2z - 4$

14. $12x^2 + 5y^2 - 2z^2 + 19$ and
$-4x^2 - 8y^2 + 9z^2 - 3$ and
$15x^2 - 2y^2 - 11z^2 + 8$

15. $0.02x^3 - 0.4x^2 + x + 0.07$ and
$0.03x^3 + 0.5x^2 + 0.84x - 0.03$

16. $0.04x^6 + 0.04x^3 - 0.23x + 0.04$ and
$0.05x^6 - 0.05x^3 + 0.4$

17. $1.23y^4 - 2.25y^3 - 3.4y - 5.2$ and
$8.23y^4 + 4.75y^3 - 8.4y + 2.1$

18. $9.22x^5 - 4.02x^3 + 8.41x^2 - 4.9$ and
$-8.34x^5 + 9.46x^3 - 3.27x^2 + 8.2$

19. $\frac{1}{4}x^4 + \frac{1}{3}x^3 + \frac{3}{8}x^2 + 6$ and
$-\frac{3}{4}x^4 + \frac{1}{8}x^2 - 9$

20. $\frac{1}{3}y^5 - \frac{1}{5}y^3 - \frac{1}{2}y - 8$ and
$\frac{1}{6}y^5 - \frac{1}{10}y^3 + \frac{1}{4}y - 11$

**▮▮ Rename each additive inverse without parentheses. (*See Examples 4–6.*)**

21. $-(5x^3 - 7x^2 + 3x - 6)$

22. $-(8y^4 - 18y^3 + 4y - 9)$

23. $-(-4y^4 + 7y^2 - 2y - 1)$

24. $-(-9x^5 - 2y^4 - 5x + 8)$

**▮▮▮ Subtract. (*See Examples 7 and 8.*)**

25. $(8x - 4) - (-5x + 2)$

26. $(9y + 3) - (-4y - 2)$

27. $(-3x^2 + 2x + 9) - (x^2 + 5x - 4)$

28. $(-9y^2 + 4y + 8) - (4y^2 + 2y - 3)$

29. $(5a - 2b + c) - (3a + 2b - 2c)$

30. $(8x - 4y + z) - (4x + 6y - 3z)$

31. $(3x^2 - 2x - x^3) - (5x^2 - 8x - x^3)$

32. $(8y^2 - 3y - 4y^3) - (3y^2 - 9y - 7y^3)$

33. $(5a^2 + 4ab - 3b^2) -$
$(9a^2 - 4ab + 2b^2)$

34. $(9y^2 - 14yz - 8z^2) -$
$(12y^2 - 8yz + 4z^2)$

35. $(12x^2 - 9x) - (14x^2 + 8x - 5)$

36. $(18a^2 - 2a) - (22a^2 + 9a - 4)$

37. $9y^3 - (3y^3 + 7y^2 - 8y + 2)$

38. $8x^4 - (2x^4 + 8x^2 - 9x + 4)$

39. $(4a - 2b - c + 3d) -$
$(-2a + 3b + c - d)$

40. $(5x - 2y - z + 4w) -$
$(-3x + 4y - 5z + 2w)$

41. $(0.04x^3 - 0.03x^2 + 0.02x) -$
$(0.05x^3 + 0.08x^2 - 5)$

42. $(0.09y^4 - 0.052y^3 + 0.93) -$
$(0.03y^4 - 0.084y^3 + 0.94y^2)$

43. $(\frac{5}{8}x^4 - \frac{1}{4}x^2 - \frac{1}{2}) -$
$(-\frac{3}{8}x^4 + \frac{3}{4}x^2 + \frac{1}{2})$

44. $(\frac{1}{5}y^5 + 3y^4 - \frac{1}{6}y^3) -$
$(-\frac{4}{5}y^5 + 9y^4 - \frac{5}{6}y^3)$

## Calculator Exercises

Subtract.

45. $(852.0092x^3 - 9.00834x - 0.0084) - (437.0148x^3 + 18.00479x + 0.04)$

46. $(8,479,768y^4 - 56,009,728y^2 - 19,429,009y) - (12,049,778y^4 - 19,118,979y^2 + 26,047,972y)$

# 6-3 Multiplication of Polynomials

After finishing Lesson 6-3, you should be able to
**I**   multiply monomials.
**II**   multiply monomials and binomials.
**III**   multiply any two polynomials.

## I Multiplying Monomials

To multiply monomials we multiply the coefficients. Then we multiply the variables. This process is based on the commutative and associative laws of multiplication.

**Examples.**   Multiply and simplify.

**1.**  $(-8x^4y^7)(5x^3y^2) = -8 \cdot 5 \cdot x^4 \cdot x^3 \cdot y^7 \cdot y^2$
                        $= -40x^7y^9$

**2.**  $(3x^2yz^5)(-6x^5y^{10}z^2) = 3 \cdot (-6) \cdot x^2 \cdot x^5 \cdot y \cdot y^{10} \cdot z^5 \cdot z^2$
                            $= -18x^7y^{11}z^7$

You should try to do this mentally, writing only the answer.

**TRY THIS** ➤

> Multiply and simplify.
>
> 1.  $9y^2$ and $-2y$
> 2.  $4x^3y$ and $6x^5y^2$
> 3.  $-5xy^7z^4$ and $18x^3y^3z^8$

## II Multiplying Monomials and Binomials

The distributive laws are the basis for multiplying polynomials other than monomials.

**Example 3.**   Multiply: $2x$ and $3x - 5$.

$2x \cdot (3x - 5) = 2x \cdot (3x) - 2x \cdot (5)$    *Using a distributive law*
             $= 6x^2 - 10x$      *Multiplying the monomials*

**TRY THIS** ➤

> Multiply.
>
> 4.  $-3y$ and $2y + 6$
> 5.  $2xy$ and $4y^2 - 5$

**Example 4.**   Multiply: $3y^2 + 4$ and $y - 2$.

$(3y^2 + 4)(y - 2) = \underset{\text{(a)}}{(3y^2 + 4)(y)} - \underset{\text{(b)}}{(3y^2 + 4)(2)}$    *Using a distributive law*

Let us consider the two parts (a) and (b) separately.

(a)   $(3y^2 + 4)(y) = (3y^2)(y) + 4 \cdot y$    *Using a distributive law*
               $= 3y^3 + 4y$      *Multiplying the monomials*

ⓑ $(3y^2 + 4)(2) = (3y^2) \cdot 2 + 4 \cdot 2$   *Using a distributive law*
$$= 6y^2 + 8 \quad \textit{Multiplying the monomials}$$

We replace the parts ⓐ and ⓑ in the original expression with their answers, and combine like terms if they exist.

$$(3y^2 + 4)(y - 2) = (3y^3 + 4y) - (6y^2 + 8)$$
$$= 3y^3 - 6y^2 + 4y - 8$$

**TRY THIS** ➡

> 6. Multiply $5x^2 - 4$ and $x + 3$.
> 7. Multiply $2y + 3$ and $3y - 4$.

### ⁍ Multiplying Any Two Polynomials

**Example 5.**  Multiply $p + 2$ and $p^4 - 2p^3 + 3$.

By the distributive laws we have:

$$(p + 2)(p^4 - 2p^3 + 3) = (p + 2)(p^4) - (p + 2)(2p^3) + (p + 2)(3)$$
$$= p \cdot (p^4) + 2(p^4) - p \cdot (2p^3) - 2(2p^3) + p \cdot (3) + 2(3)$$
$$= p^5 + 2p^4 - 2p^4 - 4p^3 + 3p + 6$$
$$= p^5 - 4p^3 + 3p + 6$$

In the last step we collected like terms.

**TRY THIS** ➡

> Multiply.
> 8.  $p - 3$ and $p^3 + 4p^2 - 5$
> 9.  $2x^3 + 4x - 5$ and $x - 4$

Now we can see how to multiply any two polynomials.

To multiply two polynomials, multiply each term of one by every term of the other. Then add the results.

We can use columns for long multiplications. We multiply each term at the top by every term at the bottom, keeping like terms in columns. Then we add.

**Example 6.**  Multiply $5x^3 + x - 4$ and $-2x^2 + 3x + 6$.

$$
\begin{array}{l}
5x^3 + \ x - 4 \\
-2x^2 + 3x + 6 \\
\hline
-10x^5 \qquad\quad - \ 2x^3 + \ 8x^2 \qquad \textit{Multiplying by } -2x^2 \\
\qquad\quad 15x^4 \qquad\qquad + \ 3x^2 - 12x \qquad \textit{Multiplying by } 3x \\
\qquad\qquad\quad 30x^3 \qquad\qquad + \ 6x - 24 \qquad \textit{Multiplying by } 6 \\
\hline
-10x^5 + 15x^4 + 28x^3 + 11x^2 - \ 6x - 24 \qquad \textit{Adding}
\end{array}
$$

> 10.  Multiply $-4x^3 - 2x + 1$ and $-2x^2 - 3x + 6$.

**TRY THIS** ➡

## Exercise Set 6-3

▌Multiply. (*See Examples 1 and 2.*)
  1. $(2y^2)(5y)$
  2. $(3x^2)(2x)$
  3. $(-3y^2)(4xy)$
  4. $(-8x^2)(5xy)$
  5. $(5x)(-4x^2y)$
  6. $(2y)(-9y^2z)$
  7. $(-3ab^2)(2a^2b)$
  8. $(-5xy^3)(7x^2y)$
  9. $(2x^3y^2)(-5x^2y^4)$
  10. $(7a^2bc^4)(-8ab^3c^2)$

▌▌Multiply. (*See Examples 3 and 4.*)
  11. $3x(5x - 2)$
  12. $9y(4y - 7)$
  13. $-4t(2t - 9)$
  14. $-7y(8y - 6)$
  15. $-2x(3 - x - x^2)$
  16. $-9y(4 - y - y^3)$
  17. $3ab(a + b - 2)$
  18. $2xy(2x - 3y + 7xy)$
  19. $a^2(1 - a + 2a^2 - 5a^3)$
  20. $y^3(2 - y + 3y^2 + 8y^3)$
  21. $(x + 3)(x + 4)$
  22. $(y + 2)(y + 5)$
  23. $(x - 2)(x - 5)$
  24. $(y - 4)(y - 9)$
  25. $(2x + 3)(x + 4)$
  26. $(4y + 5)(y + 3)$
  27. $(2x + 5)(3x - 4)$
  28. $(3t + 7)(2t - 5)$
  29. $(s + 3t)(s - 3t)$
  30. $(2y + 4)(2y - 4)$
  31. $(x - y)(x - y)$
  32. $(a + 2b)(a + 2b)$
  33. $(y + 8x)(2y - 7x)$
  34. $(a + 9b)(3a - 4b)$
  35. $(x^2 + y)(x^2 - 2y)$
  36. $(y^2 + z)(y^2 - 3z)$
  37. $(a^2 - 2b^2)(a^2 - 3b^2)$
  38. $(x^2 - 5y^2)(x^2 - 4y^2)$

▌▌▌Multiply. (*See Examples 5 and 6.*)
  39. $(x - 4)(x^2 + 4x + 16)$
  40. $(y - 2)(y^2 + 5y + 10)$
  41. $(y + 3)(y^2 - 3y + 9)$
  42. $(x + 2)(x^2 - 4x + 16)$
  43. $(x^2 - 2x + 1)(x^2 + x + 2)$
  44. $(y^2 - 3y - 7)(y^2 + 4y - 8)$
  45. $(3x^3 - x + 9)(-2x^2 + 4x - 3)$
  46. $(2x^3 - 3x + 1)(-4x^2 + x - 5)$
  47. $(x + y)(x^2 - xy + y^2)$
  48. $(a - b)(a^2 + ab + b^2)$
  49. $(3a^2 - 1)(a^2 + 4a - 5)$
  50. $(5x^2 - 2)(x^2 + 8x - 7)$
  51. $(2m^3 - 3)(m^2 + 5m - 7)$
  52. $(5t^3 - 5)(t^2 - 4t + 8)$
  53. $(4x + 7y)(2x^2 + 3xy + 4y^2)$
  54. $(8p + 9q)(5p^2 + 8pq + 7q^2)$

---

### Challenge Exercises

Multiply.
  55. $(4a^2b - 2ab + 3b^2)(5a^2b - 6ab + 7b^2)$
  56. $(2x^2 + y^2 - 2xy)(x^2 - 2y^2 - xy)$
  57. $(3x^3 + 5x^2 - 7x + 19)(x^2 + 4x - 2)$
  58. $(2y^4 + 3y^2 - 8y + 7)(y^2 + 5y - 6)$
  59. $(x - p)(x + p)(x^2 - p^2)$
  60. $(y^2 + a)(y^2 + a)(y^4 - 2ay^2 - a^2)$

# 6-4 Special Products of Polynomials

After finishing Lesson 6-4, you should be able to
**I**   multiply two binomials using the FOIL rule.
**II**  square binomials.

## I Products of Two Binomials

We know that to multiply two polynomials, we multiply each term of one polynomial by every term of the other. To multiply two *binomials,* we multiply the FIRST terms. Then we multiply the OUTSIDE terms, then the INSIDE terms, and finally the LAST terms. If there are like terms we collect them. We can abbreviate the rule like this: F O I L.

**Examples.** Multiply.

$$\overset{\text{F} \quad\text{O} \quad\text{I} \quad\text{L}}{}$$

**1.** $(x + 5)(x - 8) = x^2 - 8x + 5x - 40$
$$= x^2 - 3x - 40$$

$$\overset{\text{F} \quad\quad\text{O} \quad\quad\text{I} \quad\quad\text{L}}{}$$

**2.** $(p - 3q)(2p - 5q) = 2p^2 - 5pq - 6pq + 15q^2$
$$= 2p^2 - 11pq + 15q^2$$

**3.** $(3xy + 2x)(x^2 + 2xy^2) = 3x^3y + 6x^2y^3 + 2x^3 + 4x^2y^2$

**TRY THIS**

> Multiply.
>
> 1. $(y - 4)(y + 10)$
> 2. $(p + 5q)(2p - 3q)$
> 3. $(x^2y + 2x)(xy^2 + y^2)$

## II Squares of Binomials

If we apply the FOIL rule to products like $(a + b)^2$ and $(a - b)^2$ we obtain:

$$(a + b)^2 = (a + b)(a + b) \qquad\qquad (a - b)^2 = (a - b)(a - b)$$
$$= a^2 + ab + ab + b^2 \qquad\qquad\quad = a^2 - ab - ab + b^2$$
$$= a^2 + 2ab + b^2 \qquad\qquad\qquad\quad = a^2 - 2ab + b^2$$

To square a binomial we square the first term. Then we take twice the product of the two terms. Next we square the second term. Then we add.

**Examples.** Multiply.

**4.** $(y - 5)^2 = y^2 - 2(5)(y) + 5^2$
$$= y^2 - 10y + 25$$

**5.** $(2x + 9)^2 = (2x)^2 + 2(2x)(9) + 9^2$
$$= 4x^2 + 36x + 81$$

Whenever possible try to find such products mentally. Try to write only the answer.

**TRY THIS** ➤

> Multiply.
>
> 4. $(x - 8)^2$
> 5. $(3x + 7)^2$

**Examples.** Multiply.

**6.** $(2x + 3y)^2 = (2x)^2 + 2(2x)(3y) + (3y)^2$
$= 4x^2 + 12xy + 9y^2$

**7.** $(3x^2 - 5xy^2)^2 = (3x^2)^2 - 2(3x^2)(5xy^2) + (5xy^2)^2$
$= 9x^4 - 30x^3y^2 + 25x^2y^4$

**TRY THIS** ➤

> Multiply.
>
> 6. $(4x + 5y)^2$
> 7. $(2y^2 - 6x^2y)^2$

## Exercise Set 6-4

▌Multiply. (*See Examples 1–3.*)

1. $(a + 2)(a + 3)$
2. $(x + 5)(x + 8)$
3. $(y + 3)(y - 2)$
4. $(x + 8)(x - 3)$
5. $(y - 4)(y + 7)$
6. $(x - 6)(x + 9)$
7. $(b - 7)(b - 5)$
8. $(y - 3)(y - 7)$
9. $(2x + 9)(x + 2)$
10. $(3y + 7)(y + 3)$
11. $(4a + 3)(a - 1)$
12. $(5x + 2)(x - 3)$
13. $(3y - 2)(y - 3)$
14. $(4x - 7)(x - 4)$
15. $(3b + 8)(2b - 5)$
16. $(7x + 2)(3x - 6)$
17. $(2x - 5)(3x - 7)$
18. $(4x - 9)(5x - 8)$
19. $(2x + 3y)(4x + 5y)$
20. $(9a + 7b)(5a + 3b)$
21. $(a^2 + b)(a^2 - 2b)$
22. $(x^2 + y)(x^2 - 5y)$
23. $(2m^2 - n^2)(m^2 + 3n^2)$
24. $(8x^2 - y^2)(x^2 + 7y^2)$
25. $(2x^2 + 3y^2)(4x^2 - 5y^2)$
26. $(4y^2 + 7z^2)(5y^2 - 9z^2)$
27. $(7m^2 - 8n^2)(3m^2 - 5n^2)$
28. $(9a^2 - 8b^2)(4a^2 - 7b^2)$

▌▌Multiply. (*See Examples 4–7.*)

29. $(x + 3)^2$
30. $(y + 7)^2$
31. $(y - 5)^2$
32. $(x - 6)^2$
33. $(2s + 3t)^2$
34. $(5x + 7y)^2$
35. $(5x - 9y)^2$
36. $(7y - 4z)^2$
37. $(3a^2 + 2)^2$
38. $(5x^2 + 6)^2$
39. $(7x^2 - 2)^2$
40. $(6y^2 - 5)^2$
41. $(2x - 3y^2)^2$
42. $(3s^2 - 4t^2)^2$
43. $(a^2b^2 + ab^2)^2$
44. $(x^2y + xy^2)^2$

# 6-5 More Special Products

After finishing Lesson 6-5, you should be able to
**I** multiply the sum and difference of the same two expressions.
**II** find special products such as those above and those found in Lesson 6-4, when they are mixed together.

## Products of Sums and Differences

If we apply the FOIL rule to a product like $(a + b)(a - b)$, we obtain:

$$(a + b)(a - b) = a^2 - ab + ab - b^2$$
$$= a^2 - b^2$$

The product of a sum and difference is the difference of two squares. To find such a product we square the first expression and square the second expression. Then write a minus sign between the squares.

**Examples.** Multiply.

**1.** $(y + 5)(y - 5) = y^2 - 5^2$
$$= y^2 - 25$$

**2.** $(3x - 2)(3x + 2) = (3x)^2 - 2^2$
$$= 9x^2 - 4$$

Whenever possible you should avoid writing a middle step as shown in the above examples. Try to write only the answer.

### TRY THIS ▶

Multiply.
1. $(x + 8)(x - 8)$
2. $(4y + 7)(4y - 7)$

**Examples.** Multiply.

**3.** $(2xy^2 + 3x)(2xy^2 - 3x) = (2xy^2)^2 - (3x)^2$
$$= 4x^2y^4 - 9x^2$$

**4.** $(5y + 4 - 3x)(5y + 4 + 3x) = (5y + 4)^2 - (3x)^2$
$$= 25y^2 + 40y + 16 - 9x^2$$

**5.** $(3xy^2 + 4y)(-3xy^2 + 4y) = (4y + 3xy^2)(4y - 3xy^2)$
$$= (4y)^2 - (3xy^2)^2$$
$$= 16y^2 - 9x^2y^4$$

**TRY THIS** ➡

Multiply.

3. $(3x^2y + 2y)(3x^2y - 2y)$
4. $(2x + 3 - 5y)(2x + 3 + 5y)$
5. $(-2x^3y^2 + 5t)(2x^3y^2 + 5t)$

## ıı Multiplications

When multiplying first see what kind of multiplication you have and then use the best method. Following are the methods we have used so far.

①  $(A + B)(A + B) = (A + B)^2 = A^2 + 2 \cdot A \cdot B + B^2$
②  $(A - B)(A - B) = (A - B)^2 = A^2 - 2 \cdot A \cdot B + B^2$
③  $(A - B)(A + B) = A^2 - B^2$
④  F O I L
⑤  The product of a monomial and any polynomial. Multiply each term of the polynomial by the monomial.

**Examples.**  Multiply.

**6.**  $(x + 4)(x - 4) = x^2 - 16$     *Using* ③

**7.**  $(x + 8)(x - 2) = x^2 + 6x - 16$     *Using* ④

**8.**  $(x - 6)(x - 6) = x^2 - 12x + 36$     *Using* ②

**9.**  $5x^3(3x^2y^2 + 2xy - 8) = 15x^5y^2 + 10x^4y - 40x^3$     *Using* ⑤

**10.**  $(2x + 7y)(2x + 7y) = 4x^2 + 28xy + 49y^2$     *Using* ①

**TRY THIS** ➡

Multiply.

6.  $(x - 8)(x - 8)$
7.  $(2x + 3)^2$
8.  $(2x + 1)(2x - 1)$
9.  $5y^2(-3x^2y^3 + 2xy^2 - 9)$
10.  $(p + 4q)(p - 7q)$

## Exercise Set 6-5

ı Multiply. *(See Examples 1–5.)*

1.  $(c + 2)(c - 2)$
2.  $(x - 3)(x + 3)$
3.  $(x + y)(x - y)$
4.  $(a + b)(a - b)$
5.  $(2a + 1)(2a - 1)$
6.  $(4y + 3)(4y - 3)$
7.  $(3 - 2x)(3 + 2x)$
8.  $(5 - 7y)(5 + 7y)$
9.  $(3m - 2n)(3m + 2n)$
10.  $(3x - 4y)(3x + 4y)$
11.  $(x^2 - 9)(x^2 + 9)$
12.  $(3a^2 + 2)(3a^2 - 2)$

13. $(5a^2 + 2b)(5a^2 - 2b)$
14. $(6y^2 + 7z)(6y^2 - 7z)$
15. $(3c^2 - 2d^2)(3c^2 + 2d^2)$
16. $(5x^2 - 4y^2)(5x^2 + 4y^2)$

■■ Multiply. (*See Examples 6–10.*)

17. $(y + 3)(y + 5)$
18. $(2x + 3)(3x + 4)$
19. $(2x - 7)(2x + 7)$
20. $(5y - 9z)(5y + 9z)$
21. $(4x + 2y)^2$
22. $(5x + 3y)^2$
23. $(9x - 5y)^2$
24. $(8t - 4w)^2$
25. $4x^3(5x^2y^2 + 4xy - 9)$
26. $3y^4(8x^2y^3 + 5xy^2 - 7)$
27. $(5x + 3)(5x + 3)$
28. $(9y - 4)(9y - 4)$
29. $(2x + 4y)(5x - 7y)$
30. $(5p - 7q)(4p + 9q)$
31. $(8y - z)(9y - 7z)$
32. $(10x - y)(5x + 8y)$
33. $(7x^2 + 3)(4x^2 - 5)$
34. $(9y^3 - 2)(8y^3 - 7)$
35. $(8x + 9y)^2$
36. $(9z - 4w)^2$
37. $(\frac{1}{5}x - \frac{2}{3}y)(\frac{1}{5}x + \frac{2}{3}y)$
38. $(\frac{1}{8}a - \frac{3}{4}b)(\frac{1}{8}a + \frac{3}{4}b)$
39. $-5y^4(8y^5 - 3y^4 - 9y^3 + y^2 - 8y + 3)$
40. $-8x^3(9x^6 + 8x^4 - 7x^3 - 3x^2 - 8x - 12)$
41. $(\frac{1}{3}x - 1)(\frac{1}{3}x + 2)$
42. $(\frac{1}{2}y - 4)(\frac{1}{2}y + 1)$

---

## Challenge Exercises

Multiply.

43. $(x + 1)(x - 1)(x^2 + 1)$
44. $(y - 2)(y + 2)(y^2 + 4)$
45. $(a + b)(a - b)(a^2 + b^2)$
46. $(2x - y)(2x + y)(4x^2 + y^2)$
47. $(a + b + 1)(a + b - 1)$
48. $(m + n + 2)(m + n - 2)$
49. $(2x + 3y + 4)(2x + 3y - 4)$
50. $(3a - 2b + c)(3a - 2b - c)$

---

## MATHEMATICAL NOTE: Theorems

One way to disprove a theorem is by counterexample. This involves finding one example that contradicts the theorem. For instance, the statement "All prime numbers are odd" can be disproved by the counterexample 2. 2 is a prime number, and 2 is not odd. So the statement is disproved by counterexample.

Research mathematicians work at proving or disproving theorems. Their proofs may take many years of careful reasoning.

# 6-6 The Compound Interest Formula

After finishing Lesson 6-6, you should be able to
∎ solve certain problems using the compound interest formula.

∎ An important and frequently used formula is the compound interest formula. We first consider simple interest.

**Example 1.** An investment is made at 8%. It grows to $783 at the end of one year. How much was originally invested?

Rewording and translating we have:

Now we solve the equation.

$$x + 8\%x = 783$$
$$x + 0.08x = 783$$
$$(1 + 0.08)x = 783$$
$$1.08x = 783$$
$$x = \frac{783}{1.08}$$
$$= 725$$

The number 725 checks in the problem situation, so the answer is $725.

**TRY THIS** ➡

> 1. An investment is made at 6%. It grows to $848 at the end of one year. How much was originally invested?

Now we consider compound interest.

**THEOREM 6-3**

If an amount $P$ is invested at an interest rate of $r$ compounded annually, in $t$ years it will grow to an amount $A$ given by

$$A = P(1 + r)^t.$$

**Example 2.** Suppose $1000 is invested at 8%, compounded annually. What amount will be in the account at the end of two years?

We use the formula of Theorem 6-3, $A = P(1 + r)^t$. We get
$$A = 1000(1 + 0.08)^2$$
$$= 1000(1.08)^2$$
$$= 1166.4$$

The answer is $1166.40.

**TRY THIS**

> 2. Suppose $500 is invested at 6%, compounded annually. What amount will be in the account at the end of two years?

Interest may be compounded more often than once a year. There is a formula that applies.

**THEOREM 6-4**

If an amount $P$ is invested at an interest rate $r$, compounded $n$ times per year, in $t$ years it will grow to an amount $A$ given by

$$A = P\left(1 + \frac{r}{n}\right)^{nt}.$$

When problems involving compound interest are translated to mathematical language, the above formula is almost always used.

**Example 3.** Suppose $1000 is invested at 8%, compounded quarterly. How much will be in the account at the end of two years?

In this case $n = 4$ and $t = 2$. We substitute into the formula.

$$A = P\left(1 + \frac{r}{n}\right)^{nt}$$
$$= 1000\left(1 + \frac{0.08}{4}\right)^{4 \cdot 2}$$
$$= 1000(1.02)^8$$
$$= 1171.66$$

The answer is $1171.66.

**TRY THIS**

> 3. Suppose $1000 is invested at 8% compounded semiannually. How much will be in the account at the end of two years?

## Exercise Set 6-6

❚Solve. (*See Examples 1 and 2.*)

1. An investment is made at 9%, compounded annually. It grows to $708.50 at the end of one year. How much was originally invested?

2. An investment is made at 7%, compounded annually. It grows to $856 at the end of one year. How much was originally invested?

3. An investment is made at 8%, compounded annually. It grows to $648 at the end of one year. How much was originally invested?

4. An investment is made at 4%, compounded annually. It grows to $572 at the end of one year. How much was originally invested?

5. Suppose $1000 is invested at 4%, compounded annually. What amount will be in the account at the end of two years?

6. Suppose $1000 is invested at 6%, compounded annually. What amount will be in the account at the end of two years?

7. Suppose $800 is invested at 8%, compounded annually. What amount will be in the account at the end of two years?

8. Suppose $750 is invested at 5%, compounded annually. What amount will be in the account at the end of two years?

Solve. (*See Example 3.*)

9. Suppose $1000 is invested at 7%, compounded semiannually. How much will be in the account at the end of one year?

10. Suppose $4000 is invested at 9%, compounded semiannually. How much will be in the account at the end of one year?

11. Suppose $2000 is invested at 8%, compounded semiannually. How much will be in the account at the end of two years?

12. Suppose $3000 is invested at 6%, compounded semiannually. How much will be in the account at the end of two years?

## Calculator Exercises

13. Suppose $1000 is invested at 6%, compounded monthly. How much will be in the account at the end of two years?

14. Suppose $500 is invested at 4%, compounded monthly. How much will be in the account at the end of two years?

# COMPUTER ACTIVITY
## Compound Interest

**PROBLEM:** Let the original amount be $100, and let it be compounded monthly at 1% interest. Compare this with $100 compounded monthly at $1\frac{1}{8}$% interest for the same number of months.

```
START
   │
   │ 1
   ▼
LET
A = 100
   │
   │ 2
   ▼
LET
B = 100
   │
   │ 3
   ▼
LET
M = 1
   │
   ▼
LET          4
A = A(1 + 0.01)
   │
   │ 5
   ▼
LET
B = B(1 + 0.01125)
   │
   ▼
PRINT
M,A,B
   │
   ▼
  IS
  M          Yes
LARGE    ────────►  STOP
ENOUGH?
   │
   │ No      6
   ▼
LET
M = M + 1
```

**Examples using the flowchart:**

| 3(6) | 1(4) | 2(5) |
|------|------|------|
| M | A | B |
|   | 100 | 100 |
| 1 | 101 | 101.125 |
| 2 | 102.01 | 102.26 |
| 3 | 103.03 | 103.41 |
| 4 |  |  |
| 5 |  |  |
| 6 |  |  |
| 7 |  |  |
| 8 |  |  |
| 9 |  |  |
| 10 |  |  |
| 11 |  |  |
| 12 |  |  |

**TRY THIS** ➤ Use a calculator to complete the examples.

BASIC PROGRAM (Optional)

```
10  PRINT "MONTHS", "A","B"    50  LET A = A*(1+0.01)
20  LET A = 100                60  LET B = B*(1+0.01125)
30  LET B = 100                70  PRINT M,A,B
40  FOR M = 1 TO 12            80  NEXT M
```

# CHAPTER 6 REVIEW

Review the material in the chapter. Then see how you have done by trying these review exercises. If you miss an exercise, restudy the indicated lesson.

6-1     Collect like terms.
1. $9x - 5y - 3x + y - 7x + 4y$
2. $8a^3 + 3a^2 - 2a + 5a + 6a^3 - a^2$

6-1     Arrange in ascending powers of $y$.
3. $-12x^3y^2 + 5xy^3 + 14xy - 8 + 9x^4y^4$

6-2     Add.
4. $5x^2 - 8x^3 + 3x - 2$ and $4x^3 + 5x^2 + 9 - x$
5. $5a^4 + 7a^3 + 6a^2 - 7$ and $3a^4 - 5a^2 + 2 - a^3$
6. $8y^2 - 4xy - 5x^2 + 8x^3$ and $7x^3 + 2x^2 - 8xy + 6y^2$
7. $p^3 + 5q^2 + 2pq$ and $3pq^3 - p^3 - 6$ and $4pq^2 + 5p^3 - pq + 6$

6-2     Subtract.
8. $(8y^2 + 3y + 6) - (-5y^2 + 4y - 3)$
9. $(8p - 5q + 7r) - (2p + 5q - 4r)$
10. $(15a - 5c + 4b) - (8b + 4c + 5a)$
11. $(8x^2 - 3xy - 7y^2) - (4x^2 - 6xy - 8y^2)$

6-3     Multiply.
12. $(-8x^2y)(4xy^2)$
13. $4a(5a + 6b)$
14. $(3x - 2y + 5z)(-3x + 4z)$
15. $(5y^3 + 3y - 6)(6y^3 - 4y + 7)$

6-4, 6-5     Find these special products.
16. $(4x - 7)(2x + 3)$
17. $(2x - 3)(2x + 3)$
18. $(7x - 5y)^2$
19. $(3x + 4y)^2$
20. $(7a - 3b)(4a - 6b)$

6-6     21. Solve.
Suppose $500 is invested at 8%, compounded annually. What amount will be in the account at the end of two years?

## CHAPTER 6 TEST

Collect like terms.
1. $6a - 3b - 4a + b - 5a + 7b$
2. $3x^3 + 2x^2 - 2x + 5x + 4x^3 - x^2$

Arrange in descending powers of $x$.
3. $18x^2y^3 + 5x^4y^4 - 13xy + 15x^3 + 9$

Add.
4. $3x^2 - 4x^3 + 2x - 1$ and $5x^3 + 4x^2 + 3 - x$
5. $4y^4 + 3y^3 + 5y^2 - 6$ and $2y^4 - 2y^2 + 3 - y^3$
6. $4y^2 - 3xy - 4x^2 + 7x^3$ and $5x^3 + 3x^2 - 2xy + 5y^2$
7. $a^3 + 2a^2 + ab$ and $ab^3 - a^3 - 1$ and $2ab^2 + 3a^3 - ab + 1$

Subtract.
8. $(7x^2 + 2x + 4) - (-2x^2 + 2x - 2)$
9. $(9a - 4b + 6c) - (3a + 2b - 5c)$
10. $(12c - 4b + 6a) - (7a + 2c + 4b)$
11. $(5r^2 - 2rs - 6s^2) - (3r^2 - 4rs - 7s^2)$

Multiply.
12. $(-4x^2y)(3xy^2)$
13. $3b(3a + 4b)$
14. $(2x - 3y + 4z)(-4x + 3z)$
15. $(3x^3 + 2x - 4)(5x^2 - 2x + 4)$

Find these special products.
16. $(3x - 5)(3x + 5)$
17. $(8x + 4y)(2x - 3y)$
18. $(9x - 4y)^2$
19. $(5x + 2y)^2$
20. $(9x - 5y)(2x - 7y)$

21. Solve.
   Suppose $800 is invested at 6%, compounded annually.
   What amount will be in the account at the end of two
   years?

## Ready for Polynomials and Factoring?

1-5    1. Evaluate $xy - xz$ when $x = -2$, $y = 4$, $z = 3$.

1-5    2. Factor: $5x + 5y$.

1-7    3. Simplify: $(3a)^2$.

1-8    Multiply and simplify.

        4. $a^4 \cdot a^7$

        5. $7^{-2} \cdot 7^{-3}$

        6. $(8x^{-3}y^4)(3x^{-9}y^{-2})$

1-8    Simplify.

        7. $(2^{-3})^4$

        8. $(x^{-2})^{-4}$

2-2    Solve.

        9. $(x - 3)(x + 5) = 0$

    10. $3x(2x + 10) = 0$

6-1   11. Is $2x - 4$ a monomial, binomial, or trinomial?

    Multiply and simplify.

6-3   12. $(2x^2yz^4)(-8x^7y^4z)$

6-3   13. $3x(4x - 7)$

6-3   14. $(4y^2 + 2)(y - 3)$

6-4   15. $(a + 6)(2a - 3)$

6-4   16. $(2xy + 3x)(x^2 + 4xy^2)$

6-4   17. $(2x - 3)^2$

6-4   18. $(3x^2y + 5y^2)^2$

6-5   19. $(4x + 3)(4x - 3)$

6-5   20. $(2xy + 4y^2)(-2xy + 4y^2)$

6-5   21. $(x + 7)(x - 1)$

6-5   22. $4x^4(2x^2y^2 + 8xy - 2)$

6-5   23. $(3x + 4y)(3x + 4y)$

# Chapter 7
# Polynomials and Factoring

*If a flower bed has an area of 108 m² and the length is 3 m longer than the width, we can find its dimensions by solving an equation.*

# 7-1 Factoring

After finishing Lesson 7-1, you should be able to
**I**   factor polynomials where the terms have a common factor.
**II**  factor polynomials by grouping.
**III** factor polynomials which are differences of squares.

## I Terms with Common Factors

Factoring is the reverse of multiplication. When factoring polynomials first look for common factors.

**Example 1.** Factor out a common factor.

$$4y^2 - 8 = 4 \cdot y^2 - 4 \cdot 2$$
$$= 4(y^2 - 2)$$

In some cases there is more than one common factor. Then we usually use the one with the largest coefficient and the largest exponent. You should try to write the answer directly.

**Examples.** Factor out a common factor.

**2.** $5x^4 - 20x^3 = 5x^3(x - 4)$

**3.** $15y^5 + 12y^4 - 27y^3 - 3y^2 = 3y^2(5y^3 + 4y^2 - 9y - 1)$

**TRY THIS** ➡

> Factor out a common factor.
>
> 1.  $3x^2 - 6x$
> 2.  $4x^5 - 8x^3$
> 3.  $P + Prt$
> 4.  $9y^4 - 15y^3 + 3y^2$

**Examples.** Factor out a common factor.

**4.** $12x^2y - 20x^3y = 4x^2y(3 - 5x)$

**5.** $10p^6q^2 - 4p^5q^3 + 2p^4q^4 = 2p^4q^2(5p^2 - 2pq + q^2)$

**TRY THIS** ➡

> Factor out a common factor.
>
> 5.  $20p^3r + 12p^2r$
> 6.  $6x^2y - 21x^3y^2 + 3x^2y^3$

## ıı Factoring by Grouping

Sometimes a common factor is itself a binomial, or sometimes pairs of terms have a common factor which can be removed.

**Example 6.** Factor.

$$y^2 + 3y + 4y + 12 = y(y + 3) + 4(y + 3)$$
$$= (y + 4)(y + 3)$$

Note that we factored two parts of the expression, $y^2 + 3y$ and $4y + 12$. Then we removed the common binomial factor, $y + 3$.

**Examples.** Factor.

**7.** $4x^2 - 3x + 20x - 15 = 4x^2 + 20x - 3x - 15$
$$= 4x(x + 5) - 3(x + 5)$$
$$= (4x - 3)(x + 5)$$

**8.** $ax^2 + ay - bx^2 - by = ax^2 + ay + (-bx^2 - by)$
$$= a(x^2 + y) - b(x^2 + y) \qquad \textit{Factoring out a and } -b$$
$$= (a - b)(x^2 + y)$$

Not all expressions with four terms can be factored by grouping.

**TRY THIS** ➡

> Factor.
>
> 7. $x^2 + 5x + 4x + 20$
> 8. $5y^2 + 2y + 10y + 4$
> 9. $px + py - qx - qy$

## ııı Difference of Squares

To factor a difference of two squares we can use the following equation.

$$A^2 - B^2 = (A + B)(A - B)$$

**Examples.** Factor.

**9.** $x^2 - 9 = x^2 - 3^2$
$$= (x + 3)(x - 3)$$

**10.** $25y^6 - 49x^2 = (5y^3 + 7x)(5y^3 - 7x)$

**TRY THIS** ➡

> Factor.
>
> 10. $y^2 - 4$
> 11. $49x^4 - 25y^{10}$
> 12. $36y^4 - 16y^6$

## Exercise Set 7-1

▌Factor. (*See Examples 1–5.*)

1. $y^2 - 5y$
2. $x^2 + 9x$
3. $4a^2 + 2a$
4. $6y^2 + 3y$
5. $y^3 + 9y^2$
6. $x^3 + 8x^2$
7. $3y^2 - 3y - 9$
8. $5x^2 - 5x + 15$
9. $6x^2 - 3x^4$
10. $8y^2 + 4y^4$
11. $4ab - 6ac + 12ad$
12. $8xy + 10xz - 14xw$
13. $4x^2y - 12xy^2$
14. $5x^2y^3 + 15x^3y^2$
15. $x^6 + x^5 - x^3 + x^2$
16. $y^4 - y^3 + y^2 + y$
17. $24x^3 - 36x^2 + 72x$
18. $16x^6 - 32x^3 - 48x^2$
19. $10a^4 + 15a^2 - 25a - 30$
20. $12t^5 - 20t^4 + 8t^2 - 16$
21. $\frac{4}{7}x^6 - \frac{6}{7}x^4 + \frac{1}{7}x^2 - \frac{3}{7}x$
22. $\frac{5}{4}y^7 - \frac{3}{4}y^5 + \frac{7}{4}y^3 - \frac{1}{4}y$

▌▌Factor. (*See Examples 6–8.*)

23. $a(b - 2) + c(b - 2)$
24. $a(x^2 - 3) - 2(x^2 - 3)$
25. $(x - 2)(x + 5) + (x - 2)(x + 8)$
26. $(m - 4)(m + 3) + (m - 4)(m - 3)$
27. $a^2(x - y) + a^2(x - y)$
28. $3x^2(x - 6) + 3x^2(x - 6)$
29. $ac + ad + bc + bd$
30. $xy + xz + wy + wz$
31. $b^3 - b^2 + 2b - 2$
32. $y^3 - y^2 + 3y - 3$
33. $y^2 - 8y - y + 8$
34. $t^2 + 6t - 2t - 12$
35. $2y^4 + 6y^2 + 5y^2 + 15$
36. $8x^4 - 12x^2 - 12x^2 + 18$
37. $2xy - x^2y - 6 + 3x$
38. $4ab - a^2b - 20 + 5a$

▌▌▌Factor. Remember to look first for a common factor. (*See Examples 9 and 10.*)

39. $x^2 - 16$
40. $y^2 - 9$
41. $9x^2 - 25$
42. $4a^2 - 49$
43. $4x^2 - 25$
44. $100y^2 - 81$
45. $6x^2 - 6y^2$
46. $8x^2 - 8y^2$
47. $3x^8 - 3y^8$
48. $5x^4 - 5y^4$
49. $4xy^4 - 4xz^4$
50. $9a^4 - a^2b^2$
51. $\frac{1}{25} - x^2$
52. $\frac{1}{16} - y^2$
53. $0.25 - y^2$
54. $0.16 - x^2$
55. $0.04x^2 - 0.09y^2$
56. $0.01x^2 - 0.04y^2$

## Challenge Exercises

Factor.

57. $(x - 3)^2 - 9$
58. $(y - 2)^2 - 16$
59. $(2y + 4)^2 - 25$
60. $(3x + 9)^2 - 81$
61. $a^{16} - 1$
62. $y^{32} - 1$

# 7-2 Factoring Trinomials

After finishing Lesson 7-2, you should be able to
▮ factor polynomials which are the squares of binomials.
▮▮ factor trinomials of the type $x^2 + ax + b$.

## ▮Factoring Squares of Binomials

Some trinomials are squares of binomials. For example,

$$x^2 + 6x + 9 = (x + 3)^2$$

Trinomials like this are sometimes called *trinomial squares*. We must first be able to recognize when a trinomial is a square of a binomial.

a)  Two of the terms must be squares ($A^2$ and $B^2$).
b)  There must be no minus sign before $A^2$ or $B^2$.
c)  If we multiply $A$ and $B$ (the square roots of these expressions) and double the result, we get the remaining term, $2 \cdot A \cdot B$, or its additive inverse, $-2 \cdot A \cdot B$.

**Example 1.**  Is $x^2 + 10x + 25$ the square of a binomial?

a)  $x^2$ and 25 are squares.
b)  There is no minus sign before $x^2$ or 25.
c)  If we multiply the square roots, $x$ and 5, and double we get the remaining term: $2 \cdot 5 \cdot x$ or $10x$.

Thus $x^2 + 10x + 25$ is the square of a binomial.

**Example 2.**  Is $x^2 + 8x + 13$ the square of a binomial?

The answer is no, since 13 is not a square.

**TRY THIS** ━━━━▶

To factor squares of binomials we use the following equations.

$$A^2 + 2 \cdot A \cdot B + B^2 = (A + B)^2$$
$$A^2 - 2 \cdot A \cdot B + B^2 = (A - B)^2$$

Which of the following are trinomial squares?

1.  $x^2 + 6x + 9$
2.  $x^2 - 8x + 16$
3.  $x^2 + 6x + 11$
4.  $4x^2 - 20x + 25$
5.  $16x^2 - 20x + 25$
6.  $5x^2 + 14x + 16$
7.  $x^2 + 8x - 16$
8.  $x^2 - 8x - 16$

**Examples.** Factor.

**3.** $x^2 - 10x + 25 = (x - 5)^2$

**4.** $16y^2 + 49 + 56y = 16y^2 + 56y + 49$
$$= (4y + 7)^2$$

**5.** $-20xy + 4y^2 + 25x^2 = 4y^2 - 20xy + 25x^2$
$$= (2y - 5x)^2$$

**TRY THIS** ➡

Factor.

9. $x^2 + 14x + 49$
10. $9y^2 + 25 - 30y$
11. $72xy + 16x^2 + 81y^2$

**Examples.** Factor.

**6.** $25x^4 + 70x^2y^3 + 49y^6 = (5x^2 + 7y^3)^2$

**7.** $-4y^2 - 144y^8 + 48y^5 = -4y^2(1 - 12y^3 + 36y^6)$
$$= -4y^2(1 - 6y^3)^2$$

*Removing a common factor first*

**TRY THIS** ➡

Factor.

12. $16x^4 - 40x^2y^3 + 25y^6$
13. $24ab - 8a^2 - 18b^2$
14. $-12x^4y^2 + 60x^2y^5 - 75y^8$

## ⸪ Factoring Trinomials of the Type $x^2 + ax + b$

Consider this product.

$$\overset{\text{F} \quad \text{O} \quad \text{I} \quad \text{L}}{(x + 3)(x + 5) = x^2 + 5x + 3x + 15}$$
$$= x^2 + 8x + 15$$

Note that the coefficient 8 is the sum of 3 and 5, and the 15 is the product of 3 and 5. In general, $(x + a)(x + b) = x^2 + (a + b)x + ab$. To factor we can use this equation in reverse.
$$x^2 + (a + b)x + ab = (x + a)(x + b)$$

**Example 8.** Factor $x^2 - 3x - 10$.

We look for pairs of integers whose product is $-10$ and whose sum is $-3$.

| Pairs of Factors | Sum of Factors |
|:---:|:---:|
| $-2, \quad 5$ | $3$ |
| $2, \ -5$ | $-3$ |
| $10, \ -1$ | $9$ |
| $-10, \quad 1$ | $-9$ |

Thus the desired integers are 2 and $-5$. Then

$$x^2 - 3x - 10 = (x + 2)(x - 5)$$

We can check by multiplying.

**TRY THIS** ▇▇▇▇▇▇▶

Factor. Check by multiplying.

15. $x^2 + 5x - 14$
16. $x^2 + 21 - 10x$
17. $y^2 - y - 2$

## Exercise Set 7-2

▌Factor. Remember to look first for a common factor. (*See Examples 3–7.*)

1. $y^2 - 6y + 9$
2. $x^2 - 8x + 16$
3. $x^2 + 14x + 49$
4. $x^2 + 16x + 64$
5. $x^2 + 1 + 2x$
6. $x^2 + 1 - 2x$
7. $a^2 + 4a + 4$
8. $a^2 - 4a + 4$
9. $y^2 + 36 - 12y$
10. $y^2 + 36 + 12y$
11. $-18y^2 + y^3 + 81y$
12. $24a^2 + a^3 + 144a$
13. $12a^2 + 36a + 27$
14. $20y^2 + 100y + 125$
15. $2x^2 - 40x + 200$
16. $32x^2 + 48x + 18$
17. $1 - 8d + 16d^2$
18. $1 + 10b + 25b^2$
19. $64 + 25y^2 - 80y$
20. $81 + 16x^2 + 72x$
21. $x^4y^4 - 8x^2y^2 + 16$
22. $a^4y^4 - 18a^2y^2 + 81$
23. $-24ab + 16a^2 + 9b^2$
24. $12rs + 4r^2 + 9s^2$
25. $9y^8 + 12y^4 + 4$
26. $16x^{10} - 8x^5 + 1$
27. $\frac{1}{36}x^8 + \frac{4}{18}x^4 + \frac{4}{9}$
28. $\frac{1}{25}y^{10} - \frac{6}{20}y^5 + \frac{9}{16}$
29. $0.25x^2 + 0.30x + .09$
30. $0.04x^2 - 0.28x + 0.49$

▌▌Factor. (*See Example 8.*)

31. $x^2 + 9x + 20$
32. $y^2 + 8y + 15$
33. $y^2 - 8y + 16$
34. $a^2 - 10a + 25$
35. $x^2 - 27 - 6x$
36. $t^2 - 15 - 2t$
37. $m^2 - 3m - 28$
38. $x^2 - 2x - 8$
39. $14x + x^2 + 45$
40. $12y + y^2 + 32$
41. $y^2 + 2y - 63$
42. $x^2 + 3x - 40$
43. $t^2 - 11t + 28$
44. $y^2 - 14y + 45$
45. $3x + x^2 - 10$
46. $x + x^2 - 6$
47. $x^2 + 5x + 6$
48. $y^2 + 8y + 7$
49. $32 + 4y - y^2$
50. $56 + x - x^2$
51. $15 + t^2 + 8t$
52. $27 + y^2 + 12y$
53. $x^4 + 11x^2 - 80$
54. $y^4 + 5y^2 - 84$
55. $x^2 - \frac{4}{25} + \frac{3}{5}x$
56. $y^2 - \frac{8}{49} + \frac{2}{7}y$
57. $y^2 + 0.4y - 0.05$
58. $t^2 + 0.6t - 0.27$

# 7-3 Trinomials of the Type $ax^2 + bx + c$

After finishing Lesson 7-3, you should be able to
▌ factor trinomials of the type $ax^2 + bx + c$.

▌Consider a multiplication.

$$
\begin{array}{cccc}
 & \text{F} & \text{O} & \text{I} & \text{L} \\
(2x + 3)(5x + 4) = & 10x^2 & + 8x & + 15x & + 12 \\
 & 10x^2 & + & 23x & + & 12
\end{array}
$$

$$
\begin{array}{|c|c|c|}
\hline
\text{F} & \text{O + I} & \text{L} \\
2 \cdot 5 & 2 \cdot 4 + 3 \cdot 5 & 3 \cdot 4 \\
\hline
\end{array}
$$

To factor $ax^2 + bx + c$ we look for two binomials

$$(\_\_x + \_\_)(\_\_x + \_\_)$$

where products of numbers in the blanks are as follows.

1. The numbers in the *first* blanks have product $a$.
2. The *outside* product and the *inside* product add up to $b$.
3. The numbers in the *last* blanks have product $c$.

**Example 1.** Factor $5x^2 - 9x - 2$.

We first look for a common factor. There is none other than 1.
We look for numbers whose product is 5. These are 1, 5 and $-1$, $-5$.

We have these possibilities.

$$(x + \quad)(5x + \quad) \quad \text{or} \quad (-x + \quad)(-5x + \quad)$$

Now we look for numbers whose product is $-2$. These are 1, $-2$ and $-1$, 2.

Then we have these as some of the possibilities for factorization.

Then we multiply each. We must get $5x^2 - 9x - 2$.

a) $(x + 1)(5x - 2)$
b) $(x - 2)(5x + 1)$
c) $(-x + 1)(-5x - 2)$
d) $(-x + 2)(-5x - 1)$

a) $5x^2 + 3x - 2$
b) $5x^2 - 9x - 2$
c) $5x^2 - 3x - 2$
d) $5x^2 - 9x - 2$

We see that b) and d) are both factorizations. We prefer to have the first coefficients positive when that is possible. Thus the factorization we prefer is $(x - 2)(5x + 1)$.

**TRY THIS** ➤

**Example 2.** Factor $12x^2 + 34x + 14$.

We first look for a common factor. The number 2 is a common factor, so we factor it out. $2(6x^2 + 17x + 7)$. Now we consider $6x^2 + 17x + 7$. We look for numbers whose product is 6. These are 6, 1 and 2, 3. (From Example 1 we found that we needed to consider only positive factors of the first term.) We then have these possibilities.

$(6x + \quad)(x + \quad)$ and $(2x + \quad)(3x + \quad)$

Next we look for pairs of numbers whose product is 7. They are

7, 1 $\qquad$ $-7, -1$ $\qquad$ (*Both positive or both negative*)

By multiplying, we find that the answer is $2(2x + 1)(3x + 7)$.

> Factor.
>
> 1. $3x^2 + 5x + 2$
> 2. $4x^2 - 3 + 4x$

**TRY THIS** ➤

**Example 3.** Factor $x^2y^2 + 5xy + 4$.

In this case, we can treat $xy$ as if it were a single variable.

$$x^2y^2 + 5xy + 4 = (xy)^2 + (4 + 1)xy + 4 \cdot 1$$
$$= (xy + 4)(xy + 1)$$

> Factor.
>
> 3. $24y^2 - 46y + 10$
> 4. $16x^2 - 12 + 16x$

**TRY THIS** ➤

Another way to factor $ax^2 + bx + c$ is as follows:

> Factor.
>
> 5. $p^2q^2 + 7pq + 12$
> 6. $2x^4y^6 - 3x^2y^3 - 20$

   a) First look for a common factor.
   b) Multiply the first and last coefficients, $a$ and $c$.
   c) Try to factor the product $ac$ so that the sum of the factors is $b$.
   d) Write the middle term, $bx$, as a sum.
   e) Factor by grouping.

**Example 4.** Factor $2x^2 - 3x - 35$.

a) First look for a common factor. There is none (other than 1).

b) Multiply the first and last coefficients, 2 and $-35$.

$$2(-35) = -70$$

c)   Try to factor $-70$ so that the sum of the factors is $-3$.

| Some Pairs of Factors | Sums of Factors |
|:---:|:---:|
| $-2,\quad 35$ | $33$ |
| $2, -35$ | $-33$ |
| $-14,\quad 5$ | $-9$ |
| $7, -10$ | $-3$ |

The desired factors are 7 and $-10$.

d)   Write $-3x$ as a sum using the results of c).

$$-3x = -10x + 7x$$

e)   Factor by grouping.

$$
\begin{aligned}
2x^2 - 3x - 35 &= 2x^2 - 10x + 7x - 35 \\
&= (2x^2 - 10x) + (7x - 35) \\
&= 2x(x - 5) + 7(x - 5) \\
&= (2x + 7)(x - 5)
\end{aligned}
$$

**TRY THIS** ➡

Factor.

7.   $3x^2 - 13x - 56$
8.   $4x^2 + 37x + 9$

## Exercise Set 7-3

▌Factor. Remember to look first for a common factor. (*See Examples 1–4.*)

1.   $3b^2 + 8b + 4$
2.   $9x^2 + 15x + 4$
3.   $6y^2 - y - 2$
4.   $3a^2 - a - 4$
5.   $-7a + 6a^2 - 10$
6.   $-35z + 12z^2 - 3$
7.   $9a^2 + 6a - 8$
8.   $4t^2 + 4t - 15$
9.   $3x^2 - 16x - 12$
10.   $6x^2 - 5x - 25$
11.   $6x^2 - 15 - x$
12.   $10y^2 - 12 - 7y$
13.   $3a^2 - 10a + 8$
14.   $12a^2 - 7a + 1$
15.   $35y^2 + 34y + 8$
16.   $9a^2 + 18a + 8$
17.   $2t + 5t^2 - 3$
18.   $4x + 15x^2 - 3$
19.   $8x^2 - 16 - 28x$
20.   $18x^2 - 24 - 6x$
21.   $3x^3 - 5x^2 - 2x$
22.   $18y^3 - 3y^2 - 10y$
23.   $24x^2 - 2 - 47x$
24.   $15y^2 - 10 - 19y$
25.   $21x^2 + 37x + 12$
26.   $10y^2 + 23y + 12$
27.   $17x + 40x^2 - 12$
28.   $2y + 24y^2 - 15$
29.   $12a^2 - 17a + 6$
30.   $20a^2 - 23a + 6$
31.   $2x^2 + xy - 6y^2$
32.   $2m^2 + mn - 10n^2$
33.   $-6xy + 8x^2 - 9y^2$
34.   $-7ts + 2t^2 - 4s^2$
35.   $7a^2b^2 + 6 + 13ab$
36.   $3m^2n^2 + 6 + 11mn$
37.   $9x^2y^2 - 4 + 5xy$
38.   $10a^2b^2 - 1 - 9ab$

# 7-4 Completing the Square

After finishing Lesson 7-4, you should be able to
▮ factor polynomials by completing the square.

▮ A difference of two squares can have more than two terms.

**Example 1.** Factor.

$$x^2 + 6x + 9 - 25 = (x^2 + 6x + 9) - 25$$
$$= (x + 3)^2 - 5^2$$

This is now a difference of two squares, one of which is a square of a binomial. When we factor, we get

$$(x + 3 + 5)(x + 3 - 5), \text{ or } (x + 8)(x - 2).$$

**TRY THIS**

> Factor.
>
> 1. $x^2 + 2x + 1 - 25$
> 2. $y^2 + 8y + 16 - 9$

**Example 2.** Factor.

$$x^2 + 10x + 25 - y^2 + 2y - 1 = (x^2 + 10x + 25) - (y^2 - 2y + 1)$$
$$= (x + 5)^2 - (y - 1)^2$$

This is now a difference of two squares. Factoring, we get

$$[(x + 5) - (y - 1)][(x + 5) + (y - 1)],$$
or $(x + 5 - y + 1)(x + 5 + y - 1),$
or $(x - y + 6)(x + y + 4).$

**TRY THIS**

> Factor.
>
> 3. $x^2 + 8x + 16 - 100$
> 4. $x^2 - 16x + 64 -$
>    $y^2 - 4y - 4$

We can use this method to factor $x^2 + 10x + 21$. This trinomial is not a square. For it to be a square, the last term would have to be 25. If we add 0, naming it $25 - 25$, we have:

$$x^2 + 10x + 21 = x^2 + 10x + (25 - 25) + 21$$
$$= (x^2 + 10x + 25) + (-25 + 21)$$
$$= (x + 5)^2 - 4$$

This is now a difference of two squares. Factoring, we get

$$(x + 5 - 2)(x + 5 + 2) \text{ or } (x + 3)(x + 7).$$

We added $25 - 25$ to make our trinomial a square.

To use this method we need to determine what the third term would have to be for it to be a square.

**Example 3.** What must be added to $x^2 - 8x$ to make a trinomial square?

To find the third term we take half of the coefficient of $x$, and then square it. Half of $-8$ is $-4$, and $(-4)^2 = 16$. Thus we must add $16$, and $x^2 - 8x + 16$ is a square.

**TRY THIS** ➡️

> What must be added to make a trinomial square?
>
> 5. $x^2 - 12x$    6. $x^2 + 6x$
> 7. $x^2 - 14x$    8. $x^2 + 22x$

**Example 4.** Factor $x^2 - 8x - 9$.

This trinomial is not a square. For it to be a square the last term would have to be 16. To see this we take half of $-8$ and square it. To get the last term to be 16 we add zero to the trinomial, naming it $16 - 16$.

$$x^2 - 8x - 9 = x^2 - 8x + (16 - 16) - 9 \quad \textit{Adding zero}$$
$$= (x^2 - 8x + 16) + (-16 - 9)$$
$$= (x^2 - 8x + 16) - 25$$
$$= (x - 4)^2 - 5^2$$
$$= (x - 4 + 5)(x - 4 - 5), \text{ or } (x + 1)(x - 9)$$

**Example 5.** Factor $y^2 + 55 + 16y$.

We first write the polynomial in descending order: $y^2 + 16y + 55$. It is not a square. For it to be a square the last term would have to be 64. To see this we take half of 16 and square it. To get the last term to be 64 we add zero to the trinomial, naming it $64 - 64$.

$$y^2 + 16y + 55 = y^2 + 16y + (64 - 64) + 55 \quad \textit{Adding zero}$$
$$= (y^2 + 16y + 64) + (-64 + 55)$$
$$= (y^2 + 16y + 64) - 9$$
$$= (y + 8)^2 - 3^2$$
$$= (y + 8 + 3)(y + 8 - 3), \text{ or } (y + 11)(y + 5)$$

This procedure is called *completing the square*. Learn to do it even though you could factor another way! We shall use it again later.

**TRY THIS**

> Factor by completing the square.
>
> 9. $x^2 + 8x + 12$
> 10. $-4y - 32 + y^2$

**Example 6.** Factor $x^2 - 5x + 4$.

This trinomial is not a square. For it to be a square, the last term would have to be $\frac{25}{4}$. To see this, we take half of $-5$ and square it. To get the last term to be $\frac{25}{4}$ we add zero to the trinomial, naming it $\frac{25}{4} - \frac{25}{4}$.

$$\begin{aligned}
x^2 - 5x + 4 &= x^2 - 5x + \left(\tfrac{25}{4} - \tfrac{25}{4}\right) + 4 \quad \textit{Adding zero} \\
&= \left(x^2 - 5x + \tfrac{25}{4}\right) + \left(-\tfrac{25}{4} + \tfrac{16}{4}\right) \\
&= \left(x^2 - 5x + \tfrac{25}{4}\right) - \tfrac{9}{4} \\
&= \left(x - \tfrac{5}{2}\right)^2 - \left(\tfrac{3}{2}\right)^2 \\
&= \left(x - \tfrac{5}{2} + \tfrac{3}{2}\right)\left(x - \tfrac{5}{2} - \tfrac{3}{2}\right), \text{ or } (x - 1)(x - 4)
\end{aligned}$$

**TRY THIS**

> Factor by completing the square.
>
> 11. $x^2 + x - \frac{3}{4}$

## Exercise Set 7-4

▌Factor by completing the square. Show your work. (*See Examples 4–6.*)

1. $c^2 + 8c + 12$
2. $x^2 + 10x + 16$
3. $t^2 - 10t + 21$
4. $a^2 - 8a + 12$
5. $-2y + y^2 - 24$
6. $-10a + a^2 - 24$
7. $x^2 - 14x + 40$
8. $y^2 - 6y + 8$
9. $r^2 + 12r - 28$
10. $y^2 + 16y - 17$
11. $m^2 - 15 + 2m$
12. $r^2 - 15 + 14r$
13. $p^2 + 8p + 15$
14. $a^2 + 8a + 12$
15. $t^2 + 12t + 11$
16. $m^2 + 14m + 13$
17. $3x^2 + 39 - 42x$
18. $2x^2 + 144 - 36x$
19. $5a^2 - 40a - 420$
20. $8x^2 - 64x - 72$
21. $x^2 + 7x + 6$
22. $x^2 + 5x - 6$
23. $x^2 - 3x + \frac{5}{4}$
24. $x^2 - 5x + \frac{9}{4}$

### Calculator Exercises

Factor by completing the square.

25. $x^2 + 4.482x - 7.403544$
26. $x^2 - 0.78x + 0.1232$
27. $5.72x^2 + 35.464x - 1319.2608$
28. $0.24x^2 + 1.4256x + 2.112312$

# 7-5 Sums or Differences of Two Cubes

After finishing Lesson 7-5, you should be able to
▮ factor polynomials that are sums or differences of two cubes.

▮ Consider the following.

$$(a + b)(a^2 - ab + b^2) = a(a^2 - ab + b^2) + b(a^2 - ab + b^2)$$
$$= a^3 - a^2b + ab^2 + a^2b - ab^2 + b^3$$
$$= a^3 + b^3$$

$$(a - b)(a^2 + ab + b^2) = a(a^2 + ab + b^2) - b(a^2 + ab + b^2)$$
$$= a^3 + a^2b + ab^2 - a^2b - ab^2 - b^3$$
$$= a^3 - b^3$$

To factor sums or differences of two cubes we use the following equations.

$$a^3 + b^3 = (a + b)(a^2 - ab + b^2)$$
$$a^3 - b^3 = (a - b)(a^2 + ab + b^2)$$

**Example 1.** Factor $x^3 - 27$.

In one set of parentheses we write the cube root of the first term, the sign of the second term, and then the cube root of the second term.

$$x^3 - 27 = (x - 3)(\qquad)$$

To get the next factor we think of $x - 3$ and do the following.

1. Square the first term: $x^2$.
2. Take the product of the first and second terms, $-3x$, and change the sign: $3x$.
3. Square the second term: $(-3)^2 = 9$.

$$= (x - 3)(x^2 + 3x + 9)$$

*Note:* We cannot factor $x^2 + 3x + 9$. It is not the square of a binomial.

**TRY THIS** ➡

Factor.

1. $x^3 - 8$
2. $y^3 - 27$

**Example 2.** Factor $125x^3 + y^3$.

$125x^3 + y^3 = (5x + y)($          $)$          *Writing the sum of the cube roots*

Now we think of $5x + y$ and get the next factor.

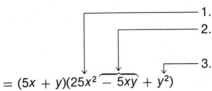

1. Square the first term: $25x^2$.
2. Take the product of the first and second terms, $5xy$, and change the sign: $-5xy$.
3. Square the last term: $y^2$.

$= (5x + y)(25x^2 - 5xy + y^2)$

**TRY THIS**

Factor.

3. $27x^3 + y^3$
4. $8y^3 + z^3$

**Example 3.** Factor.

$64y^6 - 125x^6 = (4y^2 - 5x^2)[(4y^2)^2 + (4y^2)(5x^2) + (5x^2)^2]$
$= (4y^2 - 5x^2)(16y^4 + 20y^2x^2 + 25x^4)$

**TRY THIS**

Factor.

5. $8x^6 + 27y^6$

## Exercise Set 7-5

▮Factor. Remember to look first for a common factor. (*See Examples 1–3.*)

1. $x^3 + 8$
2. $c^3 + 27$
3. $y^3 - 64$
4. $z^3 - 1$
5. $w^3 + 1$
6. $x^3 + 125$
7. $8a^3 + 1$
8. $27x^3 + 1$
9. $y^3 - 8$
10. $p^3 - 27$
11. $8 - 27b^3$
12. $64 - 125x^3$
13. $64y^3 + 1$
14. $125x^3 + 1$
15. $8x^3 + 27$
16. $27y^3 + 64$
17. $a^3 - b^3$
18. $x^3 - y^3$
19. $a^3 + \frac{1}{8}$
20. $b^3 + \frac{1}{27}$
21. $8x^3 - 27y^3$
22. $64c^3 - 125d^3$
23. $rs^3 + 64r$
24. $ab^3 + 125a$
25. $5x^3 - 40z^3$
26. $2y^3 - 54z^3$
27. $x^3 + 0.001$
28. $y^3 + 0.125$
29. $64x^6 - 8t^6$
30. $125c^6 - 8d^6$

# 7-6 Factoring: A General Strategy

After finishing Lesson 7-6, you should be able to
▮  factor polynomials using any of the methods you have learned.

▮Here is a general strategy for factoring.
A.  Always look first for a common factor.
B.  Then proceed by considering the number of terms.
   *Two terms:* Try factoring as a difference of two squares, or a sum or difference of two cubes.
   *Three terms:* (1)  Is it a square of a binomial? If so, you know how to factor.
   (2)  Is it a square of a binomial? If not, use trial and error.
   *More than three terms:* (1)  Try grouping.
   (2)  Try differences of squares again.
C.  *Always factor completely.* By this we mean whenever you obtain a factor that can still be factored, you should factor it.

**Example 1.**  Factor $10a^2x - 40b^2x$.

A.  We look first for a common factor.

$$10x(a^2 - 4b^2)$$

B.  The factor $a^2 - 4b^2$ has only two terms. It is a difference of squares. We factor it.

$$10x(a + 2b)(a - 2b)$$

C.  Have we factored completely? Yes, because no factor can be factored further.

**Example 2.**  Factor $x^6 - y^6$.

A.  We look for a common factor. There isn't one.

B.  There are only two terms. It is a difference of squares: $(x^3)^2 - (y^3)^2$. We factor it.

$$(x^3 + y^3)(x^3 - y^3)$$

One factor is a sum of two cubes, and the other factor is a difference of two cubes. We factor them.

$$(x + y)(x^2 - xy + y^2)(x - y)(x^2 + xy + y^2)$$

C.  We have factored completely because no factor can be factored further.

**TRY THIS** ➡️

> Factor completely.
>
> 1.  $2 - 32x^4$
> 2.  $7a^6 - 7$
> 3.  $3x + 12 + 4x + x^2$
> 4.  $c^2 - 2cd + d^2 - t^2 - 8t - 16$

## Exercise Set 7-6

▮ Factor completely. Remember to look first for a common factor. (*See Examples 1 and 2.*)

1.  $x^2 - 144$
2.  $y^2 - 81$
3.  $2x^2 + 11x + 12$
4.  $8a^2 + 18a - 5$
5.  $3x^4 - 12$
6.  $2xy^2 - 50x$
7.  $a^2 + 25 + 10a$
8.  $p^2 + 64 + 16p$
9.  $2x^2 - 10x - 132$
10.  $3y^2 - 15y - 252$
11.  $9x^2 - 25y^2$
12.  $16a^2 - 81b^2$
13.  $4c^2 - 4cd + d^2$
14.  $70b^2 - 3ab - a^2$
15.  $-7x^2 + 2x^3 + 4x - 14$
16.  $9m^2 + 3m^3 + 8m + 24$
17.  $4x^2 - 27x + 45$
18.  $3y^2 + 15y - 42$
19.  $8m^3 + m^6 - 20$
20.  $-37x^2 + x^4 + 36$
21.  $ac + cd - ab - bd$
22.  $xw - yw + xz - yz$
23.  $m^6 - 1$
24.  $64t^6 - 1$
25.  $x^2 + 6x - y^2 + 9$
26.  $t^2 + 10t - p^2 + 25$
27.  $36y^2 - 35 + 12y$
28.  $2b - 28a^2b + 10ab$
29.  $a^8 - b^8$
30.  $2x^4 - 32$
31.  $8p^3 + 27q^3$
32.  $125x^3 + 64y^3$
33.  $64p^3 - 1$
34.  $8y^3 - 125$
35.  $a^3b - 16ab^3$
36.  $x^3y - 25xy^3$
37.  $-23xy + 20x^2y^2 + 6$
38.  $42ab + 27a^2b^2 + 8$
39.  $2x^3 + 6x^2 - 8x - 24$
40.  $3x^3 + 6x^2 - 27x - 54$

### SCIENCE NOTE: Cosmology

How are stars formed? How large is the universe? What are the properties of space? These are questions from cosmology, a branch of astronomy that is concerned with the physical structure of the universe. (The word *cosmos* means "universe.") Many great mathematicians have contributed work to cosmology.

# 7-7 Solving Equations by Factoring

After finishing Lesson 7-7, you should be able to
▋ solve equations by factoring and using the principle of zero products.

▋ To solve equations by factoring we will restate an important theorem from Chapter 2.

**THEOREM 2-3 (The Principle of Zero Products)**
A product is 0 if and only if at least one of the factors is 0.

Notice that Theorem 2-3 says that if a factor is 0, then the product will be 0; and also that if a product is 0, then one of the factors must be 0.

To use this principle in solving equations, we make sure that there is 0 on one side of the equation and then factor the other side.

---

**Remark (if and only if).** When we use these words in a sentence, what does the sentence mean? It means two things. "*A* if and only if *B*" means "If *A* then *B*, and also if *B* then *A*." In other terms, it means "If *A* then *B*, and the converse." Let us consider Theorem 2-3 in this light. It says that if a product is 0 then one of the factors must be 0 *and also* if one of the factors is 0, then the product is 0.

What does this mean, in a logical sense, for solving equations? Suppose we have an equation $A \cdot B = 0$. Theorem 2-3 says that if either of the factors is 0 it will be true. It also says that if it is true, then at least one of the factors must be 0. Thus we get solutions by setting the factors equal to 0, and we get *all* of the solutions that way. Thus the statements $A \cdot B = 0$ and $A = 0$ or $B = 0$ are equivalent statements and have the same solutions. This is why, logically, we do not need to check possible solutions of equations found by using the principle of zero products.

---

**Example 1.** Solve $x^2 - 3x - 28 = 0$.

We first factor the polynomial. Then we use the principle of zero products.

$$x^2 - 3x - 28 = 0$$
$$(x - 7)(x + 4) = 0 \qquad \textit{Factoring}$$

The expressions $x^2 - 3x - 28$ and $(x - 7)(x + 4)$ name the same number for any replacement. Hence the equations have the same solutions.

$$x - 7 = 0 \quad \text{or} \quad x + 4 = 0 \qquad \textit{Using the principle of zero products}$$
$$x = 7 \quad \text{or} \qquad x = -4$$

Check:  For 7: $x^2 - 3x - 28 = 0$ $\qquad$ For $-4$: $x^2 - 3x - 28 = 0$

$$\begin{array}{c|c} 7^2 - 3(7) - 28 & 0 \\ 49 - 21 - 28 & \\ 0 & \end{array} \qquad \begin{array}{c|c} (-4)^2 - 3(-4) - 28 & 0 \\ 16 + 12 - 28 & \\ 0 & \end{array}$$

The solutions are 7 and $-4$.

When we use the principle of zero products, a check is not necessary except to detect errors.

**TRY THIS**

> Solve.
>
> 1. $x^2 + 8 = 6x$

**Example 2.**  Solve $7y + 3y^2 = -2$.

$$3y^2 + 7y + 2 = 0 \qquad \textit{Adding 2 to get 0 on one side and arranging in descending order}$$

$$(3y + 1)(y + 2) = 0 \qquad \textit{Factoring}$$

$$3y + 1 = 0 \quad \text{or} \quad y + 2 = 0 \qquad \textit{Using the principle of zero products}$$
$$3y = -1 \quad \text{or} \qquad y = -2$$
$$y = -\tfrac{1}{3} \quad \text{or} \qquad y = -2$$

The solutions are $-\tfrac{1}{3}$ and $-2$.

**TRY THIS**

> Solve.
>
> 2. $5y + 2y^2 = 3$

**Example 3.**  Solve $5b^2 - 10b = 0$.

$$5b(b - 2) = 0 \qquad \textit{Factoring}$$

$$5b = 0 \quad \text{or} \quad b - 2 = 0 \qquad \textit{Using the principle of zero products}$$
$$b = 0 \quad \text{or} \qquad b = 2$$

The solutions are 0 and 2.

**TRY THIS**

> Solve.
>
> 3. $8b^2 - 16b = 0$

**Example 4.** Solve $x^2 - 6x + 9 = 0$.
$$(x - 3)(x - 3) = 0 \quad \textit{Factoring}$$

$x - 3 = 0 \quad \text{or} \quad x - 3 = 0 \qquad \textit{Using the principle of zero products}$
$\qquad x = 3 \quad \text{or} \qquad x = 3$

There is only one solution, 3.

**TRY THIS**

Solve.

4.  $25 + x^2 = -10x$
5.  $4x^2 - 9 = 0$

## Exercise Set 7-7

Solve. (*See Examples 1–4.*)

1.  $x^2 + 3x - 28 = 0$
2.  $y^2 - 4y - 45 = 0$
3.  $y^2 - 8y + 16 = 0$
4.  $r^2 - 2r + 1 = 0$
5.  $x^2 - 12x + 36 = 0$
6.  $y^2 + 16y + 64 = 0$
7.  $9x + x^2 + 20 = 0$
8.  $8y + y^2 + 15 = 0$
9.  $x^2 + 8x = 0$
10.  $t^2 + 9t = 0$
11.  $x^2 - 9 = 0$
12.  $p^2 - 16 = 0$
13.  $z^2 = 36$
14.  $y^2 = 81$
15.  $x^2 + 14x + 45 = 0$
16.  $y^2 + 12y + 32 = 0$
17.  $y^2 + 2y = 63$
18.  $a^2 + 3a = 40$
19.  $p^2 - 11p = -28$
20.  $x^2 - 14x = -45$
21.  $32 + 4x - x^2 = 0$
22.  $27 + 12t + t^2 = 0$
23.  $3b^2 + 8b + 4 = 0$
24.  $9y^2 + 15y + 4 = 0$
25.  $8y^2 - 10y + 3 = 0$
26.  $4x^2 + 11x + 6 = 0$
27.  $6z - z^2 = 0$
28.  $8y - y^2 = 0$
29.  $12z^2 + z = 6$
30.  $6x^2 - 7x = 10$
31.  $5x^2 - 20 = 0$
32.  $6y^2 - 54 = 0$
33.  $2x^2 - 15x = -7$
34.  $x^2 - 9x = -8$
35.  $21r^2 + r - 10 = 0$
36.  $12a^2 - 5a - 28 = 0$
37.  $15y^2 = 3y$
38.  $18x^2 = 9x$
39.  $100x^2 = 81$
40.  $49y^2 = 36$

## Challenge Exercises

Solve.

41.  $x^2 - \frac{1}{25} = 0$
42.  $y^2 - \frac{1}{64} = 0$
43.  $x(x + 8) = 16(x - 1)$
44.  $m(m + 9) = 4(2m + 5)$
45.  $(a - 5)^2 = 36$
46.  $(x - 6)^2 = 81$

# 7-8 Solving Problems

After finishing Lesson 7-8, you should be able to
▮ solve problems by translating to equations and solving the equations.

▮ To solve some problems we can first translate the problem situation to an equation and then solve the equation. Then we check to see if the solution(s) satisfies the conditions of the problem.

**Example 1.** The square of a number minus the number is 20. Find the number.

$$\underbrace{\text{The square of a number}}_{x^2} \quad \underbrace{\text{minus}}_{-} \quad \underbrace{\text{the number}}_{x} \quad \underbrace{\text{is}}_{=} \quad \underbrace{20}_{20} \qquad \textit{Translating}$$

We solve the equation.

$$x^2 - x = 20$$
$$x^2 - x - 20 = 0 \qquad \textit{Adding} -20$$
$$(x - 5)(x + 4) = 0 \qquad \textit{Factoring}$$

$$x - 5 = 0 \quad \text{or} \quad x + 4 = 0 \qquad \textit{Using the principle of zero products}$$
$$x = 5 \quad \text{or} \qquad x = -4$$

The numbers 5 and −4 both check. They are the answers to the problem.

**TRY THIS**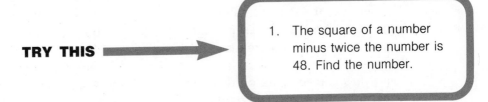

1. The square of a number minus twice the number is 48. Find the number.

It is sometimes helpful to reword a problem before translating.

**Example 2.** The width of a rectangle is 2 m less than the length. The area is 15 m². Find the dimensions.

$$\underbrace{\text{The length}}_{\ell} \quad \underbrace{\text{times}}_{\cdot} \quad \underbrace{\text{the length minus 2}}_{(\ell - 2)} \quad \underbrace{\text{is}}_{=} \quad \underbrace{15.}_{15} \qquad \textit{Rewording}$$
$$\textit{Translating}$$

We solve the equation.

$$\ell \cdot (\ell - 2) = 15$$
$$\ell^2 - 2\ell = 15 \quad \textit{Multiplying}$$
$$\ell^2 - 2\ell - 15 = 0 \quad \textit{Adding } -15$$
$$(\ell - 5)(\ell + 3) = 0 \quad \textit{Factoring}$$

$$\ell - 5 = 0 \quad \text{or} \quad \ell + 3 = 0 \quad \textit{Using the principle of zero products}$$
$$\ell = 5 \quad \text{or} \quad \ell = -3$$

The solutions of the equation are 5 and −3. Now we check in the problem. The length of a rectangle cannot be negative. Thus the length is 5 m. Since the width is 2 m less than the length, the width is 3 m.

**TRY THIS**

2. The width of a rectangle is 5 cm less than the length. The area is 24 cm². Find the dimensions.

## Exercise Set 7-8

▌Solve these problems. (*See Examples 1 and 2.*)

1. Four times the square of a number is 21 more than eight times the number. What is the number?

2. Four times the square of a number is 45 more than eight times the number. What is the number?

3. The square of a number plus the number is 132. What is the number?

4. The square of a number plus the number is 156. What is the number?

5. The length of the top of a table is 5 cm more than the width. Find the length and width if the area is 84 cm².

6. The length of the top of a work bench is 4 cm greater than the width. The area is 96 cm². Find the length and the width.

7. Sam Sylow is planning a garden 25 m longer than it is wide. The garden will have an area of 7500 m². What will its dimensions be?

8. A flower bed is to be 3 m longer than it is wide. The flower bed will have an area of 108 m². What will its dimensions be?

9. The sum of the squares of two consecutive odd positive integers is 202. Find the integers.

10. The sum of the squares of two consecutive odd positive integers is 394. Find the integers.

11. If the sides of a square are lengthened by 4 cm the area becomes 49 cm². Find the length of a side of the original square.

12. If the sides of a square are lengthened by 6 m the area becomes 144 m². Find the length of a side of the original square.

13. The base of a triangle is 9 cm greater than the height. The area is 56 cm². Find the height and base.

14. The base of a triangle is 5 cm less than the height. The area is 18 cm². Find the height and base.

15. The perimeter of a square is 4 more than its area. Find the length of a side.

16. The area of a square is 12 more than its perimeter. Find the length of a side.

17. Three consecutive even integers are such that the square of the first plus the square of the third is 136. Find the three integers.

18. Three consecutive even integers are such that the square of the third is 76 more than the square of the second. Find the three integers.

19. Find three consecutive integers such that the product of the first and third minus the second is one more than 10 times the third.

20. Find three consecutive integers such that four times the square of the third less three times the square of the first minus 41 is twice the square of the second.

## Challenge Exercises

21. A rectangular piece of tin is twice as long as it is wide. Squares 2 cm on a side are cut out of each corner and the ends are turned up to make a box whose volume is 480 cm². What are the dimensions of the piece of tin?

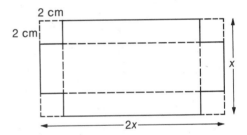

### CONSUMER NOTE: Bait and Switch

The "bait and switch" technique is a way to fool buyers. The bait is an item offered at an incredibly low price. When a person comes in, the salesperson tries to switch to something that costs much more. For instance, an ad may offer cheap repair service. But when a customer requests the service, the salesperson finds reasons to provide different repairs. The salesperson charges a much higher price for these repairs.

The bait-and-switch technique can be used to sell many things. Examples are carpets, television repairs, and home repairs.

## CHAPTER 7 REVIEW

Review the material in the chapter. Then see how you have done by trying these review exercises. If you miss an exercise, restudy the indicated lesson.

Factor completely.

7-1    1.   $4x + 4$

7-1    2.   $8y - 16$

7-1    3.   $9y^2 - 64$

7-1    4.   $3a^2 - 75$

7-2    5.   $x^2 - 14x + 49$

7-2    6.   $4x^2 + 25 + 20x$

7-2    7.   $-5x + 6 + x^2$

7-3    8.   $2y^2 - 3y - 2$

7-3    9.   $8b^2 + 9 - 18b$

7-5   10.   $a^3 + 8b^3$

7-5   11.   $27b^3 - 64c^3$

7-4   12.   Factor $x^2 + 21 - 10x$ by completing the square. Show your work.

7-7    Solve.

     13.   $x^2 + 4 = -5x$

     14.   $x^2 - 8x = 0$

7-8    Solve.

     15.   The square of a number plus 7 times the number is $-12$. Find the number.

     16.   The length of a rectangle is 3 cm more than the width and the area is 54 cm². Find its dimensions.

## CHAPTER 7 TEST

Factor completely.
1. $5y + 5$
2. $9t - 27$
3. $16x^2 - 81$
4. $5b^2 - 180$
5. $x^2 + 81 - 18x$
6. $9x^2 + 24x + 16$
7. $-2x - 15 + x^2$
8. $6x^2 + 11x - 10$
9. $-41y + 15y^2 + 28$
10. $x^3 + 27y^3$
11. $64p^3 - 125q^3$

12. Factor $-16x - 36 + x^2$ by completing the square. Show your work.

Solve.
13. $x^2 - 21 = 4x$
14. $y^2 - 9y = 0$

Solve.
15. The square of a number plus 9 times the number is $-8$. Find the number.
16. The length of a rectangle is 5 cm more than the width and the area is 84 cm². Find its dimensions.

Chemical engineers develop new methods of making chemical or petroleum products. Engineers' development work is aided by chemical technicians.

Steel workers in a rolling mill operate machines that turn steel ingots into sheets. The ingots are heated and then squeezed between giant rollers in the mill.

Electronics assemblers put together parts of electronic products. Assemblers may use hand tools, or they may operate machines that make delicate assemblies.

Welders apply heat to materials—usually metals—so they melt and join together. Welding work is needed in many kinds of manufacturing and construction.

# CAREERS IN MANUFACTURING AND CONSTRUCTION

Manufacturing is a source of goods. Some are durable. Others, such as food products, paper, clothing, and chemicals, are nondurable. They are used up before long.

Construction also is a source of goods. These include buildings, bridges, dams, and roads.

In the mid-1970s, manufacturing was the leading area of work in the United States. This is shown by the bar graph below. Contract construction, which includes construction of most large buildings, was far behind. Two other goods-producing areas, agriculture and mining, ranked below construction.

Workers (in millions)

| | 0 | 5 | 10 | 15 | 20 |
|---|---|---|---|---|---|
| Manufacturing | | Durable | | Nondurable | |
| Trade | | Retail | | Wholesale | |
| Government | | State and local | Federal | | |
| Health, repair, and other services | | | | | |
| Transportation and public utilities | | | | | |
| Finance, insurance, and real estate | | | | | |
| Contract construction | | | | | |
| Agriculture | | | | | |
| Mining | | | | | |

**United States Labor Force in 1974**

at cutters prepare meat for sale
market. Cutters may also pre-
fish and poultry for sale. They
duce portions that are ready for
king.

Roofers apply weatherproofing material to a rooftop. The material may
consist of strips of felt and coats of
asphalt or tar, or it may be metal,
tile, or slate.

Garment workers do one of the
many steps needed to make wom-
en's, men's, or children's clothing.
The steps include designing, cutting,
sewing, and pressing.

Electricians assemble and
install the electrical systems in buildings. Electricians may also use
testing devices to check
that the systems are func-
tioning properly.

Percent change

| | −40 | −30 | −20 | −10 | 0 | 10 | 20 | 30 | 40 | 50 |
| Health, repair, and other services | | | | | | | | | | |
| Government | | | | | | | | | | |
| Finance, insurance, and real estate | | | | | | | | | | |
| Contract construction | | | | | | | | | | |
| Trade | | | | | | | | | | |
| Mining | | | | | | | | | | |
| Manufacturing | | | | | | | | | | |
| Transportation and public utilities | | | | | | | | | | |
| Agriculture | | | | | | | | | | |

**Projected Changes in United States Labor Force, 1974–1985**

Projected changes in these areas are
shown above. Construction is likely to
grow fastest. Mining and manufacturing
are likely to grow less quickly.
Agriculture—including unpaid members of
farm families—is likely to shrink.

Despite the lower growth rate in
manufacturing, it will remain a much
larger area than construction. Similarly,
agriculture will remain larger than mining,
though both areas will be relatively small.
They are part of "Other" in the circle
graph.

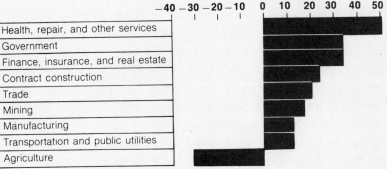

Services

Trade

Government

Various Services

Transportation,
communication,
and public utilities

Other

Construction

Manufacturing

Goods

**Projected United States Labor Force in the mid-1980s**

**Ready for Relations, Functions, and Transformations?**

3-1    1. Draw and label the first and second axes. Then plot these
        points:
        a) (3, 2)
        b) (−2, 4)
        c) (−4, −1)
        d) (2, 0)

       Graph the following equations.

3-1    2. $y − 3x = 2$

3-1    3. $2y = 3x + 2$

3-1    4. $\frac{1}{2}x = 4y − 3$

3-2    5. $2y + 4 = 3x$

3-2    6. $y = −1$

5-4    7. $y > x$

5-4    8. $3x − 6y < 9$

5-4    9. $x − 2y \geq 5$

# Chapter 8
# Relations, Functions, Transformations

The cost of operating a car is a function of speed.

# 8-1 Relations

After finishing Lesson 8-1, you should be able to
- **I** find the set of ordered pairs determined by a given relation.
- **II** list the domain and range of a given relation.
- **III** graph relations.

## I Relations and Ordered Pairs

For certain relations it is easy to determine a set of ordered pairs. We use braces to indicate that we are considering a set.

**Example 1.** Consider the set {2, 3, 5} and the relation < (is less than). This yields the following ordered pairs, in which the first member is less than the second:

(2, 3), (2, 5), (3, 5).

For certain sets of ordered pairs it is easy to determine a relation.

**Example 2.** Consider the set {2, 3, 5} and the following set of ordered pairs:

{(2, 2), (3, 3), (5, 5)}.

In each ordered pair the first member is the same as the second. This set of ordered pairs determines the relation = (is equal to).

**TRY THIS**

> 1. Consider the set {4, 5, 6}. Find the set of ordered pairs determined by the relation > (is greater than).
> {(5, 4), (6, 4), (6, 5)}

Since relations and ordered pairs are so closely associated, we shall actually *define* a relation to *be* a set of ordered pairs. To do this, we will use the idea of a Cartesian product.

## II Cartesian Products

### DEFINITION

The *Cartesian product* of two sets A and B is the set of *all* ordered pairs having the first member from set A and the second member from set B. The Cartesian product of two sets A and B is symbolized $A \times B$.

**Example 3.** Consider sets $A$ and $B$, where $A = \{1, 2, 3\}$ and $B = \{a, b\}$.

The Cartesian product, $A \times B$, is as follows.

(1, *a*)   (2, *a*)   (3, *a*)
(1, *b*)   (2, *b*)   (3, *b*)

**TRY THIS** ➡️

2.  Consider sets $A$ and $B$, where $A = \{a, b, c\}$ and $B = \{1, 2\}$. List all the ordered pairs in $A \times B$.

The sets $A$ and $B$ may be the same.

**Example 4.** Consider the set $\{2, 3, 4, 5\}$. The Cartesian product of this set by itself is as follows.

| 5 | (2, 5) | (3, 5) | (4, 5) | (5, 5) |
| 4 | (2, 4) | (3, 4) | (4, 4) | (5, 4) |
| 3 | (2, 3) | (3, 3) | (4, 3) | (5, 3) |
| 2 | (2, 2) | (3, 2) | (4, 2) | (5, 2) |
| | 2 | 3 | 4 | 5 |

The headings at the bottom and at the left are only for reference. The Cartesian product consists only of the ordered pairs.

3.  Consider the set $\{x, y, z\}$. List all the ordered pairs in the Cartesian product of the set by itself.

**TRY THIS** ➡️

In a Cartesian product we can pick out ordered pairs that make up a common relation, such as $=$ or $<$ in the next examples.

**Example 5.** This is the relation $=$ (all ordered pairs in which the first member is the same as the second).

(2, 5)   (3, 5)   (4, 5)   (5, 5)
(2, 4)   (3, 4)   (4, 4)   (5, 4)
(2, 3)   (3, 3)   (4, 3)   (5, 3)
(2, 2)   (3, 2)   (4, 2)   (5, 2)

**Example 6.** This is the relation $<$ (all ordered pairs in which the first member is less than the second).

(2, 5)   (3, 5)   (4, 5)   (5, 5)
(2, 4)   (3, 4)   (4, 4)   (5, 4)
(2, 3)   (3, 3)   (4, 3)   (5, 3)
(2, 2)   (3, 2)   (4, 2)   (5, 2)

**TRY THIS** ➡

4. Consider the Cartesian product shown in Example 6. List the ordered pairs in the relation > (all ordered pairs in which the first member is greater than the second).

There are also many relations that do not have common names and relations with which we are not already familiar. Any time we select a set of ordered pairs from a Cartesian product, we have selected some relation. This is true even if we make the selection at random.

**DEFINITION**

A *relation* from a set A to a set B is any set of ordered pairs in A × B. The set of all first members in a relation is its *domain*. The set of all second numbers in a relation is its *range*.

**Example 7.** List the domain and range of the relation {(2, 3), (4, 3), (5, 2), (5, 5)}.

The domain is {2, 4, 5}.
The range is {2, 3, 5}.

**TRY THIS** ➡

5. List the domain and range of the relation {(a, 1), (b, 2), (c, 1), (d, 2)}.

## ⅲ Relations in Real Numbers

Relations are sets of ordered pairs. Since we know how to graph ordered pairs, we can graph relations.

We shall be most interested in relations from R, the set of real numbers, to itself. To graph such relations, we picture R × R and then indicate which ordered pairs are in the relation. This is a familiar process. We draw an x-axis and a y-axis. Then each point of the plane corresponds to an ordered pair of real numbers.

This is called a Cartesian coordinate system.

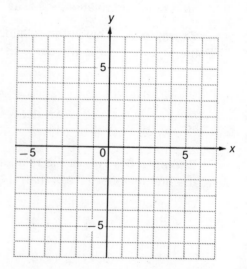

**Example 8.** Graph the relation $\{(0, -2), (1, -1), (2, 0), (3, 1)\}$
in $R \times R$.

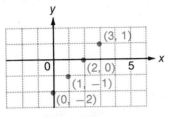

Graph these relations in $R \times R$.

6. $\{(-3, 0), (-2, 1), (-1, 2),$
   $(0, 3), (1, 4)\}$.
7. $\{(1, 1), (1, 2), (1, 3), (2, 1),$
   $(2, 2), (3, 1)\}$.

**TRY THIS** ▬▬▶

## Exercise Set 8-1

▮ For Exercises 1-6, consider the set $\{-1, 0, 1, 2\}$. (*See Example 1.*)

1. Find the set of ordered pairs determined by the relation $<$ (is less than).

2. Find the set of ordered pairs determined by the relation $>$ (is greater than).

3. Find the set of ordered pairs determined by the relation $\leq$ (is less than or equal to).

4. Find the set of ordered pairs determined by the relation $\geq$ (is greater than or equal to).

5. Find the set of ordered pairs determined by the relation $=$.

6. Find the set of ordered pairs determined by the relation $\neq$.

▮▮ List all ordered pairs in the following Cartesian products. (*See Examples 3 and 4.*)

7. $A \times B$, where $A = \{0, 2, 4, 5\}$ and $B = \{a, b, c\}$.

8. $A \times B$, where $A = \{1, 3, 5, 9\}$ and $B = \{d, e, f\}$.

9. $B \times C$, where $B = \{x, y, z\}$ and $C = \{1, 2\}$.

10. $B \times C$, where $B = \{5, 7, 10\}$ and $C = \{a, z\}$.

11. $D \times D$ where $D = \{-1, 0, 1, 2\}$

12. $E \times E$ where $E = \{-1, 1, 3, 5\}$

List the domain and range for each of the following relations. (*See Example 7.*)

13. $\{(5, 2), (6, 4), (8, 6)\}$

14. $\{(7, 1), (8, 2), (9, 5)\}$

15. $\{(6, 0), (7, 5), (8, 5)\}$

16. $\{(8, 2), (10, 1), (6, 3)\}$

17. $\{(8, 1), (8, 1), (5, 1)\}$

18. $\{(6, 2), (2, 0), (-3, 0)\}$

19. $\{(5, 6)\}$

20. $\{(7, -4)\}$

▮▮▮ Graph these relations in $R \times R$. (*See Example 8.*)

21. $\{(3, 0), (4, 2), (5, 4), (6, 6)\}$

22. $\{(1, 1), (2, 3), (3, 5), (4, 7)\}$

23. $\{(3, -4), (3, -3), (3, -2),$
    $(3, -1), (3, 0)\}$

24. $\{(-2, 1), (-2, 2), (-2, 3),$
    $(-2, 4), (-2, 5)\}$

25. $\{(4, 3), (4, 2), (3, 2), (3, 3)$
    $(5, 2), (5, 3)\}$

26. $\{(2, -2), (3, -2), (2, -3),$
    $(3, -3), (2, -4), (3, -4)\}$

27. $\{(-1, 1), (-2, 1), (-2, 2),$
    $(-3, 1), (-3, 2), (-3, 3)\}$

28. $\{(-1, -1), (-1, -2), (-1, -3),$
    $(-2, -2), (-2, -3), (-3, -3)\}$

# 8-2 Relations and Sentences

After finishing Lesson 8-2, you should be able to
▮   graph relations which are the solution sets of sentences in two variables.

▮ The set of all replacements which make a sentence true is called
its *solution set*. Some relations are solution sets of sentences in
two variables.

**Example 1.**  Graph the relation which is the solution set of the
sentence $y = 3x - 1$.

Some ordered pairs in this relation are $(-1, -4)$, $(0, -1)$ and $(2, 5)$.
The graph of this relation is also called the *graph of the equation*.

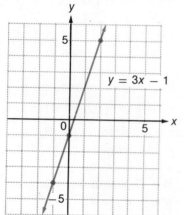

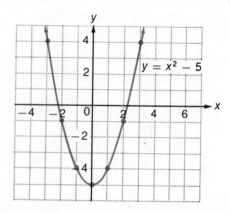

**TRY THIS**

1.   Graph the relation which is
     the solution set of the sen-
     tence $y = 2x + 1$.

**Example 2.**   Graph the relation which is the solution
set of the sentence $y \geq x^2 - 5$.

First graph $y = x^2 - 5$.

Use $(0, 0)$ as a test point.

$$\frac{y \geq x^2 - 5}{0 \;\big|\; 0^2 - 5}$$
$$-5$$

Since $(0, 0)$ makes $y > x^2 - 5$ true we shade in the region containing it.

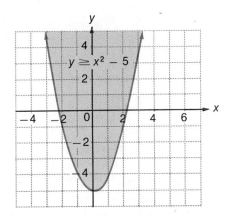

**TRY THIS**

2. Graph the relation which is the solution set of the sentence $y \geq x^2 - 1$.

## Exercise Set 8-2

▎Graph the relations which are the solution sets of the following sentences. (*See Examples 1 and 2.*)

1. $y = 4x + 1$
2. $y = 2x - 1$
3. $y \geq x^2 + 2$
4. $y \geq x^2 - 2$
5. $x = y^2 + 2$
6. $x = y^2 - 2$
7. $8x - 3y = 24$
8. $5x - 10y = 50$
9. $3x + 12 = 4y$
10. $4x - 20 = 5y$
11. $y = -2$
12. $y = 6$
13. $x = 3$
14. $x = -7$
15. $y = \dfrac{1}{x}$
16. $y = \dfrac{1}{-x}$

### Calculator Exercises

Graph.

17. $y = 3.21x^2 - 5.01x + 2.168$
18. $y = -1.055x^2 + 3.001x + 1.444$

### Challenge Exercises

Graph.

19. $y = |x + 1|$
20. $y = |x - 1|$
21. $y = |x^3|$
22. $y = \sqrt{x}$

# 8-3 Symmetry

After finishing Lesson 8-3, you should be able to
▌ identify figures which are symmetric with respect to a line.
▌▌ test the equation of a relation for symmetry with respect to the *x*-axis or *y*-axis.

## ▌ Line Symmetry

Points *P* and $P_1$ are symmetric with respect to line $\ell$.

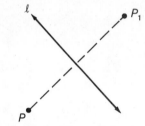

**DEFINITION**

Two points *P* and $P_1$ are said to be *symmetric* with respect to a line $\ell$ when the points are the same distance from $\ell$, measured along a perpendicular to $\ell$. Line $\ell$ is known as a line or *axis* of symmetry and $P_1$ is said to be the image of *P*.

We say, too, that the two points above are *reflections* of each other across the line. The line is known as a *line of reflection*.

**DEFINITION**

A figure, or set of points, is symmetric with respect to a line when the image of each point in the set is also in the set.

**Example 1.** The figure at the right is symmetric with respect to line $\ell$. Imagine picking this figure up and flipping it over.

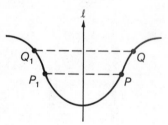

Points *P* and $P_1$ would be interchanged. Points *Q* and $Q_1$ would be interchanged. These are pairs of symmetric points. The entire figure would look exactly like it did before flipping.

**Example 2.** Which of the following figures are symmetric with respect to the given line?

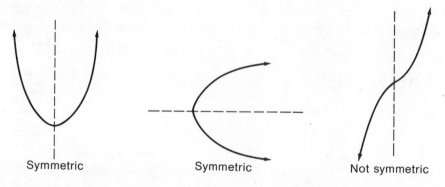

Symmetric        Symmetric        Not symmetric

TRY THIS

1. Which of the following figures are symmetric with respect to the given line?

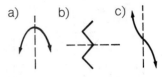

a)   b)   c)

## ıı Symmetry with Respect to the Axes

There are special and interesting kinds of symmetry in which the
$x$-axis or the $y$-axis is a line of symmetry.

### THEOREM 8-1

Two points are symmetric with respect to the $x$-axis if and only if
their $y$-coordinates are additive inverses and they have the same
$x$-coordinate. Two points are symmetric with respect to the $y$-axis
if and only if their $x$-coordinates are additive inverses and they
have the same $y$-coordinate.

**Example 3.** Plot the point $(2, -5)$ and the point symmetric to it
with respect to the $x$-axis.

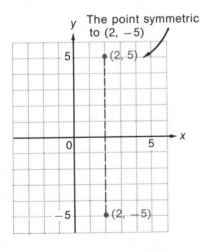

**TRY THIS**

2. Plot the point $(3, -2)$ and
   the point symmetric to it
   with respect to the $x$-axis.

**Example 4.** Plot the point (3, 5) and the point symmetric to it with respect to the *y*-axis.

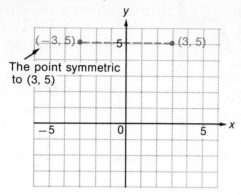

The point symmetric to (3, 5)

**TRY THIS**

3. Plot the point (4, −2) and the point symmetric to it with respect to the *y*-axis.

**Example 5.** In the relation $y = x^2$ there are points (2, 4) and (−2, 4). The first coordinates, 2 and −2, are additive inverses of each other, while the second coordinates are the same. For every point of the relation (*x*, *y*), there is another point (−*x*, *y*). So the relation $y = x^2$ is symmetric with respect to the *y*-axis.

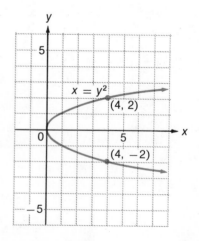

**Example 6.** In the relation $x = y^2$ there are points (4, 2) and (4, −2). The second coordinates, 2 and −2, are additive inverses of each other, while the first coordinates are the same. For every point of the relation (*x*, *y*), there is another point (*x*, −*y*). So the relation $x = y^2$ is symmetric with respect to the *x*-axis.

## THEOREM 8-2

When a relation is defined by an equation,

1. its graph is symmetric with respect to the *y*-axis if and only if replacing *x* by −*x* produces an equivalent equation.
2. its graph is symmetric with respect to the *x*-axis if and only if replacing *y* by −*y* produces an equivalent equation.

We thus have a means of testing a relation for symmetry with respect to the *x*- and *y*-axes when it is defined by an equation.

**Example 7.** Test $y = x^2 + 2$ for symmetry with respect to the axes.

We replace *x* by −*x*, and obtain $y = (-x)^2 + 2$, which is equivalent to $y = x^2 + 2$. Therefore the graph is symmetric with respect to the *y*-axis.

We replace *y* by −*y* and obtain $-y = x^2 + 2$, which is not equivalent to $y = x^2 + 2$. Therefore the graph is not symmetric with respect to the *x*-axis.

**Example 8.** Test $x^2 + y^4 + 5 = 0$ for symmetry with respect to the axes.

We replace *x* by −*x*, and obtain $(-x)^2 + y^4 + 5 = 0$, which is equivalent to the original equation. Therefore the graph is symmetric with respect to the *y*-axis.

We replace *y* by −*y* and obtain $x^2 + (-y)^4 + 5 = 0$, which is equivalent to the original equation. Therefore the graph is symmetric with respect to the *x*-axis.

**TRY THIS** ➡

> Test for symmetry with respect to the *x*-axis and *y*-axis.
>
> 4. $y = x^2 + 3$
> 5. $x^2 + y^2 = 25$

## Exercise Set 8-3

▮ Which of the following figures are symmetric with respect to the given line? (*See Examples 1 and 2.*)

1.

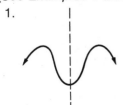

2.

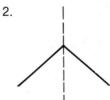

3.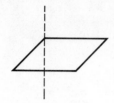

4.

5.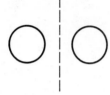

6.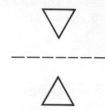

▌▌Use graph paper for Exercises 7–10. (*See Examples 3 and 4.*)

7. Plot $(3, -7)$ and the point symmetric to it with respect to the $x$-axis. List the coordinates of that point.

8. Plot $(-5, 2)$ and the point symmetric to it with respect to the $x$-axis. List the coordinates of that point.

9. Plot $(-4, 3)$ and the point symmetric to it with respect to the $y$-axis. List the coordinates of that point.

10. Plot $(1, -6)$ and the point symmetric to it with respect to the $y$-axis. List the coordinates of that point.

Test for symmetry with respect to the $x$-axis and the $y$-axis. (*See Examples 7 and 8.*)

11. $3y = x^2 + 4$

12. $5y = 2x^2 - 3$

13. $2x^4 + 3 = y^2$

14. $3y^2 = 2x^4 - 5$

15. $2x - 5 = 3y$

16. $5y = 4x + 5$

17. $y^3 = 2x^2$

18. $3y^3 = 4x^2$

19. $2y^2 = 5x^2 + 12$

20. $3x^2 - 2y^2 = 7$

21. $3y^3 = 4x^3 + 2$

22. $x^3 - 4y^3 = 12$

**Challenge Exercises**

Test for symmetry with respect to the $x$-axis and the $y$-axis.

23. $y = |x|$

24. $|x| = |y|$

25. $y = |x| + 1$

26. $y = |x| - 3$

27. $|x| + |y| = 3$

28. $|x| - |y| = 5$

# 8-4 Point Symmetry and Inverses

After finishing Lesson 8-4, you should be able to
  **I** identify figures which are symmetric with respect to a point.
  **II** test the equation of a relation for symmetry with respect to the origin.
  **III** write equations of inverses of relations.
  **IIII** test the equation of a relation for symmetry with respect to the line $y = x$.

## ▪ Point Symmetry

We now define symmetry with respect to a point.

**DEFINITION**
Two points $P$ and $P_1$ are symmetric with respect to a point $Q$ when they are the same distance from $Q$, and all three points are on a line. $P_1$ is said to be the image of $P$.

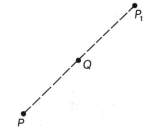

**DEFINITION**
A figure or *set* of points is symmetric with respect to a point when the image of each point in the set is also in the set.

**Example 1.** The figure at the right is symmetric with respect to point $O$. Imagine sticking a pin in this figure at $O$ and then rotating the figure 180°. Points $P$ and $P_1$ would be interchanged. Points $Q$ and $Q_1$ would be interchanged. These are pairs of symmetric points. The entire figure would look exactly as it did before rotating. This means that the image of each point of the figure is also on the figure.

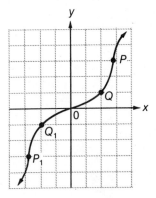

**Example 2.** Which of the following figures are symmetric with respect to the given point?

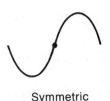

Symmetric

Symmetric

Not symmetric

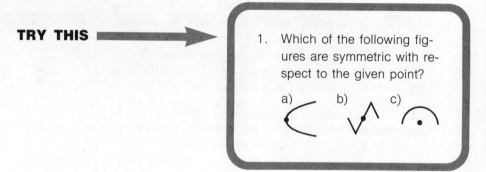

1. Which of the following figures are symmetric with respect to the given point?

   a)   b)   c)

## ιι Symmetry with Respect to the Origin

A special kind of symmetry with respect to a point is symmetry with respect to the origin.

**THEOREM 8-3**

Two points are symmetric with respect to the origin if and only if both their *x* and *y* coordinates are additive inverses of each other.

**Example 3.** Plot the point (3, 5) and the point symmetric to it with respect to the origin.

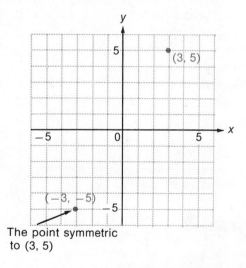

The point symmetric
to (3, 5)

**TRY THIS**

2. Plot the point (4, −2) and the point symmetric to it with respect to the origin.

**THEOREM 8-4**

A graph of a relation defined by an equation is symmetric with respect to the origin if and only if replacing $x$ by $-x$ and replacing $y$ by $-y$ produces an equivalent equation.

This gives us a means for testing a relation for symmetry with respect to the origin, when it is defined by an equation.

**Example 4.** Test $x^2 = y^2 + 2$ for symmetry with respect to the origin.

We replace $x$ by $-x$ and $y$ by $-y$, and obtain $(-x)^2 = (-y)^2 + 2$, which is equivalent to $x^2 = y^2 + 2$, the original equation. Therefore the graph is symmetric with respect to the origin.

**TRY THIS** ➡️

Test each equation for symmetry with respect to the origin.

3. $y^2 + x^2 = 16$
4. $y = x^3$
5. $y = x^2$

## ᴵᴵᴵ Inverses of Relations

**DEFINITION**

If, in a relation, we interchange first and second members in each ordered pair, then we obtain a relation called the *inverse* of the original relation.

**Example 5.** Find the inverse of the relation $\{(2, 1), (3, 1), (4, 2)\}$.

The inverse is $\{(1, 2), (1, 3), (2, 4)\}$.

**TRY THIS** ➡️

6. Find the inverse of the relation $\{(0, 1), (-2, 5), (5, -2)\}$.

**THEOREM 8-5**

Interchanging $x$ and $y$ in the equation of a relation produces an equation of the inverse relation.

**Example 6.** Find an equation of the inverse of $y = x^2 - 5$.

We interchange $x$ and $y$, and obtain $x = y^2 - 5$. This is an equation of the inverse relation.

**TRY THIS** ➡️

7. Find an equation of the inverse of $y = x^2 + 4$.

## ▐▐▐▐Inverses and Symmetry

Interchanging first and second coordinates in each ordered pair of a relation has the effect of interchanging the *x*-axis and the *y*-axis.

Interchanging the *x*-axis and the *y*-axis has the effect of reflecting across the diagonal line whose equation is $y = x$, as shown below. Thus the graphs of a relation and its inverse are always reflections of each other across the line $y = x$.

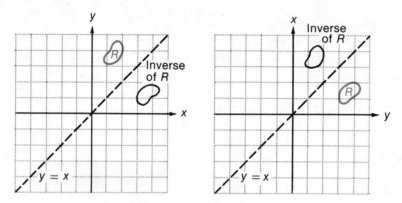

**Example 7.** Here are some graphs of relations and their inverses.

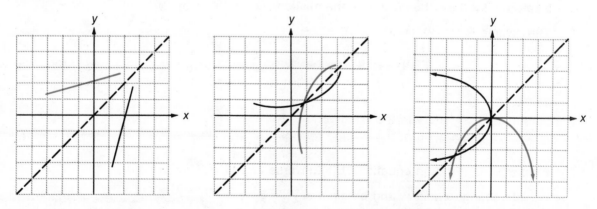

It can happen that a relation is its own inverse: that is, when *x* and *y* are interchanged, or the relation is reflected across the line $y = x$, there is no change. Such a relation is symmetric with respect to the line $y = x$.

**Example 8.** Test the relation $3x + 3y = 5$ for symmetry with respect to the line $y = x$.

We interchange $x$ and $y$ in the equation, obtaining $3y + 3x = 5$. This is equivalent to the original equation, so the graph is symmetric with respect to the line $y = x$.

**TRY THIS**

Test the relations defined by these equations for symmetry with respect to the line $y = x$.

8. $4x + 4y = 6$
9. $y = 2x^2$

## Exercise Set 8-4

❚ Which of the following figures are symmetric with respect to the given points? (*See Examples 1 and 2.*)

1.

2.

3.

4.

5.

6.

❚❚ Use graph paper for Exercises 7–10. (*See Example 3.*)

7. Plot the point $(2, -4)$ and the point symmetric to it with respect to the origin.

8. Plot the point $(4, 3)$ and the point symmetric to it with respect to the origin.

9. Plot the point $(-3, 6)$ and the point symmetric to it with respect to the origin.

10. Plot the point $(-4, -3)$ and the point symmetric to it with respect to the origin.

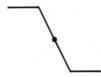

Test for symmetry with respect to the origin. (*See Example 4.*)

11. $3x^2 - 2y^2 = 3$

12. $5y^2 = -7x^2 + 4$

13. $3x + 3y = 0$

14. $7x = -7y$

15. $5x - 5y = 0$

16. $3x = 3y$

17. $3x = \dfrac{5}{y}$

18. $3y = \dfrac{7}{x}$

19. $3x^2 + 4x = 2y$

20. $5y = 7x^2 - 2x$

21. $y = |2x|$

22. $3x = |y|$

▮▮▮ Find the inverse of each of the following relations. (*See Example 5.*)

23. $\{(0, 1), (5, 6), (-2, -4)\}$

24. $\{(-1, -2), (0, 0), (3, 1)\}$

25. $\{(-1, -1), (-3, -4)\}$

26. $\{(5, -5), (6, -6)\}$

Write an equation of the inverse relation of the following. (*See Example 6.*)

27. $y = 4x - 5$

28. $y = 3x + 5$

29. $y = 3x^2 + 2$

30. $y = 5x^2 - 4$

31. $x^2 - 3y^2 = 3$

32. $2x^2 + 5y^2 = 4$

33. $xy = 7$

34. $xy = -5$

▮▮▮▮ Test for symmetry with respect to the line $y = x$. (*See Example 8.*)

35. $3x + 2y = 4$

36. $5x - 2y = 7$

37. $xy = 10$

38. $xy = 12$

39. $4x + 4y = 3$

40. $5x + 5y = -1$

41. $3x = \dfrac{4}{y}$

42. $4y = \dfrac{5}{x}$

43. $4x^2 + 4y^2 = 3$

44. $3x^2 + 3y^2 = 5$

45. $y = |2x|$

46. $3x = |2y|$

---

## Challenge Exercises

47. Graph $y = x^2 + 1$. Then by reflection across the line $y = x$, graph its inverse.

48. Graph $y = x^2 - 3$. Then by reflection across the line $y = x$, graph its inverse.

49. Graph $y = |x|$. Then by reflection across the line $y = x$, graph its inverse.

50. Graph $x = |y|$. Then by reflection across the line $y = x$, graph its inverse.

# 8-5 *Functions*

After finishing Lesson 8-5, you should be able to
 I  recognize the graph of a function.
 II  find function values.
 III  find outputs for function machines.

## I Recognizing Graphs of Functions

A function is a special kind of relation.

**DEFINITION**

A function is a relation in which no two ordered pairs have the same first coordinate and different second coordinates.

In a function, given one member of the domain, there is one and only one member of the range that goes with it. Thus each member of the domain *determines* a member of the range, but only one member. It is easy to recognize the graph of a function. We can think of vertical lines. If a vertical line could cross the graph in more than one place there would be more than one member of the range for some member of the domain. The graph would not be a graph of a function.

**Example 1.** Which of the following are graphs of functions?

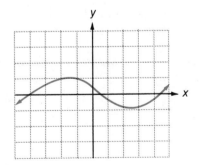
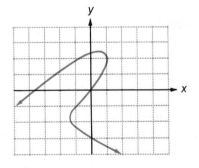
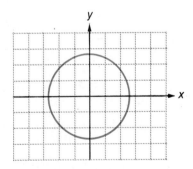

A function
No vertical line can
cross the graph
more than once.

Not a function
Vertical lines can
cross the graph
more than once.

Not a function
Vertical lines can
cross the graph
more than once.

TRY THIS ➤

Which of the following are graphs of functions?

1.   2.   3.

## ıı Function Notation

Functions are often named by letters, such as $f$ or $g$. Suppose the function $f$ is described by the equation $y = x^3 + 3$. (A function is not an equation, but the solutions of the equation yield a correspondence which is a function.) The symbol $f(x)$, read "$f$ of $x$," denotes "the number which corresponds to $x$," or "the *value* of $f$ at $x$."

We often write $f(x) = x^2 + 3$ instead of $y = x^2 + 3$. This gives us a recipe for finding the value $f(x)$ in the range which corresponds to a number $x$ in the domain.
*Note:* "$f(x)$" does *not* mean "$f$ times $x$."

**Example 2.** Consider the function $g$ defined as

$$g = \{(1, 4), (2, 3), (3, 2), (4, 4)\}.$$

Here $g(1) = 4$, $g(2) = 3$, $g(3) = 2$, and $g(4) = 4$.

TRY THIS ➤

4.  Consider the function $h$ defined as follows.
$h = \{(5, 0), (8, -3), (2, 2), (-3, -4), (-1, 6)\}$. Find
a) $h(5)$, b) $h(2)$, and
c) $h(-3)$.

**Example 3.** Given a function $f$ described by $f(x) = x^2 + 3$, find
a) $f(-5)$, b) $f(\frac{1}{2})$, c) $f(a)$, and d) $f(a - 1)$.

We find the values by substitution. (It may help to think of $f(x) = x^2 + 3$ as $f(\ ) = (\ )^2 + 3$. Then what goes in the blank on the left goes in the blank on the right.)

a)  $f(-5) = (-5)^2 + 3$
    $= 28$

b)  $f(\frac{1}{2}) = (\frac{1}{2})^2 + 3$
    $= 3\frac{1}{4}$

c)  $f(a) = (a)^2 + 3$
    $= a^2 + 3$

d)  $f(a - 1) = (a - 1)^2 + 3$
    $= a^2 - 2a + 1 + 3$
    $= a^2 - 2a + 4$

**Example 4.** The function described by $A(r) = \pi r^2$ gives the area of a circle with radius $r$. Find a) $A(3)$, b) $A(\frac{2}{5})$, and c) $A(1)$.

a)  $A(3) = \pi(3)^2$
    $= 9\pi$

b)  $A(\frac{2}{5}) = \pi(\frac{2}{5})^2$
    $= \dfrac{4\pi}{25}$

c)  $A(1) = \pi(1)^2$
    $= \pi$

**TRY THIS**

5. Given a function $f$ described by $f(x) = 3x - 4$, find a) $f(2)$, b) $f(-2)$, c) $f(0)$, d) $f(\frac{1}{4})$, e) $f(a)$. f) $f(a - 1)$, and g) $f(a + 1)$.

6. The function $A(s) = s^2$ is related to the area of a square with side $s$. Find a) $A(2)$, b) $A(3)$, c) $A(\frac{1}{4})$, and d) $A(x + 1)$.

Answers.  5. a) 2  b) −10  c) −4  d) $-\dfrac{13}{4}$  e) 3a − 4  f) 3a − 7
g) 3a − 1  6. a) 4  b) 9  c) $\dfrac{1}{16}$  d) $x^2 + 2x + 1$

## ▪▪▪ Mappings and Function Machines

Functions can be thought of as mappings. A function $f$ *maps* the set of first coordinates (the domain) to the set of second coordinates (the range).

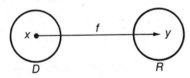

As in this diagram, each $x$ in the domain corresponds to (or is mapped to) just one $y$ in the range. That $y$ is the second coordinate of the ordered pair $(x, y)$.

**Example 5.** Consider the function $f$ for which $f(x) = 2x + 3$. Since $f(0)$ is 3, this function maps 0 to 3 and gives the ordered pair $(0, 3)$.
Since $f(3)$ is 9, this function maps 3 to 9 and gives the ordered pair $(3, 9)$.

Sometimes it is helpful to think of functions or mappings in terms of function machines. Inputs are entered into the machine. The machine then gives the proper output.

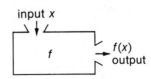

**Example 6.**  This function machine is for the function $f$ which maps each input $x$ to the output $\frac{1}{x}$. Find a) $f(2)$, b) $f(3)$, and c) $f(-2)$.

a)  $f(2) = \frac{1}{2}$

b)  $f(3) = \frac{1}{3}$

c)  $f(-2) = \frac{1}{-2}$

$\qquad = -\frac{1}{2}$

input $x$

$f(x) = \frac{1}{x}$ ➔ $\frac{1}{x}$ output

Note that $f$ is not defined for $x = 0$.

Find the indicated outputs for the function machines described below.

7.  Find a) $g(0)$,
    b) $g(-3)$,
    c) $g(7)$, and
    d) $g(\frac{1}{2})$.

    input $x$

    $g(x) = x - 4$ ➔ $x - 4$ output

8.  Find a) $h(1)$,
    b) $h(3)$,
    c) $h(-4)$,
    and d) $h(5)$.

    input $x$

    $h(x) = x^2 - x$ ➔ $x^2 - x$ output

9.  Find a) $f(2)$,
    b) $f(-4)$,
    c) $f(-3)$,
    and d) $f(\frac{1}{3})$.

    input $x$

    $f(x) = \frac{1}{-x}$ ➔ $\frac{1}{-x}$ output

**TRY THIS** ➡

## Exercise Set 8-5

❚ Which of the following are graphs of functions? (*See Example 1.*)

1.

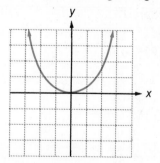

2.

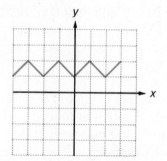

3.

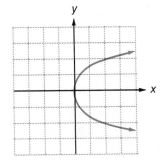

4.

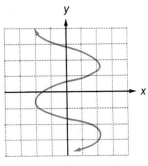

5.

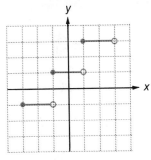

6.

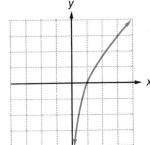

■■ For each of the functions described below find the indicated function values. (*See Examples 3 and 4.*)

7. $g(x) = x + 1$. Find:
   a) $g(0)$
   b) $g(-4)$
   c) $g(-7)$
   d) $g(8)$

8. $h(x) = x - 4$. Find:
   a) $h(4)$
   b) $h(8)$
   c) $h(-3)$
   d) $h(-4)$

9. $f(x) = 5x^2 + 4x$. Find:
   a) $f(0)$
   b) $f(-1)$
   c) $f(3)$
   d) $f(t)$

10. $g(x) = 3x^2 - 2x$. Find:
   a) $g(0)$
   b) $g(-1)$
   c) $g(3)$
   d) $g(t)$

11. $f(x) = 3x^2 + 2x - 1$. Find:
   a) $f(2)$
   b) $f(3)$
   c) $f(-3)$
   d) $f(1)$

12. $h(x) = 4x^2 - x + 2$. Find:
   a) $h(3)$
   b) $h(0)$
   c) $h(-1)$
   d) $h(-2)$

13. $f(x) = 2|x| + 3x$. Find:
   a) $f(1)$
   b) $f(-2)$
   c) $f(-4)$
   d) $f(2y)$

14. $g(x) = 3|x| - 2x$. Find:
   a) $g(1)$
   b) $g(-2)$
   c) $g(-4)$
   d) $g(3y)$

■■■ Find the indicated outputs for the function machines described below. (*See Example 6.*)

15. input $x$

$$g(x) = x + 9 \quad \xrightarrow{\quad} \quad x + 9 \text{ output}$$

Find a) $g(8)$, b) $g(-3)$, and c) $g(5)$.

16. input $x$

$$f(x) = x - 4 \quad \xrightarrow{\quad} \quad x - 4 \text{ output}$$

Find a) $f(-1)$, b) $f(13)$, and c) $f(-6)$.

17. input $x$

$$h(x) = x^2 + 2x \quad \xrightarrow{\quad} \quad x^2 + 2x \text{ output}$$

Find a) $h(1)$, b) $h(-1)$, and c) $h(4)$.

18. input $x$

$$g(x) = x^2 - 3x \quad \xrightarrow{\quad} \quad x^2 - 3x \text{ output}$$

Find a) $g(2)$, b) $g(-3)$, and c) $g(0)$.

19. input $x$

$$f(x) = 2 \cdot |x| \quad \xrightarrow{\quad} \quad 2 \cdot |x| \text{ output}$$

Find a) $f(4)$, b) $f(-4)$, and c) $f(6)$.

20. input $x$

$$g(x) = -3 \cdot |x| \quad \xrightarrow{\quad} \quad -3 \cdot |x| \text{ output}$$

Find a) $g(-2)$, b) $g(0)$, and c) $g(-7)$.

## Calculator Exercises

For each of the functions described below find the indicated function values.

21. $f(x) = 0.003x + 0.21$
    a) $f(0.01)$
    b) $f(0.03)$
    c) $f(0.08)$
    d) $f(0.09)$

22. $g(x) = 0.0004x - 0.221$
    a) $g(0.02)$
    b) $g(0.003)$
    c) $g(0.001)$
    d) $g(0.002)$

## Challenge Exercises

23. The *greatest integer* function $y = [x]$ is defined as follows: $[x]$ is the greatest integer that is less than or equal to $x$. For example, $[4.5] = 4$, $[-1] = -1$, $[-3.8] = -4$. Graph the greatest integer function for values of $x$ from $-5$ to $5$.

# 8-6 Inverses of Functions

After finishing Lesson 8-6, you should be able to
▪ find equations for inverses of functions.

▪ All functions have inverses, but the inverse is not necessarily a function. If the inverse of a function $f$ is also a function we denote it by $f^{-1}$ (read "$f$ inverse"). Recall that we obtain the inverse of a relation by interchanging the coordinates of each ordered pair. Thus the domain of a function $f$ is the range of $f^{-1}$ and the range of $f$ is the domain of $f^{-1}$.

Let us consider inverses of functions in terms of function machines. Suppose that the function $f$ programmed into the machine has an inverse that is also a function. Suppose then that the function machine has a reverse switch. When the switch is thrown the machine is programmed to do the inverse mapping $f^{-1}$. Inputs then enter at the opposite end and the entire process is reversed.

When a function is defined by an equation, we can sometimes find an equation for its inverse by thinking of interchanging $x$ and $y$.

**Example 1.** Given $f(x) = x + 1$, find an equation for $f^{-1}(x)$.

a)  Let us think of this as $y = x + 1$.
b)  To find the inverse we interchange $x$ and $y$: $x = y + 1$.
c)  Now we solve for $y$: $y = x - 1$.
d)  Thus $f^{-1}(x) = x - 1$.

In Example 1 $f$ maps any $x$ onto $x + 1$ (this function adds 1 to each number of the domain). Its inverse, $f^{-1}$, maps any number $x$ onto $x - 1$ (this inverse function subtracts 1 from each member of its domain). Thus the function and its inverse do opposite things.

**TRY THIS**

1. Given $g(x) = x + 2$, find an equation for $g^{-1}(x)$.
2. Let $g(x) = 3x + 2$. Find a formula for $g^{-1}(x)$.

**Example 2.** Let $S(x) = \sqrt{x}$. Find an equation for $S^{-1}(x)$.

a)   Let us think of this as $y = \sqrt{x}$. Note that the domain and
     range both consist of nonnegative numbers only.
b)   To find the inverse we interchange $x$ and $y$. $x = \sqrt{y}$.
c)   Now we solve for $y$, squaring both sides: $y = x^2$.
d)   Thus $S^{-1}(x) = x^2$, with the understanding that $x$ cannot be negative.

In Example 2, $S$ maps any $x$ onto $\sqrt{x}$ (this function takes
the square root of any input). Its inverse, $S^{-1}$, maps any
number $x$ onto $x^2$ (this function squares each input); thus
the function and its inverse do opposite things.

**TRY THIS** ➡

3.   Let $f(x) = \sqrt{x + 1}$.
     Find an equation
     for $f^{-1}(x)$.

Suppose the inverse of a function $f$ is also a function. Let us
suppose that we do the mapping $f$ and then do the inverse mapping $f^{-1}$. We will be back where we started. In other words, if we
find $f(x)$ for some $x$ and then find $f^{-1}$ for this number, we will be
back at $x$. In function notation the statement looks like this:

   $f^{-1}(f(x)) = x$.

This is read "$f$ inverse of $f$ of $x$ equals $x$." It means, working
from the inside out, to take $x$, then find $f(x)$, and then find $f^{-1}$ for
that number. When we do, we will be back where we started, at
$x$. For similar reasons, the following is also true:

   $f(f^{-1}(x)) = x$.

For the statements above to be true, $x$ must of course be in the
domain of the function being considered. We summarize these
ideas by stating the following theorem.

**THEOREM 8-6**
For any function $f$ whose inverse is a function: $f^{-1}(f(a)) = a$ for any $a$
in the domain of $f$. Also $f(f^{-1}(a)) = a$ for any $a$ in the domain of $f^{-1}$.

**Example 3.**   For the function $f$ of Example 1, find $f^{-1}(f(283))$.
Find also $f(f^{-1}(-12,045))$.

We note that every real number is in the domain of both $f$ and
$f^{-1}$. Thus, using Theorem 8-6, we may immediately write the answers, without calculating.

$f^{-1}(f(283)) = 283,$

$f(f^{-1}(-12,045)) = -12,045.$

**TRY THIS** ➡️

4. For the function $f$ of Example 1, find $f^{-1}(f(579))$ and $f(f^{-1}(-83,479))$.

## Exercise Set 8-6

▌In each of the following, find equations for $f^{-1}(x)$. (*See Examples 1 and 2.*)

1. $f(x) = x - 1$
2. $f(x) = x - 2$
3. $f(x) = x + 4$
4. $f(x) = x + 3$
5. $f(x) = x + 8$
6. $f(x) = x + 7$
7. $f(x) = 2x + 5$
8. $f(x) = 3x + 2$
9. $f(x) = 3x - 1$
10. $f(x) = 4x - 3$
11. $f(x) = 0.5x + 2$
12. $f(x) = 0.7x + 4$
13. $f(x) = \sqrt{x - 1}$
14. $f(x) = \sqrt{x - 2}$
15. $f(x) = \sqrt{x + 2}$
16. $f(x) = \sqrt{x + 3}$

(*See Example 3.*)

17. $f(x) = 35x - 173$. Find $f^{-1}(f(3))$. Find $f(f^{-1}(-125))$.

18. $g(x) = \dfrac{-173x + 15}{3}$. Find $g^{-1}(g(5))$. Find $g(g^{-1}(-12))$.

19. $f(x) = x^3 + 2$. Find $f^{-1}(f(12,053))$. Find $f(f^{-1}(-17,243))$.

20. $g(x) = x^3 - 486$. Find $g^{-1}(g(489))$. Find $g(g^{-1}(-17,422))$.

---

## Challenge Exercises

Functions can be combined in a way called *composition* of functions. The composition of two functions $f$ and $g$ is written $f \circ g$, where $f \circ g(x) = f(g(x))$. For example, given that $f(x) = x^2$ and $g(x) = x + 1$,

$$\begin{aligned} f \circ g(x) &= f(g(x)) \\ &= f(x + 1) \\ &= (x + 1)^2 \\ &= x^2 + 2x + 1 \end{aligned} \qquad \begin{aligned} g \circ f(x) &= g(f(x)) \\ &= g(x^2) \\ &= x^2 + 1 \end{aligned}$$

Find $f \circ g(x)$ and $g \circ f(x)$.

21. $f(x) = 2x$, $g(x) = x^2 + 1$
22. $f(x) = x^2$, $g(x) = x + 3$
23. $f(x) = 2x + 3$, $g(x) = x - 4$
24. $f(x) = 3x^2 + 2$, $g(x) = 2x - 1$
25. $f(x) = 4x^2 - 1$, $g(x) = \dfrac{2}{x}$
26. $f(x) = x^2 - 1$, $g(x) = x^2 - 1$

# 8-7 Transformations

After finishing Lesson 8-7, you should be able to
▌ sketch graphs which are vertical translations of given graphs.
▌▌ sketch graphs which are horizontal translations of given graphs.

An alteration of a relation is called a *transformation*. If such an alteration consists merely of moving the graph without changing its shape and without rotating it, the transformation is called a *translation*.

## ▍Vertical Translations

Compare the graphs of the relations $y = x^2$ and $y = 1 + x^2$.

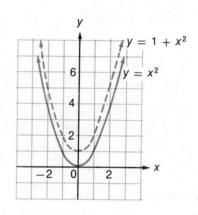

The graphs have the same shape except that $y = 1 + x^2$ is moved up a distance of 1 unit. Consider any equation $y = f(x)$ and adding a constant $a$ to produce $y = a + f(x)$. This changes each function value by the same amount $a$, but produces no change in the shape of the graph. If $a$ is positive the graph is translated upward. If $a$ is negative the graph is translated downward.

Note that $y = 1 + x^2$ is equivalent to $y - 1 = x^2$. Thus the transformation above amounts to replacing $y$ by $y - 1$ in the original equation.

**THEOREM 8-7**

In an equation of a relation, replacing $y$ by $y - a$, where $a$ is a constant, translates the graph vertically a distance of $|a|$. If $a$ is positive the translation is in the positive direction (upward). If $a$ is negative the translation is downward.

If in an equation we replace $y$ by $y + 3$, this is the same as replacing it by $y - (-3)$. In this case the constant $a$ is $-3$ and the translation is downward. If we replace $y$ by $y - 5$, the constant $a$ is 5 and the translation is upward.

**Example 1.** Sketch the graph of $y = |x|$. Then sketch the graph of $y = -2 + |x|$ by translating it.

The graph of $y = |x|$ is shown below on the left. Note that $y = -2 + |x|$ is equivalent to $y + 2 = |x|$ or $y - (-2) = |x|$. This shows the new equation can be obtained by replacing $y$ by $y - (-2)$, so by Theorem 8-7 the translation is downward, two units.

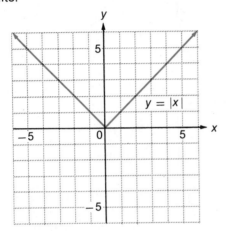
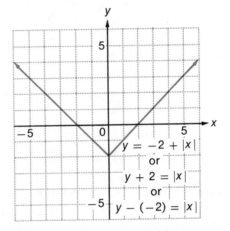

**TRY THIS** ➡️

Consider the graph of $y = |x|$ as shown in Example 1. Sketch the graph of each of the following by translating.

1. $y = -1 + |x|$
2. $y = 4 + |x|$

## ▐ Horizontal Translations

Translations can also be horizontal. If we replace $x$ by $x - b$ everywhere it occurs in an equation, we translate a distance of $|b|$ horizontally.

### THEOREM 8-8
In an equation of a relation, replacing $x$ by $x - b$, where $b$ is a constant, translates the graph horizontally a distance of $|b|$. If $b$ is positive the translation is in the positive direction (to the right). If $b$ is negative, the translation is to the left.

**Example 2.** Sketch the graph of $y = |x|$. Then sketch the graph of $y = |x + 2|$ by translating it.

Here we note that $x$ is replaced by $x + 2$, or $x - (-2)$. Thus $b = -2$, and by Theorem 8-8 the translated graph will be moved two units in the negative direction (to the left).

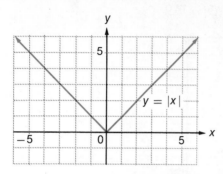

**TRY THIS**

Relations other than functions can be translated. Theorems 8-7 and 8-8 hold for any relations. A relation may be translated both horizontally and vertically.

**Example 3.** A circle centered at the origin with radius of length 1 has an equation $x^2 + y^2 = 1$. If we replace $x$ by $x - 1$ and $y$ by $y + 2$, we translate the circle so that the center is at the point $(1, -2)$.

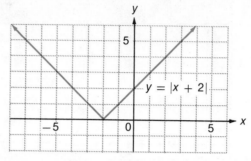

Consider the graph of $y = |x|$ as shown in Example 2. Sketch the graph of each of the following by translating it.

3. $y = |x + 3|$
4. $y = |x - 1|$

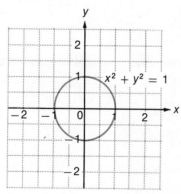

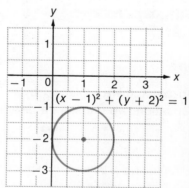

5. Consider the circle centered at the origin as shown in Example 3. If we replace $x$ by $x - 2$ and $y$ by $y + 3$, what are the coordinates of the center of the translated circle?

**TRY THIS**

## Exercise Set 8-7

▌Here is a graph of $y = |x|$. Sketch graphs of the following by translating this one. (*See Example 1.*)

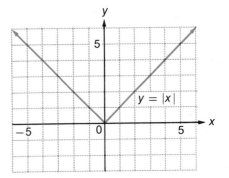

1. $y = 2 + |x|$
2. $y = 3 + |x|$
3. $y = -2 + |x|$
4. $y = -3 + |x|$
5. $y = 5 + |x|$
6. $y = 6 + |x|$
7. $y = -4 + |x|$
8. $y = -5 + |x|$
9. $y = \frac{1}{2} + |x|$
10. $y = \frac{3}{4} + |x|$

▌▌Consider the graph of $y = |x|$ as shown. Sketch graphs of the following by translating this one. (*See Example 2.*)

11. $y = |x - 3|$
12. $y = |x - 2|$
13. $y = |x + 2|$
14. $y = |x + 4|$
15. $y = |x - 4|$
16. $y = |x - 5|$
17. $y = |x + 5|$
18. $y = |x + 6|$
19. $y = |x - \frac{1}{2}|$
20. $y = |x + \frac{3}{4}|$

### Challenge Exercises

21. Consider a circle with center at (2, 4). What are the coordinates of the center of the translated circle if we replace $x$ with $x - 3$ and $y$ with $y + 5$ in the equation of the circle?

### COMPUTER NOTE: Mark I

Mark I was the first successful computer. It could add, subtract, multiply, and divide automatically. And it could store and retrieve numbers. Its construction was begun at Harvard University in 1939 and completed in 1944.

Mark I was both mechanical and electronic. It had some 750,000 parts, including 800 kilometers of wire. It weighed more than 30 tons. It could add or subtract two 23-digit numbers in about three-tenths of a second. Multiplying or dividing such numbers took from four to ten seconds.

The designer of Mark I was Howard Aiken. He later designed faster, all-electronic computers.

# 8-8 Stretching and Shrinking

After finishing Lesson 8-8, you should be able to
**Ⅰ** sketch graphs which are vertical stretchings or shrinkings of given graphs.
**Ⅱ** sketch graphs which are horizontal stretchings or shrinkings of given graphs.

## Ⅰ Vertical Stretchings and Shrinkings

Compare the graphs of $y = f(x)$, $y = 2f(x)$, and $y = \frac{1}{2}f(x)$.

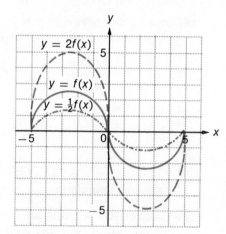

The graph of $y = 2f(x)$ looks like that of $y = f(x)$ but is stretched in a vertical direction. The graph of $y = \frac{1}{2}f(x)$ is flattened or shrunk in a vertical direction.

Consider any equation such as $y = f(x)$. Multiplying on the right by the constant 2 will double every function value, thus stretching the graph both ways away from the horizontal axis. A similar thing is true for any constant greater than 1. Multiplying on the right by $\frac{1}{2}$ will halve every function value, thus shrinking the graph both ways toward the horizontal axis. A similar thing is true for any constant between 0 and 1.

Multiplying $f(x)$ by a constant $a$ is the same as dividing $y$ by $a$. In an equation of any relation, dividing $y$ by 2 will stretch the graph in the $y$-direction. Dividing $y$ by $\frac{1}{2}$ will shrink the graph in the $y$-direction.

Now compare the graphs of $y = f(x)$, $y = -2f(x)$, and $y = -\frac{1}{2}f(x)$.

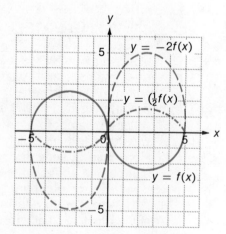

When we multiply by a negative constant, the graph is reflected across the $x$-axis as well as being stretched or shrunk. Note that if we multiply by $-1$, this has the effect of replacing $y$ by $-y$ and we obtain a reflection without stretching or shrinking.

**THEOREM 8-9**

In an equation of a relation, dividing $y$ by a constant does the following to the graph.
1. If $|c| > 1$, the graph is stretched vertically.
2. If $|c| < 1$, the graph is shrunk vertically.
3. If $c$ is negative, the graph is also reflected across the $x$-axis.

**Example 1.** Here is a graph of $y = f(x)$. Sketch a graph of $y = 2f(x)$.

$y = 2f(x)$ is equivalent to $\dfrac{y}{2} = f(x)$. By Theorem 8-9 the graph is stretched vertically. Every function value is doubled.

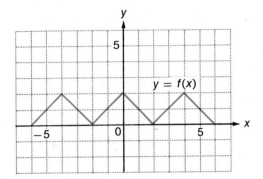

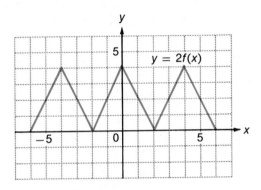

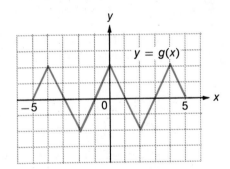

Consider the graph of $y = f(x)$ as shown in Example 1.

1. Sketch a graph of $y = 3f(x)$.
2. Sketch a graph of $y = \frac{1}{2}f(x)$.

**TRY THIS**

**Example 2.** Here is a graph of $y = g(x)$. Sketch a graph of $y = -\frac{1}{2}g(x)$.

$y = -\frac{1}{2}g(x)$ is equivalent to $\dfrac{y}{-\frac{1}{2}} = g(x)$. By theorem 8-9, the graph is shrunk in the $y$-direction and also reflected across the $x$-axis. We halve each function value and change its sign.

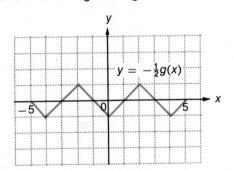

3. Consider the graph of $y = f(x)$ as shown in Example 1. Sketch a graph of $y = -\frac{1}{2}f(x)$.

**TRY THIS**

## ⅠⅠ Horizontal Stretchings and Shrinkings

If we divide $y$ by a constant, a graph is stretched or shrunk vertically. If we divide $x$ by a constant, a graph will be stretched or
shrunk horizontally.

### THEOREM 8-10

In an equation of a relation, dividing $x$ wherever it occurs by a
constant $d$ does the following to the graph.
1. If $|d| > 1$, the graph is stretched horizontally.
2. If $|d| < 1$, the graph is shrunk horizontally.
3. If $d$ is negative, the graph is also reflected across the $y$-axis.

Note that if $d = -1$, this has the effect of replacing $x$ by $-x$ and
we obtain a reflection without stretching or shrinking.

**Example 3.** Here is a graph of $y = f(x)$.
Sketch a graph of each of the following.
a) $y = f(2x)$
b) $y = f(\tfrac{1}{2}x)$
c) $y = f(-\tfrac{1}{2}x)$

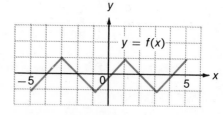

a) $f(2x) = f\left(\dfrac{x}{\frac{1}{2}}\right)$. By Theorem 8-10

the graph will be shrunk. Each
$x$-coordinate will be halved.

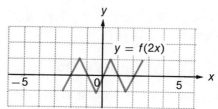

b) $f(\tfrac{1}{2}x) = f\left(\dfrac{x}{2}\right)$. The graph will be

stretched. Each $x$-coordinate will
be doubled.

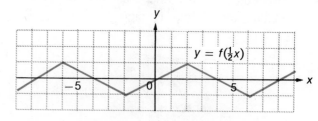

c) $f(-\tfrac{1}{2}x) = f\left(\dfrac{x}{-2}\right)$. The graph

will be stretched and reflected.

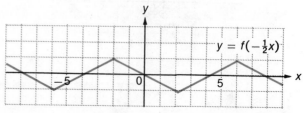

**TRY THIS** ➡

Here is a graph of $y = f(x)$.

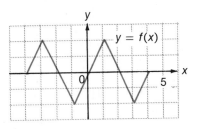

4. Sketch a graph of $y = f(2x)$.
5. Sketch a graph of $y = f(\frac{1}{2}x)$.
6. Sketch a graph of $y = f(-\frac{1}{2}x)$.

## Exercise Set 8-8

▌Here is a graph of $y = |x|$. Sketch graphs by transforming this one. (*See Examples 1 and 2.*)

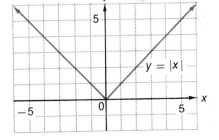

1. $y = 4|x|$
2. $y = 3|x|$
3. $y = 5|x|$
4. $y = 6|x|$
5. $y = \frac{1}{4}|x|$
6. $y = \frac{1}{3}|x|$
7. $y = -3|x|$
8. $y = -4|x|$
9. $y = -\frac{1}{4}|x|$
10. $y = -\frac{1}{3}|x|$

Here is a graph of $y = f(x)$. Sketch graphs by transforming this one. (*See Examples 1 and 2.*)

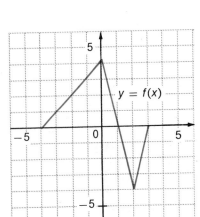

11. $y = 3f(x)$
12. $y = 2f(x)$
13. $y = -2f(x)$
14. $y = -3f(x)$
15. $y = 4f(x)$
16. $y = 5f(x)$
17. $y = \frac{1}{2}f(x)$
18. $y = \frac{1}{3}f(x)$
19. $y = -\frac{1}{2}f(x)$
20. $y = -\frac{1}{3}f(x)$

▌▌Consider the graph of $y = |x|$ above. Sketch graphs by transforming this one. (*See Example 3.*)

21. $y = |2x|$
22. $y = |3x|$
23. $y = |\frac{1}{2}x|$
24. $y = |\frac{1}{3}x|$

Consider the graph of $y = f(x)$ above. Sketch graphs by transforming this one. (*See Example 3.*)

25. $y = f(3x)$
26. $y = f(2x)$
27. $y = f(\frac{1}{2}x)$
28. $y = f(\frac{1}{3}x)$
29. $y = f(-2x)$
30. $y = f(-3x)$
31. $y = f(-\frac{1}{2}x)$
32. $y = f(-\frac{1}{3}x)$

# 8-9 Some Special Classes of Functions

After finishing Lesson 8-9, you should be able to
I  find function values for linear functions.
II  show that certain functions are either even or odd.

## I Linear Functions

### DEFINITION

A linear function is any function $f$ described by $f(x) = mx + b$ where $m$ and $b$ are constants.

**Example 1.**  A linear function $f$ is described by $f(x) = 3x - 2$. Find $f(-2)$, $f(1)$, $f(0)$, and graph $f$.

$f(-2) = 3(-2) - 2 = -8$
$f(1) = 3(1) - 2 = 1$
$f(0) = 3(0) - 2 = -2$

| $x$ | $-2$ | 1 | 0 |
|-----|------|---|---|
| $f(x)$ | $-8$ | 1 | $-2$ |

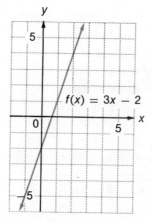

$f(x) = 3x - 2$

**TRY THIS**

1.  A linear function $f$ is described by $f(x) = -2x - 3$. Find $f(3)$, $f(0)$, and $f(-3)$. Use graph paper and graph $f$.

## II Even and Odd Functions

If the graph of a function is symmetric with respect to the $y$-axis, it is an *even* function. Recall that a function will be symmetric to the $y$-axis if in its equation we can replace $x$ by $-x$ and obtain an equivalent equation. Thus if we have a function given by $y = f(x)$, then $y = f(-x)$ will give the same function if the function is even.

### DEFINITION

A function is an even function when $f(x) = f(-x)$ for all $x$ in the domain of $f$.

**Example 2.**  Show that $f(x) = x^2 + 1$ is an even function.

$$f(-x) = (-x)^2 + 1 = x^2 + 1 = f(x)$$

Since $f(-x) = f(x)$ for all $x$ in the domain, $f$ is an even function. Note that the graph is symmetric with respect to the $y$-axis.

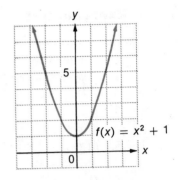

**Example 3.**  Show that $f(x) = x^2 + 3x^4$ is an even function.

$$f(-x) = (-x)^2 + 3(-x)^4 = x^2 + 3x^4 = f(x)$$

Since $f(-x) = f(x)$ for all $x$ in the domain, the function is even.

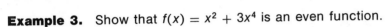

**TRY THIS**

2.  Show that $f(x) = x^4 + 2x^6$ is an even function.

$$f(-x) = (-x)^4 + 2(-x)^6 = x^4 + 2x^6 = f(x)$$

If the graph of a function is symmetric with respect to the origin, it is an *odd* function. Recall that a function will be symmetric with respect to the origin if in its equation we can replace $x$ by $-x$ and $y$ by $-y$ and obtain an equivalent equation. Thus if we have a function given by $y = f(x)$, then $-y = f(-x)$ will be equivalent if $f$ is an odd function.

**DEFINITION**

A function is an odd function when $f(-x) = -f(x)$ for all $x$ in the domain of $f$.

**Example 4.**  Show that $f(x) = x^3$ is an odd function.

a)  $f(-x) = (-x)^3 = -(x)^3$
b)  $-f(x) = -x^3$

Since $f(-x) = -f(x)$ for all $x$ in the domain, $f$ is odd. Note that the graph is symmetric with respect to the origin.

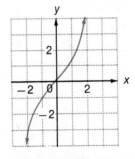

**Example 5.**  Show that $f(x) = x^3 + 5x$ is an odd function.

a)  $f(-x) = (-x)^3 + 5(-x) = -x^3 - 5x$
b)  $-f(x) = -(x^3 + 5x) = -x^3 - 5x$
Since $f(-x) = -f(x)$ for all $x$ in the domain, $f$ is odd.

3.  Show that
$$f(x) = x^5 - 3x^3$$
is an odd function.

**TRY THIS**

Answer.   3. $f(-x) = (-x)^5 - 3(-x)^3 = -x^5 + 3x^3$; $-f(x) = -(x^5 - 3x^3) = -x^5 + 3x^3$  Since $f(-x) = -f(x)$ for all $x$ in the domain, $f$ is odd.

## Exercise Set 8-9

▌For each of the linear functions described below find the indicated function values. Then graph the function. (*See Example 1.*)

1. $f(x) = x - 3$; find $f(-5)$, $f(-3)$, and $f(2)$.

2. $f(x) = x + 5$; find $f(-4)$, $f(-6)$, and $f(7)$.

3. $g(x) = 2x - 3$; find $g(2)$, $g(0)$, and $g(-4)$.

4. $g(x) = 3x + 4$; find $g(-3)$, $g(6)$, and $g(4)$.

5. $h(x) = -3x + 2$; find $h(-1)$, $h(2)$, and $h(-3)$.

6. $h(x) = -5x + 1$; find $h(0)$, $h(-2)$, and $h(6)$.

7. $f(x) = \frac{1}{2}x + 1$; find $f(6)$, $f(2)$, and $f(-8)$.

8. $f(x) = \frac{1}{3}x + 2$; find $f(3)$, $f(9)$, and $f(-6)$.

▌▌Show that the following functions are even. (*See Examples 2 and 3.*)

9. $f(x) = 2x^4 + 4x^2$

10. $f(x) = 5x^2 + 3x^4$

11. $f(x) = |2x|$

12. $f(x) = |3x|$

13. $f(x) = 3x^4 - 4x^6$

14. $f(x) = 5x^8 - 3x^2$

Show that the following functions are odd. (*See Examples 4 and 5.*)

15. $g(x) = 4x^3 - x$

16. $f(x) = -3x^3 + 2x$

17. $h(x) = 2x + 5x^3$

18. $h(x) = 4x^3 - 5x$

19. $f(x) = 4x$

20. $f(x) = -4x$

21. $f(x) = x^5 + x^3 + x$

22. $f(x) = -3x^5 - 2x^3 - x$

23. Which of the following functions are even? odd? neither even nor odd?

a)
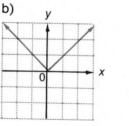

b)
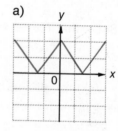

c)
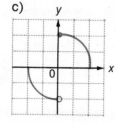

d)
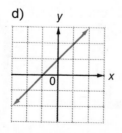

24. Which of the following functions are even? odd? neither even nor odd?

a)
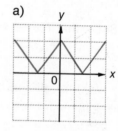

b)
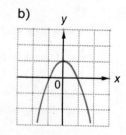

c)
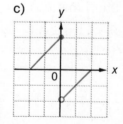

d)
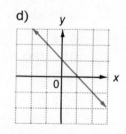

## COMPUTER ACTIVITY

## Composition of Functions

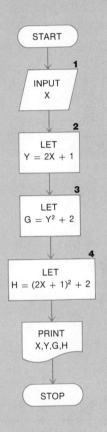

**PROBLEM:** Let F(X) = 2X + 1
and G(X) = X² + 2.
Compute H(X) = G(F(X)). (Hint: H(X) = G(F(X)) = G(2X + 1) = (2X + 1)² + 2.)

### Examples using the flowchart:

| 1 | 2 | 3 | 4 | |
|---|---|---|---|---|
| X | Y = F(X) | G = G(Y) | H = H(X) | Does G = H? |
| 1 | 3 | 11 | 11 | Yes |
| 1.25 | 3.5 | 14.25 | 14.25 | Yes |
| −5 | −9 | 83 | 83 | Yes |

**TRY THIS**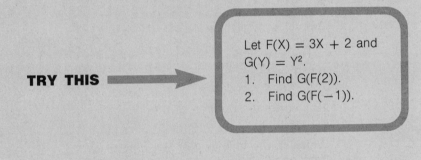

Let F(X) = 3X + 2 and
G(Y) = Y².
1. Find G(F(2)).
2. Find G(F(−1)).

BASIC PROGRAM (Optional)
10 INPUT X
20 LET Y = 2*X + 1
30 LET G = Y↑2 + 2
40 LET H =(2*X + 1)↑2 + 2
50 PRINT X,Y,G,H

## CHAPTER 8 REVIEW

Review the material in the chapter. Then see how you have done by trying these review exercises. If you miss an exercise, restudy the indicated lesson.

8-1    1. List the domain and range of the relation $\{(1, 2), (-1, 4), (0, 5), (2, -4), (-6, \sqrt{3})\}$.

8-2    2. Graph the relation which is the solution set of $y \geq x^2 + 1$.

8-3    Test for symmetry with respect to the $x$-axis and the $y$-axis.
     3. $y = 7$
     4. $y^2 = x^2 + 3$
     5. $x^2 + y^2 = 4$
     6. $x = 3$
     7. $x^3 = y^3 - y$
     8. $x^2 = y + 3$

8-4    Test for symmetry with respect to the origin.
     9. $x + y = 3$
     10. $y = x^3$
     11. $x = 2$

8-4    12. Write an equation of the inverse relation of $y = 3x^2 + 2x - 1$.

8-5    Which of the following are graphs of functions?
     13.

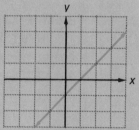

     14.

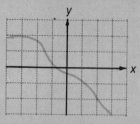

15.

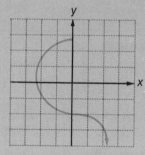

8-5    16. $f(x) = 3\sqrt{x + 2}$. Find
     a) $f(2)$
     b) $f(0)$
     c) $f(-2)$

8-6    17. $g(x) = \dfrac{\sqrt{x}}{2} + 2$. Find an equation for $g^{-1}(x)$.

Here is a graph of $g(x)$. Sketch graphs of the following equations.

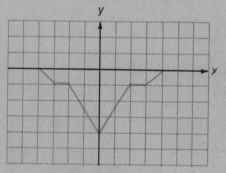

8-7    18. $y = g(x) + 2$
8-7    19. $y = g(x - 1)$
8-8    20. $y = \frac{1}{2}g(x)$

8-9    21. Show that $f(x) = -2x^2 - 2$ is an even function.

8-9    22. Show that $f(x) = x^5 + x$ is an odd function.

## CHAPTER 8 TEST

1. List the domain and range of the relation $\{(-1, 0), (\sqrt{3}, 5), (8, -4), (7, 0), (-6, -2)\}$.
2. Graph the relation which is the solution set of $y \geq x^2 + 3$

Test for symmetry with respect to the $x$-axis and the $y$-axis.

3. $y = 4$
4. $y^2 = x^2 + 8$
5. $x^2 + y^2 = 9$
6. $x = 5$
7. $x^5 = y^5 - y$
8. $x^2 - y = 4$

Test for symmetry with respect to the origin.

9. $x + y = 7$
10. $y = 2x^3$
11. $x = 4$

12. Write an equation of the inverse relation of $y = 2x^2 - 3x + 1$.

Which of the following are graphs of functions?

13.

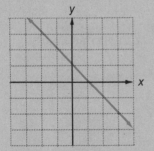

14.

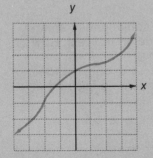

15.

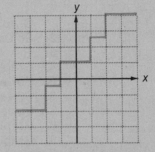

16. $g(x) = 4\sqrt{x - 3}$. Find
    a) $g(8)$
    b) $g(3)$
    c) $g(12)$

17. $f(x) = \dfrac{\sqrt{x}}{3} + 1$. Find an equation for $f^{-1}(x)$.

Here is a graph of $y = f(x)$. Sketch graphs of the following equations.

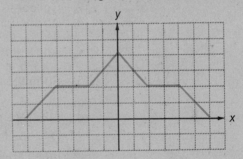

18. $y = \frac{1}{2}f(x)$
19. $y = f(x) - 2$
20. $y = f(x - 1)$

21. Show that $f(x) = -3x^4 - 2$ is an even function.
22. Show that $g(x) = x^7 + x$ is an odd function.

## CUMULATIVE REVIEW FOR CHAPTERS 5–8

5-1  1. Graph on a number line: $y \geq -5$.
5-1  2. Solve using the addition principle: $x + 12 < -3$.
5-2  3. Graph: $-6 < x \leq -1$.
5-2  4. Graph: $x \leq 3$ or $x \geq 6$.
5-2  5. Solve using the multiplication principle: $-4w \leq 28$.
5-2  6. Solve: $-3 + 7x < 2x + 9$.
5-3  7. Solve: $|4 - y| < 10$.
5-4  8. Graph: $-3x + y > 1$.
5-5  9. Graph this system: $y > x - 1$
$2x + y < 5$

5-5  10. Graph. If a polygon is formed, find the vertices.
$y \leq -x - 1$
$y \leq 3$
$y - 2x \leq 8$
$y \geq -2$

5-6  11. Find the maximum and minimum values, and where they occur.
$R = 5y - x$ subject to: $11x + 2y \leq 48$
$6x + 8y \geq -36$
$5x - 6y \geq 8$

6-1  12. Collect like terms: $5m + 2 - 3n + 6m - n + 8$.
6-1  13. Arrange in descending powers of $t$:
$6s^3t - 2s^2t^2 + 5st^3$.
6-2  14. Add: $3ab^2 - a^2b + 6a^3$ and
$-4a^2b + 5b^3 + 2ab^2$.
6-2  15. Subtract: $(-2y + 6y^2 - 3) - (-y^3 + 4y - 5y^2)$.

6-3  Multiply.
16. $(3m^2n)(-2mn^2)$     17. $(x - 3y)(2x^3)$
18. $(y^2 - y + 3)(2y + 5)$

6-4, 6-5  Find these special products.
19. $(5 - 3x)(-2 + 7x)$     20. $(3x + 2y)^2$
21. $(5x - 2)(-5x - 2)$

6-6  Solve.
22. An investment is made at 8%, compounded annually. It grows to $1053 at the end of one year. How much was originally invested?
23. Suppose $2500 is invested at 11%, compounded semiannually. How much will be in the account at the end of two years?

Factor completely.

7-1  24.  $9y - 12y^2$          25.  $7m^4 - 112m^2$
7-2  26.  $12m + 36 + m^2$      27.  $x^2 - 15 - 2x$
7-3  28.  $6 + 20y^2 - 23y$

7-4  29.  Factor $x^2 - 20 - 8x$ by completing the square. Show your work.
7-5  30.  Factor:  $16a^3 + 2b^3$.
7-5  31.  Factor:  $64 - 27n^3$.
7-7  32.  Solve:  $3 - 5x = 2x^2$.
7-8  33.  Solve:  If the sides of a square are lengthened by 8 cm the area becomes 100 cm². Find the length of the side of the original square.

8-1  34.  List the domain and range of the relation $\{(3, -6), (1, -1), (-4, -2), (0, 0), (7, -1)\}$

8-2  35.  Graph the relation which is the solution set of $3x - y = 7$.

8-3  36.  Test for symmetry with respect to the x-axis and the y-axis: $x^2 - y^3 = 8$.

8-4  37.  Test for symmetry with respect to the origin:  $x + y = 0$.

8-4  38.  Write an equation of the inverse relation of $3x - y = 2$.

8-5  39.  Is the graph at the right that of a function?

8-5  40.  $p(x) = x - 4x^2$. Find $p(-1)$ and $p(10)$.

8-6  41.  $h(x) = 3x - 5$. Find an equation for $h^{-1}(x)$.

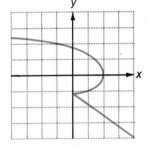

The graph of $y = f(x)$ is shown at the right. Sketch graphs of the following.

8-7  42.  $y = f(x) - 5$
8-7  43.  $y = f(x + 1)$
8-8  44.  $y = 2f(x)$

8-9  45.  Show that $f(x) = 2x^5 - x^3$ is an odd function.

8-9  46.  Show that $f(x) = -x^2 - 3$ is an even function.

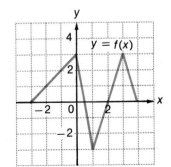

## Ready for Fractional Expressions and Equations?

1-2   1. Add: $\frac{2}{7} + (-\frac{7}{9})$.

1-3   2. Subtract: $-\frac{5}{3} - (-\frac{3}{5})$.

1-4   3. Multiply: $7 \cdot (-\frac{2}{3})$.

1-4   Find the reciprocal of each.

      4. $\frac{3}{4}$         5. 6         6. $-\frac{5}{4}$

1-4   Divide.

      7. $\frac{2}{3} \div \frac{3}{4}$       8. $-\frac{7}{8} \div \frac{1}{2}$       9. $\frac{3}{4} \div (-\frac{1}{4})$

1-5   10. Evaluate $xy - xz$ when $x = 3$, $y = -2$, $z = 4$.

1-5   Factor.

      11. $4x + 4y$       12. $3y + 6$       13. $cx - cr + cw$

1-8   Multiply and simplify.

      14. $x^2 \cdot x^5$       15. $3^4 \cdot 3^{-1}$       16. $(7x^3y^{-2})(2x^{-2}y^4)$

1-8   Divide.

      17. $\dfrac{5^9}{5^{-2}}$       18. $\dfrac{4^{-3}}{4^{-5}}$       19. $\dfrac{y^{-2}}{y^6}$       20. $\dfrac{10x^5y^2}{2xy^4}$

1-8   Simplify.

      21. $(4^3)^5$       22. $(y^{-2})^3$       23. $(2x^2y^{-4}z^3)^4$

2-2   24. Solve: $8 - 3(a - 1) = 2 + 4(3 - a)$

2-4   25. Solve $E = mc^2$, for $m$.

6-2   26. Add: $(5ax^2 + 4bx - 7)$ and $(3ax^2 - 5bx + 2)$.

6-2   27. Subtract: $(-3x^4 + x^3 - 2x^2 + 1) - (2x^4 + 3x^2 - 4)$.

6-3   28. Multiply: $(a + 3)(a^4 - 3a^2 + 2)$

7-1   Factor out a common factor.

      29. $12y^4 - 15y^3 + 3y^2$       30. $8x^2y - 28x^3y^2 + 4x^2y^3$

      Factor.

7-1   31. $x^2 - 25$       32. $16y^8 - 36x^4$

7-2   33. $x^2 - 14x + 49$       34. $4y^2 - 16xy + 16x^2$

7-2   35. $3y^2 - 24y^3 + 48y^4$       36. $x^2 - 6x + 8$

7-3   37. $6x^2 + 39x + 45$       38. $x^4y^4 + 7x^2y^2 + 6$

# Chapter 9
# Fractional Expressions and Equations

*How much garbage is produced in a city in one year?*

# 9-1 Multiplying and Dividing

After finishing Lesson 9-1, you should be able to
  ▎ multiply fractional expressions.
  ▎▎ multiply a fractional expression by 1, using an expression for 1 like $\frac{A}{A}$.
  ▎▎▎ simplify fractional expressions by factoring numerator and denominator and removing factors of 1.
  ▎▎▎▎ multiply fractional expressions and simplify.
  ▎▎▎▎▎ divide fractional expressions and simplify.

These are *fractional expressions*.

$$\frac{7}{8}, \qquad \frac{8}{y+5}, \qquad \frac{x^2 + 7xy - 4}{x^3 - y^3}$$

Fractional expressions show quotients of polynomials.

$$\frac{7}{8} \text{ means } 7 \div 8 \text{ and } \frac{8}{y+5} \text{ means } 8 \div (y + 5).$$

Certain substitutions are not sensible in fractional expressions. Since division by 0 is not defined, any number that makes a denominator 0 is not a sensible replacement. In $\frac{8}{y+5}$, $-5$ is not a sensible replacement.

## ▎Multiplying

To multiply two fractional expressions, multiply numerators and multiply denominators.

**Example 1.** Multiply.

$$\frac{x+3}{y-4} \cdot \frac{x^3}{y+5} = \frac{(x+3)x^3}{(y-4)(y+5)} \qquad \text{\textit{Multiplying numerators and multiplying denominators}}$$

$$= \frac{x^4 + 3x^3}{y^2 + y - 20} \qquad \text{\textit{Simplifying}}$$

**TRY THIS** ➡️

Multiply.

1. $\dfrac{x-2}{5} \cdot \dfrac{x+2}{x+4}$

2. $\dfrac{x+y}{x+3} \cdot \dfrac{x+y}{x-3}$

## ‖ Multiplying by 1

Any number multiplied by 1 is that same number. Any fractional expression with the same numerator and denominator names the number 1.

$$\frac{y + 5}{y + 5}, \frac{4x^2 - 5}{4x^2 - 5}, \frac{-1}{-1}$$   *All name the number 1 for all sensible replacements*

We can multiply by 1 to get equivalent expressions. For example, let us multiply $\frac{x + y}{5}$ by 1.

$$\frac{x + y}{5} \cdot \frac{x - y}{x - y} = \frac{(x + y)(x - y)}{5(x - y)}$$
$$= \frac{x^2 - y^2}{5x - 5y}$$

We know now that $\frac{x + y}{5}$ and $\frac{x^2 - y^2}{5x - 5y}$ are equivalent. This means that they will name the same number for all replacements, except those that make a denominator zero.

**Examples.**   Multiply.

**2.** $\dfrac{x^2 + 3}{x - 1} \cdot \dfrac{x + 1}{x + 1} = \dfrac{(x^2 + 3)(x + 1)}{(x - 1)(x + 1)}$
$$= \dfrac{x^3 + x^2 + 3x + 3}{x^2 - 1}$$

**3.** $\dfrac{-1}{-1} \cdot \dfrac{x - 4}{x - y} = \dfrac{-1 \cdot (x - 4)}{-1 \cdot (x - y)}$
$$= \dfrac{(-1)x - (-1)4}{(-1)x - (-1)y}$$
$$= \dfrac{-x + 4}{-x + y}$$
$$= \dfrac{4 - x}{y - x}$$

**TRY THIS** ➡

Multiply.

**3.** $\dfrac{3x + 2y}{5x + 4y} \cdot \dfrac{x}{x}$

**4.** $\dfrac{2x^2 - y}{3x + 4} \cdot \dfrac{3x + 2}{3x + 2}$

**5.** $\dfrac{-1}{-1} \cdot \dfrac{2a - 5}{a - b}$

## ⅢSimplifyingFractional Expressions

Fractional expressions can be simplified by reversing the previous procedure. That is, we factor numerator and denominator and try to "remove" a factor of 1.

**Example 4.** Simplify.

$$\frac{4a + 8}{2} = \frac{2 \cdot 2a + 2 \cdot 4}{2 \cdot 1} = \frac{2(2a + 4)}{2 \cdot 1} = \frac{2}{2} \cdot \frac{2a + 4}{1} = 2a + 4$$

### TRY THIS

Answers. 6. 7x  7. 2a + 3

**Example 5.** Simplify.

$$\frac{9x^2 + 6xy - 3y^2}{12x^2 - 12y^2} = \frac{3(x + y)(3x - y)}{12(x + y)(x - y)} \quad \textit{Factoring}$$

$$= \frac{3(x + y)}{3(x + y)} \cdot \frac{3x - y}{4(x - y)}$$

$$= \frac{3x - y}{4(x - y)} \qquad \textit{"Removing" a factor of 1}$$

### TRY THIS

Canceling is a shortcut for part of the procedure in Examples 4 and 5. The use of canceling saves a step in simplifying. Canceling gives rise to a great many errors. It should be done cautiously, if at all. *Note:* If you can't factor, you can't cancel!

Answers.  8. $\frac{3x + 2}{x + 2}$  9. $\frac{y + 2}{y - 1}$

Simplify.

6. $\dfrac{7x^2}{x}$

7. $\dfrac{6a + 9}{3}$

Simplify.

8. $\dfrac{6x^2 + 4x}{2x^2 + 4x}$

9. $\dfrac{y^2 + 3y + 2}{y^2 - 1}$

## ⅢⅢMultiplying and Simplifying

After multiplying you should usually simplify, if possible.

**Example 6.** Multiply and simplify.

$$\frac{x + 2}{x - 2} \cdot \frac{x^2 - 4}{x^2 + x - 2} = \frac{(x + 2)(x^2 - 4)}{(x - 2)(x^2 + x - 2)} \quad \textit{Multiplying numerators and also denominators}$$

$$= \frac{(x + 2)(x - 2)(x + 2)}{(x - 2)(x + 2)(x - 1)} \quad \textit{Factoring numerators and denominators}$$

$$= \frac{(x + 2)(x - 2)}{(x + 2)(x - 2)} \cdot \frac{x + 2}{x - 1}$$

$$= \frac{x + 2}{x - 1} \quad \textit{Simplifying}$$

**Example 7.** Multiply and simplify.

$$\frac{a^3 - b^3}{a^2 - b^2} \cdot \frac{a^2 + 2ab + b^2}{a^2 + ab + b^2} = \frac{(a^3 - b^3)(a^2 + 2ab + b^2)}{(a^2 - b^2)(a^2 + ab + b^2)}$$

$$= \frac{(a - b)(a^2 + ab + b^2)(a + b)(a + b)}{(a - b)(a + b)(a^2 + ab + b^2)}$$

$$= \frac{(a - b)(a^2 + ab + b^2)(a + b)}{(a - b)(a^2 + ab + b^2)(a + b)} \cdot \frac{a + b}{1}$$

$$= a + b$$

**TRY THIS**

Multiply and simplify.

10. $\dfrac{(x - y)^2}{x + y} \cdot \dfrac{3x + 3y}{x^2 - y^2}$

11. $\dfrac{a^3 + b^3}{a^2 - b^2} \cdot \dfrac{a^2 - 2ab + b^2}{a^2 - ab + b^2}$

## ▐▐▐▐▐ Dividing and Simplifying

Two expressions are reciprocals of each other if their product is 1.

To find the reciprocal of a fractional expression we interchange numerator and denominator.

**Examples.**

**8.** The reciprocal of $\dfrac{x + 2y}{3x^2y + 7}$ is $\dfrac{3x^2y + 7}{x + 2y}$.

**9.** The reciprocal of $y - 8$ is $\dfrac{1}{y - 8}$.

**TRY THIS**

Find the reciprocal.

12. $\dfrac{x + 3}{x - 5}$

13. $x + 7$

14. $\dfrac{1}{y^3 - 9}$

We can divide fractional expressions by multiplying by the reciprocal of the divisor.

We usually simplify answers if possible.

**Example 10.** Divide and simplify.

$$\frac{a^2 - 1}{a + 1} \div \frac{a^2 - 2a + 1}{a + 1} = \frac{a^2 - 1}{a + 1} \cdot \frac{a + 1}{a^2 - 2a + 1} \qquad \textit{Multiplying by the reciprocal}$$

$$= \frac{(a + 1)(a - 1)}{a + 1} \cdot \frac{a + 1}{(a - 1)(a - 1)} \qquad \textit{Factoring numerator and denominator}$$

$$= \frac{(a + 1)(a - 1)}{(a + 1)(a - 1)} \cdot \frac{a + 1}{a - 1}$$

$$= \frac{a + 1}{a - 1} \qquad \textit{Simplifying}$$

**TRY THIS** ➡

Divide and simplify.

15. $\dfrac{x^2 + 7x + 10}{y} \div \dfrac{x^2 - 3x - 10}{y}$

16. $\dfrac{a^2 - b^2}{ab} \div \dfrac{a^2 - 2ab + b^2}{2a^2b^2}$

## Exercise Set 9-1

▮ Multiply. (*See Example 1.*)

1. $\dfrac{y + 3}{4} \cdot \dfrac{y - 2}{y + 4}$

2. $\dfrac{x + 7}{5} \cdot \dfrac{x - 3}{x + 6}$

3. $\dfrac{z - 1}{z + 1} \cdot \dfrac{z + 2}{z - 3}$

4. $\dfrac{x - 4}{x + 3} \cdot \dfrac{x + 6}{x - 2}$

5. $\dfrac{x - y}{2x + y} \cdot \dfrac{x + y}{2x - y}$

6. $\dfrac{2y + 3}{y - 5} \cdot \dfrac{2y - 5}{y + 6}$

7. $\dfrac{x - 2}{x + 1} \cdot \dfrac{x^2 + 2x + 4}{x^2 - x + 1}$

8. $\dfrac{x - y}{x + y} \cdot \dfrac{x^2 + xy + y^2}{x^2 - xy + y^2}$

▮▮ Multiply. (*See Examples 2 and 3.*)

9. $\dfrac{3x}{3x} \cdot \dfrac{x + 1}{x + 3}$

10. $\dfrac{y}{y} \cdot \dfrac{4y - 3}{2y + 5}$

11. $\dfrac{4 - y^2}{6 - y} \cdot \dfrac{-1}{-1}$

12. $\dfrac{8 - x^3}{4 - x} \cdot \dfrac{-1}{-1}$

13. $\dfrac{t - 3}{t + 2} \cdot \dfrac{t - 3}{t - 3}$

14. $\dfrac{p - 4}{p + 5} \cdot \dfrac{p + 5}{p + 5}$

15. $\dfrac{4x - 3}{x + 5} \cdot \dfrac{x^2 - 1}{x^2 - 1}$

16. $\dfrac{5y - 1}{3y + 4} \cdot \dfrac{y^2 + 3}{y^2 + 3}$

▮▮▮ Simplify. (*See Examples 4 and 5.*)

17. $\dfrac{9y^2}{15y}$

18. $\dfrac{6x^3}{18x^2}$

19. $\dfrac{2a - 6}{2}$

20. $\dfrac{3a - 6}{3}$

21. $\dfrac{4y - 12}{4y + 12}$

22. $\dfrac{8x + 16}{8x - 16}$

23. $\dfrac{t^2 - 16}{t^2 - 8t + 16}$

24. $\dfrac{p^2 - 25}{p^2 + 10p + 25}$

25. $\dfrac{x^2 + 7x - 8}{4x^2 - 8x + 4}$

26. $\dfrac{y^2 + 4y - 12}{3y^2 - 12y + 12}$

27. $\dfrac{x^4 - 4x^2}{x^3 + 2x^2}$

28. $\dfrac{r^4 - 9r^2}{r^3 - 3r^2}$

29. $\dfrac{a^3 - b^3}{a^2 - b^2}$

30. $\dfrac{x^3 + y^3}{x^2 - y^2}$

▮▮▮▮ Multiply and simplify. (*See Examples 6 and 7.*)

31. $\dfrac{x^2 - 16}{x^2} \cdot \dfrac{x^2 - 4x}{x^2 - x - 12}$

32. $\dfrac{y^2 + 10y + 25}{y^2 - 9} \cdot \dfrac{y + 3}{y + 5}$

33. $\dfrac{y^2 - 16}{2y + 6} \cdot \dfrac{y + 3}{y - 4}$

34. $\dfrac{m^2 - n^2}{4m + 4n} \cdot \dfrac{m + n}{m - n}$

35. $\dfrac{x^2 - 2x - 35}{2x^3 - 3x^2} \cdot \dfrac{4x^3 - 9x}{7x - 49}$

36. $\dfrac{y^2 - 10y + 9}{y^2 - 1} \cdot \dfrac{y + 4}{y^2 - 5y - 36}$

37. $\dfrac{c^3 + 8}{c^2 - 4} \cdot \dfrac{c^2 - 4c + 4}{c^2 - 2c + 4}$

38. $\dfrac{x^3 - 27}{x^2 - 9} \cdot \dfrac{x^2 - 6x + 9}{x^2 + 3x + 9}$

39. $\dfrac{x^2 - y^2}{x^3 - y^3} \cdot \dfrac{x^2 + xy + y^2}{x^2 + 2xy + y^2}$

40. $\dfrac{64x^3 + 27y^3}{16x^2 - 9y^2} \cdot \dfrac{16x^2 - 24xy + 9y^2}{4x^2 - 12xy + 9y^2}$

▮▮▮▮▮ Divide and simplify. (*See Example 10.*)

41. $\dfrac{3y + 15}{y} \div \dfrac{y + 5}{y}$

42. $\dfrac{6x + 12}{x} \div \dfrac{x + 2}{x^3}$

43. $\dfrac{y^2 - 9}{y} \div \dfrac{y + 3}{y + 2}$

44. $\dfrac{x^2 - 4}{x} \div \dfrac{x - 2}{x + 4}$

45. $\dfrac{4a^2 - 1}{a^2 - 4} \div \dfrac{2a - 1}{a - 2}$

46. $\dfrac{25x^2 - 4}{x^2 - 9} \div \dfrac{5x - 2}{x + 3}$

47. $\dfrac{x^2 - 16}{x^2 - 10x + 25} \div \dfrac{3x - 12}{x^2 - 3x - 10}$

48. $\dfrac{y^2 - 36}{y^2 - 8y + 16} \div \dfrac{3y - 18}{y^2 - y + 12}$

49. $\dfrac{y^3 + 3y}{y^2 - 9} \div \dfrac{y^2 + 5y - 14}{y^2 + 4y - 21}$

50. $\dfrac{a^3 + 4a}{a^2 - 16} \div \dfrac{a^2 + 8a + 15}{a^2 + a - 20}$

51. $\dfrac{x^3 - 64}{x^3 + 64} \div \dfrac{x^2 - 16}{x^2 - 4x + 16}$

52. $\dfrac{8y^3 + 27}{64y^3 - 1} \div \dfrac{4y^2 - 9}{16y^2 + 4y + 1}$

## Calculator Exercises

Multiply or divide.

53. $\dfrac{834x}{y - 427.2} \cdot \dfrac{26.3x}{y + 427.2}$

54. $\dfrac{0.0049t}{t + 0.007} \cdot \dfrac{27{,}000t}{t - 0.007}$

55. $\dfrac{527}{x + 93.87} \div \dfrac{x - 93.87}{468}$

56. $\dfrac{y + 924.6}{0.003} \div \dfrac{0.421}{y - 924.6}$

# 9-2 Least Common Multiple

After finishing Lesson 9-2, you should be able to
■ find least common multiples of algebraic expressions.

■ To add fractional expressions we first find a common denominator. Consider $\frac{5}{42} + \frac{7}{12}$. We look for a common multiple of 42 and 12. Usually we try to get the smallest such number, or the *least common multiple* (LCM). To find the LCM we factor.

$$42 = 2 \cdot 3 \cdot 7$$
$$12 = 2 \cdot 2 \cdot 3$$

The LCM is the number that has 2 as a factor twice, 3 as a factor once, and 7 as a factor once. The LCM is $2 \cdot 2 \cdot 3 \cdot 7$, or 84.

To obtain the LCM we use each factor the greatest number of times it occurs in any one factorization.

**Example 1.** Find the LCM of 18 and 24.

$$18 = 3 \cdot 3 \cdot 2$$
$$24 = 2 \cdot 2 \cdot 2 \cdot 3$$

The LCM is $3 \cdot 3 \cdot 2 \cdot 2 \cdot 2$, or 72.

**TRY THIS** ➤

Find the LCM by factoring.

1. 18, 30
2. 28, 36
3. 12, 18, 24

To find the LCM of two or more algebraic expressions we factor them. Then we use each factor the greatest number of times it occurs in any one expression.

**Example 2.** Find the LCM of $12xy^2$, $15x^3y$.

$$12xy^2 = 2 \cdot 2 \cdot 3 \cdot x \cdot y \cdot y$$
$$15x^3y = 3 \cdot 5 \cdot x \cdot x \cdot x \cdot y$$

The LCM is $2 \cdot 2 \cdot 3 \cdot 5 \cdot x \cdot x \cdot x \cdot y \cdot y$, or $60x^3y^2$.

**TRY THIS** ➤

Find the LCM.

4. $18a^2b^2$, $15a^3b$

**Example 3.** Find the LCM of $y^2 + 5y + 4$, $y^2 + 2y + 1$.

$$y^2 + 5y + 4 = (y + 4)(y + 1)$$
$$y^2 + 2y + 1 = (y + 1)(y + 1)$$

The LCM is $(y + 4)(y + 1)(y + 1)$.

**Example 4.** Find the LCM of $x^2 + 8$, $x + 2$, and 7.

These expressions are not factorable, so their LCM is their product, $7(x^2 + 8)(x + 2)$.

**Example 5.** Find the LCM of $x^2 - y^2$, $x^3 + y^3$, $x^2 + 2xy + y^2$.

$$x^2 - y^2 = (x - y)(x + y)$$
$$x^3 + y^3 = (x + y)(x^2 - xy + y^2)$$
$$x^2 + 2xy + y^2 = (x + y)(x + y)$$

The LCM is $(x - y)(x + y)(x + y)(x^2 - xy + y^2)$.

If an LCM is multiplied by $-1$ we still consider the answer to be an LCM. For example, the LCM of 7 and $-7$ is either 7 or $-7$. The LCM of $x - 3$ and $3 - x$ is either $x - 3$ or $3 - x$.

**Example 6.** Find the LCM of $x^2 - y^2$ and $3y - 3x$.

$$x^2 - y^2 = (x + y)(x - y)$$
$$3y - 3x = 3(y - x)$$

The LCM is $3(x + y)(x - y)$, or $3(x + y)(y - x)$.

**TRY THIS**

Find the LCM.

5. $x^2 + 2x + 1$, $x^2 + 5x + 4$
6. $x^2 + 10$, $x - 3$, 5
7. $a^2 - b^2$, $2b - 2a$
8. $y^2 + 7y + 12$,
   $y^2 + 8y + 16$, $y + 4$

## Exercise Set 9-2

▪Find the LCM. (*See Examples 1–6.*)

1. 14, 20
2. 18, 26
3. 24, 36, 42
4. 24, 42, 60
5. $8x^2$, $12x^3$
6. $4y^2$, $24y^3$
7. $12x^2y$, $4xy$
8. $18r^2s$, $12rs^3$
9. $15ab^2$, $3ab$, $10a^3b$
10. $6x^2y^2$, $9x^3y$, $15y^3$
11. $a + b$, $a - b$
12. $x - 4$, $x + 4$
13. $3(y - 2)$, $6(2 - y)$
14. $5(y - 1)$, $10(1 - y)$
15. $y^2 - 9$, $3y + 9$
16. $a^2 - b^2$, $ab + b^2$
17. $5y - 15$, $y^2 - 6y + 9$
18. $4x - 16$, $x^2 - 8x + 16$
19. $(a + 1)$, $(a - 1)^2$, $a^2 - 1$
20. $(x - 2)$, $(x + 2)^2$, $x^2 - 4$
21. $x^2 - 4$, $2 - x$
22. $y^2 - 9$, $3 - y$
23. $x^2 + 10x + 25$, $x^2 + 2x - 15$
24. $y^2 + 8x + 16$, $y^2 - 3y - 28$
25. $2r^2 - 5r - 12$, $3r^2 - 13r + 4$
26. $3x^2 - 4x - 4$, $4x^2 - 5x - 6$
27. $2x^2 - 5x - 3$, $2x^2 - x - 1$,
    $x^2 - 6x + 9$
28. $3x^2 + 4x - 4$, $2x^2 + 7x + 6$,
    $x^2 - 4x + 4$

# 9-3 Addition and Subtraction

After finishing Lesson 9-3, you should be able to
- **I** add and subtract fractional expressions having the same denominator.
- **II** add and subtract fractional expressions whose denominators are additive inverses of each other.
- **III** add and subtract fractional expressions having different denominators.
- **IIII** simplify combined additions and subtractions of fractional expressions.

## I Addition and Subtraction, Same Denominator

When denominators are the same, we add or subtract the numerators and keep the same denominator.

**Example 1.** Add.

$$\frac{3 + x}{x} + \frac{4}{x} = \frac{7 + x}{x}$$

Example 1 shows that $\frac{3 + x}{x} + \frac{4}{x}$ and $\frac{7 + x}{x}$ are equivalent expressions.

They name the same number for all replacements except 0.

**Example 2.** Add.

$$\frac{4x^2 - 5xy}{x^2 - y^2} + \frac{2xy - y^2}{x^2 - y^2} = \frac{4x^2 - 3xy - y^2}{x^2 - y^2}$$

$$= \frac{(4x + y)(x - y)}{(x + y)(x - y)}$$

$$= \frac{x - y}{x - y} \cdot \frac{4x + y}{x + y}$$

$$= \frac{4x + y}{x + y}$$

**TRY THIS** ➡

**Example 3.** Subtract.

$$\frac{4x + 5}{x + 3} - \frac{x - 2}{x + 3} = \frac{4x + 5 - (x - 2)}{x + 3}$$

$$= \frac{4x + 5 - x + 2}{x + 3}$$

$$= \frac{3x + 7}{x + 3}$$

Add.

1. $\dfrac{5 + y}{y} + \dfrac{7}{y}$

2. $\dfrac{2x^2 + 5x - 9}{x - 5} +$ $\dfrac{x^2 - 19x + 4}{x - 5}$

In Example 3, note the use of parentheses. This is important, to make sure you subtract the entire numerator and not just part of it.

**TRY THIS** ━━━▶

## ▮ Addition and Subtraction When Denominators are Additive Inverses

When one denominator is the additive inverse of the other, we first multiply one expression by $\dfrac{-1}{-1}$. This will give us a common denominator.

**Example 4.** Add.

$$\frac{a}{2a} + \frac{a^3}{-2a} = \frac{a}{2a} + \frac{-1}{-1} \cdot \frac{a^3}{-2a} \qquad \textit{Multiplying by } \frac{-1}{-1}$$
$$= \frac{a}{2a} + \frac{-a^3}{2a}$$
$$= \frac{a - a^3}{2a}$$
$$= \frac{a(1 - a^2)}{2a}$$
$$= \frac{a}{a} \cdot \frac{1 - a^2}{2}$$
$$= \frac{1 - a^2}{2}$$

**TRY THIS** ━━━▶

**Example 5.** Subtract.

$$\frac{5x}{x - 2y} - \frac{3y - 7}{2y - x} = \frac{5x}{x - 2y} - \frac{-1}{-1} \cdot \frac{3y - 7}{2y - x}$$
$$= \frac{5x}{x - 2y} - \frac{7 - 3y}{x - 2y}$$
$$= \frac{5x - (7 - 3y)}{x - 2y} \qquad \textit{Subtracting numerators (remember the parentheses)}$$
$$= \frac{5x - 7 + 3y}{x - 2y}$$

**TRY THIS** ━━━▶

---

Subtract.

3. $\dfrac{a}{b + 2} - \dfrac{b}{b + 2}$

4. $\dfrac{4y + 7}{x^2 + y^2} - \dfrac{3y - 5}{x^2 + y^2}$

---

Add.

5. $\dfrac{b}{3b} + \dfrac{b^3}{-3b}$

6. $\dfrac{3x^2 + 4}{x - 5} + \dfrac{x^2 - 7}{5 - x}$

---

Subtract.

7. $\dfrac{3}{4y} - \dfrac{7x}{-4y}$

8. $\dfrac{4x^2}{x - y} - \dfrac{7x^2}{y - x}$

### ⅢAddition and Subtraction, Different Denominators

When denominators are different, but not additive inverses of each other, we first find a common denominator, using the LCM, and then add or subtract numerators.

**Example 6.** Add.

$$\frac{2a}{5} + \frac{3b}{2a}$$

First find the LCM of the denominators.

$$\begin{matrix} 5 \\ 2a \end{matrix} \quad \text{The LCM is } 5 \cdot 2a \text{ or } 10a.$$

Now we multiply by 1 to get the LCM in each expression. Then we add and simplify.

$$\frac{2a}{5} \cdot \frac{2a}{2a} + \frac{3b}{2a} \cdot \frac{5}{5} = \frac{4a^2}{10a} + \frac{15b}{10a} = \frac{4a^2 + 15b}{10a}$$

**TRY THIS** ➤

Add.

9. $\dfrac{3x}{7} + \dfrac{4y}{3x}$

**Example 7.** Add.

$$\frac{1}{2x} + \frac{5x}{x^2 - 1} + \frac{3}{x + 1}$$

We first find the LCM of the denominators.

$$\left. \begin{matrix} 2x = 2x \\ x^2 - 1 = (x - 1)(x + 1) \\ x + 1 = x + 1 \end{matrix} \right\} \text{The LCM is } 2x(x - 1)(x + 1).$$

Now we multiply by 1 to get the LCM in each expression. Then we add and simplify. We leave the denominator factored to ease possible simplifying at the end.

$$\frac{1}{2x} \cdot \frac{(x - 1)(x + 1)}{(x - 1)(x + 1)} + \frac{5x}{(x - 1)(x + 1)} \cdot \frac{2x}{2x} + \frac{3}{x + 1} \cdot \frac{2x(x - 1)}{2x(x - 1)}$$

$$= \frac{(x - 1)(x + 1)}{2x(x - 1)(x + 1)} + \frac{10x^2}{2x(x - 1)(x + 1)} + \frac{6x(x - 1)}{2x(x - 1)(x + 1)}$$

$$= \frac{x^2 - 1}{2x(x - 1)(x + 1)} + \frac{10x^2}{2x(x - 1)(x + 1)} + \frac{6x^2 - 6x}{2x(x - 1)(x + 1)}$$

$$= \frac{17x^2 - 6x - 1}{2x(x - 1)(x + 1)}$$

Here no simplifying can be done. We have left the denominator factored. In some cases denominators are best left this way. In other cases it is best to multiply them out.

**TRY THIS** ➡️

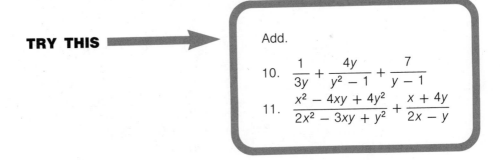

Add.

10. $\dfrac{1}{3y} + \dfrac{4y}{y^2 - 1} + \dfrac{7}{y - 1}$

11. $\dfrac{x^2 - 4xy + 4y^2}{2x^2 - 3xy + y^2} + \dfrac{x + 4y}{2x - y}$

**Example 8.** Subtract.

$$\dfrac{2y + 1}{y^2 - 7y + 6} - \dfrac{y + 3}{y^2 - 5y - 6} = \dfrac{2y + 1}{(y - 6)(y - 1)} - \dfrac{y + 3}{(y - 6)(y + 1)} \qquad \textit{The LCM is}\ (y - 6)(y - 1)(y + 1)$$

$$= \dfrac{2y + 1}{(y - 6)(y - 1)} \cdot \dfrac{y + 1}{y + 1} - \dfrac{y + 3}{(y - 6)(y + 1)} \cdot \dfrac{y - 1}{y - 1}$$

$$= \dfrac{(2y + 1)(y + 1) - (y + 3)(y - 1)}{(y - 6)(y - 1)(y + 1)}$$

$$= \dfrac{2y^2 + 3y + 1 - (y^2 + 2y - 3)}{(y - 6)(y - 1)(y + 1)}$$

$$= \dfrac{2y^2 + 3y + 1 - y^2 - 2y + 3}{(y - 6)(y - 1)(y + 1)}$$

$$= \dfrac{y^2 + y + 4}{(y - 6)(y - 1)(y + 1)} \cdot$$

**TRY THIS** ➡️

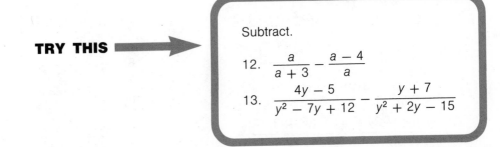

Subtract.

12. $\dfrac{a}{a + 3} - \dfrac{a - 4}{a}$

13. $\dfrac{4y - 5}{y^2 - 7y + 12} - \dfrac{y + 7}{y^2 + 2y - 15}$

## ⅠⅠⅠⅠSimplifying Combined Additions and Subtractions

**Example 9.** Simplify.

$$\frac{2x}{x^2 - 4} + \frac{5}{2 - x} - \frac{1}{2 + x} = \frac{2x}{(x - 2)(x + 2)} + \frac{5}{2 - x} - \frac{1}{2 + x}$$

$$= \frac{2x}{(x - 2)(x + 2)} + \frac{-1}{-1} \cdot \frac{5}{(2 - x)} - \frac{1}{x + 2}$$

$$= \frac{2x}{(x - 2)(x + 2)} + \frac{-5}{x - 2} - \frac{1}{x + 2} \qquad \textit{The LCM is } (x - 2)(x + 2)$$

$$= \frac{2x}{(x - 2)(x + 2)} + \frac{-5}{x - 2} \cdot \frac{x + 2}{x + 2} - \frac{1}{x + 2} \cdot \frac{x - 2}{x - 2}$$

$$= \frac{2x - 5(x + 2) - (x - 2)}{(x - 2)(x + 2)}$$

$$= \frac{2x - 5x - 10 - x + 2}{(x - 2)(x + 2)}$$

$$= \frac{-4x - 8}{(x - 2)(x + 2)}$$

$$= \frac{-4(x + 2)}{(x - 2)(x + 2)}$$

*We leave the denominator factored to ease possible simplifying at the end.*

$$= \frac{-4}{x - 2} \cdot \frac{x + 2}{x + 2}$$

$$= \frac{-4}{x - 2}$$

**TRY THIS** ➡

Simplify.

14. $\dfrac{1}{x} - \dfrac{3}{x^2} + \dfrac{5}{x + 1}$

## Exercise Set 9-3

❚Add or subtract. Simplify if possible. (*See Examples 1–3.*)

1. $\dfrac{3 - a}{a} + \dfrac{5 + 2a}{a}$

2. $\dfrac{5 - 2x}{x} + \dfrac{4 + 4x}{x}$

3. $\dfrac{a - 3b}{a + b} + \dfrac{a + 5b}{a + b}$

4. $\dfrac{x - 5y}{x + y} + \dfrac{x + 7y}{x + y}$

5. $\dfrac{5x^2 - 4x + 7}{x^3} + \dfrac{4x^2 + 9x + 3}{x^3}$

6. $\dfrac{7t^2 - 3t + 2}{t^4} + \dfrac{8t^2 + 5t - 9}{t^4}$

7. $\dfrac{4y + 3}{y - 2} - \dfrac{y - 2}{y - 2}$

8. $\dfrac{3t + 2}{t - 4} - \dfrac{t - 4}{t - 4}$

9. $\dfrac{10xy}{xy^2} - \dfrac{6xy}{xy^2}$

10. $\dfrac{12ab}{ab^2} - \dfrac{5ab}{ab^2}$

11. $\dfrac{6y^2 - 3y + 1}{2y + 1} - \dfrac{4y^2 - 3y - 1}{2y + 1}$

12. $\dfrac{5x^2 + 2x - 3}{3x - 1} - \dfrac{4x^2 - 2x + 5}{3x - 1}$

**Ⅱ** Add or subtract. Simplify when possible. (*See Examples 4 and 5.*)

13. $\dfrac{a^2}{a-b} + \dfrac{b^2}{b-a}$

14. $\dfrac{r^2}{r-s} + \dfrac{s^2}{s-r}$

15. $\dfrac{x+2}{3x-4} + \dfrac{2x-3}{4-3x} + \dfrac{5(3x-1)}{3x-4}$

16. $\dfrac{4(y-1)}{2y-5} + \dfrac{5(2y+3)}{5-2y} + \dfrac{y-4}{2y-5}$

17. $\dfrac{3}{x} - \dfrac{8}{-x}$

18. $\dfrac{2}{a} - \dfrac{5}{-a}$

19. $\dfrac{2x-10}{x^2-25} - \dfrac{5-x}{25-x^2}$

20. $\dfrac{y-9}{y^2-16} - \dfrac{7-y}{16-y^2}$

**Ⅲ** Add or subtract. Simplify when possible. Leave denominators factored. (*See Examples 6–8.*)

21. $\dfrac{y-2}{y+4} + \dfrac{y+3}{y-5}$

22. $\dfrac{x-2}{x+3} + \dfrac{x+2}{x-4}$

23. $\dfrac{4xy}{x^2-y^2} + \dfrac{x-y}{x+y}$

24. $\dfrac{5ab}{a^2-b^2} + \dfrac{a+b}{a-b}$

25. $\dfrac{9x+2}{3x^2-2x-8} + \dfrac{7}{3x^2+x-4}$

26. $\dfrac{3y+2}{2y^2-y-10} + \dfrac{8}{2y^2-7y+5}$

27. $\dfrac{4}{x+1} + \dfrac{x+2}{x^2-1} + \dfrac{3}{x-1}$

28. $\dfrac{-2}{y+2} + \dfrac{5}{y-2} + \dfrac{y+3}{y^2-4}$

29. $\dfrac{1}{x^2+y^2} + \dfrac{1}{x^2-y^2} + \dfrac{2x^2}{y^4-x^4}$

30. $\dfrac{2}{a^2-b^2} + \dfrac{2}{a^2+b^2} + \dfrac{4a^2}{a^4-b^4}$

31. $\dfrac{x-1}{3x+15} - \dfrac{x+3}{5x+25}$

32. $\dfrac{y-2}{4y+8} - \dfrac{y+6}{5y+10}$

33. $\dfrac{5ab}{a^2-b^2} - \dfrac{a-b}{a+b}$

34. $\dfrac{6xy}{x^2-y^2} - \dfrac{x+y}{x-y}$

35. $\dfrac{3y}{y^2-7y+10} - \dfrac{2y}{y^2-8y+15}$

36. $\dfrac{5x}{x^2-6x+8} - \dfrac{3x}{x^2-x-12}$

37. $\dfrac{3x-1}{x^2+2x-3} - \dfrac{x+4}{x^2-9}$

38. $\dfrac{3p-2}{p^2+2p-24} - \dfrac{p-3}{p^2-16}$

**Ⅳ** Simplify. (*See Example 9.*)

39. $\dfrac{1}{x+1} - \dfrac{x}{x-2} + \dfrac{x^2+2}{x^2-x-2}$

40. $\dfrac{2}{y+3} - \dfrac{y}{y-1} + \dfrac{y^2+2}{y^2+2y-3}$

41. $\dfrac{x-1}{x-2} - \dfrac{x+1}{x+2} + \dfrac{x-6}{x^2-4}$

42. $\dfrac{y-3}{y-4} - \dfrac{y+2}{y+4} + \dfrac{y-7}{y^2-16}$

43. $\dfrac{4x}{x^2-1} + \dfrac{3x}{1-x} - \dfrac{4}{x-1}$

44. $\dfrac{5y}{1-2y} - \dfrac{2y}{2y+1} + \dfrac{3}{4y^2-1}$

# 9-4 Complex Fractional Expressions

After finishing Lesson 9-4, you should be able to
▌ simplify complex fractional expressions.

### ▌ DEFINITION

A *complex fractional expression* is one which has a fractional expression in its numerator or its denominator, or both.

These are complex fractional expressions.

$$\frac{x}{x - \frac{1}{3}}, \quad \frac{2x - \frac{4x}{3y}}{\frac{5x^2 + 2x}{6y^2}}, \quad \frac{\frac{1}{a} + \frac{1}{b}}{\frac{1}{a} - \frac{1}{b}}$$

To simplify complex fractional expressions we first add or subtract or both to get a single fractional expression in both numerator and denominator. Then we divide and simplify.

**Example 1.**  Simplify.

$$\frac{1 + \frac{1}{x}}{1 - \frac{1}{x^2}} = \frac{\frac{x}{x} + \frac{1}{x}}{\frac{x^2}{x^2} - \frac{1}{x^2}} \qquad \textit{Finding LCM and multiplying by 1}$$

$$= \frac{\frac{x + 1}{x}}{\frac{x^2 - 1}{x^2}} \qquad \textit{Adding in the numerator and denominator}$$

$$= \frac{x + 1}{x} \cdot \frac{x^2}{x^2 - 1} \qquad \textit{Multiplying by the reciprocal of the denominator}$$

$$= \frac{(x + 1) \cdot x^2}{x(x^2 - 1)}$$

$$= \frac{(x + 1) \cdot x \cdot x}{x(x + 1)(x - 1)}$$

$$= \frac{x}{x - 1} \qquad \textit{Simplifying}$$

Example 1 shows that the expressions $\dfrac{1 + \dfrac{1}{x}}{1 - \dfrac{1}{x^2}}$ and $\dfrac{x}{x - 1}$ are equivalent.

They name the same number for all replacements except 0, 1, and $-1$.

**TRY THIS** ━━━━━━━━━━━━▶

Simplify.

1. $\dfrac{y + \frac{1}{2}}{y - \frac{1}{7}}$

2. $\dfrac{1 - \dfrac{1}{x}}{1 - \dfrac{1}{x^2}}$

**Example 2.** Simplify.

$$\dfrac{\dfrac{1}{a} + \dfrac{1}{b}}{\dfrac{1}{a^3} + \dfrac{1}{b^3}} = \dfrac{\dfrac{1}{a} \cdot \dfrac{b}{b} + \dfrac{1}{b} \cdot \dfrac{a}{a}}{\dfrac{1}{a^3} \cdot \dfrac{b^3}{b^3} + \dfrac{1}{b^3} \cdot \dfrac{a^3}{a^3}}$$

$$= \dfrac{\dfrac{b}{ab} + \dfrac{a}{ab}}{\dfrac{b^3}{a^3b^3} + \dfrac{a^3}{a^3b^3}} \qquad \textit{Adding in the numerator and denominator}$$

$$= \dfrac{\dfrac{b + a}{ab}}{\dfrac{b^3 + a^3}{a^3b^3}}$$

$$= \dfrac{b + a}{ab} \cdot \dfrac{a^3b^3}{b^3 + a^3} \qquad \textit{Multiplying by the reciprocal of the denominator}$$

$$= \dfrac{(b + a)a^3b^3}{ab(b^3 + a^3)} \qquad \textit{Simplifying}$$

$$= \dfrac{(b + a) \cdot ab \cdot a^2b^2}{ab(b + a)(b^2 - ab + a^2)}$$

$$= \dfrac{(b + a)ab}{(b + a)ab} \cdot \dfrac{a^2b^2}{b^2 - ab + a^2}$$

$$= \dfrac{a^2b^2}{b^2 - ab + a^2}$$

**TRY THIS** ━━━━━━━━━━━━▶

Simplify.

3. $\dfrac{\dfrac{1}{a} - \dfrac{1}{b}}{\dfrac{1}{a^3} - \dfrac{1}{b^3}}$

4. $\dfrac{\dfrac{1}{a} + \dfrac{1}{b}}{\dfrac{1}{a} - \dfrac{1}{b}}$

5. $\dfrac{\dfrac{1}{a} - \dfrac{1}{a + h}}{h}$

## Exercise Set 9-4

▌ Simplify. (*See Examples 1 and 2.*)

1. $\dfrac{\dfrac{1}{x} + 4}{\dfrac{1}{x} - 3}$

2. $\dfrac{\dfrac{1}{y} + 7}{\dfrac{1}{y} - 5}$

3. $\dfrac{x - \dfrac{1}{x}}{x + \dfrac{1}{x}}$

4. $\dfrac{y + \dfrac{1}{y}}{y - \dfrac{1}{y}}$

5. $\dfrac{\dfrac{3}{x} + \dfrac{4}{y}}{\dfrac{4}{x} - \dfrac{3}{y}}$

6. $\dfrac{\dfrac{2}{y} + \dfrac{5}{z}}{\dfrac{1}{y} - \dfrac{4}{z}}$

7. $\dfrac{\dfrac{x^2 - y^2}{xy}}{\dfrac{x - y}{y}}$

8. $\dfrac{\dfrac{a^2 - b^2}{ab}}{\dfrac{a - b}{b}}$

9. $\dfrac{a - \dfrac{3a}{b}}{b - \dfrac{b}{a}}$

10. $\dfrac{1 - \dfrac{2}{3x}}{x - \dfrac{4}{9x}}$

11. $\dfrac{\dfrac{1}{a} + \dfrac{1}{b}}{\dfrac{a^2 - b^2}{ab}}$

12. $\dfrac{\dfrac{1}{x} + \dfrac{1}{y}}{\dfrac{x^2 - y^2}{xy}}$

13. $\dfrac{\dfrac{1}{x^3} - x}{\dfrac{1}{x^2} - 1}$

14. $\dfrac{\dfrac{1}{y^3} + y}{\dfrac{1}{y^2} + 1}$

15. $\dfrac{\dfrac{y^2 - y - 6}{y^2 - 5y - 14}}{\dfrac{y^2 + 6y + 5}{y^2 - 6y - 7}}$

16. $\dfrac{\dfrac{x^2 - x - 12}{x^2 - 2x - 15}}{\dfrac{x^2 + 8x + 12}{x^2 - 5x - 14}}$

17. $\dfrac{\dfrac{x}{1 - x} + \dfrac{1 + x}{x}}{\dfrac{1 - x}{x} + \dfrac{x}{1 + x}}$

18. $\dfrac{\dfrac{y}{x - y} + \dfrac{x + y}{y}}{\dfrac{x - y}{x} + \dfrac{y}{x + y}}$

19. $\dfrac{\dfrac{3}{a} + \dfrac{3}{b} - \dfrac{6}{ab}}{\dfrac{4}{a} + \dfrac{4}{b} - \dfrac{8}{ab}}$

20. $\dfrac{\dfrac{5}{x} - \dfrac{5}{y} + \dfrac{10}{xy}}{\dfrac{6}{x} - \dfrac{6}{y} + \dfrac{12}{xy}}$

21. $\dfrac{\dfrac{4}{x - 5} + \dfrac{2}{x + 2}}{\dfrac{2x}{x^2 - 3x - 10} + \dfrac{3}{x - 5}}$

22. $\dfrac{\dfrac{4a}{2a^2 - a - 1} - \dfrac{4}{a - 1}}{\dfrac{1}{a - 1} + \dfrac{6}{2a + 1}}$

# 9-5 Division of Polynomials

After finishing Lesson 9-5, you should be able to
**I**   divide a polynomial by a monomial and check the result.
**II**   divide a polynomial by a divisor which is not a monomial and, if there is a remainder, express the result two ways.

## I Divisor a Monomial

Remember that fractional expressions indicate division. Division by a monomial can be done by first writing a fractional expression.

**Example 1.**   Divide $12x^3 + 8x^2 + x + 4$ by $4x$.

$$\frac{12x^3 + 8x^2 + x + 4}{4x} \qquad \textit{Writing a fractional expression}$$

$$= \frac{12x^3}{4x} + \frac{8x^2}{4x} + \frac{x}{4x} + \frac{4}{4x} \qquad \textit{Doing the reverse of adding}$$

$$= 3x^2 + 2x + \frac{1}{4} + \frac{1}{x} \qquad \textit{Simplifying}$$

**TRY THIS**

Divide.

1.   $\dfrac{x^3 + 16x^2 + 6x}{2x}$

**Example 2.**   Divide: $(8x^4 - 3x^3 + 5x^2) \div x^2$.

$$\frac{8x^4 - 3x^3 + 5x^2}{x^2} = \frac{8x^4}{x^2} - \frac{3x^3}{x^2} + \frac{5x^2}{x^2}$$

$$= 8x^2 - 3x + 5$$

You should try to write only the answer.

To divide a polynomial by a monomial we can divide each term by the monomial.

**TRY THIS**

Divide.

2.   $(15y^5 - 6y^4 + 18y^3) \div 3y^2$
3.   $(x^4 + 10x^3 + 16x^2) \div 2x^2$

## ıı **Divisor Not a Monomial**

We use a procedure very much like long division in arithmetic when the divisor is not a monomial.

**Example 3.** Divide $x^2 + 5x + 6$ by $x + 3$.

$$
\begin{array}{r}
x \phantom{aaaaaaa} \\
x + 3 \overline{)\ x^2 + 5x + 6} \\
\underline{x^2 + 3x} \phantom{aaa} \\
2x \phantom{aaaa}
\end{array}
$$

— Divide first term by first term: $\dfrac{x^2}{x} = x$

— Multiply x by divisor

— Subtract

We now "bring down" the next term of the dividend, 6.

$$
\begin{array}{r}
x\ + 2 \phantom{aaaa} \\
x + 3 \overline{)\ x^2 + 5x + 6} \\
\underline{x^2 + 3x} \phantom{aaaa} \\
2x + 6 \phantom{a} \\
\underline{2x + 6} \\
0
\end{array}
$$

— Divide first term by first term: $\dfrac{2x}{x} = 2$

— Multiply 2 by divisor

— Subtract

Answer: Quotient $x + 2$, remainder 0.

To check, we multiply quotient by divisor and add the remainder, if any, to see if we get the dividend.

$(x + 3)(x + 2) = x^2 + 5x + 6$. This answer checks.

**TRY THIS** ➡

Divide and check.

4. $x - 2 \overline{)\ x^2 + 3x - 10}$

**Example 4.** Divide: $(125y^3 - 8) \div (5y - 2)$.

$$
\begin{array}{r}
25y^2 + 10y + 4 \phantom{aa} \\
5y - 2 \overline{)\ 125y^3 \phantom{aaaaaaaa} - 8} \\
\underline{125y^3 - 50y^2} \phantom{aaaaaaaa} \\
50y^2 \phantom{aaaaaaa} \\
\underline{50y^2 - 20y} \phantom{aa} \\
20y - 8 \\
\underline{20y - 8} \\
0
\end{array}
$$

— Leave space for missing terms

**TRY THIS** ➡

Divide and check.

5. $(y^4 + y^2 - 20) \div (y + 2)$

**Example 5.** Divide: $(x^4 - 9x^2 - 5) \div (x - 2)$.

$$
\begin{array}{r}
x^3 + 2x^2 - 5x - 10 \\
x - 2 \overline{)x^4 \qquad - 9x^2 \qquad\quad - 5} \\
\underline{x^4 - 2x^3} \\
2x^3 - 9x^2 \\
\underline{2x^3 - 4x^2} \\
- 5x^2 \\
\underline{-5x^2 + 10x} \\
- 10x - 5 \\
\underline{- 10x + 20} \\
- 25
\end{array}
$$

The answer is $x^3 + 2x^2 - 5x - 10$, R $-25$, or

$$x^3 + 2x^2 - 5x - 10 + \frac{-25}{x - 2}.$$

**TRY THIS**

Divide and check.

6. $(y^3 - 11y^2 + 6) \div (y - 3)$
7. $(x^3 + 9x^2 - 5) \div (x^2 - 1)$

## Exercise Set 9-5

▌Divide. (*See Examples 1 and 2.*)

1. $\dfrac{30x^8 - 15x^6 + 40x^4}{5x^4}$

2. $\dfrac{24y^6 + 18y^5 - 36y^2}{6y^2}$

3. $\dfrac{-14a^3 + 28a^2 - 21a}{7a}$

4. $\dfrac{-32x^4 - 24x^3 - 12x^2}{4x}$

5. $(9y^4 - 18y^3 + 27y^2) \div 9y$

6. $(24a^3 + 28a^2 - 20a) \div 2a$

7. $(36x^6 - 18x^4 - 12x^2) \div -6x$

8. $(18y^7 - 27y^4 - 3y^2) \div -3y^2$

9. $(a^2b - a^3b^3 - a^5b^2) \div a^2b$

10. $(x^3y^2 - x^3y^3 - x^4y^2) \div x^2y^2$

11. $(6p^2q^2 - 9p^2q + 12pq^2) \div -3pq$

12. $(16y^4z^2 - 8y^6z^4 + 12y^8z^3) \div 4y^4z$

▌▌Divide and, if directed, check. (*See Examples 3–5.*)

13. $(x^2 + 10x + 21) \div (x + 3)$

14. $(y^2 - 8y + 16) \div (y - 4)$

15. $(a^2 - 8a - 16) \div (a + 4)$

16. $(y^2 - 10y - 25) \div (y - 5)$

17. $(x^2 + 7x + 14) \div (x + 5)$

18. $(t^2 - 7t - 9) \div (t - 3)$

19. $(y^2 - 25) \div (y + 5)$

20. $(a^2 - 81) \div (a - 9)$

21. $(y^3 - 4y^2 + 3y - 6) \div (y - 2)$

22. $(x^3 - 5x^2 + 4x - 7) \div (x - 3)$

23. $(a^3 - a + 12) \div (a - 4)$

24. $(x^3 - x + 6) \div (x + 2)$

25. $(8x^3 + 27) \div (2x + 3)$

26. $(64y^3 - 8) \div (4y - 2)$

27. $(x^4 - x^2 - 42) \div (x^2 - 7)$

28. $(y^4 - y^2 - 54) \div (y^2 - 3)$

29. $(x^4 - x^2 - x + 2) \div (x - 1)$

30. $(y^4 - y^2 - y + 3) \div (y + 1)$

# 9-6 Solving Fractional Equations

After finishing Lesson 9-6, you should be able to
■ solve fractional equations.

■ A fractional equation is an equation which contains one or more fractional expressions. These are fractional equations.

$$\frac{2}{3} + \frac{5}{6} = \frac{1}{x}, \qquad \frac{x-1}{x-5} = \frac{4}{x-5}$$

To solve a fractional equation we multiply on both sides by the LCM of all the denominators. This is called *clearing of fractions*.

**Example 1.** Solve: $\frac{2}{3} - \frac{5}{6} = \frac{1}{x}$.

The LCM of all denominators is $6x$, or $2 \cdot 3 \cdot x$. We multiply on both sides by this.

$$(2 \cdot 3 \cdot x) \cdot \left(\frac{2}{3} - \frac{5}{6}\right) = (2 \cdot 3 \cdot x) \cdot \frac{1}{x} \qquad \textit{Multiplying by LCM}$$

$$2 \cdot 3 \cdot x \cdot \frac{2}{3} - 2 \cdot 3 \cdot x \cdot \frac{5}{6} = 2 \cdot 3 \cdot x \cdot \frac{1}{x} \qquad \begin{array}{l}\textit{Multiplying to remove}\\\textit{parentheses}\end{array}$$

$$\frac{2 \cdot 3 \cdot x \cdot 2}{3} - \frac{2 \cdot 3 \cdot x \cdot 5}{6} = \frac{2 \cdot 3 \cdot x}{x}$$

$$4x - 5x = 6 \qquad \textit{Simplifying}$$

$$-x = 6$$

$$-1 \cdot x = 6$$

$$x = -6$$

Check: 
$$\frac{2}{3} - \frac{5}{6} = \frac{1}{x}$$

$$\begin{array}{c|c}
\frac{2}{3} - \frac{5}{6} & \frac{1}{-6} \\
\hline
\frac{4}{6} - \frac{5}{6} & -\frac{1}{6} \\
-\frac{1}{6} & 
\end{array}$$

Note that when we *clear of fractions* all the denominators disappear. Thus we have an equation without fractional expressions, which we know how to solve.

**TRY THIS**

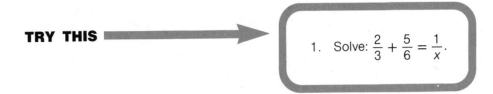

1. Solve: $\dfrac{2}{3} + \dfrac{5}{6} = \dfrac{1}{x}$.

When clearing of fractions, always be sure to multiply *all* terms in the equation by the LCM.

When we multiply by an expression with a variable, we may not get equivalent equations. Thus we must *always* check possible solutions in the original equation.

**Example 2.** Solve: $\dfrac{x-1}{x-5} = \dfrac{4}{x-5}$.

The LCM of the denominators is $x - 5$. We multiply by $x - 5$.

$$(x-5)\cdot \dfrac{x-1}{x-5} = (x-5)\cdot \dfrac{4}{x-5}$$
$$x - 1 = 4$$
$$x = 5$$

Check:  $\dfrac{x-1}{x-5} = \dfrac{4}{x-5}$

$$\begin{array}{c|c} \dfrac{5-1}{5-5} & \dfrac{4}{5-5} \\[2mm] \dfrac{4}{0} & \dfrac{4}{0} \end{array}$$

5 is not a solution of the original equation because it results in division by 0. In fact, the equation has no solution.

**TRY THIS**

2. Solve: $\dfrac{x-7}{x-9} = \dfrac{2}{x-9}$.

**Remark.** Example 2 above again illustrates the fact that when we prove a theorem we cannot make any statements about the converse of the theorem. In Example 2 we proved "If $\dfrac{x-1}{x-5} = \dfrac{4}{x-5}$, then $x = 5$." The converse of this theorem is "If $x = 5$, then $\dfrac{x-1}{x-5} = \dfrac{4}{x-5}$." The converse is not true. The check shows this.

In general, when in solving an equation we multiply by an expression containing a variable, we may get an equation having solutions that the original one does not.

**Example 3.**  Solve: $\dfrac{x^2}{x-2} = \dfrac{4}{x-2}$.

The LCM of all the denominators is $x - 2$. We multiply by $x - 2$ to clear of fractions.

$$(x-2)\cdot\frac{x^2}{x-2} = (x-2)\cdot\frac{4}{x-2}$$
$$x^2 = 4$$
$$x^2 - 4 = 0$$
$$(x+2)(x-2) = 0$$

$$x = -2 \quad \text{or} \quad x = 2 \qquad \textit{Using the principle of zero products}$$

The number $-2$ checks, but 2 does not (it results in division by 0). The solution is $-2$.

**TRY THIS**

3. Solve: $\dfrac{x^2}{x+3} = \dfrac{9}{x+3}$.

# Exercise Set 9-6

❚ Solve. (*See Examples 1–3.*)

1. $\dfrac{2}{5} + \dfrac{7}{8} = \dfrac{y}{20}$

2. $\dfrac{4}{5} + \dfrac{1}{3} = \dfrac{t}{9}$

3. $\dfrac{1}{3} - \dfrac{5}{6} = \dfrac{1}{x}$

4. $\dfrac{5}{8} - \dfrac{2}{5} = \dfrac{1}{y}$

5. $\dfrac{x}{3} - \dfrac{x}{4} = 12$

6. $\dfrac{y}{5} - \dfrac{y}{3} = 15$

7. $y + \dfrac{5}{y} = -6$

8. $x + \dfrac{4}{x} = -5$

9. $\dfrac{4}{z} + \dfrac{2}{z} = 3$

10. $\dfrac{4}{3y} - \dfrac{3}{y} = \dfrac{10}{3}$

11. $\dfrac{x-3}{x+2} = \dfrac{1}{5}$

12. $\dfrac{y-5}{y+1} = \dfrac{3}{5}$

13. $\dfrac{3}{y+1} = \dfrac{2}{y-3}$

14. $\dfrac{4}{x-1} = \dfrac{3}{x+2}$

15. $\dfrac{y-1}{y-3} = \dfrac{2}{y-3}$

16. $\dfrac{x-2}{x-4} = \dfrac{2}{x-4}$

17. $\dfrac{x+1}{x} = \dfrac{3}{2}$

18. $\dfrac{y+2}{y} = \dfrac{5}{3}$

19. $\dfrac{2}{x} - \dfrac{3}{x} + \dfrac{4}{x} = 5$

20. $\dfrac{4}{y} - \dfrac{6}{y} + \dfrac{8}{y} = 8$

21. $\dfrac{1}{2} - \dfrac{4}{9x} = \dfrac{4}{9} - \dfrac{1}{6x}$

22. $-\dfrac{1}{3} - \dfrac{5}{4y} = \dfrac{3}{4} - \dfrac{1}{6y}$

23. $\dfrac{60}{x} - \dfrac{60}{x-5} = \dfrac{2}{x}$

24. $\dfrac{50}{y} - \dfrac{50}{y-2} = \dfrac{4}{y}$

25. $\dfrac{7}{5x-2} = \dfrac{5}{4x}$

26. $\dfrac{5}{y+4} = \dfrac{3}{y-2}$

27. $\dfrac{x}{x-2} + \dfrac{x}{x^2-4} = \dfrac{x+3}{x+2}$

28. $\dfrac{3}{y-2} + \dfrac{2y}{4-y^2} = \dfrac{5}{y+2}$

29. $\dfrac{a}{2a-6} - \dfrac{3}{a^2-6a+9} = \dfrac{a-2}{3a-9}$

30. $\dfrac{2}{x+4} + \dfrac{2x-1}{x^2+2x-8} = \dfrac{1}{x-2}$

**BIOGRAPHICAL NOTE: Diophantus**

The early Greek mathematicians focused their studies on geometry. Diophantus, a Greek who lived hundreds of years after Euclid and Archimedes, focused on algebra. He introduced new symbols into mathematical writing. He also studied equations in several variables that have only positive integers as solutions. Today, these are called Diophantine equations.

Little is known about the life of Diophantus. However, one famous problem about him may give some accurate information: His boyhood lasted $\frac{1}{6}$ of his life. His beard grew after $\frac{1}{12}$ more. After $\frac{1}{7}$ more of his life he married. His son was born 5 years later. The son lived to $\frac{1}{2}$ Diophantus's age. Diophantus died 4 years after his son died. What was his age at his death? In modern terms,

$x = \frac{1}{6}x + \frac{1}{12}x + \frac{1}{7}x + 5 + \frac{1}{2}x + 4$. So $x = 84$.

Diophantus is known to have lived and worked in Alexandria, Egypt. The date of his death is about A.D. 320.

# 9-7 Formulas

After finishing Lesson 9-7, you should be able to
▮ solve a formula for a given letter.

▮As mentioned earlier the skill of solving formulas for a letter is important in applications of mathematics to many fields, such as science, engineering, and technology.

**Example 1.** Solve $\frac{PV}{T} = k$ for $T$.

We multiply by the LCM, which is $T$:

$$T \cdot \frac{PV}{T} = T \cdot k$$

$$\frac{T}{T} \cdot PV = Tk$$

$$PV = Tk$$

$$\frac{PV}{k} = T$$

**TRY THIS** ━━━━━▶

> 1.  Solve $\frac{E}{R} = I$, for $R$.

**Example 2.** Solve $\frac{1}{R} = \frac{1}{r_1} + \frac{1}{r_2}$, for $r_1$.

We multiply by the LCM, which is $Rr_1r_2$.

$$Rr_1r_2 \cdot \frac{1}{R} = Rr_1r_2 \cdot \left( \frac{1}{r_1} + \frac{1}{r_2} \right)$$

$$Rr_1r_2 \cdot \frac{1}{R} = Rr_1r_2 \cdot \frac{1}{r_1} + Rr_1r_2 \cdot \frac{1}{r_2} \qquad \text{\textit{Using a distributive law}}$$

$$\frac{R}{R} \cdot r_1r_2 = \frac{r_1}{r_1} \cdot Rr_2 + \frac{r_2}{r_2} \cdot Rr_1$$

$$r_1r_2 = Rr_2 + Rr_1 \qquad \text{\textit{Simplifying}}$$

We might be tempted at this point to multiply by $\frac{1}{r_2}$ to get $r_1$ alone on the left, BUT note that there is an $r_1$ on the right. We must get all the terms involving $r_1$ on the *same side* of the equation.

$$r_1r_2 - Rr_1 = Rr_2 \quad \text{Adding } -Rr_1$$
$$r_1(r_2 - R) = Rr_2$$
$$r_1 = \frac{Rr_2}{r_2 - R}$$

**TRY THIS** ➡

2.  Solve $\dfrac{1}{R} = \dfrac{1}{r_1} + \dfrac{1}{r_2}$, for $R$.

## Exercise Set 9-7

▮Solve each formula for the given letter. (*See Examples 1 and 2.*)

1.  $\dfrac{W_1}{W_2} = \dfrac{d_1}{d_2}$; $d_1$

2.  $\dfrac{W_1}{W_2} = \dfrac{d_1}{d_2}$; $W_2$

3.  $S = \dfrac{(v_1 + v_2)t}{2}$; $t$

4.  $S = \dfrac{(v_1 + v_2)t}{2}$; $v_1$

5.  $\dfrac{1}{R} = \dfrac{1}{R_1} + \dfrac{1}{R_2}$; $R_1$

6.  $\dfrac{1}{R} = \dfrac{1}{R_1} + \dfrac{1}{R_2}$; $R$

7.  $R = \dfrac{gs}{g + s}$; $s$

8.  $R = \dfrac{gs}{g + s}$; $g$

9.  $I = \dfrac{2V}{R + 2r}$; $r$

10.  $I = \dfrac{2V}{R + 2r}$; $R$

11.  $\dfrac{1}{p} + \dfrac{1}{q} = \dfrac{1}{f}$; $f$

12.  $\dfrac{1}{p} + \dfrac{1}{q} = \dfrac{1}{f}$; $p$

13.  $I = \dfrac{nE}{R + nr}$; $r$

14.  $I = \dfrac{nE}{R + nr}$; $n$

15.  $S = \dfrac{H}{m(t_1 - t_2)}$; $H$

16.  $\dfrac{H}{m(t_1 - t_2)}$; $t_1$

17.  $\dfrac{E}{e} = \dfrac{R + r}{r}$; $e$

18.  $\dfrac{E}{e} = \dfrac{R + r}{r}$; $r$

19.  $S = \dfrac{a - ar^n}{1 - r}$; $a$

20.  $S = \dfrac{a}{1 - r}$; $r$

**MATHEMATICAL NOTE: & = +**

One of the first mathematical symbols a student learns is $+$.
It appears in simple addition. It appears also in polynomials.
Where did the symbol come from? It may have developed
from the ampersand, &. When an ampersand is written very
quickly, it resembles a plus sign. Writers of mathematics
may have used $+$ as a quick and easy substitute for &.

# 9-8 Solving Problems

After finishing Lesson 9-8, you should be able to
▌ solve problems using fractional equations.

▌ Sometimes fractional equations can help in solving problems.

**Example 1.** The reciprocal of 2 more than a number is three times the reciprocal of the number. Find the number.

Letting $x$ represent the number, we translate.

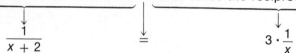

Reciprocal of 2 more than a number is three times the reciprocal of the number

$$\frac{1}{x+2} \qquad = \qquad 3 \cdot \frac{1}{x}$$

The LCM is $x(x+2)$.

$$\frac{x(x+2)}{x+2} = \frac{3x(x+2)}{x}$$
$$x = 3(x+2)$$
$$x = 3x + 6$$
$$x = -3$$

Check: Go to the original problem. The number to be checked is $-3$. Two more than this is $-1$. The reciprocal of $-1$ is $-1$. The reciprocal of the number itself is $\frac{1}{-3}$ and three times this is $-1$.

So, $-3$ is the solution.

### TRY THIS

1. The reciprocal of 2 less than a certain number is twice the reciprocal of the number itself. What is the number?

Recall the definition of speed, $r = \frac{d}{t}$, and the other two formulas easily obtained from this one, $d = rt$ and $t = \frac{d}{r}$.

**Example 2.** An airplane flies 1062 km with the wind in the same time that it takes to fly 738 km against the wind. The speed of the plane in still air is 200 km/h. Find the speed of the wind.

We first make a drawing.
We let $r$ represent the speed
of the wind and summarize the
facts in a chart.

1062 km        $t_1$ hours

200 + $r$ (The wind increases the speed.)

$t_2$ hours        738 km

200 − $r$ (The wind decreases the speed.)

|  | $r$ | $d$ | $t$ |
|---|---|---|---|
| With wind | $200 + r$ | $d_1 = 1062$ | $t_1$ |
| Against wind | $200 - r$ | $d_2 = 738$ | $t_2$ |

The times are the same, so $t_1 = t_2$. From $t = \dfrac{d}{r}$ we have

$$t_1 = \frac{1062}{200 + r} \text{ and } t_2 = \frac{738}{200 - r}.$$

Since $t_1 = t_2$ it follows that

$$\frac{1062}{200 + r} = \frac{738}{200 - r}$$

Solving for $r$, we get 36. This checks. Thus the
speed of the wind is 36 km/h.

**TRY THIS**

2. A boat travels 246 km
downstream in the same
amount of time that it takes
to travel 180 km upstream.
The speed of the current in
the stream is 5.5 km/h.
Find the speed of the boat
in still water.

Suppose a person can do a job in 5 hours. Then in 1 hour $\frac{1}{5}$ of
the job is done and in 3 hours $\frac{3}{5}$ of it can be done.

If a job can be done in $t$ hours (or days), then $\dfrac{1}{t}$ of it can be

done in 1 hour (or day).

**Example 3.** Lon Moore can mow a lawn in 4 hours. Penny
Push can mow the same lawn in 5 hours. How long would it take
both of them, working together, to mow the lawn?

Lon can mow the lawn in 4 hours. Thus he can mow $\frac{1}{4}$ of it in 1
hour. Penny can mow the lawn in 5 hours. Thus she can mow $\frac{1}{5}$
of it in 1 hour. Thus they can mow $\frac{1}{4} + \frac{1}{5}$ of it in 1 hour. Let $t$
represent the amount of time it takes them to mow the lawn if
they work together. Then they mow $\dfrac{1}{t}$ of the lawn in 1 hour. Thus

$$\frac{1}{4} + \frac{1}{5} = \frac{1}{t}.$$

Solving for $t$, we get $t = 2\frac{2}{9}$ hours. This checks. Thus it takes Lon and Penny $2\frac{2}{9}$ hours to mow the lawn working together.

**TRY THIS** ➜

3. Fred Huntinpeck does a certain typing job in 6 hours. Fran Ikfingers can do the same job in 4 hours. How long would it take both persons, working together, to do the same amount of typing?

**Example 4.** At a factory, smokestack A pollutes the air twice as fast as smokestack B. When the stacks operate together they yield a certain amount of pollution in 15 hours. Find the amount of time it would take each to yield the same amount of pollution if it operated alone.

Let $x$ represent the amount of time it takes smokestack A to yield the pollution. Then $2x$ represents the amount of time it takes smokestack B to yield the pollution. Then

$\dfrac{1}{x}$ is the amount of pollution yielded in 1 hour by A.

$\dfrac{1}{2x}$ is the amount of pollution yielded in 1 hour by B.

In 1 hour both stacks yield $\dfrac{1}{x} + \dfrac{1}{2x}$ of the pollution. They also

yield $\dfrac{1}{15}$ of it. We have the equation

$$\frac{1}{x} + \frac{1}{2x} = \frac{1}{15}.$$

Solving for $x$, we get $x = 22\frac{1}{2}$ hours, and $2x = 45$ hours. This checks. Thus stack B takes 45 hours to yield the pollution and stack A takes $22\frac{1}{2}$ hours.

**TRY THIS** ➜

4. Two pipes carry water to the same tank. Pipe A, working alone, can fill the tank three times as fast as pipe B. Working together the pipes can fill the tank in 24 hours. Find the time each would take to fill the tank alone.

# Exercise Set 9-8

▮Solve. (*See Examples 1–4.*)

1. The reciprocal of 5 plus the reciprocal of 7 is the reciprocal of what number?

2. The reciprocal of 3 plus the reciprocal of 6 is the reciprocal of what number?

3. The sum of a number and 6 times its reciprocal is −5. Find the number.

4. The sum of a number and 21 times its reciprocal is −10. Find the number.

5. In a fractional numeral the numerator is 3 more than the denominator. If 2 is added to both numerator and denominator, the result is $\frac{3}{2}$. Find the original fractional numeral.

6. In a fractional numeral the denominator is 8 more than the numerator. If 5 is added to both numerator and denominator, the result is $\frac{1}{2}$. Find the original fractional numeral.

7. The speed of a stream is 3 km/h. A boat travels 4 km upstream in the same time it takes to travel 10 km downstream. What is the speed of the boat in still water?

8. The speed of a stream is 4 km/h. A boat travels 6 km upstream in the same time it takes to travel 12 km downstream. What is the speed of the boat in still water?

9. The speed of Train A is 12 km/h slower than the speed of Train B. Train A travels 230 km in the same time it takes Train B to travel 290 km. Find the speed of each train.

10. The speed of a passenger train is 14 km/h faster than the speed of a freight train. The passenger train travels 400 km in the same time it takes the freight train to travel 330 km. Find the speed of each train.

11. George Skiff has a boat that can move at a speed of 15 km/h in still water. He rides 140 km downstream in a river in the same time it takes to ride 35 km upstream. What is the speed of the river?

12. A paddleboat can move at a speed of 2 km/h in still water. The boat is paddled 4 km downstream in a river in the same time it takes to go 1 km upstream. What is the speed of the river?

13. Ollie Carr has just enough money to rent a canoe for $1\frac{1}{2}$ hours. How far out on a lake can he paddle and return on time if he paddles out at 2 km/h and back at 4 km/h?

14. Polly Paddle has just enough money to rent a canoe for $2\frac{1}{2}$ hours. How far out on the lake can she paddle and return on time if she paddles out at 3 km/h and back at 2 km/h?

15. Sam Strong, an experienced shipping clerk, can fill a certain order in 5 hours. Willy Weak, a new clerk, needs 9 hours to do the same job. Working together, how long would it take them to fill the order?

16. Paul Putty can paint a room in 4 hours. Sally Spackle can paint the same room in 3 hours. Working together, how long would it take them to paint the room?

17. Harry Hammer can frame in a room in 5 hours. Sue Saul can do the same job in 4 hours. Working together, how long will it take them to frame in a room?

18. Sally Stilson can complete a plumbing job in 6 hours. Wally Wrench can do the same job in 4 hours. Working together, how long will it take them to complete the job?

19. A swimming pool can be filled in 12 hours if water enters through a pipe alone, or in 30 hours if water enters through a hose alone. If water is entering through the pipe and the hose, how long will it take to fill the pool?

20. A tank can be filled in 18 hours by pipe A alone and in 22 hours by pipe B alone. How long would it take to fill the tank if both pipes were working?

21. One car goes 25 km/h faster than another. While one goes 300 km the other goes 450 km. Find their speeds.

22. One car goes 30 km/h faster than another. While one goes 450 km the other goes 600 km. Find their speeds.

23. Bull Dozer can clear a lot in 5.5 hours. His partner can do the same job in 7.5 hours. How long would it take them to clear the lot working together?

24. One of Ty Psetter's printing presses can print an order of booklets in 4.5 hours. Another press can do the same job in 5.5 hours. How long would it take if both presses are used?

### SCIENCE NOTE: Weight and Mass

Weight is a measure of the pull of gravity on an object. A golf ball, for example, has a certain weight on earth. It has a different weight on the moon. The force of gravity is less there, so the golf ball weighs less.

Mass is the amount of matter in an object. It is not changed by changes in gravity. The golf ball's mass is the same on earth as it is on the moon.

Grams and kilograms are really measures of mass. Technically, a weight should not be stated in grams. The correct unit for stating weight is the newton. It is named for the great English mathematician and physicist, Sir Isaac Newton. It is a unit of force. On the surface of the earth, the force of gravity is roughly the same in all places. Differences in weight on earth are equivalent to differences in mass. So weights are commonly stated in terms of grams and kilograms.

# 9-9 Variation

After finishing Lesson 9-9, you should be able to
**I** find an equation of variation given a description of direct variation.
**II** solve problems involving direct variation.
**III** find an equation of variation given a description of inverse variation.
**IIII** solve problems involving inverse variation.

## I Direct Variation

A plumber earns $9 per hour. In 1 hour, $9 is earned. In 2 hours, $18 is earned. In 3 hours, $27 is earned, and so on. This gives rise to a set of ordered pairs of numbers, all having the same ratio:

(1, 9), (2, 18), (3, 27), (4, 36), and so on.

The ratio of earnings to time is always $\frac{9}{1}$, or 9.

Whenever a situation gives rise to pairs of numbers in which the ratio is constant, we say that there is *direct variation*. Here the earnings vary directly as the time.

$$\frac{e}{t} = 9 \text{ (a constant), or } e = 9t$$

### DEFINITION
Whenever a situation gives rise to a relation among variables $y = kx$, where $k$ is a constant, we say that there is *direct* variation, or that y *varies directly as* x. The number $k$ is called the *variation constant*.

**Example 1.** Find an equation of variation where $y$ varies directly as $x$, and $y = 32$ when $x = 2$.

First substitute to find $k$.

$$y = kx$$
$$32 = k \cdot 2$$
$$\frac{32}{2} = k, \text{ or } k = 16$$

Then the equation of variation is $y = 16x$.

**TRY THIS** ➡

Find an equation of variation where $y$ varies directly as $x$, and

1. $y = 8$ when $x = 20$
2. $y = 5.6$ when $x = 8$

## ⅠⅠ Direct Variation Problems

**Example 2.** The number of centimeters $W$ of water which is produced from melting snow varies directly as the number of centimeters $S$ of snow. Meteorologists have found that 150 cm of snow will melt to 16.8 cm of water. 200 cm of snow will melt to how many centimeters of water?

a) First find an equation of variation.

$$W = kS$$
$$16.8 = k \cdot 150$$
$$\frac{16.8}{150} = k$$
$$0.112 = k$$

The equation of variation is $W = 0.112S$.

b) Use the equation to find how many centimeters of water will result from 200 cm of snow.

$$W = 0.112S$$
$$W = 0.112(200)$$
$$W = 22.4$$

200 cm of snow will melt to 22.4 cm of water.

**TRY THIS** ▬▬▬▶

3. *Ecology Problem.* The amount of garbage $G$ produced in the United States varies directly as the number of people $N$ who produce the garbage. It is known that 50 tons of garbage is produced by 200 people in 1 year. The population of San Francisco is about 700,000. About how much garbage is produced by people in San Francisco in 1 year?

## ⅠⅠⅠ Inverse Variation

A bus is traveling a distance of 20 km. At a speed of 20 km/h, it will take 1 hour. At 40 km/h, it will take $\frac{1}{2}$ hour. At 60 km/h it will take $\frac{1}{3}$ hour, and so on. This gives rise to a set of pairs of numbers, all having the same product:

$$(20, 1), (40, \tfrac{1}{2}), (60, \tfrac{1}{3}), (80, \tfrac{1}{4}), \text{ and so on.}$$

Note that as the first number gets larger the second number gets smaller. Whenever a situation gives rise to pairs of numbers whose product is constant, we say that there is *inverse variation*. Here the *time varies inversely as the speed.*

$$rt = 20 \text{ (a constant) or } t = \frac{20}{r}$$

**DEFINITION**
Whenever a situation gives rise to a relation among variables
$y = \dfrac{k}{x}$, where $k$ is a constant, we say that there is *inverse varia-*
*tion,* or that y *varies inversely as* x. The number $k$ is called the
*variation constant.*

**Example 3.**  Find an equation of variation where $y$ varies inversely as $x$, and $y = 32$ when $x = 0.2$.

First substitute to find $k$.

$$y = \frac{k}{x}$$
$$32 = \frac{k}{0.2}$$
$$(0.2)32 = k$$
$$6.4 = k$$

The equation of variation is $y = \dfrac{6.4}{x}$.

**TRY THIS**

4.  Find an equation of variation where $y$ varies in-
versely as $x$, and
$y = 0.012$ when $x = 50$.

## ⅠⅠⅠⅠ Inverse Variation Problems

**Example 4.**  The time $t$ required to do a certain job varies inversely as the number $P$ of people who work on the job (assuming each does the same amount of work). It takes 4 hours for 12
people to erect some football bleachers. How long would it take
3 people to do the same job?

a)  First, find an equation of variation.

$$t = \frac{k}{P}$$
$$4 = \frac{k}{12} \qquad \textit{Substituting}$$
$$12 \cdot 4 = k$$
$$48 = k$$

The equation of variation is $t = \dfrac{48}{P}$.

b) Use the equation to find the time it would take 3 people to do the same job.

$$t = \frac{48}{P}$$

$$t = \frac{48}{3} \quad \text{Substituting 3 for P}$$

$$= 16$$

It would take 16 hours.

**TRY THIS**

> 5. The time $t$ required to drive a fixed distance varies inversely as the speed $r$. It takes 5 hours at 60 km/h to drive a fixed distance. How long would it take to drive the fixed distance at 40 km/h?

## Exercise Set 9-9

▪Find an equation of variation where $y$ varies directly as $x$ and the following are true. (*See Example 1.*)

1. $y = 24$ when $x = 3$
2. $y = 5$ when $x = 12$
3. $y = -6$ when $x = 1$
4. $y = 2$ when $x = 5$
5. $y = 15$ when $x = 3$
6. $y = 1$ when $x = -2$
7. $y = 30$ when $x = 8$
8. $y = -1$ when $x = 1$
9. $y = 0.8$ when $x = 0.5$
10. $y = 0.6$ when $x = 0.4$

▪▪Solve. (*See Example 2.*)

11. The electric current $I$, in amperes, in a circuit varies directly as the voltage $V$. When 12 volts are applied, the current is 4 amperes. What is the current when 18 volts are applied?

12. Hooke's law states that the distance $d$ a spring is stretched by a hanging object varies directly as the weight $w$ of the object. If the distance is 40 cm when the weight is 3 kg, what is the distance when the weight is 5 kg?

13. The number $N$ of plastic straws produced by a machine varies directly as the amount of time $t$ the machine is operating. If the machine produces 20,000 straws in 8 hours, how many straws can it produce in 50 hours?

14. The number $N$ of aluminum cans used each year varies directly as the number of people using the cans. If 250 people use 60,000 cans in one year, how many cans are used each year in Dallas, population 850,000?

15. The amount of pollution $A$ entering the atmosphere varies directly as the number of people $N$ living in an area. If 60,000 people result in 42,600 tons of pollutants entering the atmosphere, how many tons enter the atmosphere in a city with a population of 750,000?

16. The weight $M$ of an object on the moon varies directly as its weight $E$ on earth. A person who weighs 95 kg on earth weighs 15.2 kg on the moon. How much would a 105 kg person weigh on the moon?

17. The weight $M$ of an object on Mars varies directly as its weight $E$ on earth. A person who weighs 95 kilograms on earth weighs 38 kg on Mars. How much would a 100 kg person weigh on Mars?

18. The number of kilograms of water $W$ in a human body varies directly as the total weight. A person weighing 96 kg contains 64 kg of water. How many kilograms of water are in a person weighing 75 kg?

**▮▮▮** Find an equation of variation where $y$ varies inversely as $x$, and the following are true. (*See Example 3.*)

19. $y = 6$ when $x = 10$
20. $y = 16$ when $x = 4$
21. $y = 4$ when $x = 3$
22. $y = 4$ when $x = 9$
23. $y = 12$ when $x = 3$
24. $y = 9$ when $x = 5$
25. $y = 27$ when $x = \frac{1}{3}$
26. $y = 81$ when $x = \frac{1}{9}$
27. $y = 0.4$ when $x = 0.8$
28. $y = 1.5$ when $x = 0.3$

**▮▮▮▮** Solve. (*See Example 4.*)

29. The current $I$ in an electrical conductor varies inversely as the resistance $R$ of the conductor. If the current is $\frac{1}{2}$ ampere when the resistance is 240 ohms, what is the current when the resistance is 540 ohms?

30. The time $t$ required to empty a tank varies inversely as the rate $r$ of pumping. If a pump can empty a tank in 45 minutes at the rate of 600 kl per minute, how long will it take the pump to empty the same tank at the rate of 1000 kl per minute?

31. The volume $V$ of a gas varies inversely as the pressure $P$ upon it. The volume of a gas is 200 cm³ under a pressure of 32 kg/cm². What will be its volume under a pressure of 40 kg/cm²?

32. The time $T$ required to do a job varies inversely as the number of people $P$ working. It takes 5 hours for 7 bricklayers to complete a certain job. How long would it take 10 bricklayers to complete the job?

33. The time $t$ required to drive a fixed distance varies inversely as the speed $r$. It takes 5 hours at 80 km/h to drive a fixed distance; how long would it take to drive the fixed distance at 60 km/h?

34. The wavelength $W$ of a radio wave varies inversely as its frequency $F$. A wave with a frequency of 1200 kilohertz per second has a length of 300 meters. What is the length of a wave with a frequency of 800 kilohertz per second?

35. The weight $W$ that a horizontal beam can support varies inversely as the length $L$ of the beam? Suppose an 8-meter beam can support 1200 kilograms. How many kilograms can a 14-meter beam support?

36. The length $L$ of rectangles of fixed area varies inversely as the width $W$. Suppose the length is 64 m when the width is 3 m. Find the length when the width is 12 m. What is the fixed area?

## CHAPTER 9 REVIEW

Review the material in the chapter. Then see how you have done by trying these review exercises. If you miss an exercise, restudy the indicated lesson.

9-1    1.   Simplify: $\dfrac{3x^2 - 4x - 4}{4x^2 - 3x - 10}$.

9-1    2.   Multiply and simplify: $\dfrac{x^2 - 64}{8x} \cdot \dfrac{4x}{x + 8}$.

9-1    3.   Divide and simplify: $\dfrac{6y^4}{y^2 - 9} \div \dfrac{3y^2}{2y^2 + 7y + 3}$

9-3    Add.

     4.   $\dfrac{a + 9}{a + 3} + \dfrac{12 - 5a}{a + 3}$

     5.   $\dfrac{y + 2}{y - 3} + \dfrac{y}{3 - y}$

     6.   $\dfrac{5}{4x - 2} + \dfrac{x + 3}{4x^2 - 4x + 1}$

9-3    Subtract.

     7.   $\dfrac{8y}{y - 4} - \dfrac{12y}{y - 4}$

     8.   $\dfrac{a + 5}{a - 7} - \dfrac{a}{7 - a}$

     9.   $\dfrac{7}{x^2 - 81} - \dfrac{x - 4}{3x^2 - 25x - 18}$

9-4    10.   Simplify: $\dfrac{\dfrac{1}{2x} - 3}{\dfrac{1}{x} - 4}$.

9-5    11.   Divide: $2x - 3 \overline{\smash{)}4x^4 - 5x^2 + 2x - 10}$.

9-6    12.   Solve: $\dfrac{15}{y} - \dfrac{15}{y - 2} = -2$.

9-7    13.   Solve for $P$: $T = Rn + \dfrac{mn}{P}$.

9-8    14.   In a fractional numeral, the numerator is 16 more than the denominator. If the numerator is decreased by 3, the result is equal to $\frac{4}{3}$. Find the original fractional numeral.

9-9    15.   The number $N$ of parts a punch press can produce varies directly as the time it operates. It can produce 1200 parts in 2 hours. How many can it produce in 5 hours?

9-9    16.   The time $T$ required to do a certain job varies inversely as the number of people $P$ working. It takes 16 hours for 2 people to repaint a gymnasium. How long would it take 6 people to do the job?

## CHAPTER 9 TEST

1. Simplify: $\dfrac{5x^2 + 38x + 21}{3x^2 + 22x + 7}$.

2. Multiply and simplify: $\dfrac{y^2 - 100}{9y} \cdot \dfrac{3y}{y + 10}$.

3. Divide and simplify: $\dfrac{8t^5}{t^2 - 25} \div \dfrac{4t^2}{7t^2 - 34t - 5}$.

Add.

4. $\dfrac{x + 3}{x + 8} + \dfrac{14 - 5x}{x + 8}$

5. $\dfrac{t + 9}{t - 5} + \dfrac{2t}{5 - t}$

6. $\dfrac{4}{5x - 15} + \dfrac{x + 8}{4x^2 - 11x - 3}$

Subtract.

7. $\dfrac{9x}{x - 5} - \dfrac{15x}{x - 5}$

8. $\dfrac{p + 7}{3 - p} - \dfrac{p}{p - 3}$

9. $\dfrac{8}{y^2 - 64} - \dfrac{y - 5}{2y^2 - 15y - 8}$

10. Simplify: $\dfrac{\dfrac{1}{3a} - 4}{\dfrac{1}{2a} - 1}$.

11. Divide: $a + 3 \overline{\smash)2a^3 - 13a + 15}$.

12. Solve: $\dfrac{15}{x} - \dfrac{15}{x + 2} = 2$.

13. Solve for $T$: $\dfrac{E}{e} = \dfrac{T + r}{r}$.

14. One car travels 90 km in the same time a car going 10 km/h slower travels 60 km. Find the speed of each.

15. The amount of garbage $G$ produced in the United States varies directly as the number of people $N$ who produce the garbage. It is known that 50 tons of garbage is produced by 200 people in 1 year. The population of Minneapolis is 434,400. How much garbage is produced by Minneapolis in 1 year?

16. The cost $C$, per person, of renting a beach cottage varies inversely as the number of people $N$ who rent the cottage. It costs $12 per person for 4 people to rent the cottage for a day. How much does it cost per person for 6 people to rent the cottage?

## Ready for Exponents, Powers, and Roots?

1-2 Simplify.

1. $|-8|$        2. $|0|$        3. $|\sqrt{3}|$

2-2 Solve.

4. $(x + 5)(x - 7) = 0$
5. $3x(3x + 5) = 0$

1-8 Multiply and simplify.

6. $y^7 \cdot y^3$
7. $8^3 \cdot 8^{-2}$
8. $(3x^2y^{-4})(4x^3y^2)$

1-8 Divide.

9. $\dfrac{4^8}{4^2}$      10. $\dfrac{7^8}{7^{-2}}$      11. $\dfrac{5^{-3}}{5^3}$

12. $\dfrac{3^{-4}}{3^{-6}}$      13. $\dfrac{y^4}{y^6}$      14. $\dfrac{32x^3y^{10}}{4x^4y^4}$

1-8 Simplify.

15. $(4^2)^4$
16. $(a^{-3})^{-4}$
17. $(4xy^{-3})^3$
18. $(10x^3y^{-2}z^{-4})^2$

2-2 Solve.

19. $4x - 1 = 15$
20. $2(8 - 3x) = 3 - 5(x - 1)$

7-2 Factor.

21. $x^2 - 12x + 36$
22. $9y^2 - 12y + 4$
23. $4y^2 + 28xy + 49x^2$
24. $16x^4 - 40x^2y^4 + 25y^8$
25. $-27x^2 + 36x - 12$
26. $x^2 - 6x - 16$
27. $x^2 - 13x + 36$

# Chapter 10
# Exponents, Powers, and Roots

How long should the letters of a road message be
to be the most recognizable?

# 10-1 Scientific Notation

After finishing Lesson 10-1, you should be able to
**I** simplify expressions involving integer exponents.
**II** convert from decimal notation to scientific notation and from scientific notation to decimal notation.
**III** multiply and divide using scientific notation.

## I Integer Exponents

Recall some of the definitions and properties of integer exponents.

$a^1 = a$                   $a^m a^n = a^{m+n}$     (*Theorem 1-4*)

$a^0 = 1, a \neq 0$           $\dfrac{a^m}{a^n} = a^{m-n}$     (*Theorem 1-5*)

$a^{-n} = \dfrac{1}{a^n}, a \neq 0$     $(a^m)^n = a^{mn}$     (*Theorem 1-6*)

**Examples.** Simplify.

**1.** $(4xy)^1 = 4xy$

**2.** $(-8x^3y^7)^0 = 1$ assuming neither $x$ nor $y$ is 0

**3.** $5x^{-3}y^{-4} = 5 \cdot \dfrac{1}{x^3} \cdot \dfrac{1}{y^4} = \dfrac{5}{x^3y^4}$

**4.** $(-8x^5y^7)(4x^3y^{-2}) = -32x^8y^5$     *Using Theorem 1-4*

**5.** $\dfrac{42x^8y^3}{21x^4y^8} = 2x^4y^{-5}$     *Using Theorem 1-5*

**6.** $(5x^{-2}y^4)^3 = 5^3x^{-6}y^{12} = 125x^{-6}y^{12}$     *Using Theorem 1-6*

**TRY THIS** ➡

Simplify.

1. $(-9ab^2)^1$
2. $(-9x^2y)^0$
3. $-2a^{-5}b^{-6}$
4. $(x^2 + y^2)^{-3}$
5. $30a^4 \cdot 6a^{-9}$
6. $(-5a^2b^{-3})(4a^{-3}b^6)$
7. $\dfrac{-24x^{-3}y^5}{6x^5y^7}$
8. $\dfrac{10a^3b^2c^5}{15a^5b^7c^2}$
9. $(y^{-4})^6$
10. $(8a^2b^{-4})^3$

Note the following.

$$\left(\frac{x}{y}\right)^3 = \frac{x}{y} \cdot \frac{x}{y} \cdot \frac{x}{y} = \frac{x \cdot x \cdot x}{y \cdot y \cdot y} = \frac{x^3}{y^3}$$

This illustrates the following new theorem.

**THEOREM 10-1**

For any real numbers $a$ and $b$, $b \neq 0$, and any integer $n$,

$$\left(\frac{a}{b}\right)^n = \frac{a^n}{b^n}$$

**Example 7.** Simplify.

$$\left(\frac{4x^2}{y}\right)^3 = \frac{(4x^2)^3}{y^3} = \frac{4^3x^6}{y^3} = \frac{64x^6}{y^3}$$

**TRY THIS** ➡

> Simplify.
>
> 11. $\left(\dfrac{a}{b}\right)^4$
>
> 12. $\left(\dfrac{x^2y^{-3}}{3a}\right)^4$

## ▪ Scientific Notation

Scientific notation is useful when calculations involve large or small numbers.

**DEFINITION**

Scientific notation for a number consists of exponential notation for a power of 10 and, if needed, a decimal numeral for a number between 1 and 10, and a multiplication sign.

We can convert to scientific notation by multiplying by 1, choosing an appropriate symbol $\dfrac{10^k}{10^k}$ for 1.

**Example 8.** Light travels about 9,460,000,000,000 kilometers in one year. Write scientific notation for the number.

We want to move the decimal point 12 places, between the 9 and the 4, so we multiply by $\dfrac{10^{12}}{10^{12}}$.

$$9{,}460{,}000{,}000{,}000 = 9{,}460{,}000{,}000{,}000 \times \frac{10^{12}}{10^{12}}$$

*Using $10^{12}$ to "move the decimal point" between 9 and 4*

$$= \frac{9{,}460{,}000{,}000{,}000}{10^{12}} \times 10^{12}$$

$$= 9.46 \times 10^{12}$$

With practice such conversions can be performed mentally and you should try to do this as much as possible.

**TRY THIS** ➡

> 13. Convert 460,000,000,000 to scientific notation.
>
> 14. The distance from the earth to the sun is about 150,000,000 km. Write scientific notation for this number.

**Example 9.** Write scientific notation for 0.0000000000156.

We want to move the decimal point 11 places, between the 1 and the 5, so we multiply by $\frac{10^{11}}{10^{11}}$.

$$0.0000000000156 = 0.0000000000156 \times \frac{10^{11}}{10^{11}} \qquad \textit{Multiplying by 1}$$
$$= (0.0000000000156 \times 10^{11}) \times 10^{-11}$$
$$= 1.56 \times 10^{-11}$$

You should try to make such conversions mentally as much as possible.

**TRY THIS**

> 15. Convert 0.00000001235 to scientific notation.
> 16. The mass of a hydrogen atom is 0.00000000000000000000000017 grams. Write scientific notation for this number.

**Examples.** Convert to decimal notation.

**10.** $7.893 \times 10^5 = 789{,}300$    *Moving the decimal point 5 places to the right*

**11.** $4.7 \times 10^{-8} = 0.000000047$    *Moving the decimal point 8 places to the left*

**TRY THIS**

> Convert to decimal notation.
> 17. $7.893 \times 10^{11}$
> 18. $5.67 \times 10^{-5}$

### ❚❚❚ Multiplying and Dividing

Multiplying and dividing in scientific notation is easy because we can use the properties of exponents.

**Example 12.** Multiply: $(3.1 \times 10^5)(4.5 \times 10^{-3})$.

We apply the commutative and associative laws to get

$$(3.1 \times 4.5)(10^5 \times 10^{-3}) = 13.95 \times 10^2.$$

To find scientific notation for the result, we convert 13.95 to scientific notation and then simplify.

$$13.95 \times 10^2 = (1.395 \times 10^1) \times 10^2$$
$$= 1.395 \times 10^3$$

**TRY THIS** ➡️

> Multiply and write scientific notation for the answer.
>
> 19.  $(9.1 \times 10^{-17})(8.2 \times 10^3)$
> 20.  $(1.12 \times 10^{-8})(5 \times 10^{-7})$

**Example 13.** Divide:  $\dfrac{6.4 \times 10^{-7}}{8.0 \times 10^6}$.

$$\frac{6.4 \times 10^{-7}}{8.0 \times 10^6} = \frac{6.4}{8.0} \times \frac{10^{-7}}{10^6} \qquad \textit{Factoring}$$

$$= 0.8 \times 10^{-13} \qquad \textit{Doing the divisions separately}$$

$$= (8.0 \times 10^{-1}) \times 10^{-13} \qquad \textit{Converting answer to scientific notation}$$

$$= 8.0 \times 10^{-14}$$

**TRY THIS** ➡️

> Divide and write scientific notation for the answer.
>
> 21.  $\dfrac{4.2 \times 10^5}{2.1 \times 10^2}$
>
> 22.  $\dfrac{1.1 \times 10^{-4}}{2.0 \times 10^{-7}}$

## Exercise Set 10-1

Simplify. (*See Examples 1–7.*)

1.  $(-4m^2n^3)^0$
2.  $(-9x^3y^5)^0$
3.  $(x^2 + y)^1$
4.  $(y^3 + z)^1$
5.  $3a^{-1}b^{-2}$
6.  $6x^{-2}y^{-3}$
7.  $\dfrac{r^{-1}s^{-2}}{t^{-3}}$
8.  $\dfrac{x^{-4}y^{-3}}{z^{-2}}$
9.  $(x^3 + y^3)^{-2}$
10.  $(a^5 - b^4)^{-3}$
11.  $(-2a^2b^3)(6a^{-4}b^{-1})$
12.  $(-5c^3d^{-5})(7d^4c^{-1})$
13.  $\dfrac{a^2b^{-3}}{a^4b^{-2}}$
14.  $\dfrac{x^3y^{-5}}{x^5y^{-7}}$
15.  $\dfrac{-6^5y^4z^{-5}}{2^{-2}y^{-2}z^3}$
16.  $\dfrac{9^{-2}x^{-4}y}{3^{-3}x^{-3}y^2}$
17.  $(-2m^{-2}n^3)^3$
18.  $(-3x^{-3}y^5)^2$
19.  $(2x^{-4}y^{-2})^{-3}$
20.  $(4a^{-4}b^{-5})^{-3}$
21.  $\left(\dfrac{3a^{-2}b}{c^2}\right)^3$
22.  $\left(\dfrac{2x^2y^{-2}}{3a^2}\right)^3$

▮▮ Convert to scientific notation. (*See Examples 8 and 9.*)

23. 47,000,000,000
24. 2,600,000,000,000
25. 863,000,000,000,000,000
26. 957,000,000,000,000,000
27. 0.000000016
28. 0.000000263
29. 0.00000000007
30. 0.00000000009

Convert to decimal notation. (*See Examples 10 and 11.*)

31. $4 \times 10^{-4}$
32. $5 \times 10^{-5}$
33. $6.73 \times 10^{8}$
34. $9.24 \times 10^{7}$
35. $8.923 \times 10^{-10}$
36. $7.034 \times 10^{-2}$

Write scientific notation for the number in each of the following. (*See Examples 8 and 9.*)

37. The mass of an electron is 0.000000000000000000000000000911 g.
38. The population of the United States is about 215,000,000.
39. An electron carries a charge of 0.00000000048 electrostatic units.
40. A helium atom has a diameter of 0.000000022 cm.

▮▮▮ Multiply and write scientific notation for the answer. (*See Example 12.*)

41. $(2.3 \times 10^{6})(4.2 \times 10^{-11})$
42. $(6.5 \times 10^{3})(5.2 \times 10^{-8})$
43. $(2.34 \times 10^{-8})(5.7 \times 10^{-4})$
44. $(3.26 \times 10^{-6})(8.2 \times 10^{-6})$

Divide and write scientific notation for the answer. (*See Example 13.*)

45. $\dfrac{8.5 \times 10^{8}}{3.4 \times 10^{5}}$
46. $\dfrac{5.1 \times 10^{6}}{3.4 \times 10^{3}}$
47. $\dfrac{4.0 \times 10^{-6}}{8.0 \times 10^{-3}}$
48. $\dfrac{7.5 \times 10^{-9}}{2.5 \times 10^{-4}}$

**COMPUTER NOTE: Monitoring**

After heavy rains, people monitor the level of water in a river. Graphs can be drawn and analyzed. By keeping track of the level, people can tell whether flooding is likely.

Computers aid in such monitoring. They help monitor air pollution in some places by keeping track of the many different pollutants. If the pollutant level becomes too high, they give warning.

Computers also monitor the conditions of some hospital patients. These computers keep track of heart beat, respiration rate, and other life processes. They sound an alarm if any condition becomes critical.

# 10-2 *Radical Expressions*

After finishing Lesson 10-2, you should be able to
**I** find principal square roots and their additive inverses.
**II** simplify radical expressions with perfect square radicands.
**III** find principal *k*th roots of expressions.
**IIII** simplify expressions of the form $\sqrt[k]{a^k}$.

## I Square Roots

**DEFINITION**
The number *c* is a square root of *a* if $c^2 = a$.

For example,

> 5 is a square root of 25 because $(5)^2 = 5 \cdot 5 = 25$.
> $-5$ is a square root of 25 because $(-5)^2 = (-5)(-5) = 25$.

This illustrates the following theorem.

**THEOREM 10-2**
Every positive real number has two real number square roots.
The number 0 has just one square root, 0 itself.

Negative real numbers do not have real number square roots.
For example, $-4$ does not have a real number square root because there is no real number *b* such that $b^2 = -4$.

**Example 1.** Find the two square roots of 64.

The square roots are 8 and $-8$, because $8^2 = 64$ and $(-8)^2 = 64$.

**TRY THIS** ▶

Find the
square roots
of each
number.

1. 9
2. 36
3. 121

**DEFINITION**
The *principal square root* of a nonnegative number is its nonnegative
square root. The symbol $\sqrt{a}$ represents the principal square root of *a*.

**Examples.** Simplify.
**2.** $\sqrt{25} = 5$   *Remember, $\sqrt{\phantom{x}}$ means to take the principal*
   *(nonnegative) square root*

**3.** $\sqrt{\dfrac{25}{64}} = \dfrac{5}{8}$

**4.** $\sqrt{0.0049} = 0.07$

**TRY THIS** ▶

Simplify.

4. $\sqrt{1}$
5. $\sqrt{36}$
6. $\sqrt{\dfrac{81}{100}}$
7. $\sqrt{0.0064}$

To name the negative square root of $a$ we write $-\sqrt{a}$.

**Example 5.** Find $-\sqrt{64}$.

$$-\sqrt{64} = -8 \qquad \sqrt{64} = 8, \text{ so } -\sqrt{64} = -8$$

**TRY THIS**

Find the following.

8. $-\sqrt{16}$
9. $-\sqrt{49}$
10. $-\sqrt{196}$

**DEFINITION**

The symbol $\sqrt{\phantom{x}}$ is called a *radical*. An expression written with a radical is called a *radical expression*. The expression written under the radical is called the *radicand*.

These are radical expressions.

$$\sqrt{5}, \qquad \sqrt{a}, \qquad -\sqrt{5x}, \qquad \frac{\sqrt{y^2 + 7}}{\sqrt{x}}$$

**Example 6.** Identify the radicand in $\sqrt{x^2 - 9}$.

The radicand is $x^2 - 9$.

**TRY THIS**

Identify the radicand in each expression.

11. $\sqrt{28 + x}$
12. $\sqrt{\dfrac{y}{y + 3}}$

## ‖ Simplifying $\sqrt{a^2}$.

In the expression $\sqrt{a^2}$, the radicand is a perfect square.

Suppose $a = 5$. Then we have $\sqrt{5^2}$, which is $\sqrt{25}$, or 5.
Suppose $a = -5$. Then we have $\sqrt{(-5)^2}$, which is $\sqrt{25}$, or 5.
Suppose $a = 0$. Then we have $\sqrt{0^2}$, which is $\sqrt{0}$, or 0.

The symbol $\sqrt{a^2}$ does not represent a negative number. It represents the principal square root of $a^2$. Note that if $a$ represents a positive number or 0, then $\sqrt{a^2}$ represents $a$. If $a$ is negative, then $\sqrt{a^2}$ represents the additive inverse of $a$. In all cases the radical expression represents the absolute value of $a$.

**THEOREM 10-3**

For any real number $a$, $\sqrt{a^2} = |a|$. The principal (nonnegative) square root of $a^2$ is the absolute value of $a$.

**Examples.** Simplify.

7. $\sqrt{(-16)^2} = |-16|$, or 16
8. $\sqrt{(3b)^2} = |3b|$, or $3|b|$
9. $\sqrt{(x - 1)^2} = |x - 1|$

**10.** $\sqrt{x^2 + 8x + 16} = \sqrt{(x + 4)^2}$
$= |x + 4|$

**TRY THIS**

Simplify.

13. $\sqrt{y^2}$
14. $\sqrt{(-24)^2}$
15. $\sqrt{25y^2}$
16. $\sqrt{(x + 7)^2}$
17. $\sqrt{x^2 - 6x + 9}$

## III Principal *k*th Roots

**DEFINITION**
The number $c$ is the cube root of $a$ if $c^3 = a$.

For example,

2 is the cube root of 8 because $2^3 = 2 \cdot 2 \cdot 2 = 8$.
$-4$ is the cube root of $-64$ because $(-4)^3 = (-4)(-4)(-4) = -64$.

We used the word "the" with cube roots because of the following theorem.

**THEOREM 10-4**
Every real number has exactly one cube root in the system of real numbers.

The symbol $\sqrt[3]{a}$ represents the cube root of $a$.

**Examples.** Simplify.

**11.** $\sqrt[3]{8} = 2$

**12.** $\sqrt[3]{-27} = -3$

**13.** $\sqrt[3]{-\dfrac{216}{125}} = -\dfrac{6}{5}$

**TRY THIS**

Simplify.

18. $\sqrt[3]{0}$ 0
19. $\sqrt[3]{-8}$ $-2$
20. $\sqrt[3]{216}$ 6
21. $\sqrt[3]{-\dfrac{343}{64}}$ $-\frac{7}{4}$

A fourth root of a number $a$ is a number whose fourth power is $a$. Numbers can also have fifth roots, sixth roots, and so on.

**DEFINITION**
A number $c$ is a $k$th root of $a$ if $c^k = a$. The symbol $\sqrt[k]{a}$ represents the principal (nonnegative) $k$th root if one exists. If no such root exists, but there is a negative $k$th root, then $\sqrt[k]{a}$ represents that number. The number $k$ is called the *index* and must be a natural number greater than 1. If $k$ is 2, it is usually not written.

**Examples.** Simplify.

**14.** $\sqrt[5]{32} = 2$

**15.** $\sqrt[4]{81} = 3$

**16.** $\sqrt[5]{-243} = -3$

**17.** $\sqrt[4]{-26}$ does not represent a real number.

Note that $\sqrt[4]{81}$ is 3 although $-3$ is also a fourth root of 81. To represent the negative root we use $-\sqrt[4]{81}$, or $-3$.

**TRY THIS** ➤

Simplify.

22. $\sqrt[4]{16}$
23. $\sqrt[5]{-32}$
24. $\sqrt[3]{-125}$
25. $\sqrt[3]{-1}$

## ▦ Simplifying $\sqrt[k]{a^k}$

Recall that $\sqrt{a^2} = |a|$. Consider the problem of simplifying $\sqrt[3]{a^3}$.

$$\sqrt[3]{2^3} = \sqrt[3]{8} = 2, \qquad \sqrt[3]{(-4)^3} = \sqrt[3]{-64} = -4$$

Since any real number has only one real number cube root, for any real number $a$, $\sqrt[3]{a^3} = a$. We do not use absolute value when simplifying cube roots. In general,

**THEOREM 10-5**

For any real number $a$,

a) $\sqrt[k]{a^k} = |a|$, ($k$ even) We must use absolute value when $k$ is even unless $a$ is nonnegative.

b) $\sqrt[k]{a^k} = a$, ($k$ odd) We do not use absolute value when $k$ is odd.

**Examples.** Simplify.

**18.** $\sqrt[5]{x^5} = x$

**19.** $\sqrt[8]{(-9)^8} = |-9|$, or 9

**20.** $\sqrt[4]{(y + 7)^4} = |y + 7|$

**21.** $\sqrt[3]{(4xy)^3} = 4xy$

**TRY THIS** ➤

Simplify.

26. $\sqrt[6]{a^6}$
27. $\sqrt[5]{(y + 7)^5}$
28. $\sqrt[4]{(-5)^4}$
29. $\sqrt[244]{(5xy)^{244}}$

## Exercise Set 10-2

▮ Find the square roots of each number. (*See Example 1.*)

1. 16
2. 225
3. 144
4. 9
5. 400
6. 81

Find the following. (*See Examples 2–5.*)

7. $-\sqrt{\dfrac{49}{36}}$

8. $-\sqrt{\dfrac{361}{9}}$

9. $\sqrt{289}$

10. $\sqrt{441}$

11. $-\sqrt{\dfrac{16}{81}}$

12. $-\sqrt{\dfrac{81}{144}}$

13. $\sqrt{0.09}$

14. $\sqrt{0.36}$

15. $-\sqrt{0.0049}$

16. $\sqrt{0.0144}$

Identify the radicand in each expression. (*See Example 6.*)

17. $5\sqrt{p^2 + 4}$

18. $-7\sqrt{y^2 - 8}$

19. $x^2 y^2 \sqrt{\dfrac{x}{y + 4}}$

20. $a^2 b^3 \sqrt{\dfrac{a}{a^2 - b}}$

▮▮ Simplify. (*See Examples 7–10.*)

21. $\sqrt{16x^2}$

22. $\sqrt{25t^2}$

23. $\sqrt{(-7c)^2}$

24. $\sqrt{(-6b)^2}$

25. $\sqrt{(a + 1)^2}$

26. $\sqrt{(5 - b)^2}$

27. $\sqrt{x^2 - 4x + 4}$

28. $\sqrt{y^2 + 16y + 64}$

29. $\sqrt{4x^2 + 28x + 49}$

30. $\sqrt{9x^2 - 30x + 25}$

▮▮▮ Simplify. (*See Examples 11–17.*)

31. $\sqrt[3]{8}$

32. $\sqrt[3]{64}$

33. $\sqrt[3]{-27}$

34. $\sqrt[3]{-125}$

35. $\sqrt[3]{-216}$

36. $\sqrt[3]{-1000}$

37. $\sqrt[3]{0.343}$

38. $\sqrt[3]{0.000008}$

39. $\sqrt[4]{625}$

40. $\sqrt[4]{256}$

41. $\sqrt[5]{-1}$

42. $\sqrt[5]{-32}$

43. $\sqrt[5]{-\dfrac{32}{243}}$

44. $\sqrt[5]{-\dfrac{1}{32}}$

▮▮▮▮ Simplify. (*See Examples 18–21.*)

45. $\sqrt[6]{x^6}$

46. $\sqrt[8]{y^8}$

47. $\sqrt[4]{(5a)^4}$

48. $\sqrt[4]{(7b)^4}$

49. $\sqrt[10]{(-6)^{10}}$

50. $\sqrt[12]{(-10)^{12}}$

51. $\sqrt[414]{(a + b)^{414}}$

52. $\sqrt[1976]{(2a + b)^{1976}}$

# 10-3 Multiplying and Simplifying

After finishing Lesson 10-3, you should be able to
- ▌ multiply with radical notation.
- ▌▌ simplify radical expressions.
- ▌▌▌ multiply and simplify radical expressions.
- ▌▌▌▌ simplify and approximate expressions using a square root table.

## ▌ Multiplying

Notice that $\sqrt{4}\,\sqrt{25} = 2 \cdot 5 = 10$.
Also $\sqrt{4 \cdot 25} = \sqrt{100} = 10$.
Likewise, $\sqrt[3]{27}\,\sqrt[3]{8} = 3 \cdot 2 = 6$ and $\sqrt[3]{27 \cdot 8} = \sqrt[3]{216} = 6$.

These examples suggest the following theorem.

### THEOREM 10-6

For any nonnegative real numbers $a$ and $b$, and any index $n$,
$\sqrt[n]{a} \cdot \sqrt[n]{b} = \sqrt[n]{ab}$.

**Examples.** Multiply.

**1.** $\sqrt{x+2}\,\sqrt{x-2} = \sqrt{(x+2)(x-2)} = \sqrt{x^2 - 4}$

**2.** $\sqrt[3]{4}\,\sqrt[3]{5} = \sqrt[3]{4 \cdot 5} = \sqrt[3]{20}$

**3.** $\sqrt[4]{\dfrac{y}{5}}\,\sqrt[4]{\dfrac{7}{x}} = \sqrt[4]{\dfrac{y}{5} \cdot \dfrac{7}{x}} = \sqrt[4]{\dfrac{7y}{5x}}$

**TRY THIS** ➡

Multiply.
1. $\sqrt{19}\,\sqrt{7}$
2. $\sqrt{x+2y}\,\sqrt{x-2y}$
3. $\sqrt[4]{403}\,\sqrt[4]{7}$
4. $\sqrt[3]{8x}\,\sqrt[3]{x^4 + 5}$

## ▌▌ Simplifying

From Theorem 10-6 we have $\sqrt[n]{ab} = \sqrt[n]{a} \cdot \sqrt[n]{b}$. This shows a way to simplify radical expressions. Consider $\sqrt{20}$. The number 20 has the factor 4, which is a perfect square. Therefore

$$\begin{aligned}
\sqrt{20} &= \sqrt{4 \cdot 5} \\
&= \sqrt{4} \cdot \sqrt{5} \\
&= 2\sqrt{5}
\end{aligned}$$

To simplify radical expressions containing just one radical sign, we usually look for factors of the radicand which are perfect powers. so that we can simplify by "removing" them.

In many situations, expressions never represent negative numbers. In such situations, absolute value notation is not necessary.

**Examples.** Simplify.

**4.** $\sqrt{5x^2} = \sqrt{x^2 \cdot 5}$
$\phantom{\sqrt{5x^2}} = \sqrt{x^2} \cdot \sqrt{5}$
$\phantom{\sqrt{5x^2}} = |x| \cdot \sqrt{5}$
$\phantom{\sqrt{5x^2}} = x\sqrt{5}$ if we know that $x \geq 0$

**5.** $\sqrt{2x^2 - 4x + 2} = \sqrt{2(x-1)^2}$
$\phantom{\sqrt{2x^2 - 4x + 2}} = \sqrt{(x-1)^2} \cdot \sqrt{2}$
$\phantom{\sqrt{2x^2 - 4x + 2}} = |x-1| \cdot \sqrt{2}$
$\phantom{\sqrt{2x^2 - 4x + 2}} = (x-1)\sqrt{2}$ if we know that $(x-1) \geq 0$

**6.** $\sqrt{216x^5y^3} = \sqrt{36 \cdot 6 \cdot x^4 \cdot x \cdot y^2 \cdot y}$
$\phantom{\sqrt{216x^5y^3}} = \sqrt{36 \cdot x^4 \cdot y^2 \cdot 6 \cdot x \cdot y}$
$\phantom{\sqrt{216x^5y^3}} = 6 \cdot |x^2| \cdot |y| \cdot \sqrt{6xy}$
$\phantom{\sqrt{216x^5y^3}} = 6x^2 \cdot |y| \cdot \sqrt{6xy}$

Since $x^2$ is never negative we need not write $|x^2|$. Then if we know that $y \geq 0$, we have $6x^2y\sqrt{6xy}$.

**TRY THIS**

> Simplify. Assume that all expressions represent nonnegative numbers. Hence, no absolute value signs will be needed.
>
> 5. $\sqrt{300}$
> 6. $\sqrt{36y^2}$
> 7. $\sqrt{3x^2 + 12x + 12}$
> 8. $\sqrt{12ab^3c^2}$

**Example 7.** Simplify.

$\sqrt[3]{32} = \sqrt[3]{8 \cdot 4}$
$\phantom{\sqrt[3]{32}} = \sqrt[3]{8} \cdot \sqrt[3]{4}$
$\phantom{\sqrt[3]{32}} = 2\sqrt[3]{4}$

**TRY THIS**

> Simplify.
>
> 9. $\sqrt[3]{16}$
> 10. $\sqrt[4]{81x^4y^8}$
> 11. $\sqrt[3]{(a+b)^4}$

## ⅠⅠⅠ Multiplying and Simplifying

Sometimes after we multiply we can then simplify.

**Examples.** Multiply and simplify. Assume that all expressions represent nonnegative numbers.

**8.** $3\sqrt[3]{25} \cdot 2\sqrt[3]{5} = 6 \cdot \sqrt[3]{25 \cdot 5}$
$= 6 \cdot \sqrt[3]{125}$
$= 6 \cdot 5$, or 30

**9.** $\sqrt[3]{18y^3}\,\sqrt[3]{4x^2} = \sqrt[3]{18y^3 \cdot 4x^2} = \sqrt[3]{72y^3x^2}$
$= \sqrt[3]{8y^3 \cdot 9x^2}$
$= \sqrt[3]{8y^3}\,\sqrt[3]{9x^2}$
$= 2y\sqrt[3]{9x^2}$

**TRY THIS** ➡

Multiply and simplify.

12. $\sqrt{3}\,\sqrt{6}$
13. $\sqrt{18y}\,\sqrt{14y}$
14. $\sqrt[3]{3x^2y}\,\sqrt[3]{36x}$
15. $\sqrt{7a}\,\sqrt{21b}$
16. $\sqrt[3]{2(y+5)}\,\sqrt[3]{4(y+5)^4}$

## ⅠⅠⅠⅠ Approximating Square Roots

Table 1 in the back of the book contains approximate square roots for the natural numbers 1 through 100. If a radicand is not listed in the table we can factor the radical expression, find exact or approximate square roots of the factors, and then find the product of these square roots.

**Example 10.** Simplify and approximate to the nearest tenth.

$\sqrt{275} = \sqrt{25 \cdot 11}$
$= \sqrt{25} \cdot \sqrt{11}$
$\approx 5 \times 3.317$
$\approx 16.6$ $\quad \approx$ means approximately equal

**TRY THIS** ➡

Simplify and approximate to the nearest tenth.

17. $\sqrt{160}$
18. $\sqrt{341}$
(*Hint:* $341 = 11 \cdot 31$)

**Example 11.** Simplify and approximate to the nearest tenth.

$$\frac{20 - \sqrt{44}}{4} = \frac{20 - \sqrt{4 \cdot 11}}{4}$$

$$= \frac{20 - 2\sqrt{11}}{4}$$

$$= \frac{10 - \sqrt{11}}{2}$$

$$\approx \frac{10 - 3.317}{2} \quad \textit{Using Table 1}$$

$$\approx \frac{6.683}{2}$$

$$\approx 3.342$$

$$\approx 3.3$$

**TRY THIS**

Simplify and approximate to the nearest tenth.

19. $\dfrac{20 + \sqrt{44}}{4}$

20. $\dfrac{12 - \sqrt{45}}{6}$

## Exercise Set 10-3

▌Assume that all expressions represent nonnegative numbers. Multiply. (*See Examples 1–3.*)

1. $\sqrt{3}\,\sqrt{2}$
2. $\sqrt{5}\,\sqrt{7}$
3. $\sqrt[3]{2}\,\sqrt[3]{5}$
4. $\sqrt[3]{7}\,\sqrt[3]{2}$
5. $\sqrt[4]{8}\,\sqrt[4]{9}$
6. $\sqrt[4]{6}\,\sqrt[4]{3}$
7. $\sqrt{3a}\,\sqrt{10b}$
8. $\sqrt{2x}\,\sqrt{13y}$
9. $\sqrt[5]{9t^2}\,\sqrt[5]{2t}$
10. $\sqrt[5]{8y^3}\,\sqrt[5]{10y}$
11. $\sqrt{x - a}\,\sqrt{x + a}$
12. $\sqrt{y - b}\,\sqrt{y + b}$
13. $\sqrt[3]{0.3x}\,\sqrt[3]{0.2x}$
14. $\sqrt[3]{0.7y}\,\sqrt[3]{0.3y}$
15. $\sqrt[4]{x - 1}\,\sqrt[4]{x^2 + x + 1}$
16. $\sqrt[4]{y + 1}\,\sqrt[4]{y^2 - y + 1}$
17. $\sqrt[5]{x - 2}\,\sqrt[5]{(x - 2)^2}$
18. $\sqrt[5]{y - 4}\,\sqrt[5]{(y - 4)^3}$
19. $\sqrt{\dfrac{6}{x}}\,\sqrt{\dfrac{y}{5}}$
20. $\sqrt{\dfrac{7}{t}}\,\sqrt{\dfrac{s}{11}}$

▌▌Simplify. (*See Examples 4–7.*)

21. $\sqrt{8}$
22. $\sqrt{18}$
23. $\sqrt{24}$
24. $\sqrt{20}$
25. $\sqrt{40}$
26. $\sqrt{90}$
27. $\sqrt{180x^4}$
28. $\sqrt{175y^6}$
29. $\sqrt[3]{54x^8}$
30. $\sqrt[3]{40y^3}$
31. $\sqrt[3]{80x^8}$
32. $\sqrt[3]{108m^5}$
33. $\sqrt[4]{32}$
34. $\sqrt[4]{80}$

35. $\sqrt[4]{162c^4d^6}$
36. $\sqrt[4]{243x^8y^{10}}$
37. $\sqrt[3]{(x + y)^4}$
38. $\sqrt[3]{(p - q)^5}$
39. $\sqrt{2x^2 + 12x + 18}$
40. $\sqrt{3x^2 - 24x + 48}$

**▌▌▌**Multiply and simplify. (*See Examples 8 and 9.*)

41. $\sqrt{3}\,\sqrt{6}$
42. $\sqrt{5}\,\sqrt{10}$
43. $\sqrt{15}\,\sqrt{6}$
44. $\sqrt{2}\,\sqrt{32}$
45. $\sqrt{6}\,\sqrt{8}$
46. $\sqrt{18}\,\sqrt{14}$
47. $\sqrt[3]{3}\,\sqrt[3]{18}$
48. $\sqrt[3]{2}\,\sqrt[3]{20}$
49. $\sqrt{45}\,\sqrt{60}$
50. $\sqrt{24}\,\sqrt{75}$
51. $\sqrt{5b^3}\,\sqrt{10c^4}$
52. $\sqrt{2x^3y}\,\sqrt{12xy}$
53. $\sqrt[3]{y^4}\,\sqrt[3]{16y^5}$
54. $\sqrt[3]{5^2t^4}\,\sqrt[3]{5^4t^6}$
55. $\sqrt[3]{(b + 3)^4}\,\sqrt[3]{(b + 3)^2}$
56. $\sqrt[3]{(x + y)^3}\,\sqrt[3]{(x + y)^5}$
57. $\sqrt{12a^3b}\,\sqrt{8a^4b^2}$
58. $\sqrt{18x^2y^3}\,\sqrt{6xy^4}$
59. $\sqrt[3]{3c^2d^5}\,\sqrt[3]{16c^2d^2}$
60. $\sqrt[3]{5a^3b^7}\,\sqrt[3]{32a^2b^4}$

**▌▌▌▌**Simplify and approximate to the nearest tenth. (*See Examples 10 and 11.*)

61. $\sqrt{180}$
62. $\sqrt{124}$
63. $\sqrt{195}$
64. $\sqrt{115}$
65. $\dfrac{10 + \sqrt{20}}{4}$
66. $\dfrac{10 - \sqrt{20}}{4}$
67. $\dfrac{8 - \sqrt{124}}{10}$
68. $\dfrac{-8 - \sqrt{124}}{10}$

---

### Calculator Exercises

*Wind Chill Temperature.* In cold weather we feel colder if there is wind than if there is not. *Wind chill temperature* is the temperature at which, without wind, we would feel as cold as in an actual situation with wind. Here is a formula for finding wind chill temperature.

$$T_w = 33 - \frac{(10.45 + 10\sqrt{v} - v)(33 - T)}{22}$$

where $T$ is the actual temperature given in degrees Celsius and $v$ is the wind speed in m/s. Find the wind chill temperature when

69. $T = 7°C$, $v = 8$ m/s
70. $T = 0°C$, $v = 12$ m/s
71. $T = -5°C$, $v = 14$ m/s
72. $T = -23°C$, $v = 15$ m/s

# 10-4 Simplifying and Dividing

After finishing Lesson 10-4, you should be able to
 ▮ simplify radical expressions where the radicand is a quotient.
 ▮▮ divide and simplify radical expressions.
 ▮▮▮ find roots of powers.

## ▮ Simplifying

Notice that $\sqrt[3]{\dfrac{27}{8}} = \dfrac{3}{2}$ and $\dfrac{\sqrt[3]{27}}{\sqrt[3]{8}} = \dfrac{3}{2}$. These examples suggest
the following.

**THEOREM 10-7**
For any nonnegative number $a$, any positive number $b$, and any

index $n$, $\sqrt[n]{\dfrac{a}{b}} = \dfrac{\sqrt[n]{a}}{\sqrt[n]{b}}$.

**Examples.** Simplify.

**1.** $\sqrt[3]{\dfrac{27}{125}} = \dfrac{\sqrt[3]{27}}{\sqrt[3]{125}} = \dfrac{3}{5}$

**2.** $\sqrt{\dfrac{25}{y^2}} = \dfrac{\sqrt{25}}{\sqrt{y^2}} = \dfrac{5}{y}$

**3.** $\sqrt{\dfrac{16x^3}{y^4}} = \dfrac{\sqrt{16x^3}}{\sqrt{y^4}} = \dfrac{\sqrt{16x^2 \cdot x}}{\sqrt{y^4}} = \dfrac{4x\sqrt{x}}{y^2}$

**4.** $\sqrt[3]{\dfrac{27y^5}{343x^3}} = \dfrac{\sqrt[3]{27y^5}}{\sqrt[3]{343x^3}} = \dfrac{\sqrt[3]{27y^3 \cdot y^2}}{\sqrt[3]{343x^3}} = \dfrac{\sqrt[3]{27y^3} \cdot \sqrt[3]{y^2}}{\sqrt[3]{343x^3}} = \dfrac{3y\sqrt[3]{y^2}}{7x}$

**TRY THIS** ➡

> Simplify.
>
> 1. $\sqrt{\dfrac{25}{36}}$
>
> 2. $\sqrt[3]{\dfrac{1000}{27}}$
>
> 3. $\sqrt{\dfrac{x^2}{100}}$
>
> 4. $\sqrt{\dfrac{4a^3}{b^4}}$
>
> 5. $\sqrt[3]{\dfrac{54x^5}{125}}$

## ▮▮ Dividing

From Theorem 10-7, we have

$$\dfrac{\sqrt[n]{a}}{\sqrt[n]{b}} = \sqrt[n]{\dfrac{a}{b}}.$$

This shows a way to divide radical expressions.

**Example 5.** Divide and simplify.

$$\frac{\sqrt{72xy}}{2\sqrt{2}} = \frac{1}{2}\frac{\sqrt{72xy}}{\sqrt{2}} = \frac{1}{2}\sqrt{\frac{72xy}{2}} = \frac{1}{2}\sqrt{36xy} = \frac{1}{2}\sqrt{36}\sqrt{xy} = \frac{1}{2}\cdot 6\sqrt{xy} = 3\sqrt{xy}$$

**TRY THIS** ➤

> Divide and simplify.
>
> 6. $\dfrac{\sqrt{75}}{\sqrt{3}}$
>
> 7. $\dfrac{14\sqrt{128xy}}{2\sqrt{2}}$
>
> 8. $\dfrac{\sqrt{50a^3}}{\sqrt{2a}}$

**Examples.** Divide and simplify.

6. $\dfrac{5\sqrt[3]{32}}{\sqrt[3]{2}} = 5\sqrt[3]{\dfrac{32}{2}} = 5\sqrt[3]{16} = 5\sqrt[3]{8\cdot 2} = 5\sqrt[3]{8}\sqrt[3]{2} = 5\cdot 2\sqrt[3]{2} = 10\sqrt[3]{2}$

7. $\dfrac{\sqrt[4]{32a^5b^3}}{\sqrt[4]{2b^{-1}}} = \sqrt[4]{\dfrac{32a^5b^3}{2b^{-1}}} = \sqrt[4]{16a^5b^4} = \sqrt[4]{16a^4b^4\cdot a} = \sqrt[4]{16a^4b^4}\sqrt[4]{a} = 2ab\sqrt[4]{a}$

**TRY THIS** ➤

> Divide and simplify.
>
> 9. $\dfrac{4\sqrt[3]{250}}{7\sqrt[3]{2}}$
>
> 10. $\dfrac{\sqrt[3]{8a^3b}}{\sqrt[3]{27b^{-2}}}$

## ▫ Roots of Powers

Another property of radicals is as follows.

**THEOREM 10-8**

For any nonnegative number $a$, any index $n$, and any natural number $m$, $(\sqrt[n]{a})^m = \sqrt[n]{a^m}$.

**Examples.** Simplify.

8. $(\sqrt{5x})^3 = \sqrt{(5x)^3} = \sqrt{(5x)^2\cdot 5x} = \sqrt{(5x)^2}\sqrt{5x} = 5x\sqrt{5x}$

9. $(\sqrt[3]{25})^2 = \sqrt[3]{(25)^2} = \sqrt[3]{(5\cdot 5\cdot 5)\cdot 5} = 5\sqrt[3]{5}$

**TRY THIS** ➤

> Simplify.
>
> 11. $(\sqrt[3]{9})^2$
> 12. $(\sqrt{6y})^3$

## Exercise Set 10-4

**▌** Simplify. (*See Examples 1–4.*)

1. $\sqrt{\dfrac{25}{36}}$

2. $\sqrt{\dfrac{100}{81}}$

3. $\sqrt[3]{\dfrac{64}{27}}$

4. $\sqrt[3]{\dfrac{343}{512}}$

5. $\sqrt{\dfrac{49}{y^2}}$

6. $\sqrt{\dfrac{121}{x^2}}$

7. $\sqrt{\dfrac{25y^3}{x^4}}$

8. $\sqrt{\dfrac{36a^5}{b^6}}$

9. $\sqrt[3]{\dfrac{8x^5}{27y^3}}$

10. $\sqrt[3]{\dfrac{64x^7}{216y^6}}$

**▌▌** Divide and simplify. (*See Examples 5–7.*)

11. $\dfrac{\sqrt{21a}}{\sqrt{3a}}$

12. $\dfrac{\sqrt{28y}}{\sqrt{4y}}$

13. $\dfrac{\sqrt[3]{54}}{\sqrt[3]{2}}$

14. $\dfrac{\sqrt[3]{40}}{\sqrt[3]{5}}$

15. $\dfrac{\sqrt{40xy^3}}{\sqrt{8x}}$

16. $\dfrac{\sqrt{56ab^3}}{\sqrt{7a}}$

17. $\dfrac{\sqrt[3]{96a^4b^2}}{\sqrt[3]{12a^2b}}$

18. $\dfrac{\sqrt[3]{189x^5y^7}}{\sqrt[3]{7x^2y^2}}$

19. $\dfrac{\sqrt{72xy}}{2\sqrt{2}}$

20. $\dfrac{\sqrt{75ab}}{3\sqrt{3}}$

21. $\dfrac{\sqrt{x^3 - y^3}}{\sqrt{x - y}}$

22. $\dfrac{\sqrt{r^3 + s^3}}{\sqrt{r + s}}$

**▌▌▌** Simplify. (*See Examples 8 and 9.*)

23. $(\sqrt{6a})^3$

24. $(\sqrt{7y})^3$

25. $(\sqrt[3]{16b^2})^2$

26. $(\sqrt[3]{25r^2})^2$

27. $(\sqrt{18a^2b})^3$

28. $(\sqrt{12x^2y})^3$

29. $(\sqrt[3]{12c^2d})^2$

30. $(\sqrt[3]{9x^2y})^2$

# 10-5 Addition and Subtraction

After finishing Lesson 10-5, you should be able to
▮ add or subtract with radical notation.

▮Any two real numbers can be added. For instance, the sum of 7
and $\sqrt{3}$ can be expressed as

$$7 + \sqrt{3}.$$

We cannot simplify this name for the sum. However, when we
have *like radicals* or radicals having the same index and radicand we can use the distributive laws to simplify.

**Examples.**  Simplify.

**1.**  $6\sqrt{7} + 4\sqrt{7} = (6 + 4)\sqrt{7}$    *Using the distributive law (factoring out $\sqrt{7}$)*
$$= 10\sqrt{7}$$

**2.**  $6\sqrt[5]{4x} + 4\sqrt[5]{4x} - \sqrt[3]{4x} = (6 + 4)\sqrt[5]{4x} - \sqrt[3]{4x}$
$$= 10\sqrt[5]{4x} - \sqrt[3]{4x}$$

**TRY THIS**

Simplify.

1.  $5\sqrt{2} + 8\sqrt{2}$
2.  $7\sqrt[4]{5x} + 3\sqrt[4]{5x} - \sqrt{7}$

Sometimes we need to simplify in order to have like radicals.

**Example 3.**  Simplify.

$5\sqrt[3]{16y^4} + 7\sqrt[3]{2y} = 5\sqrt[3]{8y^3} \cdot \sqrt[3]{2y} + 7\sqrt[3]{2y}$    *Using Theorem 10-6*
$$= 5 \cdot 2y \cdot \sqrt[3]{2y} + 7\sqrt[3]{2y}$$    *Simplifying $\sqrt[3]{8y^3}$*
$$= 10y\sqrt[3]{2y} + 7\sqrt[3]{2y}$$
$$= (10y + 7)\sqrt[3]{2y}$$    *Factoring out $\sqrt[3]{2y}$*

**TRY THIS**

Simplify.

3.  $7\sqrt{45} - 2\sqrt{5}$
4.  $3\sqrt[3]{y^5} + 4\sqrt[3]{y^2} + \sqrt[3]{8y^6}$

**Example 4.** Simplify.

$$\sqrt{9x + 9} - \sqrt{4x + 4} = \sqrt{9(x + 1)} - \sqrt{4(x + 1)} \quad \textit{Factoring radicands}$$
$$= \sqrt{9}\sqrt{x + 1} - \sqrt{4}\sqrt{x + 1}$$
$$= 3\sqrt{x + 1} - 2\sqrt{x + 1}$$
$$= \sqrt{x + 1}$$

**TRY THIS** ⟹

> Simplify.
>
> 5. $\sqrt{25x - 25} - \sqrt{9x - 9}$

## Exercise Set 10-5

▌Simplify. (*See Examples 1–4.*)

1. $6\sqrt{3} + 2\sqrt{3}$
2. $8\sqrt{5} + 9\sqrt{5}$
3. $9\sqrt[3]{5} - 6\sqrt[3]{5}$
4. $14\sqrt[5]{2} - 6\sqrt[5]{2}$
5. $4\sqrt[3]{y} + 9\sqrt[3]{y}$
6. $6\sqrt[4]{t} - 3\sqrt[4]{t}$
7. $8\sqrt{2} - 6\sqrt{2} + 5\sqrt{2}$
8. $2\sqrt{6} + 8\sqrt{6} - 3\sqrt{6}$
9. $4\sqrt[3]{5} - \sqrt{3} + 2\sqrt[3]{5} + \sqrt{3}$
10. $5\sqrt{7} - 8\sqrt[4]{11} + \sqrt{7} + 9\sqrt[4]{11}$
11. $6\sqrt{8} + 11\sqrt{2}$
12. $2\sqrt{12} + 5\sqrt{3}$
13. $8\sqrt{27} - 3\sqrt{3}$
14. $9\sqrt{50} - 4\sqrt{2}$
15. $8\sqrt{45} + 7\sqrt{20}$
16. $9\sqrt{12} + 16\sqrt{27}$
17. $18\sqrt{72} + 2\sqrt{98}$
18. $12\sqrt{45} - 8\sqrt{80}$
19. $3\sqrt[3]{16} + \sqrt[3]{54}$
20. $\sqrt[3]{27} - 5\sqrt[3]{8}$
21. $5\sqrt[3]{32} - 2\sqrt[3]{108}$
22. $9\sqrt[3]{40} - 7\sqrt[3]{135}$
23. $2\sqrt{128} - \sqrt{18} + 4\sqrt{32}$
24. $5\sqrt{50} - 2\sqrt{18} + 9\sqrt{32}$
25. $\sqrt{5a} + 2\sqrt{45a^3}$
26. $4\sqrt{3x^3} - \sqrt{12x}$
27. $\sqrt[3]{24x} - \sqrt[3]{3x^4}$
28. $\sqrt[3]{54x} - \sqrt[3]{2x^4}$
29. $2\sqrt[3]{125a^4} - 5\sqrt[3]{8a}$
30. $9\sqrt[3]{16x^5y} - 2\sqrt[3]{128x^2y}$
31. $\sqrt{8y - 8} + \sqrt{2y - 2}$
32. $\sqrt{12t + 12} + \sqrt{3t + 3}$
33. $\sqrt{x^3 - x^2} + \sqrt{9x - 9}$
34. $\sqrt{4x - 4} - \sqrt{x^3 - x^2}$

## HISTORICAL NOTE: The Euclid of Algebra

Euclid is famous for his basic work in geometry. Around 300 B.C. he put geometry into a logical framework. George Peacock, a British mathematician, tried to do the same for algebra. Around 1850 he gave statements of the commutative, associative and distributive laws. These laws underlie algebraic proofs. For that reason, he is sometimes called the Euclid of algebra.

# 10-6 More Multiplication

After finishing Lesson 10-6, you should be able to
▮ multiply expressions involving radicals, where some of the expressions may contain more than one term.

▮ To multiply expressions involving radicals where some of the expressions contain more than one term we use many of the procedures for multiplying polynomials.

**Example 1.**  Multiply.

$$\sqrt[3]{y}(\sqrt[3]{y^2} + \sqrt[3]{2}) = \sqrt[3]{y} \cdot \sqrt[3]{y^2} + \sqrt[3]{y} \cdot \sqrt[3]{2} \quad \text{\textit{Using the distributive law}}$$
$$= \sqrt[3]{y^3} + \sqrt[3]{2y} \quad \text{\textit{Using Theorem 10-6}}$$
$$= y + \sqrt[3]{2y} \quad \text{\textit{Simplifying}}$$

**TRY THIS** ➡

Multiply.

1.  $\sqrt{2}(5\sqrt{3} + 3\sqrt{7})$
2.  $\sqrt[3]{a^2}(\sqrt[3]{3a} - \sqrt[3]{2})$

**Example 2.**  Multiply.

$$(4\sqrt{3} + \sqrt{2})(\sqrt{3} - 5\sqrt{2}) = 4(\sqrt{3})^2 - 20\sqrt{3} \cdot \sqrt{2} + \sqrt{2} \cdot \sqrt{3} - 5(\sqrt{2})^2$$
$$= 4 \cdot 3 - 20\sqrt{6} + \sqrt{6} - 5 \cdot 2 \quad \text{\textit{Simplifying}}$$
$$= 12 - 20\sqrt{6} + \sqrt{6} - 10$$
$$= 2 - 19\sqrt{6}$$

**TRY THIS** ➡

Multiply.

3.  $(\sqrt{3} - 5\sqrt{2})(2\sqrt{3} + \sqrt{2})$
4.  $(\sqrt{2} + 2\sqrt{3})(3\sqrt{2} - 4\sqrt{3})$

**Example 3.**  Multiply.

$$(\sqrt{5} + \sqrt{7})(\sqrt{5} - \sqrt{7}) = (\sqrt{5})^2 - (\sqrt{7})^2$$
$$= 5 - 7$$
$$= -2$$

**TRY THIS** ➡

Multiply.

5.  $(\sqrt{2} + \sqrt{5})(\sqrt{2} - \sqrt{5})$

**Example 4.** Multiply.

$$(\sqrt{3} + x)^2 = (\sqrt{3})^2 + 2x\sqrt{3} + x^2$$
$$= 3 + 2x\sqrt{3} + x^2$$

**TRY THIS**

Multiply.

6. $(2\sqrt{5} - 3)^2$
7. $(3\sqrt{6} + 2)^2$

## Exercise Set 10-6

▌Multiply. (*See Examples 1–4.*)

1. $\sqrt{6}(2 - 3\sqrt{6})$
2. $\sqrt{3}(4 + \sqrt{3})$
3. $\sqrt{2}(\sqrt{3} - \sqrt{5})$
4. $\sqrt{5}(\sqrt{5} - \sqrt{2})$
5. $\sqrt{3}(2\sqrt{5} - 3\sqrt{4})$
6. $\sqrt{2}(3\sqrt{10} - 2\sqrt{2})$
7. $\sqrt[3]{2}(\sqrt[3]{4} - 2\sqrt[3]{32})$
8. $\sqrt[3]{3}(\sqrt[3]{9} - 4\sqrt[3]{21})$
9. $\sqrt[3]{a}(\sqrt[3]{2a^2} + \sqrt[3]{16a^2})$
10. $\sqrt[3]{x}(\sqrt[3]{3x^2} - \sqrt[3]{81x^2})$
11. $(\sqrt{3} - \sqrt{2})(\sqrt{3} + \sqrt{2})$
12. $(\sqrt{5} + \sqrt{6})(\sqrt{5} - \sqrt{6})$
13. $(\sqrt{8} + 2\sqrt{5})(\sqrt{8} - 2\sqrt{5})$
14. $(\sqrt{18} + 3\sqrt{7})(\sqrt{18} - 3\sqrt{7})$
15. $(\sqrt{a} + \sqrt{b})(\sqrt{a} - \sqrt{b})$
16. $(\sqrt{x} - \sqrt{y})(\sqrt{x} + \sqrt{y})$
17. $(3 - \sqrt{5})(2 + \sqrt{5})$
18. $(2 + \sqrt{6})(4 - \sqrt{6})$
19. $(\sqrt{3} + 1)(2\sqrt{3} + 1)$
20. $(4\sqrt{3} + 5)(\sqrt{3} - 2)$
21. $(2\sqrt{7} - 4\sqrt{2})(3\sqrt{7} + 6\sqrt{2})$
22. $(4\sqrt{5} + 3\sqrt{3})(3\sqrt{5} - 4\sqrt{3})$
23. $(\sqrt{a} + \sqrt{2})(\sqrt{a} + \sqrt{3})$
24. $(2 - \sqrt{x})(1 - \sqrt{x})$
25. $(2\sqrt[3]{3} + \sqrt[3]{2})(\sqrt[3]{3} - 2\sqrt[3]{2})$
26. $(3\sqrt[4]{7} + \sqrt[4]{6})(2\sqrt[4]{9} - 3\sqrt[4]{6})$
27. $(2 + \sqrt{3})^2$
28. $(\sqrt{5} + 1)^2$
29. $(3\sqrt{2} - \sqrt{3})^2$
30. $(5\sqrt{3} + 3\sqrt{5})^2$

## Challenge Exercises

Multiply.

31. $(\sqrt{x + 3} - 3)(\sqrt{x + 3} + 3)$
32. $(\sqrt{x + h} - \sqrt{x})(\sqrt{x + h} + \sqrt{x})$

## COMPUTER NOTE: Maps by Computer

Computers can provide information in many ways. They can print lists of numbers. They can make drawings of molecules, new car designs, and other objects. Special output units can even produce maps showing rainfall, average temperature, and many other kinds of information.

# *10-7 Rationalizing Denominators or Numerators*

After finishing Lesson 10-7, you should be able to
- **I**   rationalize the denominator of a radical expression.
- **II**   rationalize the numerator of a radical expression.
- **III**   rationalize denominators or numerators having two terms.

## **I Rationalizing Denominators**

To simplify expressions like $\sqrt{\dfrac{1}{2}}$ we multiply by 1, choosing an

appropriate symbol $\dfrac{n}{n}$.

**Example 1.**   Simplify $\sqrt{\dfrac{1}{2}}$.

We multiply by 1, choosing $\dfrac{2}{2}$ for 1. This makes the denominator
a perfect square.

$$\sqrt{\frac{1}{2}} = \sqrt{\frac{1}{2} \cdot \frac{2}{2}} \qquad \textit{Multiplying by 1}$$

$$= \sqrt{\frac{2}{2 \cdot 2}}$$

$$= \frac{\sqrt{2}}{2} \qquad \textit{Using Theorem 10-6}$$

Notice that there is no radical in the denominator. We have a rational number in the denominator. Thus we say we have *rationalized the denominator*. Radical expressions are usually considered simpler when the denominator is free of radicals.

**Example 2.**   Rationalize the denominator.

$$\sqrt[3]{\frac{7}{9}} = \sqrt[3]{\frac{7}{3 \cdot 3} \cdot \frac{3}{3}} \qquad \textit{Multiplying by } \tfrac{3}{3} \textit{ to make the denominator}$$
$$\textit{a perfect cube}$$

$$= \sqrt[3]{\frac{21}{3 \cdot 3 \cdot 3}}$$

$$= \frac{\sqrt[3]{21}}{3}$$

**TRY THIS** ➡

Rationalize the
denominator.

1.   $\sqrt{\dfrac{2}{3}}$

2.   $\sqrt{\dfrac{10}{7}}$

3.   $\sqrt[3]{\dfrac{3}{6}}$

We can use another method for rationalizing denominators.

**Example 3.** Rationalize the denominator.

$$\sqrt{\frac{2a}{5b}} = \frac{\sqrt{2a}}{\sqrt{5b}}$$

$$= \frac{\sqrt{2a}}{\sqrt{5b}} \cdot \frac{\sqrt{5b}}{\sqrt{5b}} \quad \textit{Multiplying by 1}$$

$$= \frac{\sqrt{10ab}}{\sqrt{25b^2}} \quad \textit{The denominator is a perfect square.}$$

$$= \frac{\sqrt{10ab}}{5|b|} \quad \textit{Simplifying}$$

**TRY THIS**

Rationalize the denominator.

4. $\sqrt{\dfrac{4a}{3b}}$

5. $\dfrac{\sqrt{4x^5}}{\sqrt{3y^3}}$

**Example 4.** Rationalize the denominator.

$$\frac{\sqrt[3]{a}}{\sqrt[3]{9x}} = \frac{\sqrt[3]{a}}{\sqrt[3]{9x}} \cdot \frac{\sqrt[3]{3x^2}}{\sqrt[3]{3x^2}} \quad \textit{Multiplying by 1}$$

$$= \frac{\sqrt[3]{3ax^2}}{\sqrt[3]{27x^3}} \quad \textit{The denominator is a perfect cube.}$$

$$= \frac{\sqrt[3]{3ax^2}}{3x}$$

**TRY THIS**

Rationalize the denominator.

6. $\dfrac{\sqrt[3]{7}}{\sqrt[3]{2}}$

7. $\sqrt[3]{\dfrac{3x^5}{2y}}$

## ∎ Rationalizing Numerators

Sometimes it is necessary to rationalize the numerator. We use the same procedure.

**Examples.** Rationalize the numerator.

**5.** $\dfrac{\sqrt{7}}{\sqrt{5}} = \dfrac{\sqrt{7}}{\sqrt{5}} \cdot \dfrac{\sqrt{7}}{\sqrt{7}} \quad \textit{Multiplying by 1}$

$$= \frac{\sqrt{49}}{\sqrt{35}} \quad \textit{The numerator is a perfect square.}$$

$$= \frac{7}{\sqrt{35}}$$

**6.** $\dfrac{\sqrt[3]{5}}{\sqrt[3]{3}} = \dfrac{\sqrt[3]{5}}{\sqrt[3]{3}} \cdot \dfrac{\sqrt[3]{5^2}}{\sqrt[3]{5^2}}$   *Multiplying by 1*

$= \dfrac{\sqrt[3]{5^3}}{\sqrt[3]{75}}$

$= \dfrac{5}{\sqrt[3]{75}}$

**TRY THIS** ⟹

Rationalize the numerator.

**8.** $\dfrac{\sqrt{11}}{\sqrt{6}}$

**9.** $\dfrac{\sqrt[3]{7}}{\sqrt[3]{4}}$

Why do we consider these procedures? Suppose we wanted to approximate $\dfrac{\sqrt{3}}{\sqrt{2}}$. We could do it by looking up the approximations for $\sqrt{3}$ and $\sqrt{2}$ in Table 1 and then do the division $\dfrac{1.732}{1.414}$. But this is a rather complicated division. Having rationalized the numerator we could look up $\sqrt{6}$ in the table and do the division $\dfrac{3}{2.449}$. This is an easier computation. But, if we rationalized the denominator the division would have been $\dfrac{2.449}{2}$, which is the easiest of the three. Here is a reason for rationalizing denominators: to ease computations when approximating. In calculus courses it is important to be able to rationalize the numerator. Thus we consider both procedures here.

### Ⅲ Rationalizing When There are Two Terms

When the denominator to be rationalized has two terms, choose a symbol for 1 as illustrated below.

**Example 7.** Rationalize the denominator.

$\dfrac{4 + \sqrt{2}}{\sqrt{5} - \sqrt{2}} = \dfrac{4 + \sqrt{2}}{\sqrt{5} - \sqrt{2}} \cdot \dfrac{\sqrt{5} + \sqrt{2}}{\sqrt{5} + \sqrt{2}}$   *Multiplying by 1*

$= \dfrac{(4 + \sqrt{2})(\sqrt{5} + \sqrt{2})}{(\sqrt{5} - \sqrt{2})(\sqrt{5} + \sqrt{2})}$

$= \dfrac{4\sqrt{5} + 4\sqrt{2} + \sqrt{2}\sqrt{5} + (\sqrt{2})^2}{(\sqrt{5})^2 - (\sqrt{2})^2}$

$$= \frac{4\sqrt{5} + 4\sqrt{2} + \sqrt{10} + 2}{5 - 2}$$

$$= \frac{4\sqrt{5} + 4\sqrt{2} + \sqrt{10} + 2}{3}$$

Note that the denominator in this example was $\sqrt{5} - \sqrt{2}$. We choose a symbol for 1 which had $\sqrt{5} + \sqrt{2}$ in the numerator and denominator. If the denominator had been $\sqrt{5} + \sqrt{2}$ we would have chosen $\dfrac{\sqrt{5} - \sqrt{2}}{\sqrt{5} - \sqrt{2}}$ for 1.

**Examples.** What symbol for 1 would you use to rationalize the denominator?

| | **Expression** | **Symbol for 1** |
|---|---|---|
| **8.** | $\dfrac{3}{2 + \sqrt{7}}$ | $\dfrac{2 - \sqrt{7}}{2 - \sqrt{7}}$ |
| **9.** | $\dfrac{4 + \sqrt{3}}{\sqrt{3} - \sqrt{11}}$ | $\dfrac{\sqrt{3} + \sqrt{11}}{\sqrt{3} + \sqrt{11}}$ |

**TRY THIS**

What symbol for 1 would you use to rationalize the denominator?

10. $\dfrac{\sqrt{5} + 1}{\sqrt{3} - 1}$

11. $\dfrac{1}{\sqrt{2} + \sqrt{3}}$

**Example 10.** Rationalize the denominator.

$$\frac{4}{\sqrt{3} + 1} = \frac{4}{\sqrt{3} + 1} \cdot \frac{\sqrt{3} - 1}{\sqrt{3} - 1}$$

$$= \frac{4(\sqrt{3} - 1)}{(\sqrt{3} + 1)(\sqrt{3} - 1)}$$

$$= \frac{4(\sqrt{3} - 1)}{(\sqrt{3})^2 - 1^2}$$

$$= \frac{4(\sqrt{3} - 1)}{3 - 1}$$

$$= \frac{4(\sqrt{3} - 1)}{2}$$

$$= 2(\sqrt{3} - 1)$$

**TRY THIS**

Rationalize the denominator.

12. $\dfrac{5}{1 - \sqrt{2}}$

We can also rationalize numerators.

**Example 11.** Rationalize the numerator.

$$\frac{4 + \sqrt{2}}{\sqrt{5} - \sqrt{2}} = \frac{4 + \sqrt{2}}{\sqrt{5} - \sqrt{2}} \cdot \frac{4 - \sqrt{2}}{4 - \sqrt{2}}$$

$$= \frac{16 - (\sqrt{2})^2}{4\sqrt{5} - \sqrt{5}\sqrt{2} - 4\sqrt{2} + (\sqrt{2})^2}$$

$$= \frac{16 - 2}{4(\sqrt{5} - \sqrt{2}) - \sqrt{5}\sqrt{2} + 2}$$

$$= \frac{14}{4(\sqrt{5} - \sqrt{2}) - \sqrt{10} + 2}$$

**TRY THIS** ➤

> Rationalize the numerator.
>
> 13. $\dfrac{3 + \sqrt{5}}{\sqrt{2} - \sqrt{6}}$

## Exercise Set 10-7

▌Rationalize the denominator. (*See Examples 1–4.*)

1. $\sqrt{\dfrac{6}{5}}$

2. $\sqrt{\dfrac{11}{6}}$

3. $\sqrt{\dfrac{10}{7}}$

4. $\sqrt{\dfrac{22}{3}}$

5. $\dfrac{6\sqrt{5}}{5\sqrt{3}}$

6. $\dfrac{2\sqrt{3}}{5\sqrt{2}}$

7. $\sqrt[3]{\dfrac{16}{9}}$

8. $\sqrt[3]{\dfrac{3}{9}}$

9. $\dfrac{\sqrt[3]{3a}}{\sqrt[3]{5c}}$

10. $\dfrac{\sqrt[3]{7x}}{\sqrt[3]{3y}}$

11. $\dfrac{\sqrt[3]{2y^4}}{\sqrt[3]{6x^4}}$

12. $\dfrac{\sqrt[3]{3a^4}}{\sqrt[3]{7b^2}}$

13. $\dfrac{1}{\sqrt[3]{xy}}$

14. $\dfrac{1}{\sqrt[3]{ab}}$

▌▌Rationalize the numerator. (*See Examples 5 and 6.*)

15. $\dfrac{\sqrt{7}}{\sqrt{3}}$

16. $\dfrac{\sqrt{6}}{\sqrt{5}}$

17. $\sqrt{\dfrac{14}{21}}$

18. $\sqrt{\dfrac{12}{15}}$

19. $\dfrac{4\sqrt{13}}{3\sqrt{7}}$

20. $\dfrac{5\sqrt{21}}{2\sqrt{6}}$

21. $\dfrac{\sqrt[3]{7}}{\sqrt[3]{2}}$

22. $\dfrac{\sqrt[3]{5}}{\sqrt[3]{4}}$

23. $\sqrt{\dfrac{7x}{3y}}$

24. $\sqrt{\dfrac{6a}{2b}}$

25. $\dfrac{\sqrt[3]{5y^4}}{\sqrt[3]{6x^5}}$

26. $\dfrac{\sqrt[3]{3a^5}}{\sqrt[3]{7b^2}}$

27. $\dfrac{\sqrt{ab}}{3}$

28. $\dfrac{\sqrt{xy}}{5}$

**▮▮▮ Rationalize the denominator.** (*See Examples 7–10.*)

29. $\dfrac{5}{8 - \sqrt{6}}$

30. $\dfrac{7}{9 + \sqrt{10}}$

31. $\dfrac{-4\sqrt{7}}{\sqrt{5} - \sqrt{3}}$

32. $\dfrac{-3\sqrt{2}}{\sqrt{3} - \sqrt{5}}$

33. $\dfrac{\sqrt{5} - 2\sqrt{6}}{\sqrt{3} - 4\sqrt{5}}$

34. $\dfrac{\sqrt{6} - 3\sqrt{5}}{\sqrt{3} - 2\sqrt{7}}$

35. $\dfrac{\sqrt{x} - \sqrt{y}}{\sqrt{x} + \sqrt{y}}$

36. $\dfrac{\sqrt{a} + \sqrt{b}}{\sqrt{a} - \sqrt{b}}$

37. $\dfrac{5\sqrt{3} - 3\sqrt{2}}{3\sqrt{2} - 2\sqrt{3}}$

38. $\dfrac{7\sqrt{2} + 4\sqrt{3}}{4\sqrt{3} - 3\sqrt{2}}$

**Rationalize the numerator.** (*See Example 11.*)

39. $\dfrac{\sqrt{3} + 5}{8}$

40. $\dfrac{3 - \sqrt{2}}{5}$

41. $\dfrac{\sqrt{3} - 5}{\sqrt{2} + 5}$

42. $\dfrac{\sqrt{6} - 3}{\sqrt{3} + 7}$

43. $\dfrac{\sqrt{5} - \sqrt{2}}{\sqrt{2} + \sqrt{3}}$

44. $\dfrac{\sqrt{7} - \sqrt{3}}{\sqrt{5} + \sqrt{2}}$

45. $\dfrac{4\sqrt{6} - 5\sqrt{3}}{2\sqrt{3} + 7\sqrt{6}}$

46. $\dfrac{8\sqrt{2} + 5\sqrt{3}}{5\sqrt{3} - 7\sqrt{2}}$

---

**Challenge Exercises**

Rationalize the numerator. Assume all expressions represent nonnegative numbers.

47. $\dfrac{\sqrt{x + 1} + 1}{\sqrt{x}}$

48. $\dfrac{\sqrt{a + h} - \sqrt{a}}{h}$

# 10-8 Rational Numbers as Exponents

After finishing Lesson 10-8, you should be able to
 **I**    write expressions with and without fractional exponents.
 **II**   write expressions without negative rational exponents.
 **III**  use fractional exponents to simplify radical expressions.

## I Fractional Exponents

Expressions like $a^{\frac{1}{2}}$, $5^{-\frac{1}{4}}$, and $(2y)^{\frac{4}{5}}$ have not yet been defined. We shall define such expressions in such a way that the usual properties of exponents hold.

Consider $a^{\frac{1}{2}} \cdot a^{\frac{1}{2}}$. If we still want to multiply by adding exponents it must follow that $a^{\frac{1}{2}} \cdot a^{\frac{1}{2}} = a^{\frac{1}{2}+\frac{1}{2}}$, or $a^1$. Thus we should define $a^{\frac{1}{2}}$ to be a square root of $a$, $\sqrt{a}$ or $-\sqrt{a}$. Similarly, $a^{\frac{1}{3}} \cdot a^{\frac{1}{3}} \cdot a^{\frac{1}{3}} = a^{\frac{1}{3}+\frac{1}{3}+\frac{1}{3}}$, or $a^1$, so $a^{\frac{1}{3}}$ should be defined to mean $\sqrt[3]{a}$.

### DEFINITION

For any nonnegative number $a$, and any index $n$, $a^{\frac{1}{n}}$ means $\sqrt[n]{a}$ (the principal $n$th root of $a$).

**Examples.** Rewrite without fractional exponents.

**1.** $x^{\frac{1}{2}} = \sqrt{x}$

**2.** $27^{\frac{1}{3}} = \sqrt[3]{27}$, or 3

**3.** $(abc)^{\frac{1}{5}} = \sqrt[5]{abc}$

**TRY THIS** ➡

Rewrite without fractional exponents.

1. $y^{\frac{1}{4}}$
2. $(3a)^{\frac{1}{2}}$
3. $16^{\frac{1}{4}}$
4. $(125)^{\frac{1}{3}}$
5. $(a^3b^2c)^{\frac{1}{5}}$

**Examples.** Rewrite with fractional exponents.

**4.** $\sqrt[5]{7xy} = (7xy)^{\frac{1}{5}}$

**5.** $\sqrt[7]{\dfrac{x^3y}{9}} = \left(\dfrac{x^3y}{9}\right)^{\frac{1}{7}}$

**TRY THIS** ➡

Rewrite with fractional exponents.

6. $\sqrt[3]{19}$
7. $\sqrt{abc}$
8. $\sqrt[5]{\dfrac{x^2y}{16}}$

How should we define $a^{\frac{2}{3}}$? If the usual properties of exponents are to hold, we have $a^{\frac{2}{3}} = (a^{\frac{1}{3}})^2$, or $(\sqrt[3]{a})^2$, or $\sqrt[3]{a^2}$. We make the definition accordingly.

**DEFINITION**

For any natural numbers $m$ and $n$, and any nonnegative number $a$, $a^{\frac{m}{n}}$ means $\sqrt[n]{a^m}$.

Thus $a^{\frac{m}{n}}$ represents the principal $n$th root of $a^m$. Since, by Theorem 10-8, we know that $\sqrt[n]{a^m} = (\sqrt[n]{a})^m$ it follows that $a^{\frac{m}{n}}$ also represents $(\sqrt[n]{a})^m$.

**Examples.** Rewrite without fractional exponents.

**6.** $(27)^{\frac{2}{3}} = (\sqrt[3]{27})^2$
　　　$= (3)^2$
　　　$= 9$

**7.** $4^{\frac{3}{2}} = (\sqrt[2]{4})^3$
　　　$= 2^3$
　　　$= 8$

**TRY THIS** ━━▶

> Rewrite without fractional exponents.
>
> 9. $x^{\frac{3}{2}}$
> 10. $8^{\frac{2}{3}}$
> 11. $4^{\frac{5}{2}}$

**Examples.** Rewrite with fractional exponents.

**8.** $(\sqrt[4]{7xy})^5 = (7xy)^{\frac{5}{4}}$

**9.** $\sqrt[3]{8^4} = 8^{\frac{4}{3}}$

**TRY THIS** ━━▶

> Rewrite with fractional exponents.
>
> 12. $(\sqrt[3]{7abc})^4$
> 13. $\sqrt[5]{6^7}$

## ▌Negative Rational Exponents

We now define negative rational number exponents.

**DEFINITION**

For any rational number $\frac{m}{n}$ and any positive real number $a$, $a^{-\frac{m}{n}}$ means $\dfrac{1}{a^{\frac{m}{n}}}$.

**Examples.** Rewrite with positive exponents.

**10.** $4^{-\frac{1}{2}} = \dfrac{1}{4^{\frac{1}{2}}}$

**11.** $(5xy)^{-\frac{4}{5}} = \dfrac{1}{(5xy)^{\frac{4}{5}}}$

**TRY THIS** ━━▶

> Rewrite with positive exponents.
>
> 14. $5^{-\frac{1}{4}}$
> 15. $(3xy)^{-\frac{7}{8}}$

### ⅢSimplifying Radical Expressions

Some simplifying can be done more easily when we use fractional exponents.
Note that we have defined fractional exponents *only* for nonnegative radicands.
Thus we need not use absolute value notation for an expression like $x^{\frac{2}{2}}$, which
means $\sqrt{x^2}$, or $x$, since $x$ is assumed to be nonnegative.

**Examples.** Write an exponential expression. Then simplify if
possible. Write radical notation for the answer, if appropriate.

**12.** $\sqrt[6]{x^3} = x^{\frac{3}{6}}$
$\qquad = x^{\frac{1}{2}}$
$\qquad = \sqrt{x}$

**13.** $\sqrt[6]{4} = 4^{\frac{1}{6}}$
$\qquad = (2^2)^{\frac{1}{6}}$
$\qquad = 2^{\frac{2}{6}}$
$\qquad = 2^{\frac{1}{3}}$
$\qquad = \sqrt[3]{2}$

**TRY THIS** ➡

> Write an exponential expression. Then simplify, if possible.
> Write radical notation for the answer, if appropriate.
>
> 16. $\sqrt[4]{a^2}$
> 17. $\sqrt[4]{x^4}$
> 18. $\sqrt[6]{8}$

**Example 14.** Write an exponential expression. Then simplify, if
possible. Assume variables stand for nonnegative numbers. Write
radical notation for the answer, if appropriate.

$\sqrt[8]{a^2b^4} = (a^2b^4)^{\frac{1}{8}}$
$\qquad = a^{\frac{2}{8}} \cdot b^{\frac{4}{8}}$
$\qquad = a^{\frac{1}{4}} \cdot b^{\frac{2}{4}}$
$\qquad = (ab^2)^{\frac{1}{4}}$
$\qquad = \sqrt[4]{ab^2}$

**TRY THIS** ➡

> Write an exponential expression. Then simplify, if possible.
> Assume variables stand for nonnegative numbers. Write
> radical notation for the answer, if appropriate.
>
> 19. $\sqrt[5]{a^5b^{10}}$
> 20. $\sqrt[4]{x^4y^{12}}$

We can use properties of fractional exponents to
write a single radical expression for a product or
quotient.

**Examples.** Write a single radical expression.

**15.** $\sqrt[3]{5} \cdot \sqrt{2} = 5^{\frac{1}{3}} \cdot 2^{\frac{1}{2}}$
$\qquad = 5^{\frac{2}{6}} 2^{\frac{3}{6}}$
$\qquad = (5^2 \cdot 2^3)^{\frac{1}{6}}$
$\qquad = \sqrt[6]{5^2 \cdot 2^3}$
$\qquad = \sqrt[6]{200}$

**16.** $\sqrt{x-2} \cdot \sqrt[4]{3y} = (x-2)^{\frac{1}{2}}(3y)^{\frac{1}{4}}$
$= (x-2)^{\frac{2}{4}}(3y)^{\frac{1}{4}}$
$= [(x-2)^2(3y)]^{\frac{1}{4}}$
$= \sqrt[4]{(x^2 - 4x + 4) \cdot 3y}$
$= \sqrt[4]{3x^2y - 12xy + 12y}$

**17.** $\dfrac{\sqrt[4]{(x+y)^3}}{\sqrt{x+y}} = \dfrac{(x+y)^{\frac{3}{4}}}{(x+y)^{\frac{1}{2}}}$
$= (x+y)^{\frac{3}{4}-\frac{1}{2}}$
$= (x+y)^{\frac{1}{4}}$
$= \sqrt[4]{x+y}$

**TRY THIS**

> Write a single radical expression.
>
> 21. $\sqrt[4]{7} \cdot \sqrt{3}$
>
> 22. $\dfrac{\sqrt[4]{(x+2)^3} \cdot \sqrt[5]{(x+2)}}{\sqrt{x+2}}$

**Example 18.** Write a single radical expression.

$a^{\frac{1}{2}}b^{-\frac{1}{2}}c^{\frac{5}{6}} = a^{\frac{3}{6}}b^{-\frac{3}{6}}c^{\frac{5}{6}} = (a^3b^{-3}c^5)^{\frac{1}{6}} = \sqrt[6]{a^3b^{-3}c^5}$

**TRY THIS**

> Write a single radical expression.
>
> 23. $x^{\frac{2}{3}}y^{\frac{1}{2}}z^{\frac{5}{6}}$     24. $\dfrac{a^{\frac{1}{2}}b^{\frac{3}{8}}}{a^{\frac{1}{4}}b^{\frac{1}{8}}}$

## Exercise Set 10-8

❚ Rewrite without fractional exponents. (*See Examples 1–3, 6, and 7.*)

1. $x^{\frac{1}{4}}$

2. $y^{\frac{1}{5}}$

3. $(8)^{\frac{1}{3}}$

4. $(16)^{\frac{1}{2}}$

5. $(a^2b^2)^{\frac{1}{5}}$

6. $(x^3y^3)^{\frac{1}{4}}$

7. $a^{\frac{2}{3}}$

8. $b^{\frac{3}{2}}$

9. $16^{\frac{3}{4}}$

10. $4^{\frac{7}{2}}$

Rewrite with fractional exponents. (*See Examples 4, 5, 8, and 9.*)

11. $\sqrt[3]{20}$

12. $\sqrt[3]{19}$

13. $\sqrt{17}$

14. $\sqrt{6}$

15. $\sqrt[4]{cd}$

16. $\sqrt[5]{xy}$

17. $\sqrt[5]{xy^2z}$

18. $\sqrt[7]{x^3y^2z^2}$

19. $(\sqrt{3mn})^3$

20. $(\sqrt[3]{7xy})^4$

21. $(\sqrt[7]{8x^2y})^5$

22. $(\sqrt[6]{2a^5b})^7$

❚❚ Rewrite with positive exponents. (*Examples 10 and 11.*)

23. $x^{-\frac{1}{3}}$

24. $y^{-\frac{1}{4}}$

25. $(2rs)^{-\frac{3}{4}}$

26. $(5xy)^{-\frac{5}{8}}$

27. $(\frac{1}{10})^{-\frac{2}{3}}$

28. $(\frac{1}{8})^{-\frac{3}{4}}$

29. $\dfrac{1}{x^{-\frac{2}{3}}}$

30. $\dfrac{1}{x^{-\frac{5}{8}}}$

■■■ Write an exponential expression. Then simplify if possible. Assume variables stand for nonnegative numbers. Write radical notation for the answer, if appropriate. (*See Examples 12–14.*)

31. $\sqrt[6]{a^4}$                           32. $\sqrt[6]{y^2}$

33. $\sqrt[3]{8y^6}$                          34. $\sqrt{x^4 y^6}$

35. $\sqrt[5]{32c^{10}d^{15}}$                36. $\sqrt[4]{16x^{12}y^{16}}$

37. $\sqrt[6]{\dfrac{m^{12}n^{24}}{64}}$      38. $\sqrt[5]{\dfrac{x^{15}y^{20}}{32}}$

39. $\sqrt[8]{r^4 s^2}$                       40. $\sqrt[3]{27a^3 b^9}$

41. $\sqrt[12]{64t^6 s^6}$                    42. $\sqrt[4]{81x^8 y^8}$

Write a single radical expression. (*See Examples 15–18.*)

43. $\sqrt{x}\ \sqrt[3]{x-2}$                 44. $\sqrt[4]{3x}\ \sqrt{y+4}$

45. $\dfrac{\sqrt[3]{(a+b)^2}}{\sqrt{(a+b)}}$ 46. $\dfrac{\sqrt[3]{(x+y)^2}}{\sqrt[4]{(x+y)^3}}$

47. $a^{\frac{2}{3}}\cdot b^{\frac{3}{4}}$    48. $x^{\frac{1}{3}}\cdot y^{\frac{1}{4}}\cdot z^{\frac{1}{6}}$

49. $\dfrac{s^{\frac{7}{12}}\cdot t^{\frac{5}{6}}}{s^{\frac{1}{3}}\cdot t^{-\frac{1}{6}}}$ 50. $\dfrac{x^{\frac{8}{15}}\cdot y^{\frac{4}{5}}}{x^{\frac{1}{3}}\cdot y^{-\frac{1}{5}}}$

---

### Challenge Exercises

51. *Road Pavement Messages.* In a psychological study it was determined that the proper length $L$ of the letters of a word printed on pavement is given by

$$L = \frac{(0.00252)d^{2.27}}{h},$$

where $d$ is the distance of a car from the lettering and $h$ is the height of the eye above the surface of the road. All units are in meters. This formula says that if a person is $h$ meters above the surface of the road and is to be able to recognize a message $d$ meters away, that message will be the most recognizable if the length of the letters is $L$. Find $L$, given the values of $d$ and $h$.

a) $h = 1$ m, $d = 60$ m

b) $h = 2.4$ m, $d = 80$ m

c) $h = 0.9906$ m, $d = 75$ m

d) $h = 1.1$ m, $d = 100$ m

e) Find a road pavement message near the school. See if it conforms to this formula. (*Hint:* Don't do your measurements in the middle of a road.)

# 10-9 Solving Radical Equations

After finishing Lesson 10-9, you should be able to
**I** solve radical equations with one radical term.
**II** solve radical equations with two radical terms.

## I The Principle of Powers

These are radical equations.

$$\sqrt{2x} + 1 = 5, \qquad \sqrt[3]{x} + \sqrt[3]{4x - 2} = 7$$

A radical equation is an equation in which variables occur in one
or more radicands. To solve such equations we need a new principle for equations. Suppose the equation $a = b$ is true. When
we square both sides we still get a true equation, $a^2 = b^2$. This
can be generalized.

**THEOREM 10-9 (The Principle of Powers)**
For any natural number $n$, if an equation $a = b$ is true, then the
equation $a^n = b^n$ is true.

**Remark.** The converse of Theorem 10-9 is not true. For example,
$(3)^2 = (-3)^2$ is true, but $3 = -3$ is not true.

**Example 1.** Solve: $\sqrt{x} - 3 = 4$.

$$\sqrt{x} = 7 \qquad \textit{Adding 3}$$
$$x = 7^2, \text{ or } 49 \qquad \textit{Principle of powers}$$

Check: 
$$\begin{array}{c|c} \sqrt{x} - 3 = 4 \\ \hline \sqrt{49} - 3 & 4 \\ 7 - 3 & \\ 4 & \end{array}$$

The solution is 49.

Since the converse of Theorem 10-9 is not true, the principle of
powers does *not* always give equivalent equations.

**Example 2.** Solve: $\sqrt{x} = -3$.

We might observe at the outset that this equation has no solution because the principal square root of a number is never negative. Let us continue as above, for comparison.

$x = (-3)^2$, or 9    *Principle of powers*

Check:  $\dfrac{\sqrt{x} = -3}{\begin{array}{c|c} \sqrt{9} & -3 \\ 3 & \end{array}}$

The number 9 does not check. Hence the equation has no solution.

In solving radical equations, possible solutions found using the principle of powers *must* be checked!

**TRY THIS** ➞

Solve.

1. $\sqrt{x} - 7 = 3$
2. $\sqrt{x} = -2$

**Example 3.** Solve: $x - 5 = \sqrt{x + 7}$.

$x - 5 = \sqrt{x + 7}$    *The radical is already isolated*

$(x - 5)^2 = (\sqrt{x + 7})^2$    *Principle of powers: squaring both sides*

$x^2 - 10x + 25 = x + 7$

$x^2 - 11x + 18 = 0$

$(x - 9)(x - 2) = 0$    *Factoring*

$x = 9$ or $x = 2$    *Using the principle of zero products*

The possible solutions are 9 and 2. Let us check.

For 9:  $\dfrac{x - 5 = \sqrt{x + 7}}{\begin{array}{c|c} 9 - 5 & \sqrt{9 + 7} \\ 4 & 4 \end{array}}$    For 2:  $\dfrac{x - 5 = \sqrt{x + 7}}{\begin{array}{c|c} 2 - 5 & \sqrt{2 + 7} \\ -3 & 3 \end{array}}$

Since 9 checks but 2 does not, the solution is 9.

**TRY THIS** ➞

3. Solve: $x - 1 = \sqrt{x + 5}$.

## ‖ Equations With Two Radical Terms

A general strategy for solving equations with two radical terms is as follows:

1. Isolate one of the radical terms.
2. Use Theorem 10-9, the principle of powers.
3. If a radical remains, perform steps 1 and 2 again.
4. Check possible solutions.

**Example 4.** Solve: $\sqrt{2x - 5} = 1 + \sqrt{x - 3}$.

$$(\sqrt{2x - 5})^2 = (1 + \sqrt{x - 3})^2 \qquad \textit{One radical is already isolated; we square both sides}$$

$$2x - 5 = 1 + 2\sqrt{x - 3} + (x - 3)$$
$$x - 3 = 2\sqrt{x - 3} \qquad \textit{Isolating the remaining radical}$$
$$(x - 3)^2 = (2\sqrt{x - 3})^2 \qquad \textit{Squaring both sides}$$
$$x^2 - 6x + 9 = 4(x - 3)$$
$$x^2 - 6x + 9 = 4x - 12$$
$$x^2 - 10x + 21 = 0$$
$$(x - 7)(x - 3) = 0 \qquad \textit{Factoring}$$

$x = 7$ or $x = 3$    *Using the principle of zero products*

The numbers 7 and 3 check and are the solutions.

**TRY THIS**

4. Solve: $\sqrt{3x + 1} = 1 + \sqrt{x + 4}$.

## Exercise Set 10-9

‖ Solve. (*See Examples 1–3.*)

1. $\sqrt{2x - 3} = 1$
2. $\sqrt{x + 3} = 6$
3. $\sqrt{y + 1} - 5 = 8$
4. $\sqrt{x - 2} - 7 = -4$
5. $\sqrt[3]{x + 5} = 2$
6. $\sqrt[3]{x - 2} = 3$
7. $\sqrt[4]{y - 3} = 2$
8. $\sqrt[4]{x + 3} = 3$
9. $\sqrt{3y + 1} = 9$
10. $\sqrt{2y + 1} = 13$
11. $3\sqrt{x} = 6$
12. $8\sqrt{y} = 2$
13. $\sqrt[3]{x} = -3$
14. $\sqrt[3]{y} = -4$
15. $\sqrt{y + 3} - 20 = 0$
16. $\sqrt{x + 4} - 11 = 0$
17. $\sqrt{x + 2} = -4$
18. $\sqrt{y - 3} = -2$
19. $8 = \dfrac{1}{\sqrt{x}}$
20. $3 = \dfrac{1}{\sqrt{y}}$
21. $\sqrt[3]{6x + 9} + 8 = 5$
22. $\sqrt[3]{3y + 6} + 2 = 3$

∎ Solve. (*See Example 4.*)

23. $\sqrt{3y + 1} = \sqrt{2y + 6}$

24. $\sqrt{5x - 3} = \sqrt{2x + 3}$

25. $2\sqrt{1 - x} = \sqrt{5}$

26. $2\sqrt{2y - 3} = \sqrt{4y}$

27. $2\sqrt{t - 1} = \sqrt{3t - 1}$

28. $\sqrt{y + 10} = 3\sqrt{2y + 3}$

29. $\sqrt{y - 5} + \sqrt{y} = 5$

30. $\sqrt{x - 9} + \sqrt{x} = 1$

31. $3 + \sqrt{z - 6} = \sqrt{z + 9}$

32. $\sqrt{4x - 3} = 2 + \sqrt{2x - 5}$

33. $\sqrt{20 - x} + 8 = \sqrt{9 - x} + 11$

34. $4 + \sqrt{10 - x} = 6 + \sqrt{4 - x}$

35. $\sqrt{x + 2} + \sqrt{3x + 4} = 2$

36. $\sqrt{6x + 7} - \sqrt{3x + 3} = 1$

37. $\sqrt{4y + 1} - \sqrt{y - 2} = 3$

38. $\sqrt{y + 15} - \sqrt{2y + 7} = 1$

39. $\sqrt{2m - 3} = \sqrt{m + 7} - 2$

40. $\sqrt{3x - 5} + \sqrt{2x + 3} + 1 = 0$

## Challenge Exercises

Solve.

41. $\sqrt{x + 2} - \sqrt{x - 2} = \sqrt{2x}$

42. $\sqrt{\sqrt{x + 25} - \sqrt{x}} = 5$

43. $\dfrac{x + \sqrt{x + 1}}{x - \sqrt{x + 1}} = \dfrac{5}{11}$

44. $(x - 5)^{\frac{1}{5}} - 3 = 7$

45. $x^{\frac{1}{3}} + 5 = 7$

46. $x^{\frac{1}{5}} - 7 = 4$

---

### CONSUMER NOTE: Calculating Discounts

Many stores offer discount prices. A discount-store price tag may say, "Original price: $23.80. Our price: $19.04." The difference between these prices is the discount. It is $4.76. To find the rate of discount, divide the difference by the original price. $4.76 \div 23.80 = 0.20$, or 20%. So the discount rate is 20%.

A store may advertise the discount rate. "This week, all tagged items are 12% off." To calculate the discount, multiply the original price by the rate. If an item cost $34.75 originally, a 12% discount is $34.75 \times 0.12$. That is 4.17, so the discount is $4.17. The discount subtracted from the original price gives the sale price: $30.58.

Remember, an item you do not really want is no bargain at any discount. Thomas Jefferson said it this way: "Never buy what you do not want, because it is cheap."

## COMPUTER ACTIVITY

## Finding a Square Root Using the Newton-Raphson Iteration

**PROBLEM:** Approximate R, the square root of N.

**Examples using the flowchart:**

| 1 | 2(6) | 3 | 4 | 5 |
|---|---|---|---|---|
| Input Number N | Estimate E | Sum S | Average A | Approxi-mation of Root R |
| 20 | 4.5 | 8.9444 No | 4.4722 | 4.4720 |
| | 4.4720← | 8.9442 | 4.4721 | 4.4721 |
| 45 | 5 | 14 No | 7 | 6.4285 |
| | 6.4285← | 13.4285 No | 6.7142 | 6.7021 |
| | 6.7021← | 13.4164 | 6.7082 | 6.7082 |
| 169 | 12 | 26.0833 No | 13.0416 | 12.9584 |
| | 12.9584← | 26.0001 No | 13 | 12.9999 |
| | 12.9999← | 26 | 13 | 13 |

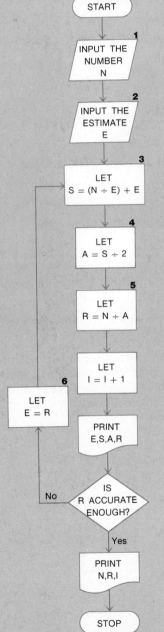

**TRY THIS** ➡ Find the square roots of these input numbers.
1. 225  2. 175

BASIC PROGRAM (Optional)

```
10  INPUT N
20  INPUT E
30  LET S = N/E + E
40  LET A = S/2
50  LET R = N/A
60  PRINT "E ="E, "S ="S,
        "A ="A, "R ="R
70  LET I = I + 1
80  IF ABS(A − R) < 0.0001
        THEN 110
90  LET E = R
100 GO TO 30
110 PRINT "NUMBER ="N,
        "ROOT ="R,
        "ITERATIONS ="I
120 END
```

## CHAPTER 10 REVIEW

Review the material in the chapter. Then see how you have done by trying these review exercises. If you miss an exercise, restudy the indicated lesson.

10-1    Convert to scientific notation.
1. 80,200,000,000
2. 0.000000074

10-1    Convert to decimal notation.
3. $7.6 \times 10^{14}$
4. $2.02 \times 10^{-12}$

10-2    Simplify.
5. $\sqrt{36}$
6. $-\sqrt{81}$
7. $\sqrt{16x^2}$
8. $\sqrt{x^2 - 2x + 1}$
9. $\sqrt[3]{\dfrac{8}{27}}$
10. $\sqrt[3]{0.008}$
11. $\sqrt[4]{(2x)^4}$

10-3    Multiply.
12. $\sqrt{5}\sqrt{7}$
13. $\sqrt[3]{2a}\sqrt[3]{3b}$
14. $\sqrt[4]{8}\sqrt[4]{9}$

10-3    Simplify.
15. $\sqrt{48}$    16. $\sqrt[3]{24x^3y^4}$

10-3    Multiply and simplify.
17. $\sqrt{18}\sqrt{12}$
18. $\sqrt[3]{a^2b}\sqrt[3]{a^4b^6}$

10-4    Simplify.
19. $\sqrt{\dfrac{25}{49}}$    20. $\sqrt[3]{\dfrac{x^3}{27}}$

10-4    Divide and simplify.
21. $\dfrac{\sqrt{48}}{\sqrt{16}}$

22. $\dfrac{\sqrt{6b^2}}{\sqrt{3b}}$

23. $\dfrac{\sqrt[3]{32}}{\sqrt[3]{2}}$

10-4    Simplify.
24. $(\sqrt[3]{16})^2$    25. $(\sqrt{3x})^3$

10-5    Simplify.
26. $\sqrt{32} + \sqrt{50}$
27. $\sqrt[3]{24} - \sqrt[3]{81}$

10-6    Multiply.
28. $(7 - 4\sqrt{3})(7 + 4\sqrt{3})$
29. $(2\sqrt{5} + 3\sqrt{2})(\sqrt{5} + \sqrt{2})$

10-7    Rationalize the denominator.
30. $\dfrac{\sqrt{8}}{\sqrt{3}}$    31. $\dfrac{6}{3 - \sqrt{7}}$

10-7    Rationalize the numerator.
32. $\dfrac{\sqrt{3}}{4}$    33. $\dfrac{\sqrt{2} + 5}{7 - \sqrt{3}}$

10-8    Rewrite without fractional exponents.
34. $16^{\frac{3}{4}}$    35. $(xy^2)^{\frac{1}{3}}$

10-8    Rewrite with fractional exponents.
36. $\sqrt[4]{9}$    37. $\sqrt[7]{8x^2y^3}$

10-8    Write an exponential expression. Then simplify if possible. Assume variables stand for nonnegative numbers. Write radical notation for the answer, if appropriate.
38. $\sqrt{a^6b^4}$
39. $\sqrt[3]{\dfrac{27}{a^6}}$
40. $\sqrt[6]{8x^9y^{12}}$

10-9    Solve.
41. $\sqrt{5 - 3x} = 6$
42. $\sqrt{7 - 4x} - \sqrt{3 - 2x} = 1$

# CHAPTER 10 TEST

Convert to scientific notation.
1. 90,400,000,000
2. 0.00000752

Convert to decimal notation.
3. $8.5 \times 10^{12}$
4. $3.05 \times 10^{-11}$

Simplify.
5. $\sqrt{81}$
6. $-\sqrt{121}$
7. $\sqrt{36y^2}$
8. $\sqrt{x^2 + 4x + 4}$
9. $\sqrt[3]{\dfrac{27}{125}}$
10. $\sqrt[3]{-0.027}$
11. $\sqrt[6]{(3y)^6}$

Multiply.
12. $\sqrt{6}\,\sqrt{5}$
13. $\sqrt[3]{3x}\,\sqrt[3]{4y}$
14. $\sqrt[4]{7}\,\sqrt[4]{6}$

Simplify.
15. $\sqrt{96}$
16. $\sqrt[3]{54a^3b^5}$

Multiply and simplify.
17. $\sqrt{20}\,\sqrt{18}$
18. $\sqrt[3]{x^2y^4}\,\sqrt[3]{x^5y^2}$

Simplify.
19. $\sqrt{\dfrac{36}{100}}$
20. $\sqrt[3]{\dfrac{y^3}{125}}$

Divide and simplify.
21. $\dfrac{\sqrt{54}}{\sqrt{18}}$

22. $\dfrac{\sqrt{8x^2}}{\sqrt{2x}}$

23. $\dfrac{\sqrt[3]{750}}{\sqrt[3]{3}}$

Simplify.
24. $(\sqrt[3]{18})^2$     25. $(\sqrt{4y})^3$

Simplify.
26. $\sqrt{27} + \sqrt{108}$
27. $\sqrt[3]{40} - \sqrt[3]{135}$

Multiply.
28. $(8 + 5\sqrt{6})(8 - 5\sqrt{6})$
29. $(2\sqrt{7} - 3\sqrt{5})(\sqrt{7} - \sqrt{5})$

Rationalize the denominator.
30. $\dfrac{\sqrt{5}}{\sqrt{7}}$     31. $\dfrac{\sqrt{3} + 7}{8 - \sqrt{5}}$

Rationalize the numerator.
32. $\dfrac{\sqrt{6}}{5}$     33. $\dfrac{\sqrt{5} - \sqrt{2}}{8}$

Rewrite without fractional exponents.
34. $8^{\frac{2}{3}}$     35. $(pq^3)^{\frac{1}{4}}$

Rewrite with fractional exponents.
36. $\sqrt[5]{7}$     37. $\sqrt[6]{9a^2b^4}$

Write an exponential expression. Then simplify if possible. Assume variables stand for nonnegative numbers. Write radical notation for the answer, if appropriate.
38. $\sqrt{a^8b^4}$
39. $\sqrt[3]{\dfrac{n^{24}}{a^8}}$
40. $\sqrt[4]{81x^8y^8}$

Solve.
41. $x - 5 = \sqrt{x + 7}$
42. $\sqrt{2x - 5} = 1 + \sqrt{x - 3}$

Clothing buyers for department stores visit manufacturers' showrooms. Buyers inspect clothing and choose styles that are likely to sell well in their stores.

Salesworkers for building materials wholesalers offer many different materials to builders. Salesworkers stress the convenience and reliability of their services.

Restaurant managers are responsible for purchasing food from wholesalers and selling meals to customers. In small restaurants, managers may also work as cooks.

Produce clerks in a food store maintain displays of fruits and vegetables. Clerks prepare these foods for sale and arrange displays so they will look attractive.

# CAREERS IN TRADE

Trade careers involve the sale of goods. People who work in trade include salespersons, shipping clerks, receiving clerks, stock clerks, cashiers, and store managers.

The most visible trade workers are in retail trade. They work in stores and restaurants in every town and city. The following pictograph shows relative numbers of retail trade workers in various kinds of trade.

| | |
|---|---|
| General merchandise | 🧍🧍🧍 |
| Food stores | 🧍🧍 |
| Apparel and accessories | 🧍 |
| Furniture and home furnishings | 🧍 |
| Eating and drinking places | 🧍🧍🧍🧍 |
| Other retail trade | 🧍🧍🧍🧍 |

**Retail Trade Workers**

Many people work in retail trade. Each complete figure above represents more than a million workers.

rniture salesworkers in a depart-
ent store or furniture store guide
stomer choices. Salesworkers
ve information about furniture
odels and materials.

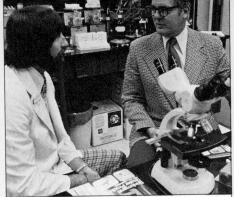

Salesworkers for wholesalers of scientific instruments call on schools
and research firms. Salesworkers
use catalogs or samples to give
product information.

Service station owners sell gasoline,
oil, tires, batteries, fan belts, wind-
shield wiper blades, and so on.
Owners may also provide repair and
maintenance service.

Clerks in catalog stores
take customer orders.
Generally, clerks use catalog order numbers.
When merchandise comes
in, clerks notify customers
of its arrival.

Workers in wholesale trade are not so visible. They help to sell
goods, generally in large quantities, to retail stores. They work in
offices and warehouses. The following pictograph shows relative
numbers of wholesale and retail trade workers.

Wholesale
Retail

**Retail and Wholesale Trade Workers**

In this pictograph, each figure represents roughly 5 million
workers.

According to projections made by analysts
in the United States Bureau of Labor Statistics, the number of trade careers will grow
steadily in the 1980s. Trade careers are not
likely to grow as quickly as careers in government or various services. But they probably will grow more quickly than careers in
manufacturing. By the mid-1980s, trade and
manufacturing will be about equal in numbers of workers. This near equality is repre-
sented in the circle graph.

Services

Trade

Government

Transportation,
communication,
and public utilities

Various Services

Other

Construction

Manufacturing

Goods

**Projected United States Labor Force in the mid-1980s**

## Ready for Complex Numbers?

1-5    1.   Collect like terms:   $3x - 2y + 4x - 8y$.

1-7    2.   Rewrite without exponents:   $i^2$.

2-2

Solve.

3.   $9x + 7 - 2x = -12 - 4x + 5$

4.   $(x - 5)(x + 3) = 0$

Multiply.

6-3    5.   $2 - 3y$ and $1 + 4y$

6-4    6.   $(3x + 8)^2$

6-5    7.   $(2x - 3)(2x + 3)$

7-1    8.   Factor:   $x^2 - 1$.

9-1    9.   Find the reciprocal:   $x - 3$.

10-2    10.   Simplify:   $\sqrt{64}$.

10-3    11.   Multiply:   $\sqrt{2}\,\sqrt{7}$.

Simplify.

10-3    12.   $\sqrt{98}$

10-3    13.   $\sqrt{3x^2}$

10-5    14.   $3\sqrt{2} + 8\sqrt{2}$

10-6    15.   Multiply:   $(\sqrt{5} + x)^2$.

10-7    16.   Rationalize the denominator:   $\dfrac{3}{2 - \sqrt{5}}$.

# Chapter 11
# Complex Numbers

*Complex numbers are used in the design of electrical equipment.*

# 11-1 Imaginary and Complex Numbers

After finishing Lesson 11-1, you should be able to
**I** name numbers such as $\sqrt{-7}$ in the form $bi$.
**II** multiply imaginary numbers.
**III** add and subtract complex numbers.

## I Imaginary Numbers

In the set of real numbers, negative numbers do not have square roots. An equation like

$$x^2 = -1$$

has no solution. A new kind of number, called *imaginary,* was invented so that negative numbers would have square roots and certain equations would have solutions. These numbers were devised, starting with an imaginary unit, named $i$, with the agreement that

$$i^2 = -1, \text{ or } i = \sqrt{-1}.$$

We assume that $i$ acts like a real number in other respects. Square roots of all negative numbers can then be expressed as a product of $i$ and a real number.

**Examples.** Express these numbers in terms of $i$.

**1.** $\sqrt{-5} = \sqrt{-1 \cdot 5}$
$= \sqrt{-1}\,\sqrt{5}$
$= i\sqrt{5} \text{ or } \sqrt{5}i$

**2.** $-\sqrt{-7} = -\sqrt{-1 \cdot 7}$
$= -\sqrt{-1}\,\sqrt{7}$
$= -i\sqrt{7} \text{ or } -\sqrt{7}i$

**3.** $\sqrt{-99} = \sqrt{-1 \cdot 99}$
$= \sqrt{-1}\,\sqrt{99}$
$= i\sqrt{9}\,\sqrt{11}$
$= 3i\sqrt{11} \text{ or } 3\sqrt{11}i$

**TRY THIS**

Express these numbers in terms of $i$.

1. $\sqrt{-7}$
2. $-\sqrt{-36}$
3. $\sqrt{-160}$

**DEFINITION**

The *imaginary* numbers consist of all numbers $bi$, where $b$ is a real number and $i$ is the imaginary unit, with the property that $i^2 = -1$.

## ❚❚ Products

To multiply imaginary numbers or an imaginary number by a real number, it is important first to express the imaginary numbers in terms of $i$.

**Examples.** Multiply.

**4.** $47i \cdot 2 = 94i$

**5.** $\sqrt{-5} \cdot 2i = \sqrt{5}i \cdot 2i$
$$= 2\sqrt{5}i^2$$
$$= -2\sqrt{5}$$

**6.** $-\sqrt{-3} \cdot \sqrt{-7} = -i\sqrt{3} \cdot i\sqrt{7}$
$$= -i^2\sqrt{21}$$
$$= -(-1)\sqrt{21}$$
$$= \sqrt{21}$$

**TRY THIS** ➡

Multiply.

4.  $6i \cdot 3i$
5.  $\sqrt{-3} \cdot 3i$
6.  $\sqrt{-3} \cdot \sqrt{-6}$

## ❚❚❚ Complex Numbers

To construct a complete number system, we shall define sums of real and imaginary numbers. We call these *complex numbers*.

**DEFINITION**

The *complex* numbers consist of all sums $a + bi$, where $a$ and $b$ are real numbers and $i$ is the imaginary unit. $a$ is called the real part and $bi$ is called the imaginary part.

Every real number $a$ is a complex number because $a = a + 0 \cdot i$. Thus the complex numbers are an extension of the real number system. All imaginary numbers $bi$ are also complex because $bi = 0 + bi$.

We assume that $i$ acts like a real number, obeying the commutative, associative, and distributive laws. Thus to add or subtract complex numbers we can treat $i$ as we would treat a variable. We combine like terms.

**Examples.** Add.

**7.** $7i + 9i = (7 + 9)i$
$= 16i$

**8.** $(-5 + 6i) + (2 - 11i) = -5 + 6i + 2 - 11i$
$= -3 - 5i$

**TRY THIS** ➡

> Add.
>
> 7.  $3i + 4i$
> 8.  $(2 + 3i) + (2 + 4i)$
> 9.  $(-7 + 4i) + (5 - 9i)$
> 10. $(-2 + 3i) + (2 - 3i)$

**Examples.** Subtract.

**9.** $7i - 9i = (7 - 9)i$
$= -2i$

**10.** $(2 + 3i) - (4 + 2i) = 2 + 3i - 4 - 2i$
$= -2 + i$

**11.** $(-6 + 5i) - (-6 + 5i) = -6 + 5i + 6 - 5i$
$= 0$

**TRY THIS** ➡

> Subtract.
>
> 11. $3i - 4i$
> 12. $(2 - 3i) - (5 - 8i)$
> 13. $(-4 + 10i) - (-2 + 3i)$
> 14. $(9 - 7i) - (15 + 2i)$

---

**Remark.** The set of complex numbers is closed under addition. To see this, consider any two complex numbers $a + bi$ and $c + di$. We add them. $(a + bi) + (c + di) = (a + c) + (b + d)i$. The answer is again a complex number.

Addition is commutative and associative. There is an additive identity, the number 0 (or $0 + 0i$). Every complex number has an additive inverse (the inverse of $a + bi$ is $-a - bi$). Thus under addition the complex numbers form a *commutative group*.

---

## Exercise Set 11-1

▌Express these numbers in terms of $i$. (See Examples 1–3.)

1.  $\sqrt{-2}$                     2.  $\sqrt{-3}$
3.  $\sqrt{-36}$                    4.  $\sqrt{-25}$
5.  $-\sqrt{-9}$                    6.  $-\sqrt{-16}$
7.  $\sqrt{-128}$                   8.  $\sqrt{-12}$
9.  $\sqrt{-\dfrac{9}{16}}$         10. $\sqrt{-\dfrac{25}{4}}$
11. $-\sqrt{-80}$                   12. $-\sqrt{-75}$

▌▌Multiply. *(See Examples 4–6.)*

13. $23i \cdot 4$

14. $-12i \cdot (-3)$

15. $\sqrt{-3} \cdot 4i$

16. $\sqrt{-5} \cdot 6i$

17. $\sqrt{-2} \sqrt{-3}$

18. $\sqrt{-5} \sqrt{-3}$

19. $-\sqrt{-2} \sqrt{-18}$

20. $-\sqrt{-3} \sqrt{-15}$

21. $\sqrt{-3} \sqrt{-15}$

22. $\sqrt{-10} \sqrt{-2}$

23. $-\sqrt{-10}(-\sqrt{-10})$

24. $-\sqrt{-7}(-\sqrt{-7})$

▌▌▌Add. *(See Examples 7 and 8.)*

25. $5i + 4i$

26. $-7i + 10i$

27. $4i + (-10i)$

28. $-2i + (-3i)$

29. $3i + (8 - 5i)$

30. $-2i + (-3 + 8i)$

31. $(3 + 2i) + (5 - i)$

32. $(-2 + 3i) + (7 + 8i)$

33. $(4 - 3i) + (5 - 2i)$

34. $(-2 - 5i) + (1 - 3i)$

Subtract. *(See Examples 9–11.)*

35. $5i - 4i$

36. $-7i - 10i$

37. $6i - (-8i)$

38. $-3i - (-4i)$

39. $2i - (4 - 3i)$

40. $3i - (5 - 2i)$

41. $(3 - i) - (5 + 2i)$

42. $(-2 + 8i) - (7 + 3i)$

43. $(4 - 2i) - (5 - 3i)$

44. $(-2 - 3i) - (1 - 5i)$

45. $(9 + 5i) - (-2 - i)$

46. $(6 - 3i) - (2 + 4i)$

---

**Calculator Exercises**

Simplify.

47. $(56.4325 + 789.5097i) + (-456.892 + 809.0568i)$

48. $(76.5773 - 567.9076i) - (907.238 - 7890.67i)$

**Challenge Exercises**

*Powers of i.* These four powers of $i$ are the keys to finding higher powers of $i$:

$$i^1 = i, \qquad i^2 = -1, \qquad i^3 = -i, \qquad i^4 = 1.$$

For example, $i^{31} = i^{28} \cdot i^3 = (i^4)^7 \cdot i^3 = 1^7 \cdot (-i) = 1 \cdot (-i) = -i$.

Simplify.

49. $i^{13}$

50. $i^{20}$

51. $i^{18}$

52. $i^{27}$

53. $i^{99}$

54. $i^{71} - i^{49}$

55. $i^{68} - i^{72} + i^{76} - i^{80}$

# 11-2 More About Complex Numbers

After finishing Lesson 11-2, you should be able to
■ solve equations like $3x + yi = 5x + 1 + 2i$ for $x$ and $y$.
■■ multiply complex numbers.
■■■ find conjugates of complex numbers and multiply a complex number by its conjugate.
■■■■ divide complex numbers.
■■■■■ find the reciprocal of a complex number and name in the form $a + bi$.

## ■ Equality for Complex Numbers

Equality for complex numbers is the same as for real numbers. A sentence $a + bi = c + di$ says that $a + bi$ and $c + di$ are two names of the same number. For this to be true, $a$ and $c$ must be the same and $b$ and $d$ must be the same. Thus $a + bi = c + di$ when $a = b$ and $c = d$.

**Example 1.** Suppose that $3x + yi = 5x + 1 + 2i$. Find $x$ and $y$.

We equate the real parts.

$$3x = 5x + 1$$
$$x = -\tfrac{1}{2} \quad \textit{Solving}$$

We equate the imaginary parts.

$$yi = 2i$$
$$y = 2 \quad \textit{Solving}$$

**TRY THIS** ➡

Solve.

1. Suppose $3x + 1 + (y + 2)i = 2x + 2yi$. Find $x$ and $y$.

## ■■ Multiplication

We multiply complex numbers as we would multiply monomials or binomials, treating the imaginary parts as like terms. Of course, we remember that $i^2 = -1$.

**Examples.** Multiply.

**2.** $3i \cdot 4i = (3 \cdot 4)i^2$
$\qquad = 12(-1)$
$\qquad = -12$

**3.** $(7i)^2 = 7^2 i^2$
$\qquad = 49(-1)$
$\qquad = -49$

**4.** $(4 + 3i) \cdot (7 + 2i) = 28 + 8i + 21i + 6i^2$
$\qquad\qquad\qquad = 28 + (8i + 21i) + 6(-1)$   *(Since* $i^2 = -1$*)*
$\qquad\qquad\qquad = 28 + 29i - 6$
$\qquad\qquad\qquad = 22 + 29i$

**5.** $(2 - 3i)^2 = 4 - 12i + 9i^2$
$\qquad\qquad = 4 - 12i - 9$
$\qquad\qquad = -5 - 12i$

**TRY THIS** ➡️

> Multiply.
>
> 2.  $5i \cdot 6i$
> 3.  $(10i)^2$
> 4.  $(7 + 2i)(5 + 5i)$
> 5.  $(-2 - 3i)(6 + 5i)$
> 6.  $(5 - 7i)^2$

## ⅲ Conjugates

**DEFINITION**

The *conjugate* of a complex number $a + bi$ is $a - bi$ and the conjugate of $a - bi$ is $a + bi$.

**Examples.**

**6.** The conjugate of $3 + 4i$ is $3 - 4i$.
**7.** The conjugate of $-4 - 7i$ is $-4 + 7i$.
**8.** The conjugate of $5i$ is $-5i$.
**9.** The conjugate of $6$ is $6$.

**TRY THIS** ➡️

> Find the conjugate of each number.
>
> 7.  $6 + 3i$
> 8.  $-9 - 5i$
> 9.  $-7i$
> 10.  $-8$

The special product $(A + B)(A - B) = A^2 - B^2$ applies to multiplying a number by its conjugate.

**Examples.**   Multiply.

**10.** $(5 + 7i)(5 - 7i) = 5^2 - (7i)^2$
$\qquad\qquad\qquad = 25 - (49i^2)$
$\qquad\qquad\qquad = 25 + 49$
$\qquad\qquad\qquad = 74$

**11.** $(a + bi)(a - bi) = a^2 - (bi)^2$
$\qquad\qquad\qquad = a^2 - b^2i^2$
$\qquad\qquad\qquad = a^2 + b^2$

**THEOREM 11-1**

The product of a nonzero complex number $a + bi$ and its conjugate $a - bi$ is the positive real number $a^2 + b^2$.

**TRY THIS** ➡️

> Multiply.
>
> 11.  $(7 - 2i)(7 + 2i)$
> 12.  $(-3 + i)(-3 - i)$
> 13.  $(p - qi)(p + qi)$

## IIII **Division**

To divide complex numbers we can multiply by 1. In choosing the notation for 1, we use the conjugate of the divisor.

**Examples.** Divide.

**12.** $\dfrac{-5 + 9i}{1 - i} = \dfrac{-5 + 9i}{1 - i} \cdot \dfrac{1 + i}{1 + i}$

$\quad\quad\quad = \dfrac{-14 + 4i}{1 - i^2}$

$\quad\quad\quad = \dfrac{-14 + 4i}{2}$

$\quad\quad\quad = -7 + 2i$

**13.** $\dfrac{2 - 3i}{3 + 5i} = \dfrac{2 - 3i}{3 + 5i} \cdot \dfrac{3 - 5i}{3 - 5i}$

$\quad\quad\quad = \dfrac{-9 - 19i}{9 - 25i^2}$

$\quad\quad\quad = \dfrac{-9 - 19i}{34}$

$\quad\quad\quad = \dfrac{-9}{34} - \dfrac{19}{34}i$

**TRY THIS** ➡

Divide.

**14.** $\dfrac{6 + 2i}{1 - 3i}$

**15.** $\dfrac{2 + 3i}{-1 + 4i}$

## IIIII **Reciprocals**

The reciprocal of a number $a + bi$ is of course that number by which we multiply $a + bi$ to get 1. By definition of division this is $\dfrac{1}{a + bi}$. To express it in the form $a + bi$ we can do this division.

**Example 14.** Find the reciprocal of $2 - 3i$ and express it in the form $a + bi$.

**a)** The reciprocal of $2 - 3i$ is $\dfrac{1}{2 - 3i}$.

**b)** We can express it in the form $a + bi$ as follows.

$\dfrac{1}{2 - 3i} = \dfrac{1}{2 - 3i} \cdot \dfrac{2 + 3i}{2 + 3i}$

$\quad\quad\quad = \dfrac{2 + 3i}{2^2 - 3^2 i^2}$

$$= \frac{2 + 3i}{4 + 9}$$

$$= \frac{2}{13} + \frac{3}{13}i$$

**TRY THIS** ➤

> 16. Find the reciprocal of $3 + 4i$ and express it in the form $a + bi$.

---

**Remark.** Multiplication of complex numbers is commutative and associative. There is an identity, the number 1, or $1 + 0i$. Every complex number except 0 has a reciprocal. Thus the set of nonzero complex numbers form a *commutative group*.

Multiplication is distributive over addition, tying the two operations together. Earlier we showed that addition of complex numbers is associative and commutative, 0 is the identity, and every complex number has an additive inverse. So the complex numbers form a *field*.

## Exercise Set 11-2

▌Solve for $x$ and $y$. (*See Example 1.*)

1. $4x + 7i = -6 + yi$
2. $8 + 8yi = 4x - 2i$
3. $-5x - yi = 10 + 8i$
4. $-3y - 4xi = 2 + 2i$
5. $3x + 4y - 7i = 18 + (x - 3y)i$
6. $-4 + (x + y)i = 2x - 5y + 5i$

▌▌Multiply. (*See Examples 2–5.*)

7. $7i \cdot 9i$
8. $3i \cdot i$
9. $(9i)^2$
10. $(13i)^2$
11. $(-3i)^2$
12. $(-5i)^2$
13. $(3 + 2i)(1 + i)$
14. $(4 + 3i)(2 + i)$
15. $(2 + 3i)(6 - 2i)$
16. $(5 + 6i)(2 - i)$
17. $(6 - 5i)(3 + 4i)$
18. $(5 - 6i)(4 + 8i)$
19. $(7 - 2i)(2 - 6i)$
20. $(-4 + 5i)(3 - 4i)$
21. $(5 - 2i)^2$
22. $(3 - 5i)^2$
23. $(1 + 3i)^2$
24. $(-2 + 2i)^2$

▌▌▌Find the conjugate of each number. (*See Examples 6–9.*)

25. $-4 + 8i$
26. $-8 + 5i$
27. $6 - 5i$
28. $7 - i$
29. $\sqrt{2} - \frac{1}{2}i$
30. $\sqrt{3} + 0.4i$
31. $r - ti$
32. $-m + ni$

Multiply. (*See Examples 10 and 11.*)

33. $(3 + 4i)(3 - 4i)$

34. $(2 - i)(2 + i)$

35. $(1 - i)(1 + i)$

36. $(6 + 3i)(6 - 3i)$

37. $(\frac{1}{2} + i)(\frac{1}{2} - i)$

38. $(1 + \frac{1}{3}i)(1 - \frac{1}{3}i)$

39. $(\sqrt{3} - i)(\sqrt{3} + i)$

40. $(3 - \sqrt{2}i)(3 + \sqrt{2}i)$

▌▌▌▌ Divide. (*See Examples 12 and 13.*)

41. $\dfrac{1 + i}{1 - i}$

42. $\dfrac{2 - i}{2 + i}$

43. $\dfrac{3 + 2i}{2 + i}$

44. $\dfrac{4 + 5i}{5 - i}$

45. $\dfrac{5 - 2i}{2 + 5i}$

46. $\dfrac{3 - 2i}{4 + 3i}$

47. $\dfrac{8 - 3i}{-2 + 7i}$

48. $\dfrac{5 - 10i}{-3 + 4i}$

49. $\dfrac{\sqrt{2} + i}{\sqrt{2} - i}$

50. $\dfrac{\sqrt{3} - i}{\sqrt{3} + i}$

51. $\dfrac{3 + 2i}{i}$

52. $\dfrac{2 + 3i}{i}$

53. $\dfrac{i}{2 + i}$

54. $\dfrac{i}{1 - i}$

▌▌▌▌▌ Find the reciprocal of each number and express it in the form $a + bi$. (*See Example 14.*)

55. $i$

56. $-i$

57. $2 - 4i$

58. $-3 - 5i$

59. $-4 + 7i$

60. $-2 + 6i$

---

### Calculator Exercises

Simplify.

61. $(43.21 - 5.674i)^2$

62. $(45.23 - 56.1i)(45.23 + 56.1i)$

### Challenge Exercises

Simplify to the form $a + bi$.

63. $i^{-3}$

64. $i^2$

65. $i^{-9}$

66. $i^{-8}$

67. $\dfrac{1 - i}{(1 + i)^2}$

68. $\dfrac{1 + i}{(1 - i)^2}$

69. $\dfrac{a + 2bi}{2a - bi}$

70. $\dfrac{3x + 2yi}{x - yi}$

71. Let $z = a + bi$. Find a general expression for $\dfrac{1}{z}$.

72. Let $z = a + bi$ and $w = c + di$. Find a general expression for $\dfrac{w}{z}$.

# 11-3 Solutions of Equations

After finishing Lesson 11-3, you should be able to
**I**    determine whether a complex number is a solution of an equation.
**II**    find an equation having given complex numbers as solutions.
**III**    solve first-degree equations having complex numbers as solutions.
**IIII**    verify that a given complex number is a square root of another complex number, then find the other square root.

## I Complex Numbers as Solutions of Equations

**Example 1.** Determine whether $1 + \sqrt{7}i$ is a solution of $x^2 - 2x + 8 = 0$.

$$x^2 - 2x + 8 = 0$$

$$
\begin{array}{c|c}
(1 + \sqrt{7}i)^2 - 2(1 + \sqrt{7}i) + 8 & 0 \\
1 + 2(\sqrt{7}i) + (\sqrt{7}i)^2 - 2 - 2\sqrt{7}i + 8 & \\
1 + 2\sqrt{7}i - 7 - 2 - 2\sqrt{7}i + 8 & \\
0 &
\end{array}
$$

$1 + \sqrt{7}i$ is a solution.

**TRY THIS** ➡

1. Determine whether $3i$ and $-3i$ are solutions of $x^2 + 9 = 0$.
2. Determine whether $1 + i$ is a solution of $x^2 - 2x + 2 = 0$.
3. Determine whether $1 - i$ is a solution of $x^2 + 2x + 1 = 0$.

## II Writing Equations with Given Solutions

The principle of zero products for real numbers states that a product is 0 if and only if at least one of the factors is 0. This principle also holds for complex numbers. Since the principle holds for complex numbers we can write equations having given solutions.

**Example 2.** Find an equation having $-1$, $i$, and $1 + i$ as solutions.

The factors we use will be $x - (-1)$, $x - i$, and $x - (1 + i)$. Next we set the product of these factors equal to 0.

$$[x - (-1)][x - i][x - (1 + i)] = 0$$

Now we multiply and simplify.

$$(x^2 + x - ix - i)(x - 1 - i) = 0$$
$$x^3 - 2ix^2 - ix - 2x - 1 + i = 0$$

**TRY THIS** ➤➤➤➤

## ⅲ Solving Equations

First-degree equations in complex numbers are solved very much like first-degree equations in real numbers.

**Example 3.** Solve $3ix + 4 - 5i = (1 + i)x + 2i$.

$$3ix + 4 - 5i - (1 + i)x = 2i \qquad \textit{Adding } -(1 + i)x$$

$$3ix - (1 + i)x = -4 + 7i \qquad \textit{Adding } -(4 - 5i)$$

$$(-1 + 2i)x = -4 + 7i \qquad \textit{Simplifying}$$

$$x = \frac{-4 + 7i}{-1 + 2i} \qquad \textit{Dividing}$$

$$x = \frac{-4 + 7i}{-1 + 2i} \cdot \frac{-1 - 2i}{-1 - 2i}$$

$$x = \frac{18 + i}{5}$$

$$x = \frac{18}{5} + \frac{1}{5}i$$

**TRY THIS** ━━━━▶

Find an equation having the given numbers as solutions.

4. $i, 1 + i$
5. $2, i, -i$

Solve.
6. $3 - 4i + 2ix = 3i - (1 - i)x$

Linear equations always have solutions. Complex numbers were invented so that certain other equations would have solutions. Suppose we ask what kinds of equations do have solutions. The answer depends upon a very important theorem.

**THEOREM 11-2 (The Fundamental Theorem of Algebra)**
Every polynomial with complex coefficients and of degree $n$ (where $n > 1$) can be factored into $n$ linear factors.

The factors of a polynomial are not always easy to find, but they exist.

**Example 4.** Show that $(x + i)(x - i)$ is a factorization of $x^2 + 1$.

We multiply.

$$(x + i)(x - i) = x^2 + ix - ix - i^2$$
$$= x^2 + 1$$

7. Show that $(x + 2i)(x - 2i)$ is a factorization of $x^2 + 4$.

**TRY THIS** ━━━━▶

We can now answer the question about solutions of equations.

**THEOREM 11-3**
Every polynomial equation of degree $n$ ($n \geq 1$) with complex coefficients has at least one solution and at most $n$ solutions in the
system of complex numbers.

---

**A Proof of Theorem 11-3**
Let us consider a polynomial equation of degree $n$.

$$P(x) = 0.$$

The polynomial $P(x)$ is either of degree 1, in which case there is a solution, or by the fundamental theorem of algebra, it can be factored
into $n$ linear factors. We then have

$$(x - a_1)(x - a_2) \ldots (x - a_n) = 0.$$

By the principle of zero products, we get

$$x = a_1 \text{ or } x = a_2 \text{ or } x = a_3 \text{ or } \ldots \text{ or } x = a_n.$$

Thus the equation has solutions $a_1, a_2, \ldots, a_n$. Some of these may be
the same. So there is at least one solution, and there are not more
than $n$ solutions.

---

## Square Roots of Complex Numbers

The fundamental theorem of algebra can be used to show that
all complex numbers have square roots.

**THEOREM 11-4**
Every nonzero complex number has two square roots. They are
additive inverses of each other. Zero has just one square root.

**Example 5.** Show that $1 + i$ is a square root of $2i$. Then find
the other square root.

We square $(1 + i)$ to show that we get $2i$.

$$\begin{aligned}
(1 + 1)^2 &= 1 + 2i + i^2 \\
&= 1 + 2i - 1 \\
&= 2i
\end{aligned}$$

By Theorem 11-4, the other square root of $2i$ is the additive inverse of $1 + i$, so it is $-1 - i$.

**TRY THIS**

8. Show that $(-1 + i)$ is a square root of $-2i$. Then find the other square root.

## Exercise Set 11-3

▌ Determine whether the given numbers are solutions of the equation. (*See Example 1.*)

1. $2i, -2i; x^2 + 4 = 0$
2. $4i, -4i; x^2 + 16 = 0$
3. $\sqrt{2}i, -\sqrt{3}i; x^2 + 3 = 0$
4. $\sqrt{3}i, -\sqrt{2}i; x^2 + 2 = 0$
5. $-1 + i, -1 - i; z^2 + 2z + 2 = 0$
6. $2 - i, 2 + i; z^2 - 4z + 5 = 0$

▌▌ Find an equation having the specified numbers as solutions. (*See Example 2.*)

7. $5i, -5i$
8. $7i, -7i$
9. $1 + i, 1 - i$
10. $2 + i, 2 - i$
11. $2 + 3i, 2 - 3i$
12. $4 + 3i, 4 - 3i$
13. $3, i$
14. $5, i$
15. $1, 3i, -3i$
16. $1, 2i, -2i$
17. $2, 1 + i, i$
18. $3, 1 - i, i$
19. $i, 2i, -i$
20. $i, -2i, -i$

▌▌▌ Solve. (*See Example 3.*)

21. $(3 + i)x + i = 5i$
22. $(2 + i)x - i = 5 + i$
23. $2ix + 5 - 4i = (2 + 3i)x - 2i$
24. $5ix + 3 + 2i = (3 - 2i)x + 3i$
25. $(1 + 2i)x + 3 - 2i = 4 - 5i + 3ix$
26. $(1 - 2i)x + 2 - 3i = 5 - 4i + 2x$
27. $(5 + i)x + 1 - 3i = $
    $(2 - 3i)x + 2 - i$
28. $(5 - i)x + 2 - 3i = $
    $(3 - 2i)x + 3 - i$

(*See Example 4.*)

29. Show that $(2x + i)(2x - i)$ is a factorization of $4x^2 + 1$.
30. Show that $(2x + 2i)(2x - 2i)$ is a factorization of $4x^2 + 4$.

▌▌▌▌ (*See Example 5.*)

31. Show that $(2 + i)$ is a square root of $3 + 4i$. Then find the other square root.
32. Show that $(2 - i)$ is a square root of $3 - 4i$. Then find the other square root.

# 11-4 Graphical Representation

After finishing Lesson 11-4, you should be able to
▌ graph complex numbers in the plane.
▌▌ find absolute values of complex numbers.

## ▌Graphical Representation

The real numbers are graphed on a line. We graph $a + bi$ in the same way we graph ordered pairs of real numbers $(a, b)$. In place of an $x$-axis we have a *real* axis, and in place of a $y$-axis we have an imaginary axis.

**Example 1.** Graph

A: $3 + 2i$
B: $-4 + 5i$
C: $-5 - 4i$
D: $i$

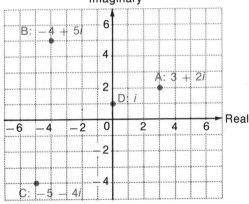

Horizontal distance corresponds to the real part of a number. Vertical distance corresponds to the imaginary part.

**TRY THIS** ━━━▶

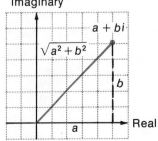

1.  Graph
    A: $5 - 3i$
    B: $-3 + 4i$
    C: $-5 - 2i$
    D: $-5i$

## Absolute Value

From the graph at the right we see that the length of the line drawn from the origin to $a + bi$ is $\sqrt{a^2 + b^2}$. Note that this quantity is a real number. It is called the *absolute value* of $a + bi$ and is denoted $|a + bi|$.

## DEFINITION

The *absolute value* of a complex number $a + bi$ is denoted $|a + bi|$ and is defined to be $\sqrt{a^2 + b^2}$.

**Example 2.** Find $|-3 + 4i|$.

$$\begin{aligned} |-3 + 4i| &= \sqrt{(-3)^2 + 4^2} \\ &= \sqrt{9 + 16} \\ &= \sqrt{25} \\ &= 5 \end{aligned}$$

**TRY THIS**

Find the following absolute values.

2. $|4 - 3i|$
3. $|-12 - 5i|$
4. $|1 + i|$

## Exercise Set 11-4

▌Graph. (*See Example 1.*)

1. $3 + 2i, 2 - 5i, -4 - 2i$
2. $3 - 4i, -5 + 3i, -2 - 3i$
3. $-4 + 2i, -3 - 4i, 2 - 3i$
4. $-5 + 4i, 3 - 2i, -5 + 5i$
5. $-2 - 5i, 5 + 3i, -3 - 4i$
6. $2 + 2i, -3 - 3i, 2 - 3i$

▌▌Find the following absolute values. (*See Example 2.*)

7. $|-4 - 3i|$
8. $|-3 - 4i|$
9. $|8 + 15i|$
10. $|7 - 24i|$
11. $|1 - 3i|$
12. $|-2 + i|$
13. $|3i|$
14. $|-2i|$
15. $|c - di|$
16. $|-c + di|$

---

## Challenge Exercises

17. Show that for any complex number $z$, $|z| = |-z|$. (*Hint:* Let $z = a + bi$.)

18. Show that for any complex number $z$, $|z| = |$the conjugate of $z|$. (*Hint:* Let $z = a + bi$.)

19. Let $z = a + bi$ and $w = c + di$. Find a general formula for $z \cdot w$.

20. Let $z = a + bi$ and $w = c + di$. Find a general formula for $\dfrac{z}{w}$.

21. Show that $|z \cdot w| = |z| \cdot |w|$.

22. Show that $\left|\dfrac{z}{w}\right| = \dfrac{|z|}{|w|}$.

# 11-5 *Conjugates of Polynomials*

After finishing Lesson 11-5, you should be able to
▌ find a polynomial in $\bar{z}$ that is the conjugate of a polynomial in $z$.

We can name a complex number $a + bi$ as $z$. For the conjugate of $z$, we write $\bar{z}$, or $\overline{a + bi}$. By definition of conjugates, $\overline{a + bi} = a - bi$ and $\overline{a - bi} = a + bi$. We have already noted (Theorem 11-1) that the product of a number and its conjugate is a real number. We restate that theorem and consider some others.

**THEOREM 11-5**
For any complex number $z$, $z \cdot \bar{z}$ is a real number.

The sum of a number and its conjugate is also always real.

**THEOREM 11-6**
For any complex number, $z$, $z + \bar{z}$ is a real number.

---

**A Proof of Theorem 11-5**
We have said that for any complex number $z$, $z \cdot \bar{z}$ is a real number. Let us prove this.
   Let $z = a + bi$. Then $(a - bi)$ is $\bar{z}$, and

$$z \cdot \bar{z} = (a + bi)(a - bi),$$
$$= a^2 - b^2 i^2,$$
$$= a^2 + b^2.$$

Since $a$ and $b$ are real numbers, so is $a^2 + b^2$. Thus $z \cdot \bar{z}$ is a real number.

---

Taking the conjugate of a sum gives the same result as adding the conjugates.

**THEOREM 11-7**
For any complex numbers $z$ and $w$, $\overline{z + w} = \bar{z} + \bar{w}$.

**Example 1.** Compare $\overline{(2 + 4i) + (5 + i)}$ and $\overline{(2 + 4i)} + \overline{(5 + i)}$

$$\overline{(2 + 4i) + (5 + i)} = \overline{7 + 5i} \qquad \textit{Adding the complex numbers}$$
$$= 7 - 5i \qquad \textit{Taking the conjugate}$$

$$\overline{(2 + 4i)} + \overline{(5 + i)} = (2 - 4i) + (5 - i) \qquad \textit{Taking conjugates}$$
$$= 7 - 5i \qquad \textit{Adding}$$

**TRY THIS** ⟶

1. Compare $\overline{(3 + 2i) + (4 - 5i)}$ with $\overline{(3 + 2i)} + \overline{(4 - 5i)}$.

---

### A Proof of Theorem 11-7

We have said that for any complex numbers $z$ and $w$, $\overline{z + w} = \overline{z} + \overline{w}$.
Let us prove this.

Let $z = a + bi$ and $w = c + di$. Then

$$\begin{aligned}
\overline{z + w} &= \overline{(a + bi) + (c + di)}, \\
&= \overline{(a + c) + (b + d)i}, & \text{Adding} \\
&= (a + c) - (b + d)i. & \text{Taking the conjugate}
\end{aligned}$$

Now,

$$\begin{aligned}
\overline{z} + \overline{w} &= \overline{(a + bi)} + \overline{(c + di)}, \\
&= (a - bi) + (c - di), & \text{Taking the conjugates} \\
&= (a + c) - (b + d)i. & \text{Adding}
\end{aligned}$$

This is the same result as before. Thus $\overline{z + w} = \overline{z} + \overline{w}$.

---

Let us next consider the conjugate of a product. The conjugate of a product is the product of the conjugates.

### THEOREM 11-8

For any complex numbers $z$ and $w$, $\overline{z \cdot w} = \overline{z} \cdot \overline{w}$.

**Example 2.** Compare $\overline{(3 + 2i)(4 - 5i)}$ and $\overline{(3 + 2i)} \cdot \overline{(4 - 5i)}$.

$$\begin{aligned}
\overline{(3 + 2i)(4 - 5i)} &= \overline{22 - 7i} & \text{Multiplying} \\
&= 22 + 7i & \text{Taking the conjugate} \\
\overline{(3 + 2i)} \cdot \overline{(4 - 5i)} &= (3 - 2i)(4 + 5i) & \text{Taking conjugates} \\
&= 22 + 7i & \text{Multiplying}
\end{aligned}$$

**TRY THIS** ⟶

2. Compare $\overline{(2 + 5i)(1 + 3i)}$ and $\overline{(2 + 5i)} \cdot \overline{(1 + 3i)}$.

Let us now consider conjugates of powers, using the preceding result. The conjugate of a power is the power of the conjugate.

### THEOREM 11-9

For any complex number $z$, $\overline{z^n} = \overline{z}^n$, where $n$ is a natural number.

**Example 3.** Show that for any complex number $z$, $\overline{z^2} = \overline{z}^2$

$$\overline{z^2} = \overline{z \cdot z} \qquad \text{By definition of exponents}$$
$$= \overline{z} \cdot \overline{z} \qquad \text{Using Theorem 11-8}$$
$$= \overline{z}^2 \qquad \text{By definition of exponents}$$

**TRY THIS** ➡

> 3. Show that for any complex number $z$, $\overline{z^3} = \overline{z}^3$.

The conjugate of a real number $a + 0i$ is $a - 0i$, and both are equal to $a$. Thus a real number is its own conjugate.

### THEOREM 11-10

If $z$ is a real number, then $\overline{z} = z$.

## Conjugates of Polynomials

Given a polynomial in $z$, where $z$ is a variable for a complex number, we can find its conjugate in terms of $\overline{z}$.

**Example 4.** Find a polynomial in $\overline{z}$ that is the conjugate of $3z^2 + 2z - 1$.

We write the expression for the conjugate and then use the properties of conjugates.

$$\overline{3z^2 + 2z - 1} = \overline{3z^2} + \overline{2z} - \overline{1} \qquad \text{Using Theorem 11-7}$$
$$= \overline{3} \cdot \overline{z^2} + \overline{2} \cdot \overline{z} - \overline{1} \qquad \text{Using Theorem 11-8}$$
$$= 3\overline{z^2} + 2\overline{z} - 1 \qquad \text{Using Theorem 11-10}$$
$$= 3\overline{z}^2 + 2\overline{z} - 1 \qquad \text{Using Theorem 11-9}$$

**TRY THIS** ➡

> Find a polynomial in $\overline{z}$ that is the conjugate of the following.
>
> 4. $5z^3 + 4z^2 - 2z + 1$
> 5. $7z^5 - 3z^3 + 8z^2 + z$

## Exercise Set 11-5

▮Find a polynomial in $\bar{z}$ that is the conjugate. (*See Example 4.*)

1. $z^2 - 3z + 5$
2. $z^2 + 4z - 1$
3. $3z^5 - 4z^2 + 3z - 5$
4. $5z^4 - 2z^3 + 5z - 3$
5. $7z^4 + 5z^3 - 12z$
6. $4z^7 - 3z^5 + 4z$
7. $5z^{10} - 7z^8 + 13z^2 - 4$
8. $8z^{12} - 8z^7 + 12z^5 - 8$
9. $7z^{100} - 15z^{89} + z^2$
10. $17z^{45} + 70z^3 - 14z + 2$

### Challenge Exercises

11. Prove Theorem 11-6.
12. Prove Theorem 11-8.

### MATHEMATICAL NOTE: The Rule of False Position

Suppose you know that a number plus a seventh of the number is nineteen. How can you find the number?

One way is to write a linear equation, $x + \frac{1}{7}x = 19$, and solve it for $x$. Another way is to use the rule of false position.

To use the rule of false position, choose any value for $x$. Then try it in the equation. Suppose $x = 7$. Then $x + \frac{1}{7}x = 8$, not 19. But you can use your false answer to find the true answer. The ratio of the true value of $x$ is to 7 as 19 is to 8. That is, $\frac{x}{7} = \frac{19}{8}$. The answer then is $\frac{17 \cdot 19}{8}$, or $16\frac{5}{8}$.

This rule was known to mathematicians in both ancient Egypt and ancient China. It appears in texts from the Middle Ages through the 1800s.

# COMPUTER ACTIVITY

## Finding the Quotient of Two Complex Numbers

**PROBLEM:** Find the quotient $(A + BI) \div (C + DI)$.

**Examples using the flowchart:**

| | | | | 1 | | 2 | 3 | 4 |
|---|---|---|---|---|---|---|---|---|
| A | B | C | D | | E $(C^2 + D^2)$ | | X | Y |
| 2 | 3 | 4 | −1 | | 17 | | 0.29411 | 0.82352 |
| 3 | −1 | −1 | 2 | | 5 | | −1 | −1 |

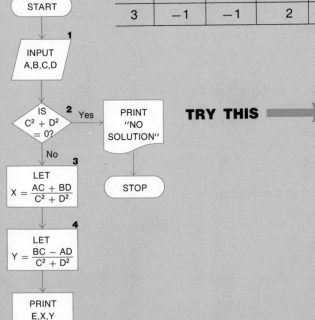

**TRY THIS** →

Use the flowchart to find the quotients.
1. $(5 - 6I) \div (2 + 3I)$
2. $(2 + 3I) \div (5 - 6I)$

BASIC PROGRAM (Optional)

```
10   INPUT A,B,C,D
20   LET E = C↑2 + D↑2
30   IF E = 0 THEN 90
40   LET X = ((A*C) + (B*D))/E
50   LET Y = ((B*C) − (A*D))/E
60   PRINT "E ="E, "X ="X,
         "Y ="Y
70   PRINT "QUOTIENT ="X;" + "Y;"I"
80   GO TO 100
90   PRINT "NO SOLUTION"
100  STOP
```

## CHAPTER 11 REVIEW

Review the material in the chapter. Then see how you have done by trying these review exercises. If you miss an exercise, restudy the indicated lesson.

11-1    1.  Add: $(6 + 2i) + (-4 - 3i)$.

11-1    2.  Subtract: $(3 - 5i) - (2 - i)$.

11-2    3.  Solve for $x$ and $y$: $4x + 2i = 8 - (2 + y)i$.

11-2   Multiply.

        4.  $(7i)^2$

        5.  $(2 - 2i)(3 + 4i)$

        6.  $(5 + 3i)^2$

11-2    7.  Find the conjugate of $-8 - 9i$.

11-2    8.  Multiply: $(2 - 3i)(2 + 3i)$.

11-2    9.  Divide: $\dfrac{2 - 3i}{1 - 3i}$.

11-2   10.  Find the reciprocal of $4 + i$, and express it in the form $a + bi$.

11-3   11.  Find an equation having the solutions $1 - 2i$, $1 + 2i$.

11-3   12.  Solve: $2ix - 5 + 3i = (2 - i)x + i$.

11-4   13.  Graph $-3 - 2i$ and $4 + 5i$.

11-4   14.  Find $|4 - 8i|$.

11-5   15.  Find a polynomial in $\bar{z}$ that is the conjugate of $3z^2 + z - 7$.

## CHAPTER 11 TEST

1. Add: $(3 + 2i) + (2 - 3i)$.
2. Subtract: $(9 - 4i) - (3 + 2i)$.
3. Solve for $x$ and $y$: $3x + i = -4 + yi$.

Multiply.

4. $8i \cdot 3i$.
5. $(1 - 2i)(2 - i)$.
6. $(1 - 2i)^2$.

7. Find the conjugate of $-2 + i$.
8. Multiply: $(2 + 5i)(2 - 5i)$.
9. Divide: $\dfrac{4 + 3i}{2 - i}$.
10. Find the reciprocal of $5 - 2i$ and express it in the form $a + bi$.
11. Find an equation having the solutions $2 - i$, $2 + i$.
12. Solve: $-5ix + 8i - 4 = (7 + i)x + 10i$.
13. Graph $3 - i$ and $4 + 6i$.
14. Find $|4 + 2i|$.
15. Find a polynomial in $\bar{z}$ that is the conjugate of $2z^6 - 4z^3 + z + 1$.

## CUMULATIVE REVIEW FOR CHAPTERS 9–11

9-1    1.  Simplify: $\dfrac{2x^2 + 5x - 3}{2x^2 - 11x + 5}$.

9-1    2.  Multiply and simplify: $\dfrac{x^2 + x - 12}{5x - 5} \cdot \dfrac{x - 1}{x - 3}$.

9-1    3.  Divide and simplify: $\dfrac{4x^3}{2x^2 + 11x - 21} \div \dfrac{12x}{x^2 + 8x + 7}$.

9-3    Add.

4.  $\dfrac{2x + 1}{5 - x} + \dfrac{x - 6}{-x + 5}$     5.  $\dfrac{5x - 1}{x^2 - x} + \dfrac{-x}{x - x^2}$

6.  $\dfrac{7x + 5}{x + 3} + \dfrac{x^2 - 3}{x^2 + 2x - 3}$

9-3    Subtract.

7.  $\dfrac{y^2}{y + 9} - \dfrac{-4y^2}{y + 9}$     8.  $\dfrac{3m^2 + 1}{8 - m} - \dfrac{2m^2}{-8 + m}$

9.  $\dfrac{7x + 3}{3x^2 - 4x - 4} - \dfrac{x - 1}{3x + 2}$

9-4    10.  Simplify: $\dfrac{x - \dfrac{3}{x}}{\dfrac{1}{x^2} + 4}$.

9-5    11.  Divide: $(a^4 - 3a^3 + 7a - 8) \div (a^2 - 5)$.

9-6    12.  Solve: $\dfrac{5}{4y} = \dfrac{7}{5y - 2}$.

9-7    13.  Solve for $v_s$:  $F_L = F_s \left( \dfrac{v + v_L}{v - v_s} \right)$.

9-8    14.  Solve:  The speed of a river is 8 km/h. A boat could only travel 8 km upstream in the same time it would take to travel 40 km downstream. What is the speed of the boat in still water?

9-9    15.  In physics, the amount of power (measured in watts) it takes to do a fixed amount of work (measured in joules) varies inversely with the time it takes to do the work. If an 18 kilowatt motor can raise an elevator 6 stories in 16 seconds, how much power would a motor need to do the job in 25 seconds?

| | | |
|---|---|---|
| 10-1 | 16. | Convert to scientific notation: 0.0000825. |
| 10-1 | 17. | Convert to decimal notation: $2.003 \times 10^4$. |
| 10-2 | 18. | Simplify: $\sqrt[3]{125x^6}$. |
| 10-3 | 19. | Multiply: $\sqrt{11} \sqrt{5}$. |
| 10-3 | 20. | Simplify: $\sqrt{92}$. |
| 10-3 | 21. | Multiply and simplify: $\sqrt{20y^3} \sqrt{32y}$. |
| 10-4 | 22. | Simplify: $\sqrt[3]{\frac{125}{8}}$. |
| 10-4 | 23. | Divide and simplify: $\dfrac{\sqrt{14m^3}}{\sqrt{2m}}$. |
| 10-4 | 24. | Simplify: $(\sqrt[3]{9y})^2$. |
| 10-5 | 25. | Simplify: $\sqrt{27} + \sqrt{147}$. |
| 10-7 | 26. | Rationalize the denominator: $\sqrt{\dfrac{3y^2}{2x}}$. |
| 10-7 | 27. | Rationalize the numerator: $\sqrt[3]{\dfrac{4}{9x}}$. |
| 10-7 | 28. | Rationalize the denominator: $\dfrac{\sqrt{2x}}{\sqrt{5} + \sqrt{x}}$. |
| | 29. | Rewrite without fractional exponents: $(m^5n^5)^{\frac{1}{3}}$. |
| 10-8 | 30. | Rewrite with fractional exponents: $\sqrt[3]{x^7}$. |
| 10-8 | 31. | Use exponential notation to write the expression $\sqrt[6]{m^3n^2}$. Then simplify if possible. Assume variables stand for nonnegative numbers. Write radical notation for the answer, if appropriate. |
| 10-9 | 32. | Solve: $\sqrt{2x + 3} = 4$. |
| 10-9 | 33. | Solve: $2\sqrt{10 - 3x} = 1 + \sqrt{51 - 14x}$. |
| 11-1 | 34. | Add: $(-5 - 2i) + (4 + 3i)$. |
| 11-1 | 35. | Subtract: $(7 - 2i) - (3 - 4i)$. |
| 11-2 | 36. | Solve for $x$ and $y$: $-5y + 15i = 30 - 3xi$. |
| 11-2 | 37. | Multiply: $(3 + 5i)(2 - 6i)$. |
| 11-2 | 38. | Find the conjugate of $-3 + 7i$. |
| 11-2 | 39. | Multiply: $(-4 + 2i)(-4 - 2i)$. |
| 11-2 | 40. | Divide: $\dfrac{3 + 2i}{1 - 3i}$. |
| 11-2 | 41. | Find the reciprocal of $-2 + 3i$ and express it in the form $a + bi$. |
| 11-3 | 42. | Find an equation having the solutions $2 - 3i$, $2 + 3i$. |
| 11-3 | 43. | Solve: $(3 - 2i)x - 5ix - 2i = 3 - 3i$. |
| 11-4 | 44. | Graph: $2 - 3i$ and $-8 + 6i$. |
| 11-4 | 45. | Find: $|-3 + 2i|$. |
| 11-5 | 46. | Find a polynomial in $\bar{z}$ that is the conjugate of $7z^2 + z$. |

## Ready for Quadratic Equations?

Solve.

2-2    1. $(x - 5)(x + 3) = 0$

7-7    2. $x^2 - 5x - 14 = 0$

7-7    3. $4x^2 - 8x = 0$

7-7    4. $x^2 + 10x + 25 = 0$

7-7    5. $x^2 - 9 = 0$

7-8    6. The length of a rectangle is 5m more than the width. The area is 24m². Find the dimensions.

Simplify.

10-2    7. $\sqrt{49}$

10-3    8. $\sqrt{88}$

10-3    9. Simplify and approximate to the nearest tenth: $\dfrac{14 - \sqrt{88}}{10}$

10-7    10. Rationalize the denominator: $\sqrt{\dfrac{2}{5}}$

11-1    Express in terms of $i$.

         11. $\sqrt{-7}$

         12. $\sqrt{-20}$

11-2    13. Find the conjugate of $-2 + 3i$.

11-3    14. Determine whether $1 + i$ is a solution of $x^2 + 2x + 1 = 0$.

# Chapter 12
# Quadratic Equations

How long would it take an object dropped from
the top of the arch to reach the ground?

# 12-1 Introduction to Quadratic Equations

After finishing Lesson 12-1, you should be able to
▪ solve equations of the type $ax^2 = k$, where $k \neq 0$.

▪Equations of second degree are called *quadratic*.

### DEFINITION

An equation of the type $ax^2 + bx + c = 0$, where $a$, $b$ and $c$ are constants and $a \neq 0$, is called the *standard form of a quadratic equation*.

We first consider solving equations in which $b = 0$, that is equations $ax^2 + c = 0$, or $ax^2 = -c$. In other words, equations in which we have $ax^2$ equal to some constant.

**Example 1.** Solve: $3x^2 = 6$.
$$x^2 = 2 \qquad \textit{Multiplying by } \tfrac{1}{3}$$

By Theorem 11-4, every complex number has two square roots that are additive inverses of each other. We take the two square roots.

$$\sqrt{x^2} = \sqrt{2} \qquad \sqrt{x^2} = -\sqrt{2}$$

We have

$$x = \sqrt{2} \text{ or } x = -\sqrt{2}.$$

Abbreviating, we have $x = \pm\sqrt{2}$.

**TRY THIS** ➡

Solve.

1. $5x^2 = 15$
2. $7x^2 = 0$

Sometimes we rationalize denominators to simplify answers.

**Example 2.** Solve: $-5x^2 + 2 = 0$.
$$-5x^2 = -2 \qquad \textit{Adding } -2$$
$$x^2 = \frac{2}{5} \qquad \textit{Multiplying by } -\frac{1}{5}$$

$$x = \sqrt{\frac{2}{5}} \quad \text{or} \quad x = -\sqrt{\frac{2}{5}} \qquad \textit{Taking square roots}$$

$$x = \sqrt{\frac{2}{5} \cdot \frac{5}{5}} \quad \text{or} \quad x = -\sqrt{\frac{2}{5} \cdot \frac{5}{5}} \qquad \textit{Rationalizing the denominators}$$

$$x = \frac{\sqrt{10}}{5} \quad \text{or} \quad x = -\frac{\sqrt{10}}{5}$$

The solutions are $\dfrac{\sqrt{10}}{5}$ and $-\dfrac{\sqrt{10}}{5}$.

**TRY THIS** ➡

> Solve.
>
> 3. $-3x^2 + 8 = 0$

**Example 3.** Solve: $4x^2 + 9 = 0$.

$$4x^2 = -9 \qquad \text{\textit{Adding} } -9$$
$$x^2 = -\tfrac{9}{4} \qquad \text{\textit{Multiplying by} } \tfrac{1}{4}$$
$$x = \sqrt{-\tfrac{9}{4}} \quad \text{or} \quad x = -\sqrt{-\tfrac{9}{4}} \qquad \text{\textit{Taking square roots (Theorem 11-4)}}$$
$$x = \tfrac{3}{2}i \qquad \text{or} \quad x = -\tfrac{3}{2}i$$

**TRY THIS** ➡

> Solve.
>
> 4. $2x^2 + 1 = 0$

## Exercise Set 12-1

▌Solve. (*See Examples 1–3.*)

1. $4x^2 = 20$
2. $3x^2 = 21$
3. $10x^2 = 0$
4. $9x^2 = 0$
5. $2x^2 - 3 = 0$
6. $3x^2 - 7 = 0$
7. $-3x^2 + 5 = 0$
8. $-2x^2 + 1 = 0$
9. $4x^2 - 1 = 0$
10. $9x^2 - 1 = 0$
11. $25x^2 + 4 = 0$
12. $9x^2 + 16 = 0$
13. $3x^2 + 1 = 0$
14. $5x^2 + 1 = 0$
15. $x^2 + 5 = 0$
16. $x^2 + 6 = 0$
17. $2x^2 + 14 = 0$
18. $3x^2 + 15 = 0$
19. $\tfrac{4}{9}x^2 - 1 = 0$
20. $\tfrac{16}{25}x^2 - 1 = 0$

## Calculator Exercises

Solve.

21. $16.3x^2 = 798.7$
22. $14.24x^2 = 512.64$
23. $25.55x^2 - 1635.2 = 0$
24. $24.48x^2 - 1982.88 = 0$

## Challenge Exercises

Solve for $x$.

25. $ax^2 - b = 0$
26. $ax^2 + b = 0$

# 12-2 Solving by Factoring

After finishing Lesson 12-2, you should be able to

■ solve quadratic equations of the type $ax^2 + bx = 0$, $a \neq 0$, $b \neq 0$, by factoring.

■■ solve certain quadratic equations of the type $ax^2 + bx + c = 0$, $a \neq 0$, $b \neq 0$, $c \neq 0$, by factoring.

## ■ Equations of the Type $ax^2 + bx = 0$

When $c$ is 0 ($a \neq 0$, $b \neq 0$), we can factor and use the principle of zero products.

**Example 1.** Solve: $3x^2 + 5x = 0$.

$$x(3x + 5) = 0 \qquad \textit{Factoring}$$

$x = 0$ or $3x + 5 = 0$    *Principle of zero products*
$x = 0$ or $3x = -5$
$x = 0$ or $x = -\frac{5}{3}$

The solutions are 0 and $-\frac{5}{3}$.

A quadratic equation of this type will always have 0 as one solution and a nonzero number as the other solution.

**TRY THIS** ➡

> Solve.
>
> 1. $4x^2 - 3x = 0$

## ■■ Equations of the Type $ax^2 + bx + c = 0$

By the fundamental theorem of algebra, every quadratic polynomial $ax^2 + bx + c$ with complex coefficients can be factored into two linear factors. However, the factors may not be easy to find. Factoring offers a good method of solving if the factoring is easy.

**Example 2.** Solve $3x^2 + x - 2 = 0$.

$$(3x - 2)(x + 1) = 0 \qquad \textit{Factoring}$$

$3x - 2 = 0$ or $x + 1 = 0$
$3x = 2$ or $x = -1$
$x = \frac{2}{3}$ or $x = -1$

The solutions are $\frac{2}{3}$ and $-1$.

**TRY THIS** ➡

> Solve.
>
> 2. $5x^2 - 8x + 3 = 0$

**Example 3.** A rectangular garden is 60 m by 80 m. Part of the garden is torn up to install a strip of lawn of uniform width around the garden. The new area of the garden is $\frac{1}{6}$ of the old area. How wide is the strip of lawn?

First make a drawing.
Let $x$ represent the width of the strip of lawn. Then,

Area of old garden $= 60 \cdot 80$     *Multiplying length and width*
Area of new garden $= (60 - 2x)(80 - 2x)$

Since the new garden is $\frac{1}{6}$ of the old we have

$$(60 - 2x)(80 - 2x) = \tfrac{1}{6} \cdot 60 \cdot 80$$
$$4800 - 160x - 120x + 4x^2 = 800$$
$$4x^2 - 280x + 4000 = 0 \quad \text{\textit{Writing the standard form}}$$
$$x^2 - 70x + 1000 = 0$$
$$(x - 20)(x - 50) = 0$$

$$x = 20 \quad \text{or} \quad x = 50$$

Checking in the original problem we see that 50 is not a solution because when $x = 50$, $60 - 2x = -40$, and the width of the garden cannot be negative. The number 20 checks. Thus the width of the strip of lawn is 20 cm.

**TRY THIS** ➡

3. An open box is to be made from a 10 cm by 20 cm rectangular piece of cardboard by cutting a square from each corner. The area of the bottom of the box is 96 cm². What is the length of the sides of the squares which are cut from the corners?

**Example 4.** Bicycles $A$ and $B$ leave the same point $P$ at the same time at right angles. $B$ travels 7 km/h faster than $A$. After 3 hours they are 39 km apart. Find the speed of each.

We first make a drawing, letting $r$ be the speed of $A$ and $r + 7$ be the speed of $B$. Since they both travel 3 hr, their distances from $P$ are $3r$ and $3(r + 7)$, respectively. To translate we use the Pythagorean Theorem.

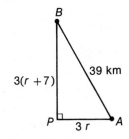

$$[3(r + 7)]^2 + [3r]^2 = 39^2$$
$$9(r + 7)^2 + 9r^2 = 1521$$
$$(r + 7)^2 + r^2 = 169 \quad \text{\textit{Multiplying by }} \tfrac{1}{9}$$
$$r^2 + 14r + 49 + r^2 = 169$$
$$2r^2 + 14r + 49 = 169$$

We write the equation in standard form.

$$2r^2 + 14r - 120 = 0$$
$$r^2 + 7r - 60 = 0 \quad \textit{Multiplying by } \tfrac{1}{2}$$
$$(r + 12)(r - 5) = 0$$

$$r + 12 = 0 \quad \text{or} \quad r - 5 = 0$$
$$r = -12 \quad \text{or} \quad r = 5$$

The solutions of the equation are $-12$ and $5$. Since speed cannot be negative in this problem, $-12$ is not a solution. The number $5$ checks, so the speed of $A$ is 5 km/h and the speed of $B$ is 12 km/h.

**TRY THIS** ➡

4. Joggers $A$ and $B$ leave the same point $P$ at right angles. $A$ jogs 1 km/h faster than $B$. After 2 hours they are 10 km apart. Find the speed of each.

## Exercise Set 12-2

▮ Solve. (*See Example 1.*)

1. $x^2 - 5x = 0$
2. $x^2 - 6x = 0$
3. $5x^2 + 10x = 0$
4. $3x^2 + 12x = 0$
5. $3x^2 - 2x = 0$
6. $7x^2 - 3x = 0$
7. $14x^2 + 9x = 0$
8. $19x^2 + 8x = 0$
9. $11x^2 - 55x = 0$
10. $13x^2 + 65x = 0$

▮▮ Solve. (*See Example 2.*)

11. $x^2 - 6x + 5 = 0$
12. $x^2 - 7x + 6 = 0$
13. $x^2 - 4x - 5 = 0$
14. $x^2 - 6x - 7 = 0$
15. $x^2 + 8x + 15 = 0$
16. $x^2 + 9x + 14 = 0$
17. $6x^2 - x - 2 = 0$
18. $2x^2 + 13x + 15 = 0$
19. $9t^2 + 15t + 4 = 0$
20. $3y^2 + 10y - 8 = 0$
21. $6x^2 + 4x = 10$
22. $3x^2 + 7x = 20$
23. $2x(4x - 5) = 3$
24. $t(2t + 9) = -7$
25. $(p - 3)(p - 4) = 42$
26. $16(t - 1) = t(t + 8)$
27. $4x(x - 2) - 5x(x - 1) = 2$
28. $14(x - 4) - (x + 2) = (x + 2)(x - 4)$

Solve. (*See Examples 3 and 4.*)

29. A picture frame measures 14 cm by 20 cm. 160 cm² of picture shows. Find the width of the frame.
30. A picture frame measures 12 cm by 20 cm. 84 cm² of picture shows. Find the width of the frame.
31. The width of a rectangle is 4 m less than the length. The area is 12 m². Find the length and width.
32. The width of a rectangle is 5 m less than the length. The area is 24 m². Find the length and width.

33. The length of a rectangle is twice the width. The area is 288 m². Find the length and width.

34. The length of a rectangle is twice the width. The area is 338 km². Find the length and width.

35. The hypotenuse of a right triangle is 5 m long. One leg is 1 m less than the other. Find the lengths of the legs.

36. The hypotenuse of a right triangle is 13 m long. One leg is 7 m longer than the other. Find the lengths of the legs.

37. The hypotenuse of a right triangle is 26 m long. The length of one leg is 14 m longer than the other. Find the lengths of the legs.

38. The hypotenuse of a right triangle is 25 km long. The length of one leg is 17 km less than the other. Find the lengths of the legs.

39. Trains *A* and *B* leave the same city at the same time at right angles. Train *B* travels 5 km/h faster than Train *A*. After 2 hr they are 50 km apart. Find the speed of each train.

40. Boats *A* and *B* leave the same point at the same time at right angles. *B* travels 7 km/h slower than *A*. After 4 hr they are 68 km apart. Find the speed of each boat.

## Challenge Exercises

Solve.

41. $(3x^2 - 7x - 20)(2x - 5) = 0$     42. $(12x^2 - 5x - 2)(8x + 11) = 0$

43. The sum of the squares of two consecutive positive integers is 61. What are the integers?

44. Find three consecutive integers such that the square of the first plus the product of the other two is 46.

45. During the first part of a trip a man travels 80 km at a certain speed. He travels 35 km on the second part of the trip at a speed which is 5 km/h slower. The total time for the trip is 3 hours. How fast did he travel on each part of the trip?

46. A woman travels 280 km at a certain speed. If she had increased her speed 5 km/h, she could have made the trip in 1 hour less time. Find her actual speed.

47. Airplane *A* travels 2800 km at a certain speed. Airplane *B* travels 2000 km at a speed which is 50 km/h faster than Plane *A* in 3 hours less time. Find the speed of each plane.

48. Two pipes are connected to the same tank. When working together they can fill the tank in 2 hours. The pipes are of different size. The larger one, working alone, can fill the tank in 3 hours less time than the smaller one. How long would the smaller one take, working alone, to fill the tank?

# *12-3 The Quadratic Formula*

After finishing Lesson 12-3, you should be able to
▌ solve quadratic equations using the quadratic formula.
▌▌ find approximate solutions using a square root table.

## ▌Solving Equations Using the Quadratic Formula

Here is a formula for finding the solutions of any quadratic equation.

**THEOREM 12-1**

The solutions of any quadratic equation (with complex coefficients)
$ax^2 + bx + c = 0$ are given by $x = \dfrac{-b \pm \sqrt{b^2 - 4ac}}{2a}$.

The equation $x = \dfrac{-b \pm \sqrt{b^2 - 4ac}}{2a}$ is called the *quadratic formula*.

**Example 1.** Solve: $5x^2 - 8x = 3$.

First find standard form and determine $a$, $b$, and $c$.

$$5x^2 - 8x - 3 = 0$$
$$a = 5, \, b = -8, \, c = -3$$

Then use the quadratic formula.

$$x = \frac{-b \pm \sqrt{b^2 - 4ac}}{2a}$$

$$x = \frac{-(-8) \pm \sqrt{(-8)^2 - 4 \cdot 5 \cdot (-3)}}{2 \cdot 5}$$

$$x = \frac{8 \pm \sqrt{64 + 60}}{10}$$

$$x = \frac{8 \pm \sqrt{124}}{10}$$

$$x = \frac{8 \pm \sqrt{4 \cdot 31}}{10}$$

$$x = \frac{8 \pm 2\sqrt{31}}{10}$$

$$= \frac{4 \pm \sqrt{31}}{5}$$

The solutions are $\dfrac{4 + \sqrt{31}}{5}$ and $\dfrac{4 - \sqrt{31}}{5}$.

**TRY THIS** ➤

We can get complex solutions.

**Example 2.**  Solve: $x^2 + x + 1 = 0$.

$a = 1, b = 1, c = 1$

$$x = \frac{-b \pm \sqrt{b^2 - 4ac}}{2a}$$

$$x = \frac{-1 \pm \sqrt{1^2 - 4 \cdot 1 \cdot 1}}{2 \cdot 1}$$

$$x = \frac{-1 \pm \sqrt{1 - 4}}{2}$$

$$x = \frac{-1 \pm \sqrt{-3}}{2}$$

$$= \frac{-1 \pm i\sqrt{3}}{2}$$

The solutions are $\dfrac{-1 + i\sqrt{3}}{2}$ and $\dfrac{-1 - i\sqrt{3}}{2}$.

**TRY THIS** ➤

> Solve using the quadratic formula.
>
> 1.  $3x^2 + 2x = 7$

> Solve.
>
> 2.  $x^2 - x + 2 = 0$

---

**A Proof of Theorem 12-1**

Let us consider any quadratic equation $ax^2 + bx + c = 0$. The coefficients can be any complex numbers except that $a \neq 0$. We multiply on both sides by $4a$, to obtain $4a^2x^2 + 4abx + 4ac = 0$. Now we add $b^2 - b^2$ on the left and rearrange. This gives us

$$4a^2x^2 + 4abx + b^2 - (b^2 - 4ac) = 0$$

or
$$4a^2x^2 + 4abx + b^2 = b^2 - 4ac$$

or
$$(2ax + b)^2 = b^2 - 4ac.$$

By Theorem 11-4, every complex number has two square roots that are additive inverses of each other. We take the two square roots.

$$2ax + b = \sqrt{b^2 - 4ac} \text{ or } 2ax + b = -\sqrt{b^2 - 4ac}$$

Solving for $x$, we get

$$x = \frac{-b + \sqrt{b^2 - 4ac}}{2a} \text{ or } x = \frac{-b - \sqrt{b^2 - 4ac}}{2a}.$$

**Example 3.** Solve: $2 + \dfrac{7}{x} = \dfrac{4}{x^2}$

First find standard form.

$$2x^2 + 7x = 4 \qquad \textit{Multiplying by } x^2\textit{, the LCM of the denominators}$$
$$2x^2 + 7x - 4 = 0 \qquad \textit{Adding } -4$$

$a = 2,\ b = 7,\ c = -4$

$$x = \frac{-7 \pm \sqrt{7^2 - 4 \cdot 2 \cdot (-4)}}{2 \cdot 2}$$

$$x = \frac{-7 \pm \sqrt{49 + 32}}{4}$$

$$x = \frac{-7 \pm \sqrt{81}}{4} = \frac{-7 \pm 9}{4}$$

$$x = \frac{-7 + 9}{4} = \frac{1}{2} \text{ or } x = \frac{-7 - 9}{4} = -4$$

The solutions are $\dfrac{1}{2}$ and $-4$.

The solutions of a quadratic equation can *always* be found using the quadratic formula. They are not always easy to find by factoring. A general strategy for solving quadratic equations is

    a)  Try factoring.
    b)  If factoring seems difficult, use the quadratic formula; it *always works!*

**TRY THIS** ➡️

Solve.

3. $3 - \dfrac{5}{x} = \dfrac{2}{x^2}$

## ▮ Approximating Solutions

A square root table can be used to approximate solutions.

**Example 4.** Approximate the solutions of the equation in Example 1.

From Table 1 in the back of the book, $\sqrt{31} \approx 5.568$.

$$\frac{4 + \sqrt{31}}{5} \approx \frac{4 + 5.568}{5}$$

$$\approx \frac{9.568}{5}$$

$$\approx 1.9 \text{ (Rounded to the nearest tenth)}$$

$$\frac{4 - \sqrt{31}}{5} \approx \frac{4 - 5.568}{5}$$

$$\approx \frac{-1.568}{5}$$

$$\approx -0.3 \text{ (Rounded to the nearest tenth)}$$

**TRY THIS**

> 4. Approximate the solutions to TRY THIS Exercise 1. Round to the nearest tenth.

## Exercise Set 12-3

▌Solve. (*See Examples 1–3.*)

1. $x^2 + 6x + 4 = 0$
2. $x^2 - 6x - 4 = 0$
3. $x^2 + 4x - 5 = 0$
4. $x^2 - 2x - 15 = 0$
5. $y^2 + 7y = 30$
6. $y^2 - 7y = 30$
7. $2t^2 - 3t - 2 = 0$
8. $5m^2 + 3m - 2 = 0$
9. $3p^2 = -8p - 5$
10. $3u^2 = 18u - 6$
11. $x^2 - x + 1 = 0$
12. $x^2 + x + 2 = 0$
13. $1 + \dfrac{2}{x} + \dfrac{5}{x^2} = 0$
14. $1 + \dfrac{5}{x^2} = \dfrac{2}{x}$
15. $x^2 - 2x + 5 = 0$
16. $x^2 - 4x + 5 = 0$
17. $x^2 + 13 = 4x$
18. $x^2 + 13 = 6x$
19. $z^2 + 5 = 0$
20. $t^2 + 3 = 0$
21. $r^2 + 3r = 8$
22. $h^2 + 4 = 6h$
23. $2x^2 = 5$
24. $3x^2 = 2$
25. $3x + x(x - 2) = 0$
26. $4x + x(x - 3) = 0$
27. $5x^2 + 2x + 1 = 0$
28. $3x^2 + x + 2 = 0$
29. $(2t - 3)^2 + 17t = 15$
30. $2y^2 - (y + 2)(y - 3) = 12$
31. $(x - 2)^2 + (x + 1)^2 = 0$
32. $(x + 3)^2 + (x - 1)^2 = 0$
33. $x + \dfrac{1}{x} = \dfrac{13}{6}$
34. $\dfrac{3}{x} + \dfrac{x}{3} = \dfrac{5}{2}$

▌▌Use the square root table, Table 1, in the back of the book to approximate solutions to the nearest tenth. (*See Example 4.*)

35. $x^2 + 4x - 7 = 0$
36. $x^2 + 6x + 4 = 0$
37. $x^2 - 6x + 4 = 0$
38. $x^2 - 4x + 1 = 0$
39. $2x^2 - 3x - 7 = 0$
40. $3x^2 - 3x - 2 = 0$
41. $3x^2 + 8x + 2 = 0$
42. $5x^2 + 7x + 1 = 0$

## Calculator Exercises

Solve.

43. $t^2 + 0.2t - 0.3 = 0$

44. $p^2 + 0.3p - 0.2 = 0$

45. $x^2 - 0.75x - 0.5 = 0$

46. $z^2 + 0.84z - 0.4 = 0$

47. $5.33x^2 - 8.23x - 3.24 = 0$

48. $0.034x^2 + 7.01x - 0.0356 = 0$

## Challenge Exercises

Solve.

49. $x^2 + x - \sqrt{2} = 0$

50. $x^2 - x - \sqrt{3} = 0$

51. $x^2 + \sqrt{5}x - \sqrt{3} = 0$

52. $\sqrt{2}x^2 + 5x + \sqrt{2} = 0$

53. $x^2 + 3x + i = 0$

54. $ix^2 - 2x + 1 = 0$

55. The hypotenuse of a right triangle is 6 cm long. One leg is 1 cm less than the other. Find the lengths of the legs. Round to the nearest tenth.

56. The hypotenuse of a right triangle is 8 m long. One leg is 2 m longer than the other. Find the lengths of the legs. Round to the nearest tenth.

57. A boat travels 2 km upstream and 2 km downstream. The total time for both parts of the trip is 1 hour. The speed of the stream is 2 km/h. What is the speed of the boat in still water? Round to the nearest tenth.

58. Person *A* can do a certain job in 3 hours less time than Person *B*. Together they can do the same job in 6 hours. How long would each take to do the job alone? Give an approximate answer. Round to the nearest tenth.

59. Solve $3x^2 + xy + 4y^2 - 9 = 0$ for $x$ terms of $y$.

60. Derive the quadratic formula by completing the square. Assume $a > 0$ in the standard form.

61. One solution of $kx^2 + 3x - k = 0$ is $-2$. Find the other.

62. Prove that the solutions of $ax^2 + bx + c = 0$ are
    a) the reciprocals of the solutions of $cx^2 - bx + a = 0$.
    b) the additive inverses of the solutions of $ax^2 - bx + c = 0$.

63. Prove that if $ac \neq 0$, then the following could be used as a formula for solving quadratic equations.

$$x = \frac{2c}{-b \pm \sqrt{b^2 - 4ac}}$$

# 12-4 The Discriminant

After finishing Lesson 12-4, you should be able to
∎ determine the nature of the solutions of a quadratic equation with real coefficients, without solving it.

∎ We now consider quadratic equations with real number coefficients. The expression

$$b^2 - 4ac$$

in the quadratic formula is called the *discriminant*. From this number we can determine the nature of the solutions.

### THEOREM 12-2
An equation $ax^2 + bx + c = 0$, with $a \neq 0$ and all coefficients real numbers, has
a) Exactly one real number solution if $b^2 - 4ac = 0$.
b) Two real number solutions if $b^2 - 4ac > 0$.
c) Two complex, but not real, number solutions that are conjugates of each other if $b^2 - 4ac < 0$.

**Example 1.** Determine the nature of the solutions of $9x^2 - 12x + 4 = 0$.

$a = 9$, $b = -12$, and $c = 4$.
We compute the discriminant.

$$
\begin{aligned}
b^2 - 4ac &= (-12)^2 - 4 \cdot 9 \cdot 4 \\
&= 144 - 144 \\
&= 0
\end{aligned}
$$

By Theorem 12-2, there is just one solution and it is a real number.

**Example 2.** Determine the nature of the solutions of $x^2 + 5x + 8 = 0$.

$a = 1$, $b = 5$, and $c = 8$.
We compute the discriminant.

$$
\begin{aligned}
b^2 - 4ac &= 5^2 - 4 \cdot 1 \cdot 8 \\
&= 25 - 32 \\
&= -7
\end{aligned}
$$

Since the discriminant is negative, there are two nonreal solutions that are complex conjugates of each other.

**Example 3.** Determine the nature of the solutions of
$x^2 + 5x + 6 = 0$.

$a = 1$, $b = 5$, and $c = 6$.

$$b^2 - 4ac = 5^2 - 4 \cdot 1 \cdot 6$$
$$= 1$$

Since the discriminant is positive, there are two
solutions and they are real numbers.

**TRY THIS** ➡

> Determine the nature of the so-
> lutions of each equation.
>
> 1. $x^2 + 5x - 3 = 0$
> 2. $9x^2 - 6x + 1 = 0$
> 3. $3x^2 - 2x + 1 = 0$

## Exercise Set 12-4

▌Determine the nature of the solutions of each equation. (*See Examples 1–3.*)

1. $x^2 - 6x + 9 = 0$
2. $x^2 + 10x + 25 = 0$
3. $x^2 + 7 = 0$
4. $x^2 + 2 = 0$
5. $x^2 - 2 = 0$
6. $x^2 - 5 = 0$
7. $4x^2 - 12x + 9 = 0$
8. $4x^2 + 8x - 5 = 0$
9. $x^2 - 2x + 4 = 0$
10. $x^2 + 3x + 4 = 0$
11. $9t^2 - 3t = 0$
12. $4m^2 + 7m = 0$
13. $y^2 = \frac{1}{2}y + \frac{3}{5}$
14. $y^2 + \frac{9}{4} = 4y$
15. $4x^2 - 4\sqrt{3}x + 3 = 0$
16. $6y^2 - 2\sqrt{3}y - 1 = 0$

### Challenge Exercises

In each of the following find $k$ so that: a) there are two real number
solutions, b) there is one real number solution, and c) there are two
solutions which are complex conjugates.

17. $x^2 + 3x + k = 0$
18. $x^2 + x + k = 0$
19. $kx^2 - 4x + 1 = 0$
20. $x^2 - x + 3x + k = 0$
21. $x^2 + x = 1 - k$
22. $3x^2 + 4x = k - 5$

Suppose in a quadratic equation $ax^2 + bx + c = 0$, $a$, $b$, and $c$ are integers.
23. Prove that the quadratic equation has two rational number solutions if
the discriminant is positive and a perfect square.
24. Use the result of Exercise 23 to determine if each equation has rational solutions.
    a) $6x^2 + 5x + 1 = 0$    b) $x^2 + 4x - 2 = 0$
25. Prove that every polynomial equation with rational coefficients is
equivalent to one with integer coefficients.
26. Prove Theorem 12-2. (*Hint:* Use the quadratic formula.)

# 12-5 Solutions and Coefficients

After finishing Lesson 12-5, you should be able to
**I** find, without solving, the sum and product of the solutions of a quadratic equation.
**II** find a quadratic equation for which the sum and product of the solutions are given.
**III** find an equation having specified numbers as solutions.

## ▮Sum and Product of Solutions

**THEOREM 12-3**
For the equation $ax^2 + bx + c = 0$,

the *sum* of the solutions is $-\dfrac{b}{a}$,

the *product* of the solutions is $\dfrac{c}{a}$.

Note that if we express $ax^2 + bx + c = 0$ in the equivalent form,

$x^2 + \dfrac{b}{a}x + \dfrac{c}{a} = 0$, then the sum of the solutions is the additive

inverse of the $x$ coefficient and their product is the constant
term.

**Example 1.** Without solving, find the sum and product of the solutions of $2x^2 = 6x + 5$.

Let $x_1$ and $x_2$ represent the solutions.

Since $2x^2 - 6x - 5 = 0$, we have $a = 2$, $b = -6$, and $c = -5$

Then, $x_1 + x_2 = -\dfrac{b}{a}$

$$= -\left(\dfrac{-6}{2}\right)$$

$$= 3,$$

$$x_1 \cdot x_2 = \dfrac{c}{a}$$

$$= \dfrac{-5}{2}.$$

**TRY THIS**

Find, without solving, the sum and product of the solutions.

1. $3x^2 + 4 = 12x$
2. $x^2 + \sqrt{2}x - 4 = 0$

## ⅠⅠ Sum and Product Given

**Example 2.** Find a quadratic equation for which the *sum* of the solutions is $-\frac{4}{5}$ and the *product* of the solutions is $\frac{2}{3}$

$$x^2 - \left(-\frac{b}{a}\right)x + \frac{c}{a} = x^2 - \left(-\frac{4}{5}\right)x + \frac{2}{3} = x^2 + \frac{4}{5}x + \frac{2}{3} = 0$$

Thus we have $x^2 + \frac{4}{5}x + \frac{2}{3} = 0$, or $15x^2 + 12x + 10 = 0$.

**TRY THIS** ⟹

> 3. Find a quadratic equation for which the sum of the solutions is 3 and the product is $-\frac{1}{4}$.

## ⅠⅠⅠ Writing Equations from Solutions

We can use the principle of zero products to write a quadratic equation whose solutions are known.

**Example 3.** Find a quadratic equation whose solutions are 3 and $-\frac{2}{5}$.

$$x = 3 \quad \text{or} \quad x = -\tfrac{2}{5}$$
$$x - 3 = 0 \quad \text{or} \quad x + \tfrac{2}{5} = 0$$

$$(x - 3)(x + \tfrac{2}{5}) = 0 \qquad \textit{Multiplying}$$
$$x^2 - \tfrac{13}{5}x - \tfrac{6}{5} = 0, \text{ or } 5x^2 - 13x - 6 = 0$$

When radicals are involved, it is sometimes easier to use the properties of the sum and product.

**Example 4.** Find a quadratic equation whose solutions are $2 + \sqrt{5}$ and $2 - \sqrt{5}$.

$$x_1 + x_2 = (2 + \sqrt{5}) + (2 - \sqrt{5})$$
$$= 4$$

$$x_1 \cdot x_2 = (2 + \sqrt{5}) \cdot (2 - \sqrt{5})$$
$$= 4 - 5 = -1$$

$$x^2 - \left(-\frac{b}{a}\right)x + \frac{c}{a} = x^2 - (4)x + (-1) = 0;$$

or $x^2 - 4x - 1 = 0$

**TRY THIS** ⟹

> Find a quadratic equation whose solutions are the following.
>
> 4. $-4, \dfrac{5}{3}$
>
> 5. $-7, 8$
>
> 6. $m, n$
>
> 7. $8, -9$
>
> 8. $3 + \sqrt{2}, 3 - \sqrt{2}$
>
> 9. $\dfrac{2 + \sqrt{5}}{2}, \dfrac{2 - \sqrt{5}}{2}$

## Exercise Set 12-5

**I** Without solving, find the sum and product of the solutions. (*See Example 1.*)

1.  $x^2 + 7x + 8 = 0$
2.  $x^2 - 2x + 10 = 0$
3.  $x^2 - x + 1 = 0$
4.  $x^2 + x - 1 = 0$
5.  $8 - 2x^2 + 4x = 0$
6.  $4 + x + 2x^2 = 0$
7.  $m^2 = 25$
8.  $t^2 = 49$
9.  $(2 + 3x)^2 = 7x$
10. $2x - 1 = (1 - 5x)^2$
11. $5(t - 3)^2 = 4(t + 3)^2$
12. $3(y + 4)^2 = 2(y + 5)^2$

**II** Find a quadratic equation for which the: (*See Example 2.*)

13. Sum of solutions $= -5$; product $= \frac{1}{2}$.
14. Sum of solutions $= -\pi$; product $= \frac{1}{4}$.
15. Sum of solutions $= \sqrt{3}$; product $= 8$.
16. Sum of solutions $= 5$; product $= -\sqrt{2}$.

**III** Find a quadratic equation whose solutions are the following. (*See Example 3.*)

17. $-11, 9$
18. $-4, 4$
19. $7$, only solution
20. $-5$, only solution
21. $-\frac{2}{5}, \frac{6}{5}$
22. $-\frac{1}{4}, -\frac{1}{2}$
23. $\frac{c}{2}, \frac{d}{2}$
24. $\frac{k}{3}, \frac{m}{4}$
25. $\sqrt{2}, 3\sqrt{2}$
26. $-\sqrt{3}, 2\sqrt{3}$
27. $\pi, -2\pi$
28. $-3\pi, 4\pi$

Use the sum and product properties to write a quadratic equation whose solutions are the following. (*See Example 4.*)

29. $4, 3$
30. $5, 6$
31. $-2, \frac{5}{4}$
32. $-6, \frac{1}{4}$
33. $1 + \sqrt{2}, 1 - \sqrt{2}$
34. $2 + \sqrt{3}, 2 - \sqrt{3}$
35. $\dfrac{2 + \sqrt{3}}{2}, \dfrac{2 - \sqrt{3}}{2}$
36. $\dfrac{1 + \sqrt{13}}{2}, \dfrac{1 - \sqrt{13}}{2}$
37. $\dfrac{m}{n}, -\dfrac{n}{m}$
38. $\dfrac{g}{h}, -\dfrac{h}{g}$
39. $2 - 5i, 2 + 5i$
40. $4 + 3i, 4 - 3i$

---

### Challenge Exercises

For each equation under the given condition, a) find the other solution, and b) find $k$.

41. $kx^2 - 17x + 33 = 0$; one solution is $3$
42. $kx^2 - 2x + k = 0$; one solution is $-3$
43. $x^2 - kx - 25 = 0$; one solution is $-5$
44. Find $k$ if $kx^2 - 4x + (2k - 1) = 0$ and the product of the solutions is $3$.
45. Prove Theorem 12-3. (*Hint:* Use the quadratic formula.)

# 12-6 Formulas

After finishing Lesson 12-6, you should be able to
▮ solve a formula for a given letter.

▮ To solve a formula for a given letter, we try to get the letter alone on one side.

**Example 1.** Solve $T = 2\pi\sqrt{\dfrac{m}{g}}$, for $m$.

$$\frac{T}{2\pi} = \sqrt{\frac{m}{g}}$$

$$\left(\frac{T}{2\pi}\right)^2 = \left(\sqrt{\frac{m}{g}}\right)^2 \quad \textit{Squaring both sides}$$

$$\frac{T^2}{4\pi^2} = \frac{m}{g}$$

$$\frac{gT^2}{4\pi^2} = m \quad \textit{Multiplying by g}$$

In most formulas the letters represent nonnegative numbers, so absolute values are not needed when taking principal square roots.

**Example 2.** Solve $c^2 = a^2 + b^2$, for $c$.

$$c = \sqrt{a^2 + b^2} \quad \textit{Taking square root}$$

**Example 3.** Solve $h = v_0 t + 16t^2$, for $t$

$$16t^2 + v_0 t - h = 0 \quad \textit{Finding standard form}$$

$$a = 16, \; b = v_0, \; c = -h$$

$$t = \frac{-b \pm \sqrt{b^2 - 4ac}}{2a}$$

$$t = \frac{-v_0 \pm \sqrt{v_0{}^2 - 4 \cdot 16 \cdot (-h)}}{2 \cdot 16} \quad \begin{array}{l}\textit{Substituting into}\\\textit{the quadratic}\\\textit{formula}\end{array}$$

$$t = \frac{-v_0 \pm \sqrt{v_0{}^2 + 64h}}{32}$$

We choose the plus sign, $\dfrac{-v_0 + \sqrt{v_0{}^2 + 64h}}{32}$, because the negative square root would give a negative answer.

**TRY THIS** ➡

Solve for the indicated letter.

1. $A = \sqrt{\dfrac{w_1}{w_2}}$; $w_2$.

2. $V = \pi r^2 h$; $r$.

3. $Ls^2 - Rs = C$; $s$.

## Exercise Set 12-6

❙ Solve for the indicated letter. (*See Examples 1–3.*)

1. $P = 4s^2$; $s$

2. $A = \pi r^2$; $r$

3. $F = \dfrac{Gm_1m_2}{r^2}$; $r$

4. $K = \dfrac{Qab}{t^2}$; $t$

5. $T = 4\pi\sqrt{\dfrac{L}{g}}$; $L$

6. $\sqrt{\dfrac{E}{m}} = c$; $E$

7. $x^2 + y^2 = r^2$; $r$

8. $a^2 + b^2 = h^2$; $h$

9. $x^2 + y^2 + z^2 = d^2$; $z$

10. $a^2 + b^2 + c^2 = t^2$; $b$

11. $h = v_0t - 16t^2$; $t$

12. $A = \pi rs + \pi r^2$; $r$

13. $S = \dfrac{1}{2}gt^2$; $t$

14. $h = \dfrac{V^2}{2g}$; $V$

15. $A = 2\pi r^2 + 2\pi rh$; $r$

16. $h = 2v_0 + 10t^2$; $t$

17. $\sqrt{2}t^2 + 3k = \pi t$; $t$

18. $\sqrt{3}t^2 - 4\pi = 0.2t$; $t$

### Challenge Exercises

Solve for the indicated letter.

19. $m = \dfrac{m_0}{\sqrt{1 - \dfrac{v^2}{c^2}}}$; $v$

20. $T = \sqrt{\dfrac{a^2 + b^2}{a^2}}$; $a$

### HISTORICAL NOTE: How Many Rabbits? How Many Pheasants?

Several ancient Chinese books included problems that can be solved by systems of equations. *Arithmetical Rules in Nine Sections* was a book of 246 problems compiled by Chang Tsang, who died in 152 B.C. One of the problems is: Suppose there are a number of rabbits and pheasants confined in a cage. In all, there are 35 heads and 94 feet. How many rabbits are there? How many pheasants are there?

Chang Tsang based his book on an older text. It includes problems about proportion, square roots, and right triangles. It is the earliest work to mention negative numbers.

# 12-7 Solving Problems

After finishing Lesson 12-7, you should be able to
**I** use quadratic equations to solve certain interest problems.
**II** use quadratic equations to solve motion problems.

## I Interest Problems

An amount of money $P$ is invested at interest rate $r$. In $t$ years it will grow to the amount $A$ given by

$$A = P(1 + r)^t,$$

where interest is compounded annually.

**Example 1.** $2560 is invested at an interest rate $r$, and grows to $3240 in 2 years. What is the interest rate?

We substitute 2560 for $P$, 3240 for $A$, and 2 for $t$ in the formula

$$A = P(1 + r)^t$$
$$3240 = 2560(1 + r)^2$$
$$\frac{3240}{2560} = (1 + r)^2$$
$$\pm\sqrt{\frac{324}{256}} = 1 + r \qquad \textit{Taking square root}$$
$$\pm\frac{18}{16} = 1 + r$$

$$-1 + \frac{18}{16} = r \quad \text{or} \quad -1 - \frac{18}{16} = r$$
$$\frac{2}{16} = r \quad \text{or} \quad -\frac{34}{16} = r$$

Since the interest rate cannot be negative,
$r = \frac{2}{16} = \frac{1}{8} = 0.125 = 12.5\%.$

**TRY THIS** ⟹

1. $2560 is invested at interest rate $r$, and grows to $2890 in 2 years. What is the interest rate?

## II Motion Problems

When an object is dropped or thrown downward, the distance, in meters, that it falls in $t$ seconds is given by

$$s = 4.9t^2 + v_0 t.$$

In this formula $v_0$ is the initial velocity.

**Example 2.**

**a)** An object is dropped from the top of the Gateway Arch in St. Louis, which is 195 meters high. How long does it take to reach the ground?

Since the object was *dropped* its initial velocity was 0. So we substitute $0$ for $v_0$ and $195$ for $s$ and then solve for $t$:

$$195 = 4.9t^2 + 0 \cdot t$$
$$195 = 4.9t^2$$
$$t^2 \approx 39.8$$
$$t \approx \sqrt{39.8} \qquad \text{\textit{We take the positive square root because} t}$$
$$t \approx 6.31 \qquad \text{\textit{cannot be negative}}$$

Thus it takes about 6.31 seconds to reach the ground.

**b)** An object is thrown downward from the top of the arch at an initial velocity of 16 meters per second (m/s). How long does it take to reach the ground?

We substitute $195$ for $s$ and $16$ for $v_0$ and solve for $t$:

$$195 = 4.9t^2 + 16t$$
$$0 = 4.9t^2 + 16t - 195$$

By the quadratic formula we obtain

$$t = -8.15 \text{ or } t = 4.88.$$

The negative answer is meaningless in this problem, so the answer is 4.88 seconds.

**c)** How far will an object fall in 3 seconds if it is thrown downward from the top of the arch at an initial velocity of 16 m/s?

We substitute $16$ for $v_0$ and $3$ for $t$ and solve for $s$.

$$s = 4.9t^2 + v_0 t$$
$$= 4.9(3)^2 + 16 \cdot 3$$
$$= 92.1$$

Thus the object falls 92.1 meters in 3 seconds.

**TRY THIS** ➡

Solve.

2. a) An object is dropped from the top of the Statue of Liberty, which is 92 meters high. How long does it take to reach the ground?

   b) An object is thrown downward from the top of the statue at an initial velocity of 40 m/s. How long does it take to reach the ground?

   c) How far will an object fall in 1 second, thrown downward from the top of the statue at an initial velocity of 40 m/s?

## Exercise Set 12-7

▌What is the interest rate? (*See Example 1.*)

1. $1000 grows to $1690 in 2 years.
2. $1000 grows to $1210 in 2 years.
3. $2560 grows to $4000 in 2 years.
4. $2560 grows to $3610 in 2 years.
5. $6400 grows to $8100 in 2 years.
6. $6250 grows to $7290 in 2 years.
7. For $1000 to triple itself in 2 years, what would the interest rate have to be?
8. For $1000 to double itself in 2 years, what would the interest rate have to be?

▌▌Solve. For Exercises 9 and 10 use the formula $s = 4.9t^2 + v_0 t$. (*See Example 2.*)

9.  a) An object is dropped 75 m from an airplane. How long does it take to reach the ground?
    b) An object is thrown downward from the plane at an initial velocity of 30 m/s. How long does it take to reach the ground?
    c) How far will an object fall in 2 seconds, thrown downward at an initial velocity of 30 m/s?

10. a) An object is dropped 500 m from an airplane. How long does it take to reach the ground?
    b) An object is thrown downward from the plane at an initial velocity of 30 m/s. How long does it take to reach the ground?
    c) How far will an object fall in 5 seconds, thrown downward at an initial velocity of 30 m/s?

### Calculator Exercises

Solve.

11. $1000 is invested at interest rate $r$. In 2 years it grows to $1166.40. What is the interest rate?
12. $1000 is invested at interest rate $r$. In 2 years it grows to $1144.90. What is the interest rate?
13. $8000 is invested at interest rate $r$. In 2 years it grows to $9856.80. What is the interest rate?
14. $6000 is invested at interest rate $r$. In 2 years it grows to $6615. What is the interest rate?

### Challenge Exercises

Solve.

15. What is the interest rate when $4913 grows to $5832 in 3 years?
16. What is the interest rate when $9826 grows to $13,704 in 3 years?

# 12-8 Equations Quadratic in Form

After finishing Lesson 12-8, you should be able to
▌ solve equations which are quadratic in form.

▌Look for a pattern.

a) $x^4 - 9x^2 + 8 = 0$, let $u = x^2$. Then $u^2 - 9u + 8 = 0$
b) $x - 5\sqrt{x} + 4 = 0$, let $u = \sqrt{x}$. Then $u^2 - 5u + 4 = 0$
c) $(x^2 - 1)^2 - (x^2 - 1) - 2 = 0$, let $u = x^2 - 1$. Then $u^2 - u - 2 = 0$

The equations on the left are not quadratic, but after a substitution we get quadratic equations. Such equations are said to be *quadratic in form*.

To solve such equations, we first make a substitution, solve for the new variable, then solve for the original variable.

**Example 1.** Solve: $x^4 - 9x^2 + 8 = 0$.

Let $u = x^2$. Then we solve the equation found by substituting $u$ for $x^2$.

$$u^2 - 9u + 8 = 0$$
$$(u - 8)(u - 1) = 0$$

$$u - 8 = 0 \quad \text{or} \quad u - 1 = 0$$
$$u = 8 \quad \text{or} \quad u = 1$$

Now we substitute $x^2$ for $u$ and solve these equations.

$$x^2 = 8 \quad \text{or} \quad x^2 = 1$$
$$x = \pm\sqrt{8} \quad \text{or} \quad x = \pm 1$$
$$x = \pm 2\sqrt{2} \quad \text{or} \quad x = \pm 1$$

To check first note that when $x = 2\sqrt{2}$, $x^2 = 8$ and $x^4 = 64$.
Also, when $x = -2\sqrt{2}$, $x^2 = 8$ and $x^4 = 64$. Similarly, when
$x = 1$, $x^2 = 1$ and $x^4 = 1$, and when $x = -1$, $x^2 = 1$ and $x^4 = 1$.
Thus instead of making four checks we can shorten them to two.

Check:  for $\pm 2\sqrt{2}$: $x^4 - 9x^2 + 8 = 0$   for $\pm 1$: $x^4 - 9x^2 + 8 = 0$

$$
\begin{array}{c|c}
(\pm 2\sqrt{2})^4 - 9(\pm 2\sqrt{2})^2 + 8 & 0 \\
64 - 9 \cdot 8 + 8 & \\
0 &
\end{array}
\qquad
\begin{array}{c|c}
(\pm 1)^4 - 9(\pm 1)^2 + 8 & 0 \\
1 - 9 + 8 & \\
0 &
\end{array}
$$

The solutions are $1, -1, 2\sqrt{2}, -2\sqrt{2}$.

**TRY THIS**

Solve.

1. $x^4 - 10x^2 + 9 = 0$

**Example 2.** Solve: $x - 3\sqrt{x} - 4 = 0$.

Let $u = \sqrt{x}$. Then we solve the equation found by substituting $u$ for $\sqrt{x}$.

$$u^2 - 3u - 4 = 0$$
$$(u - 4)(u + 1) = 0$$

$$u = 4 \quad \text{or} \quad u = -1$$

Now we substitute $\sqrt{x}$ for $u$ and solve these equations.

$$\sqrt{x} = 4 \quad \text{or} \quad \sqrt{x} = -1$$

Squaring the first equation we get $x = 16$. The second equation has no real solution since principal square roots are never negative.

The number 16 checks and is the solution.

**TRY THIS**

2. Solve $x + 3\sqrt{x} - 10 = 0$. Be sure to check.

**Example 3.** Solve: $(x^2 - 1)^2 - (x^2 - 1) - 2 = 0$.

Let $u = x^2 - 1$. Then we solve the equation found by substituting $u$ for $x^2 - 1$.

$$u^2 - u - 2 = 0$$
$$(u - 2)(u + 1) = 0$$

$$u = 2 \quad \text{or} \quad u = -1$$

Now we substitute $x^2 - 1$ for $u$ and solve these equations.

$$x^2 - 1 = 2 \quad \text{or} \quad x^2 - 1 = -1$$
$$x^2 = 3 \quad \text{or} \quad x^2 = 0$$
$$x = \pm\sqrt{3} \quad \text{or} \quad x = 0$$

The numbers $\sqrt{3}$, $-\sqrt{3}$, and 0 check. They are the solutions.

**TRY THIS**

Solve.

3. $(x^2 - x)^2 - 14(x^2 - x) + 24 = 0$

**Example 4.** Solve: $t^{\frac{2}{5}} - t^{\frac{1}{5}} - 2 = 0$.

Let $u = t^{\frac{1}{5}}$. Then solve the equation found by substituting $u$ for $t^{\frac{1}{5}}$.

$$u^2 - u - 2 = 0$$
$$(u - 2)(u + 1) = 0$$

$$u = 2 \quad \text{or} \quad u = -1$$

Now we substitute $t^{\frac{1}{5}}$ for $u$ and solve.

$$t^{\frac{1}{5}} = 2 \quad \text{or} \quad t^{\frac{1}{5}} = -1$$
$$t = 32 \quad \text{or} \quad t = -1 \qquad \textit{Principal of powers; raising to the 5th power}$$

The numbers 32 and $-1$ check and are the solutions.

**TRY THIS**

Solve.

4. $t^{\frac{2}{3}} - 3t^{\frac{1}{3}} - 10 = 0$

## Exercise Set 12-8

Solve. (*See Examples 1–4.*)

1. $x - 10\sqrt{x} + 9 = 0$
2. $2x - 9\sqrt{x} + 4 = 0$
3. $x^4 - 10x^2 + 25 = 0$
4. $x^4 - 3x^2 + 2 = 0$
5. $t^{\frac{2}{3}} + t^{\frac{1}{3}} - 6 = 0$
6. $w^{\frac{2}{3}} - 2w^{\frac{1}{3}} - 8 = 0$
7. $z^{\frac{1}{2}} - z^{\frac{1}{4}} - 2 = 0$
8. $m^{\frac{1}{3}} - m^{\frac{1}{6}} - 6 = 0$
9. $(x^2 - 6x)^2 - 2(x^2 - 6x) - 35 = 0$
10. $(1 + \sqrt{x})^2 + (1 + \sqrt{x}) - 6 = 0$
11. $(y^2 - 5y)^2 - 2(y^2 - 5y) - 24 = 0$
12. $(2t^2 + t)^2 - 4(2t^2 + t) + 3 = 0$
13. $w^4 - 4w^2 - 2 = 0$
14. $t^4 - 5t^2 + 5 = 0$
15. $x^{-2} - x^{-1} - 6 = 0$
16. $4x^{-2} - x^{-1} - 5 = 0$
17. $2x^{-2} + x^{-1} - 1 = 0$
18. $m^{-2} + 9m^{-1} - 10 = 0$

### Calculator Exercises

Solve. Check possible solutions by substituting into the original equation.

19. $6.75x - 35\sqrt{x} - 5.36 = 0$
20. $\pi x^4 - \pi^2 x^2 - \sqrt{99.3} = 0$

### Challenge Exercises

Solve.

21. $\left(\dfrac{x^2 - 2}{x}\right)^2 - 7\left(\dfrac{x^2 - 2}{x}\right) - 18 = 0$
22. $\left(\dfrac{x^2 + 1}{x}\right)^2 - 8\left(\dfrac{x^2 + 1}{x}\right) + 15 = 0$
23. $\dfrac{x}{x - 1} - 6\sqrt{\dfrac{x}{x - 1}} - 40 = 0$
24. $5\left(\dfrac{x + 2}{x - 2}\right)^2 - 3\left(\dfrac{x + 2}{x - 2}\right) - 2 = 0$

## CHAPTER 12 REVIEW

Review the material in the chapter. Then see how you have done by trying these review exercises. If you miss an exercise, restudy the indicated lesson.

Solve.

12-1   1.  $4x^2 + 2 = 0$

12-2   2.  $7x^2 - 6x = 0$

12-2   3.  $3x^2 + 10x - 8 = 0$

12-3   4.  $x^2 + 4x - 7 = 0$

12-3   5.  $x^2 + x + 4 = 0$

12-3   6.  Use the square root table, Table 1, in the back of the book to approximate solutions of $x^2 - 8x + 5 = 0$ to the nearest tenth.

12-4   7.  Determine the nature of the solutions of $4y^2 + 5y + 1 = 0$.

12-5   8.  Without solving, find the sum and product of the solutions of $5s^2 - 4s + 2 = 0$.

12-5   9.  Find a quadratic equation whose solutions are $-3$ and $-\frac{1}{2}$.

12-6  10.  Solve $v = \sqrt{2gh}$ for $h$.

12-7  11.  $2000 is invested at interest rate $r$. In 2 years it grows to $3920. What is the interest rate?

12-7  12.  From a height of 200 m, an object is thrown downward at an initial velocity of 20 m/s. How long does it take to reach the ground? Round to the nearest hundredth.

12-8  13.  Solve: $y^4 - 2y^2 + 1 = 0$.

## CHAPTER 12 TEST

Solve.
1. $16x^2 = -9$
2. $5x^2 + 8x = 0$
3. $x^2 - 6x + 7 = 0$
4. $5x^2 + 13x - 6 = 0$
5. $2x^2 - x - 1 = 0$

6. Use the square root table, Table 1, in the back of the book to approximate solutions of $x^2 + 6x + 7 = 0$ to the nearest tenth.
7. Determine the nature of the solutions of $t^2 - 12t + 12 = 0$.
8. Without solving, find the sum and product of the solutions of $6y^2 + 8y - 7 = 0$.
9. Find a quadratic equation whose solutions are $3 + \sqrt{2}$ and $3 - \sqrt{2}$.
10. Solve $A^2 + a^2 = 1$ for $A$.
11. $2000 is invested at interest rate $r$. In 2 years it grows to $3380. What is the interest rate?
12. An object is dropped from a height of 980 m. How long does it take to reach the ground?
13. Solve: $(x^2 + 1)^2 - 15(x^2 + 1) + 50 = 0$.

## Ready for Quadratic Functions?

3-1  1.  Graph:  $2y = \frac{1}{3}x - 1$.

3-2  2.  Find the intercepts of $2x - 5y = 10$.

7-4  Factor by completing the square.

    3.  $x^2 - 8x + 12$

    4.  $x^2 - 3x - 4$

8-3  5.  Which of the figures is symmetric with respect to the given line?

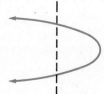

a)                                      b)

8-5  6.  Which are graphs of functions?

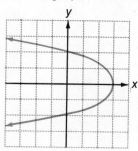

a)                                      b)

Given this graph of $y = f(x)$,

8-7  7.  Graph $y = f(x) - 2$.

8-7  8.  Graph $y = f(x + 2)$.

8-8  9.  Graph $y = 2f(x)$.

8-8  10.  Graph $y = -\frac{1}{2}f(x)$.

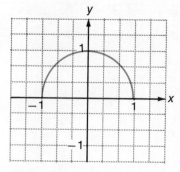

# Chapter 13
# Quadratic Functions

The price of pizza can be expressed as a quadratic function of diameter.

# 13-1 Graphs of $f(x) = ax^2$

After finishing Lesson 13-1, you should be able to
**I** graph a function $f(x) = ax^2$ and determine the vertex and the line of symmetry.
**II** graph a function $f(x) = a(x - h)^2$ and determine the vertex and the line of symmetry.

## I Graphs of $f(x) = ax^2$

A quadratic function can be described using a second degree polynomial with real coefficients.

### DEFINITION

A *quadratic function* is a function that can be described as follows: $f(x) = ax^2 + bx + c, a \neq 0$.

Graphs of quadratic functions are called *parabolas*.
  Consider the graph of $f(x) = x^2$ shown among those at the right. This function is even because $f(-x) = f(x)$ for all $x$. Thus the $y$-axis is a line of symmetry. The point $(0, 0)$, where the graph crosses the line of symmetry, is called the *vertex* of the parabola.
  Next consider $f(x) = ax^2$, where $a$ is a positive number. By Theorem 8-9, we know the following about its graph.

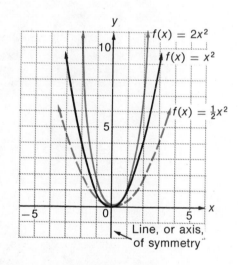

  Compared with the graph of $f(x) = x^2$,
  a) if $|a| > 1$ the graph is stretched vertically.
  b) if $|a| < 1$ the graph is shrunk vertically.

**TRY THIS**

1. a)  Graph $f(x) = 3x^2$.
   b)  Does the graph open upward or downward?
   c)  What is the line of symmetry?
   d)  What is the vertex?

Now consider $f(x) = ax^2$, where $a$ is negative. By Theorem 8-9, we know the following.

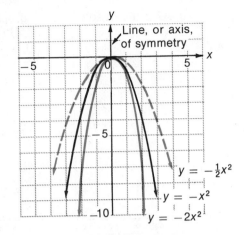

Compared with the graph of $f(x) = x^2$,
a)  If $|a| > 1$, the graph is stretched vertically.
b)  If $|a| < 1$ the graph is shrunk vertically.
c)  Since $a < 0$, the graph is reflected across the $x$-axis.

**TRY THIS** ➡

2.  a)  Graph $f(x) = -\frac{1}{4}x^2$
    b)  Does the graph open upward or downward?
    c)  What is the line of symmetry?
    d)  What is the vertex?

## ‖ Graphs of $f(x) = a(x - h)^2$

In $f(x) = ax^2$, let us replace $x$ by $x - h$. By Theorem 8-8, if $h$ is positive the graph will be translated to the right. If $h$ is negative the translation will be to the left. The line, or axis, of symmetry and the vertex will also be translated the same way. Thus for $f(x) = a(x - h)^2$

the line, or axis, of symmetry is $x = h$, and the vertex is $(h, 0)$.

**Example.**  a)  Graph $f(x) = 2x^2$.

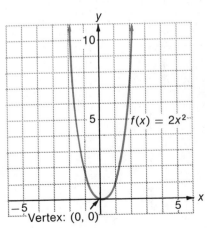

**b)** Use the graph in a) to graph $f(x) = 2(x + 3)^2$.

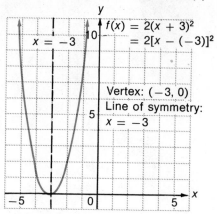

$f(x) = 2(x + 3)^2$
$= 2[x - (-3)]^2$

$x = -3$

Vertex: $(-3, 0)$
Line of symmetry:
$x = -3$

**c)** Use the graph in a) to graph $f(x) = 2(x - 1)^2$.

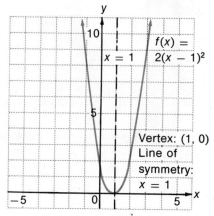

$f(x) = 2(x - 1)^2$

$x = 1$

Vertex: $(1, 0)$
Line of
symmetry:
$x = 1$

**d)** Use the graph in a) to graph $f(x) = -2(x - 1)^2$.

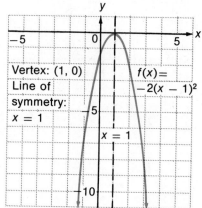

Vertex: $(1, 0)$
Line of
symmetry:
$x = 1$

$f(x) = -2(x - 1)^2$

$x = 1$

**TRY THIS** ➡

3. a) Graph $f(x) = 3x^2$.
   b) Use the graph in a) to graph $f(x) = 3(x - 2)^2$.
   c) What is the vertex?
   d) What is the line of symmetry?
   e) Does the graph open upward or downward?
   f) Is the graph of $f(x) = 3(x - 2)^2$ a horizontal translation to the left or to the right?

4. a) Graph $f(x) = -3x^2$.
   b) Use the graph in a) to graph $f(x) = -3(x + 2)^2 = -3[x - (-2)]^2$.
   c) What is the vertex?
   d) What is the line of symmetry?
   e) Does the graph open upward or downward?
   f) Is the graph of $f(x) = -3(x + 2)^2$ a horizontal translation to the left or to the right?

## Exercise Set 13-1

▌▌For each of the following functions,

    a) graph the function.
    b) find the vertex.
    c) find the line of symmetry.

*(See the Example.)*

1. $f(x) = x^2$
2. $f(x) = -x^2 \ (-x^2 = -1 \cdot x^2)$
3. $f(x) = -4x^2$
4. $f(x) = 2x^2$
5. $f(x) = (x - 3)^2$
6. $f(x) = (x - 7)^2$
7. $f(x) = 2(x - 3)^2$
8. $f(x) = -4(x - 7)^2$
9. $f(x) = -2(x + 9)^2$
10. $f(x) = 2(x + 7)^2$
11. $f(x) = 3(x - 1)^2$
12. $f(x) = -4(x - 2)^2$
13. $f(x) = -2(x + \frac{1}{2})^2$
14. $f(x) = -3(x - \frac{1}{2})^2$

## Challenge Exercises

Graph these quadratic inequalities.

15. $y \le x^2$
16. $y > x^2$
17. $y > 2x^2$
18. $y \le 2x^2$
19. $y < -x^2$
20. $y \ge -x^2$

# 13-2 Graphs of $f(x) = a(x - h)^2 + k$

After finishing Lesson 13-2, you should be able to
**I** graph a function $f(x) = a(x - h)^2 + k$ and determine the vertex, the line of symmetry, and the maximum value or minimum value.
**II** without graphing determine the vertex, the line of symmetry, and the maximum or minimum value of a function $f(x) = a(x - h)^2 + k$.

## I Graphs of $f(x) = a(x - h)^2 + k$

In $f(x) = a(x - h)^2$, let us replace $f(x)$ by $f(x) - k$. This amounts to the same thing as replacing the right side by $a(x - h)^2 + k$. By Theorem 8-7, we know that the graph will be translated upward if $k$ is positive and downward if $k$ is negative.

The vertex will be translated the same way. The line, or axis, of symmetry will not be affected. Thus, for $f(x) = a(x - h)^2 + k$,

the line of symmetry is $x = h$,
the vertex is $(h, k)$.

The maximum or the minimum function value occurs at the vertex.

If a graph opens upward ($a > 0$) there is a minimum function value, $k$.
If a graph opens downward ($a < 0$) there is a maximum function value $k$.

**Example 1.**

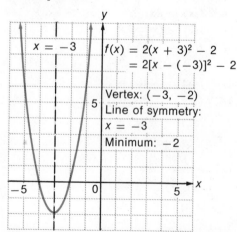

$x = -3$

$f(x) = 2(x + 3)^2 - 2$
$\quad\quad = 2[x - (-3)]^2 - 2$

Vertex: $(-3, -2)$
Line of symmetry:
$x = -3$
Minimum: $-2$

**Example 2.**

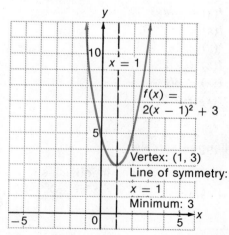

$x = 1$

$f(x) = 2(x - 1)^2 + 3$

Vertex: $(1, 3)$
Line of symmetry:
$x = 1$
Minimum: $3$

**Example 3.**

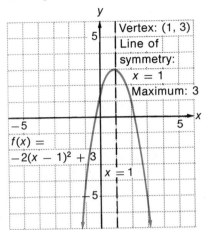

Vertex: (1, 3)
Line of symmetry: $x = 1$
Maximum: 3

$f(x) = -2(x - 1)^2 + 3$

$x = 1$

**TRY THIS** ➡

1. a) Graph $f(x) = 3(x - 2)^2 + 4$.
   b) What is the vertex?
   c) What is the line of symmetry?
   d) Is there a minimum? If so, what is it?
   e) Is there a maximum? If so, what is it?

2. a) Graph $f(x) = -3(x + 2)^2 - 1$
      $\qquad = -3[x - (-2)]^2 - 1$
   b) What is the vertex?
   c) What is the line of symmetry?
   d) Is there a minimum? If so, what is it?
   e) Is there a maximum? If so, what is it?

## ▮ Analyzing $f(x) = a(x - h)^2 + k$ Without Graphing

Without actually graphing, we can determine a lot of information about a function

$$f(x) = a(x - h)^2 + k.$$

The following table contains examples.

| Function | $f(x) = 3(x - \frac{1}{4})^2 - 2$ | $g(x) = -3(x + 5)^2 + 7$ $= -3[x - (-5)]^2 + 7$ |
|---|---|---|
| a) What is the vertex? | $(\frac{1}{4}, -2)$ | $(-5, 7)$ |
| b) What is the line of symmetry? | $x = \frac{1}{4}$ | $x = -5$ |
| c) Is there a maximum? What is it? | No, graph extends upward, $3 > 0$ | Yes, 7, graph extends downward, $-3 < 0$ |
| d) Is there a minimum? What is it? | Yes, $-2$, graph extends upward, $3 > 0$ | No, graph extends downward, $-3 < 0$ |

**TRY THIS**

Without graphing, answer the following questions for each function.

a) What is the vertex?
b) What is the line of symmetry?
c) Is there a minimum? If so, what is it?
d) Is there a maximum? If so, what is it?

3. $f(x) = (x - 5)^2 + 40$
4. $f(x) = -3(x - 5)^2$
5. $f(x) = 2(x + \frac{3}{4})^2 - 6$
6. $f(x) = -\frac{1}{4}(x + 9)^2 + 3$

## Exercise Set 13-2

▮ For each of the following,

a) graph the function.
b) find the vertex.
c) find the line of symmetry.
d) find the maximum value, or the minimum value.

*(See Examples 1–3.)*

1. $f(x) = (x - 3)^2 + 1$
3. $f(x) = (x + 1)^2 - 2$
5. $f(x) = 2(x - 1)^2 - 3$
7. $f(x) = -3(x + 4)^2 + 1$

2. $f(x) = (x + 2)^2 - 3$
4. $f(x) = (x - 1)^2 + 2$
6. $f(x) = 2(x + 1)^2 + 4$
8. $f(x) = -2(x - 5)^2 - 3$

▮▮ Without graphing,

a) find the vertex.
b) find the line of symmetry.
c) find the maximum value, or the minimum value.

*(See page 401.)*

9. $f(x) = 8(x - 9)^2 + 5$
11. $f(x) = 5(x + \frac{1}{4})^2 - 13$
13. $f(x) = -7(x - 10)^2 - 20$
15. $f(x) = \sqrt{2}(x + 4.58)^2 + 65\pi$

10. $f(x) = 10(x + 5)^2 - 8$
12. $f(x) = 6(x - \frac{1}{4})^2 + 19$
14. $f(x) = -9(x + 12)^2 + 23$
16. $f(x) = 4\pi(x - 38.2)^2 - \sqrt{34}$

# 13-3 Standard Form for Quadratic Functions

After finishing Lesson 13-3, you should be able to
■ given a function described by $f(x) = ax^2 + bx + c$, complete the square to express it as $f(x) = a(x - h)^2 + k$. Then find the vertex, line of symmetry, and the maximum value or the minimum value.
■■ solve maximum and minimum problems involving quadratic functions.

## ■ Completing the Square

Consider a quadratic function described by

$$f(x) = ax^2 + bx + c.$$

By completing the square we can describe it

$$f(x) = a(x - h)^2 + k.$$

**Example 1.** For $f(x) = x^2 - 6x + 4$,
**a)** find an equation of the type $f(x) = a(x - h)^2 + k$.
**b)** find the vertex, line of symmetry, and the maximum or minimum value.

**a)** $f(x) = x^2 - 6x + 4$
$\quad\quad = (x^2 - 6x) + 4$

We complete the square inside the parentheses. We take half the $x$ coefficient:

$$\tfrac{1}{2} \cdot (-6) = -3$$

We square it:

$$(-3)^2 = 9$$

Then we add $9 - 9$ inside the parentheses.

$f(x) = (x^2 - 6x + 9 - 9) + 4$
$\quad\quad = (x^2 - 6x + 9) + (-9 + 4)$   *Rearranging terms*
$\quad\quad = 1 \cdot (x - 3)^2 - 5$

**b)** The vertex is $(3, -5)$.
The line of symmetry is $x = 3$.
Since the coefficient, 1, is positive, there is a minimum function value. It is $-5$.

**TRY THIS** ⟹

> 1. For $f(x) = x^2 - 4x + 7$,
>    a) find an equation of the type $f(x) = a(x - h)^2 + k$.
>    b) find the vertex, line of symmetry, and the maximum or minimum value.

**Example 2.** For $f(x) = -2x^2 + 10x - 7$,
**a)** find an equation of the type $f(x) = a(x - h)^2 + k$.
**b)** find the vertex, line of symmetry, and the maximum or minimum value.

**a)** We first factor the expression $-2x^2 + 10x$. Then we proceed as before

$$f(x) = -2x^2 + 10x - 7$$

We "remove" $-2$ from the first two terms. This makes the coefficient of $x^2$ inside the parentheses a 1.

$$f(x) = -2(x^2 - 5x) - 7$$

We take half of the $x$-coefficient and square it, to get $\frac{25}{4}$. Then we add $\frac{25}{4} - \frac{25}{4}$ inside the parentheses.

$$
\begin{aligned}
f(x) &= -2(x^2 - 5x + \tfrac{25}{4} - \tfrac{25}{4}) - 7 \\
&= -2(x^2 - 5x + \tfrac{25}{4}) + 2(\tfrac{25}{4}) - 7 \qquad \text{\textit{Multiplying by} } -2, \text{ \textit{using the distributive}} \\
&= -2(x - \tfrac{5}{2})^2 + \tfrac{11}{2} \qquad\qquad\qquad \text{\textit{law, and rearranging terms}}
\end{aligned}
$$

**b)** The vertex is $(\frac{5}{2}, \frac{11}{2})$.
The line of symmetry is $x = \frac{5}{2}$.
The coefficient $-2$ is negative, so there is a maximum. It is $\frac{11}{2}$.

**TRY THIS**

> 2. For $f(x) = -4x^2 + 12x - 5$,
> a) find an equation of the type $f(x) = a(x - h)^2 + k$.
> b) find the vertex, line of symmetry, and the maximum or minimum value.

## ıı Maximum and Minimum Problems

Some maximum or minimum problems involve quadratic functions. To solve such a problem, we translate by finding the appropriate function. Then we find the maximum or minimum value of that function.

**Example 3.** What are the dimensions of the largest rectangular pen that can be enclosed with 64 meters of fence?

We make a drawing and label it.
The perimeter must be 64 m,
so we have

$$2w + 2l = 64. \qquad \textbf{(1)}$$

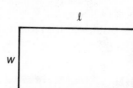

We wish to find the maximum area, so we try to find a quadratic function for the area.

$$A = lw$$

Solving **(1)** for $l$, we get $l = 32 - w$.
Substituting, we get

$$A = (32 - w)w$$
$$= -w^2 + 32w$$

Completing the square, we get

$$A = -(w - 16)^2 + 256$$

The maximum function value is 256. It occurs when $w = 16$. Thus the dimensions are 16 m by 16 m.

**TRY THIS** ➡

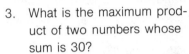

3. What is the maximum product of two numbers whose sum is 30?
4. What are the dimensions of the largest rectangular pen that can be enclosed with 100 meters of fence?

## Exercise Set 13-3

▌For each function,

    a) find an equation of the type $f(x) = a(x - h)^2 + k$.
    b) find the vertex, line of symmetry, and the maximum or minimum value.

(*See Examples 1 and 2.*)

1. $f(x) \doteq x^2 - 2x - 3$
3. $f(x) = -x^2 + 4x + 6$
5. $f(x) = x^2 + 3x - 10$
7. $f(x) = x^2 - 9x$
9. $f(x) = 3x^2 - 24x + 50$
11. $f(x) = \frac{3}{4}x^2 + 9x$
13. $f(x) = -2x^2 + 2x + 1$

2. $f(x) = x^2 + 2x - 5$
4. $f(x) = -x^2 - 4x + 3$
6. $f(x) = x^2 + 5x + 4$
8. $f(x) = x^2 + x$
10. $f(x) = 4x^2 + 8x - 3$
12. $f(x) = \frac{3}{2}x^2 - 3x$
14. $f(x) = -2x^2 - 2x + 3$

▌▌(*See Example 3.*)

15. A rancher is fencing off a rectangular area with a fixed perimeter of 76 m. What dimensions would yield the maximum area? What is the maximum area?

16. A carpenter is building a rectangular room with a fixed perimeter of 68 m. What dimensions would yield the maximum area? What is the maximum area?

17. What is the maximum product of two numbers whose sum is 22? What numbers yield this product?

18. What is the maximum product of two numbers whose sum is 45? What numbers yield this product?

19. What is the minimum product of two numbers whose difference is 4? What are the numbers?

20. What is the minimum product of two numbers whose difference is 6? What are the numbers?

21. What is the minimum product of two numbers whose difference is 5? What are the numbers?

22. What is the minimum product of two numbers whose difference is 7? What are the numbers?

---

**Calculator Exercises**

Find the maximum or minimum value for each function.

23. $f(x) = 2.31x^2 - 3.135x - 5.89$    24. $f(x) = -18.8x^2 + 7.92x + 6.18$

**Challenge Exercises**

25. What is the minimum product of two numbers whose difference is 4.932? What are the numbers?

26. The sum of the base and height of a triangle is 20. Find the dimensions for which the area is a maximum.

27. Find the dimensions and area of the largest rectangle which can be inscribed as shown in a right triangle ABC whose sides have lengths 9 cm, 12 cm, and 15 cm.

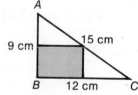

28. Bea Yeld wants to build a rectangular fence near a river. She is going to use 120 m of fencing. What is the largest area she can enclose? Note that she does not fence in the side next to the river.

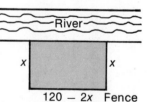

---

**COMPUTER NOTE: Traffic Flow**

Some cities use computers to keep traffic flowing during rush hours. The computers are linked to traffic lights. During rush hours, the computers receive information about the flow of cars. Then the computers adjust the timing of traffic signals to prevent traffic jams.

# 13-4 x-Intercepts and Graphs

After finishing Lesson 12-4, you should be able to
▌ find the x-intercepts of the graph of a quadratic function, if they exist.

▌The points at which a graph crosses the x-axis are
called its x-*intercepts*. These are of course the
points at which $y = 0$.

   To find the x-intercepts of a quadratic function
$f(x) = ax^2 + bx + c$ we solve the equation

   $0 = ax^2 + bx + c$.

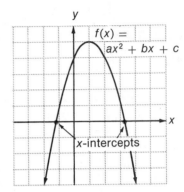

**Example.** Find the x-intercepts of the graph of
$f(x) = x^2 - 2x - 2$.

We solve the equation

   $0 = x^2 - 2x - 2$.

The equation is difficult to factor, so we use the quadratic
formula and get $x = 1 \pm \sqrt{3}$. Thus the x-intercepts are
$(1 - \sqrt{3}, 0)$ and $(1 + \sqrt{3}, 0)$. We sometimes refer to the
x-coordinates of these points as *intercepts*.

**TRY THIS** ▶

Find the x-intercepts.

1. $f(x) = x^2 - 2x - 5$

The discriminant, $b^2 - 4ac$, tells us how many real number solutions the equation $0 = ax^2 + bx + c$ has, so it also indicates
how many intercepts there are. Compare.

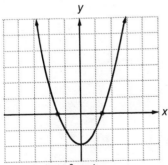

$y = ax^2 + bx + c$
$b^2 - 4ac > 0$
Two real solutions
Two x-intercepts

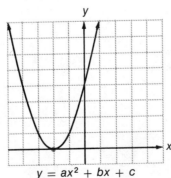

$y = ax^2 + bx + c$
$b^2 - 4ac = 0$
One real solution
One x-intercept

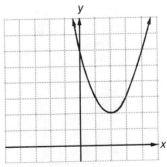

$y = ax^2 + bx + c$
$b^2 - 4ac < 0$
No real solutions
No x-intercepts

**TRY THIS** ➡

Find the *x*-intercepts, if they exist.

2. $f(x) = x^2 - 2x - 3$
3. $f(x) = x^2 + 8x + 16$
4. $f(x) = -2x^2 - 4x - 3$

## Exercise Set 13-4

▌ Find the *x*-intercepts. (*See the Example.*)

1. $f(x) = x^2 - 4x + 1$
3. $f(x) = -x^2 + 2x + 3$
5. $f(x) = 2x^2 - 4x + 6$
7. $f(x) = x^2 - x + 2$
9. $f(x) = 4x^2 + 12x + 9$

2. $f(x) = x^2 + 6x + 10$
4. $f(x) = -x^2 + 3x + 4$
6. $f(x) = 2x^2 + 4x - 1$
8. $f(x) = x^2 - x + 1$
10. $f(x) = 3x^2 - 6x + 1$

### Calculator Exercises

Find the *x*-intercepts.

11. $f(x) = 0.05x^2 - 4.735x + 100.23$

12. $f(x) = 1.13x^2 + 2.809x - 7.114$

### Challenge Exercises

Graph these quadratic inequalities.

13. $y < x^2 - 4x - 1$
15. $y > 3x^2 + 6x + 2$

14. $y \geq x^2 + 3x - 4$
16. $y > 2x^2 + 4x - 2$

### HISTORICAL NOTE: Parabolas

In ancient Greece, pebbles were used to make calculations. Pebbles also can be used to demonstrate an important curve, the parabola. Simply toss a pebble into the air. The path it describes is a parabola. Wind or air resistance will affect the path a little, so it won't be a perfect parabola. But it will be close. A pop fly in baseball and a punt in football follow parabolic paths.

The first person to notice that the path of a tossed object is a parabola was Galileo. He discovered this fact in the early 1600s.

# 13-5 *Applications of Quadratic Functions*

After finishing Lesson 13-5, you should be able to
- fit a quadratic function to three data points and solve related problems.
- solve problems involving quadratic functions.

## Fitting Quadratic Functions to Data

In many problems, a quadratic function can be used to describe the situation. We can find a quadratic function if we know three inputs and their outputs. Each such ordered pair is called a *data point*.

**Example 1.** Pizza Unlimited has the following prices for pizzas.

| Diameter in cm | Price |
|---|---|
| 20 | $3.00 |
| 30 | $4.25 |
| 40 | $5.75 |

Is price a quadratic function of diameter? Probably so, because the price should be proportional to the area, and the area is a quadratic function of the diameter (the area of a circular region is given by $A = \pi r^2$ or $A = \frac{\pi}{4}d^2$).

**a)** Fit a quadratic equation to the data points (20, 3) (30, 4.25), and (40, 5.75).

**b)** Use the function to find the price of a 35 cm pizza.

**a)** We use the three data points to obtain $a$, $b$, and $c$ in
$f(x) = ax^2 + bx + c$.

$$3.00 = a \cdot 20^2 + b \cdot 20 + c$$
$$4.25 = a \cdot 30^2 + b \cdot 30 + c$$
$$5.75 = a \cdot 40^2 + b \cdot 40 + c$$

Simplifying, we get the system

$$3.00 = 400a + 20b + c$$
$$4.25 = 900a + 30b + c$$
$$5.75 = 1600a + 40b + c$$

We solve this system obtaining (0.00125, 0.0625, 1.25).
$a = 0.00125$, $b = 0.0625$, and $c = 1.25$. Thus the function
$f(x) = 0.00125x^2 + 0.0625x + 1.25$.

**b)** To find the price of 35-cm pizza, we find $f(35)$:

$$f(35) = 0.00125(35)^2 + 0.0625(35) + 1.25$$
$$= \$4.97 \quad \textit{Rounded to the nearest cent}$$

It should be noted that this price function always gives results greater than \$1.25 since $f(0) = 1.25$. The \$1.25 is the
fixed cost involved in making a pizza.

**TRY THIS**

1. Find the quadratic function
   that fits the data points
   $(1, 0)$, $(-1, 4)$, and $(2, 1)$.
2. The following table shows
   the accident records in a
   city. It has values that a
   quadratic function will fit.

| Age of driver | Number of accidents (in a year) |
|---|---|
| 20 | 400 |
| 40 | 150 |
| 60 | 400 |

a) Assuming that a quad-
   ratic function will describe the situation,
   find the number of ac-
   cidents as a function of
   age.
b) Use the function to calculate the number of
   accidents a typical 16-
   year-old is involved in.

## ॥ Solving Problems

A theory from physics shows that when an object
such as a bullet or ball is shot or thrown upward
with an initial velocity $v_0$, its height is given, approximately, by a quadratic function.

$$s = -4.9t^2 + v_0 t + h,$$

where $h$ is the starting height (in meters), $s$ is the actual height
(in meters), and $t$ is the time from projection in seconds.

**Example 2.** A model rocket is fired upward. At the end of the burn it has an upward velocity of 49 m/s and is 155 m high. Find
**a)** its maximum height and when it is attained;
**b)** when it reaches the ground.

**a)** We will start counting time at the end of the burn. Thus $v_0 = 49$ and $h = 155$. We will graph the appropriate function, and we begin by completing the square.

$$s = -4.9\left(t^2 - \frac{49}{4.9}t\right) + 155$$
$$= -4.9(t^2 - 10t) + 155$$
$$= -4.9(t^2 - 10t + 25 - 25) + 155$$
$$= -4.9(t^2 - 10t + 25) + (-4.9)(-25) + 155$$
$$= -4.9(t - 5)^2 + 277.5$$

The vertex of the graph is the point (5, 277.5). The graph is shown at the right. The maximum height reached is 277.5 m and it is attained 5 seconds after the end of the burn.

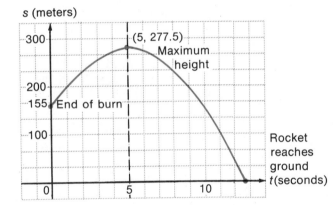

**b)** To find when the rocket reaches the ground, we set $s = 0$ in our equation and solve for $t$.

$$-4.9(t - 5)^2 + 277.5 = 0$$
$$(t - 5)^2 = \frac{277.5}{4.9}$$
$$t - 5 = \sqrt{\frac{277.5}{4.9}}$$
$$t - 5 \approx 7.525$$
$$t \approx 12.525.$$

The rocket will reach the ground about 12.525 seconds after the end of the burn.

**TRY THIS**

3. A ball is thrown upward from the top of a cliff 12 meters high, at a velocity of 2.8 m/s. Find
   a) its maximum height and when it is attained.
   b) when it reaches the ground.

## Exercise Set 13-5

▌Find the quadratic function which fits each set of data points. (*See Example 1.*)

1. (1, 4), (−1, −2), (2, 13)
2. (1, 4), (−1, 6), (−2, 16)
3. (1, 5), (2, 9), (3, 7)
4. (1, −4), (2, −6), (3, −6)

▌▌(*See Example 2.*)

5. *Predicting earnings.* A business earns $38 in the first week, $66 in the second week, and $86 in the third week. The manager graphs the points (1, 38) (2, 66), and (3, 86) and uses a quadratic function to describe the situation.
   a) Find a quadratic function that fits the data.
   b) Using the function, predict the earnings for the fourth week.

6. *Predicting earnings.* A business earns $1000 in its first month, $2000 in the second month, and $8000 in the third month. The manager plots the points (1, 1000), (2, 2000), and (3, 8000) and uses a quadratic function to describe the situation.
   a) Find a quadratic function that fits the data.
   b) Using the function, predict the earnings for the fourth month.

7. a) Find a quadratic function that fits the following data.

| Travel Speed in km/h | Number of Daytime Accidents (For every 200 million km) |
|---|---|
| 60 | 200 |
| 80 | 130 |
| 100 | 100 |

   b) Use your function to calculate the number of daytime accidents which occur at 50 km/h.

8. a) Find a quadratic function that fits the following data.

| Travel Speed in km/h | Number of Nighttime Accidents (for every 200 million km) |
|---|---|
| 60 | 400 |
| 80 | 250 |
| 100 | 250 |

   b) Use the function to calculate the number of nighttime accidents which occur at 50 km/h.

9. A rocket is fired upward from ground level at a velocity of 147 m/s. Find
   a) its maximum height and when it is attained;
   b) when it reaches the ground.

10. A rocket is fired upward from ground level at a velocity of 245 m/s. Find
   a) its maximum height and when it is attained;
   b) when it reaches the ground.

## Calculator Exercises

Find the quadratic function which fits each set of data points.
11.   (20.34, −5.86), (34.67, −6.02), (28.55, −8.46)
12.   (0.789, 245), (0.988, 350), (1.233, 404)

## Challenge Exercises

13.   *Maximizing revenue.* When a theatre owner charges $3 for admission he averages 100 people attending. For each 10¢ increase in admission price the average number attending decreases by 1. What should he charge to make the most money?

### SCIENCE NOTE: Ice Ages

There have been several ice ages in the history of the earth. The most recent one began about 70,000 years ago. For some reason, the earth's average temperature fell about 3 or 4°C. That caused an increase in the accumulation of snow each year. As more and more snow stayed unmelted each year, glaciers formed. They moved slowly southward from the northern ice cap at the rate of about 1 kilometer each 20 years.

The ice sheets made four major advances in the most recent ice age. They reached as far south as St. Louis, Cleveland, and New York City. About 10,000 years ago, they began their last retreat. They are still retreating.

During each ice age, as more water turned to snow and ice, there was less water for the oceans. The level of the oceans dropped by as much as 90 meters. When the ocean level dropped, more land was exposed. Part of the exposed land connected Asia and Alaska. The first people to reach North America probably walked across this land. The land they crossed is now under the water of the Bering Strait, off Alaska.

# 13-6 *Quadratic Variation*

After finishing Lesson 13-6, you should be able to
**I**   given a type of variation, find an equation of variation.
**II**  solve problems involving variation.

## I Finding Equations of Variation

We now consider variation when the equations involved are of second degree, or higher. Consider the equation for the area of a circle.

$$A = \pi r^2$$

We say that the area varies directly as the square of the radius. When $(r_1, A_1)$ and $(r_2, A_2)$ are solutions of the equation we have $A_1 = \pi r_1^2$ and $A_2 = \pi r_2^2$. Then

$$\frac{A_1}{A_2} = \frac{\pi r_1^2}{\pi r_2^2} = \frac{r_1^2}{r_2^2}.$$

A proportion like $\dfrac{A_1}{A_2} = \dfrac{r_1^2}{r_2^2}$ can be helpful in solving problems.

**DEFINITION**

*y* varies directly as the square of *x* if there is some positive number *k* such that $y = kx^2$.

**Example 1.**   Find an equation of variation where *y* varies directly as the square of *x*, and $y = 12$ when $x = 2$.

We write an equation of variation and find *k*.

$y = kx^2$, so $12 = k \cdot 2^2$ and $3 = k$.

Thus $y = 3x^2$.

**TRY THIS**

> 1.   Find an equation of variation where *y* varies directly as the square of *x* and $y = 175$ when $x = 5$.

From the law of gravity, we know that the weight *W* of an object varies inversely as the square of the distance *d* from the center of the earth.

$$W = \frac{k}{d^2}$$

When $(d_1, W_1)$ and $(d_2, W_2)$ are solutions of the equation we have
$W_1 = \dfrac{k}{d_1^2}$ and $W_2 = \dfrac{k}{d_2^2}$. Then

$$\frac{W_1}{W_2} = \frac{\dfrac{k}{d_1^2}}{\dfrac{k}{d_2^2}} = \frac{k}{d_1^2} \cdot \frac{d_2^2}{k} = \frac{d_2^2}{d_1^2}.$$

A proportion like $\dfrac{W_1}{W_2} = \dfrac{d_2^2}{d_1^2}$ can be helpful in solving problems.

**DEFINITION**

$y$ varies inversely as the square of $x$ if there is some positive number $k$ such that $y = \dfrac{k}{x^2}$.

**Example 2.** Find an equation of variation where $W$ varies inversely as the square of $d$, and $W = 3$ when $d = 5$.

$$W = \frac{k}{d^2}, \text{ so } 3 = \frac{k}{5^2} \text{ and } 75 = k.$$

Thus $W = \dfrac{75}{d^2}$.

**TRY THIS**

> 2. Find an equation of variation where $y$ varies inversely as the square of $x$, and $y = \frac{1}{4}$ when $x = 6$.

Consider the equation for the area $A$ of a triangle with height $h$ and base $b$.

$$A = \tfrac{1}{2}bh$$

We say that the area varies *jointly* as the height and the base. From two solutions of the equation we get the proportion

$$\frac{A_1}{A_2} = \frac{b_1 h_1}{b_2 h_2}.$$

**DEFINITION**

$y$ varies jointly as $x$ and $z$ if there is some positive number $k$ such that $y = kxz$.

**Example 3.** Find an equation of variation where $y$ varies jointly as $x$ and $z$, and $y = 42$ when $x = 2$ and $z = 3$.

$$y = kxz, \text{ so } 42 = k \cdot 2 \cdot 3 \text{ and } 7 = k.$$

Thus $y = 7xz$.

**TRY THIS** ➤

The equation

$$y = k \cdot \frac{xz^3}{w}$$

asserts that $y$ varies jointly as $x$ and the cube of $z$, and inversely as $w$.

> 3. Find an equation of variation where $y$ varies jointly as $x$ and $z$, and $y = 65$ when $x = 10$ and $z = 13$.

**Example 4.** Find an equation of variation where $y$ varies jointly as $x$ and $z$ and inversely as the square of $w$, and $y = 105$ when $x = 3$, $z = 20$ and $w = 2$.

$$y = k \cdot \frac{xz}{w^2}, \text{ so } 105 = k \cdot \frac{3 \cdot 20}{2^2} \text{ and } k = 7.$$

Thus $y = 7 \cdot \dfrac{xz}{w^2}$.

**TRY THIS** ➤

> 4. Find an equation of variation where $y$ varies jointly as $x$ and the square of $z$ and inversely as $w$, and $y = 80$ when $x = 4$, $z = 10$, and $w = 25$.

## ▪ Solving Problems

Many problem situations can be described with equations of variation.

**Example 5.** The volume of wood $V$ in a tree varies jointly as the height $h$ and the square of the girth $g$ (girth is distance around). If the volume of a redwood tree is 216 m³ when the height is 30 m and the girth is 1.5 m, what is the height of a tree whose volume is 960 m³ and girth is 2 m?

*Method 1:* First find $k$ using the first set of data. Then solve for $h$ using the second set of data.

$$V = khg^2$$
$$216 = k \cdot 30 \cdot 1.5^2$$
$$3.2 = k$$

Then

$$960 = 3.2 \cdot h \cdot 2^2$$
$$75 = h$$

*Method 2:* Let $h_1$ represent the height of the first tree and $h_2$ the height of the second tree. Use a proportion to solve for $h_2$ without first finding the variation constant.

$$\frac{V_1}{V_2} = \frac{h_1 \cdot g_1{}^2}{h_2 \cdot g_2{}^2}$$

$$\frac{216}{960} = \frac{30 \cdot 1.5^2}{h_2 \cdot 2^2}$$

$$h_2 = \frac{960 \cdot 67.5}{4 \cdot 216}$$

$$h_2 = 75 \text{ m}$$

**Example 6.** The intensity *I* of a TV signal varies inversely as the square of the distance *d* from the transmitter. If the intensity is 23 watts per square meter (W/m²) at a distance of 2 km, what is the intensity at a distance of 6 km?

We use the proportion.

$$\frac{I_1}{I_2} = \frac{d_2{}^2}{d_1{}^2}$$

$$\frac{I_2}{23} = \frac{2^2}{6^2}$$

$$I_2 = \frac{4 \cdot 23}{36}$$

$$I_2 = 2.56 \text{ W/m}^2 \qquad \text{*Rounded to the nearest hundredth*}$$

**TRY THIS** ➡

5. The distance *s* that an object falls when dropped from some point above the ground varies directly as the square of the time *t* it falls. If the object falls 19.6 m in 2 seconds, how far will the object fall in 10 seconds?

6. At a fixed temperature, the resistance *R* of a wire varies directly as the length *l* and inversely as the square of its diameter *d*. If the resistance is 0.1 ohm when the diameter is 1 mm and the length is 50 cm, what is the resistance when the length is 2000 cm and the diameter is 2 mm?

7. In Example 6, why is the equation not appropriate when the distance is 0 km from a transmitter whose initial signal is 316,000 W/m²?

## Exercise Set 13-6

▌Find an equation of variation where: (*See Examples 1–4.*)

1. *y* varies directly as the square of *x*, and $y = 0.15$ when $x = 0.1$.

2. *y* varies directly as the square of *x*, and $y = 6$ when $x = 3$.

3. *y* varies inversely as the square of *x*, and $y = 0.15$ when $x = 0.1$.

4. *y* varies inversely as the square of *x*, and $y = 6$ when $x = 3$.

5. *y* varies jointly as *x* and *z*, and *y* = 56 when *x* = 7 and *z* = 8.

6. *y* varies directly as *x* and inversely as *z*, and *y* = 4 when *x* = 12 and *z* = 15.

7. *y* varies jointly as *x* and the square of *z*, and *y* = 105 when *x* = 14 and *z* = 5.

8. *y* varies jointly as *x* and *z* and inversely as *w*, and $y = \frac{3}{2}$ when *x* = 2, *z* = 3, and *w* = 4.

9. *y* varies jointly as *x* and *z* and inversely as the product of *w* and *p*, and $y = \frac{3}{28}$ when *x* = 3, *z* = 10, *w* = 7, and *p* = 8.

10. *y* varies jointly as *x* and *z* and inversely as the square of *w*, and $y = \frac{12}{5}$ when *x* = 16, *z* = 3, and *w* = 5.

▮▮ Solve. (*See Examples 5 and 6.*)

11. *Stopping Distance of a Car.* The stopping distance *d* of a car after the brakes are applied varies directly as the square of the speed *r*. If a car traveling 60 km/h can stop in 80 m, how many feet will it take the same car to stop when it is traveling 90 km/h?

12. *Area of a Cube.* The area of a cube varies directly as the square of the length of a side. If a cube has an area 168.54 m² when the length of a side is 5.3 m, what will the area be when the length of a side is 10.2 m?

13. *Weight of an Astronaut.* The weight *W* of an object varies inversely as the square of the distance *d* from the center of the earth. At sea level (6400 km from the center of the earth) an astronaut weighs 100 kg. Find his weight when 200 km above the surface of the earth and the spacecraft is not in motion.

14. *Intensity of Light.* The intensity of light *I* from a light bulb varies inversely as the square of the distance *d* from the bulb. Suppose *I* is 90 W/m² when the distance is 5 m. Find the intensity at a distance of 10 m.

15. *Earned Run Average.* A pitcher's earned run average *A* varies directly as the number of earned runs *R* allowed and inversely as the number *I* of innings pitched. In a recent year Tom Seaver had an earned run average of 2.92. He gave up 85 earned runs in 262 innings. How many earned runs would he have given up had he pitched 300 innings? Round to the nearest whole number.

16. *Volume of a Gas.* The volume *V* of a given mass of a gas varies directly as the temperature *T* and inversely as the pressure *P*. If *V* = 231 cm³ when *T* = 42° and *P* = 20 kg/cm², what is the volume when *T* = 30° and *P* = 15 kg/cm²?

## Calculator Exercises

17. *A sighting problem.* The distance $d$ that one can see to the horizon varies directly as the square root of the height above sea level. If a person 19.5 m above sea level can see 15.46 km, how high above sea level must one be to see 54.32 km?

18. *Electrical resistance.* At a fixed temperature and chemical composition, the resistance of a wire varies directly as the length $l$ and inversely as the square of the diameter $d$. If the resistance of a certain kind of wire is 0.112 ohms when the diameter is 0.254 cm and the length is 15.24 m, what is the resistance of a wire whose length is 608.7 m and whose diameter is 0.478 cm?

## Challenge Exercises

19. The area of a circle varies directly as the square of the length of a diameter. What is the variation constant?

20. The area of a circle varies directly as the square of its circumference. What is the variation constant?

21. *The Gravity Model in Sociology.* It has been determined that the average number of telephone calls in a day $N$, between two cities, is directly proportional to the populations $P_1$ and $P_2$ of the cities and inversely proportional to the square of the distance $d$ between the cities. That is, $N = \dfrac{kP_1P_2}{d^2}$.

    a) The population of Indianapolis is 744,624 and the population of Cincinnati is 452,524 and the distance between the cities is 174 km. The average number of daily phone calls between the two cities is 11,153. Find the value $k$ and write the equation of variation.

    b) The population of Detroit is 1,511,482 and it is 446 km from Indianapolis. Find the average number of daily phone calls between Detroit and Indianapolis.

    c) The average number of daily phone calls between Indianapolis and New York is 4270 and the population of New York is 7,895,563. Find the distance between Indianapolis and New York.

    d) Why is this model not appropriate for adjoining cities such as Minneapolis and St. Paul? Sociologists say that as the communication between two cities increases, the cities tend to merge.

## CHAPTER 13 REVIEW

Review the material in the chapter. Then see how you have done by trying these review exercises. If you miss an exercise, restudy the indicated lesson.

Graph.

13-1    1.  $f(x) = -2x^2$

13-1    2.  $f(x) = -2(x + 1)^2$

13-2    3.  $f(x) = -2(x + 1)^2 + 3$

13-2    4.  For $f(x) = -2(x + 1)^2 + 3$, find the vertex, line of symmetry, and the maximum value or the minimum value.

13-3    For each function,
    a) find an equation of the type $f(x) = a(x - h)^2 + k$.
    b) find the vertex, line of symmetry, and the maximum value or minimum value.
    5.  $f(x) = x^2 - 8x + 5$
    6.  $f(x) = \frac{4}{5}x^2 - 16x$

13-4    7.  Find the $x$-intercepts of $f(x) = -2x^2 - 4x + 3$, if they exist.

13-4    8.  Find the $x$-intercepts of $f(x) = -x^2 - 2x + 4$, if they exist.

13-5    9.  Find the quadratic function that fits data points $(1, -3)$, $(-1, 5)$, and $(2, -13)$.

13-5    10. A rocket is fired upward from ground level at a velocity of 98 m/s. Find
    a) its maximum height and when it is attained;
    b) when it reaches the ground.

13-6    11. The area of a sphere varies directly as the square of its radius. If the area is 1257 m² when the radius is 10 m, what is the area when the radius is 3 m?

## CHAPTER 13 TEST

Graph.

1. $f(x) = 2x^2$
2. $f(x) = 2(x - 5)^2$
3. $f(x) = 2(x - 5)^2 - 4$

4. For $f(x) = 10(x + 3)^2 + 14$, find the vertex, line of symmetry, and the maximum or minimum value.

For each function,
a) find an equation of the type $f(x) = a(x - h)^2 + k$.
b) find the vertex, line of symmetry, and the maximum or minimum value.

5. $f(x) = -x^2 - 6x + 7$
6. $f(x) = 2x^2 - 10x - 7$

7. Find the $x$-intercepts of $f(x) = 2x^2 - 5x + 8$, if they exist.
8. Find the $x$-intercepts of $f(x) = -x^2 - 2x + 2$, if they exist.
9. Find the quadratic equation which fits the data points $(-1, 6)$, $(1, 4)$, and $(2, 9)$.
10. An appliance store sells 10 TV's the first month, 20 TV's the second month, and 40 TV's the third month. The manager graphs the points $(1, 10)$, $(2, 20)$, and $(3, 40)$, and finds that a quadratic function might fit the data.
    a) Find a quadratic function that fits the data.
    b) Using your function, predict the sales for the fourth month.
11. The time $T$ which it takes a group of people to do a certain job varies inversely as the product of the number of people and the time $t$, in hours per day, they work. If 16 people work 5 hours per day they can complete a certain job in 9 days. How many days will it take 15 people working 6 hours per day to complete the same job?

Science teachers in public high schools specialize in one area of science. Teachers direct students' laboratory activities and scientific problem solving.

Firefighters reduce the destructiveness of fires in towns or cities. Firefighters work as members of teams to reach fires quickly and to control them.

School librarians organize books and other items, and guide student in using them. Librarians work with teachers and supervisors to give in formation.

Construction inspectors visit sites to see that builders have proper permits and meet safety standards. Inspectors may visit a large project many times.

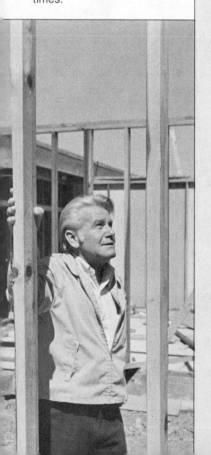

## CAREERS IN GOVERNMENT

The words *careers in government* make many people think of work for the Federal government. In fact, most careers in government in the United States exist on state and local levels. Government careers at these levels have grown significantly since 1950, as the line graph shows. Careers at the Federal level have grown relatively little in that time.

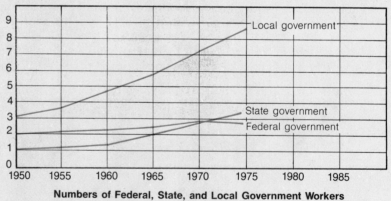

Workers (in millions)

**Numbers of Federal, State, and Local Government Workers**

Professors of mathematics at large state universities do teaching and research. Professors may teach both graduate and undergraduate students.

Social workers help individuals, families, or larger groups cope with problems such as alcoholism, the illness or death of a parent, or legal disputes.

Members of the United States Foreign Service work to support the diplomatic actions of the nation. Their careers usually call for living in various countries.

Soil conservationists for the Federal government advise farmers and ranchers about soil use. Conservationists may draw maps, write plans, and estimate costs.

## Government Employment in the Mid-1970s

Workers (in millions)

| | 0 | 1 | 2 | 3 | 4 | 5 | 6 |

- Education — State and local government / Federal government
- Health and hospitals
- National defense and international relations
- Postal service
- Police protection
- Highways
- General control
- Natural resources
- Financial administration
- All other

About three of every seven government workers are in education. The bar graph above indicates the importance of education in government work. Note that nearly all workers in education are state and local employees, as shown in the graph.

Some people who follow careers in government are pictured here. The projected place of such careers in the total labor force is shown in the circle graph.

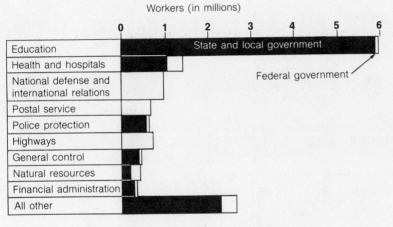

**Circle graph — Projected United States Labor Force in the mid-1980s**

Services: Trade, Government, Various Services, Transportation, communication, and public utilities, Other

Goods: Manufacturing, Construction

**Projected United States Labor Force in the mid-1980s**

## Ready for Equations of Second Degree?

Simplify.

10-2    1. $\sqrt{169}$

10-3    2. $\sqrt{48}$

7-4    Factor by completing the square.

     3. $x^2 - 2x - 15$

     4. $y^2 - 9y + 14$

Graph.

3-1    5. $y = 3x - 1$

13-1    6. $y = 3x^2$

4-2    7. Solve: $6x + 3y = -12$

                $6x - 3y = \phantom{0}18$

Solve.

7-7    8. $x^2 - 9x + 14 = 0$

12-1    9. $x^2 = 5$

12-8    10. $x^4 - 20x^2 + 64 = 0$

# Chapter 14
# Equations of Second Degree

*Some comets travel in elliptical paths. A famous comet, Halley's comet, last seen in 1910 will return in 1985.*

# 14-1 The Distance Formula

After finishing Lesson 14-1, you should be able to
  ▌ use the distance formula to find the distance between any two points in the plane.
  ▌▌ find the coordinates of the midpoint of a segment, given the endpoints.

## ▌ The Distance Formula

The following formula is important in many ways.

**THEOREM 14-1 (The Distance Formula)**
The distance between any two points $(x_1, y_1)$ and $(x_2, y_2)$ is given
by $d = \sqrt{(x_1 - x_2)^2 + (y_1 - y_2)^2}$.

**Example 1.** Find the distance between the points $(8, 7)$ and $(3, -5)$.

We substitute the coordinates into the distance formula.

$$d = \sqrt{(8 - 3)^2 + [7 - (-5)]^2}$$
$$= \sqrt{5^2 + 12^2}$$
$$= \sqrt{25 + 144}$$
$$= \sqrt{169}$$
$$= 13$$

**TRY THIS** ➡

Find the distance between the points.

1. $(-5, 3)$ and $(2, -7)$
2. $(3, 3)$ and $(-3, -3)$

---

### A Proof of Theorem 14-1

The proof of this theorem involves two cases, one where the points are on either a horizontal or vertical line, and the other where the points are not on a horizontal or vertical line. We prove the latter case as follows.

Consider any two points not on a horizontal or vertical line, $(x_1, y_1)$ and $(x_2, y_2)$. These points are vertices of a right triangle as shown. The other vertex is $(x_2, y_1)$. The legs of the triangle have lengths $|x_1 - x_2|$ and $|y_1 - y_2|$. By the Pythagorean Theorem, $d^2 = |x_1 - x_2|^2 + |y_1 - y_2|^2$. We can do away with the absolute value signs since squares of numbers are never negative. Thus $d^2 = (x_1 - x_2)^2 + (y_1 - y_2)^2$.
Taking the principal square root, we get $d = \sqrt{(x_1 - x_2)^2 + (y_1 - y_2)^2}$.

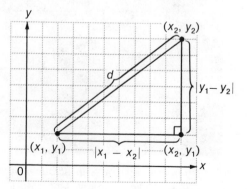

## ▪▪ Midpoints of Segments

The distance formula can be used to verify a formula for finding the coordinates of the midpoint of a segment when the coordinates of the endpoints are known.

### THEOREM 14-2 (The Midpoint Formula)

If the endpoints of a segment are $(x_1, y_1)$ and $(x_2, y_2)$, then the coordinates of the midpoint are $\left(\dfrac{x_1 + x_2}{2}, \dfrac{y_1 + y_2}{2}\right)$.

The coordinates of the midpoint can be found by averaging those of the endpoints.

**Example 2.** Find the midpoint of the segment with endpoints $(-3, 5)$ and $(4, -7)$.

Using the midpoint formula, we get

$$\left(\frac{-3 + 4}{2}, \frac{5 + (-7)}{2}\right), \text{ or } (\tfrac{1}{2}, -1).$$

**TRY THIS** ➡

Find the midpoints of the segments having endpoints as given.

3. $(-2, 1)$ and $(5, -6)$
4. $(9, -6)$ and $(9, -4)$

## Exercise Set 14-1

▪ Find the distance between the points. (*See Example 1.*)

1. $(-3, -2)$ and $(1, 1)$
2. $(5, 9)$ and $(-1, 6)$
3. $(0, -7)$ and $(3, -4)$
4. $(2, 2)$ and $(-2, -2)$
5. $(9, 5)$ and $(6, 1)$
6. $(1, 10)$ and $(7, 2)$
7. $(5, 6)$ and $(5, -2)$
8. $(5, 6)$ and $(0, 6)$
9. $(a, -3)$ and $(2a, 5)$
10. $(5, 2k)$ and $(-3, k)$
11. $(0, 0)$ and $(a, b)$
12. $(\sqrt{2}, \sqrt{3})$ and $(0, 0)$
13. $(\sqrt{a}, \sqrt{b})$ and $(-\sqrt{a}, \sqrt{b})$
14. $(c - d, c + d)$ and $(c + d, d - c)$

▪▪ Find the midpoints of the segments having the following endpoints. (*See Example 2.*)

15. $(-4, 7)$ and $(3, -9)$
16. $(4, 5)$ and $(6, -7)$
17. $(2, -5)$ and $(-9, -10)$
18. $(8, -4)$ and $(-3, 9)$
19. $(2, 2)$ and $(6, 6)$
20. $(-2, 0)$ and $(3, 0)$
21. $(a, b)$ and $(a, -b)$
22. $(-c, d)$ and $(c, d)$

### Challenge Exercises

23. Prove that the distance between pairs of points on either a horizontal line or a vertical line can be found using the distance formula.
24. Prove the midpoint formula, Theorem 14-2.

# 14-2 Circles

After finishing Lesson 14-2, you should be able to
  **I**  given the center and radius of a circle, find an equation for the circle.
  **II** find the center and radius of a circle by putting the equation in the form $(x - h)^2 + (y - k)^2 = r^2$. Then graph the circle.

## I Circles

Some equations of second degree have graphs that are circles.

**DEFINITION**

A *circle* is the set of all points in a plane which are at a fixed distance from a fixed point. The fixed point is the *center*. The fixed distance is the *radius*.

**THEOREM 14-3**

The equation (in standard form) of the circle centered at the origin with radius $r$ is $x^2 + y^2 = r^2$.

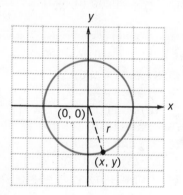

**Example 1.** What is the radius of the circle with the equation $x^2 + y^2 = 25$?

$$r^2 = 25$$
$$r = 5$$

**TRY THIS** ➡

What is the radius of each circle?

1. $x^2 + y^2 = 36$
2. $x^2 + y^2 = 100$
3. $x^2 + y^2 = 50$

### A Proof of Theorem 14-3

We must prove that a point $(x, y)$ is on the circle centered at the origin with radius $r$ if and only if $x^2 + y^2 = r^2$. To prove a sentence '$P$ if and only if $Q$' we must prove 'If $P$, then $Q$' and 'If $Q$, then $P$'. Thus there are two parts to the proof.

i) Assume $(x, y)$ is on the circle. Then it is a distance $r$ from $(0, 0)$. By the distance formula,

$$r = \sqrt{(x - 0)^2 + (y - 0)^2},$$
or $\quad r^2 = x^2 + y^2.$

We have now shown that if $(x, y)$ is on the circle then $x^2 + y^2 = r^2$.

ii) Now assume $x^2 + y^2 = r^2$ is true for a point $(x, y)$. This can be expressed as

$$(x - 0)^2 + (y - 0)^2 = r^2$$

Taking the principal square root we get

$$\sqrt{(x - 0)^2 + (y - 0)^2} = r.$$

Thus the distance from $(x, y)$ to $(0, 0)$ is $r$, so $(x, y)$ is on the circle. We have now shown that if $x^2 + y^2 = r^2$, then $(x, y)$ is on the circle.

The two parts of the proof together show that the equation

$$x^2 + y^2 = r^2$$

gives *all* the points of the circle, *and no others*.

By Theorems 8-7 and 8-8, when a circle is translated so its center is $(h, k)$, we can find an equation for it by replacing $x$ by $x - h$ and $y$ by $y - k$.

### THEOREM 14-4

The equation (in standard form) of a circle with center $(h, k)$ and radius $r$ is $(x - h)^2 + (y - k)^2 = r^2$.

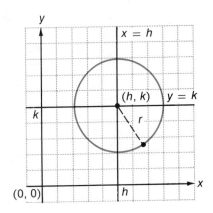

**Example 2.** Find an equation of a circle with center at $(-1, 3)$ and radius $\sqrt{2}$.

$$[x - (-1)]^2 + (y - 3)^2 = (\sqrt{2})^2$$
$$(x + 1)^2 + (y - 3)^2 = 2$$

**TRY THIS**

Find an equation of a circle with center and radius as given.

4. Center: $(5, -2)$
   Radius: $\sqrt{3}$
5. Center: $(-2, -6)$
   Radius: $\sqrt{7}$

## ▪ Finding the Center and Radius

**Example 3.** Find the center and radius of $(x - 2)^2 + (y + 3)^2 = 16$. Then graph the circle.

We may first rewrite the equation as

$$(x - 2)^2 + [y - (-3)]^2 = 4^2.$$

Then the *center* is $(2, -3)$ and the *radius* is 4. The graph is then easy to draw, as shown, using a compass.

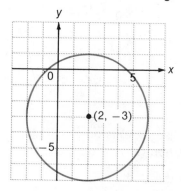

6. Find the center and radius of
   $$(x + 1)^2 + (y - 3)^2 = 4.$$
   Then graph the circle.

**TRY THIS**

Completing the square allows us to find the standard form for the equation of a circle.

**Example 4.** Find the center and radius of the circle $x^2 + y^2 + 8x - 2y + 15 = 0$.

We complete the square twice to get the standard form.

$$(x^2 + 8x + \quad) + (y^2 - 2y + \quad) = -15$$
$$(x^2 + 8x + 16) + (y^2 - 2y + 1) = -15 + 16 + 1$$
$$(x + 4)^2 + (y - 1)^2 = 2$$
$$[x - (-4)]^2 + (y - 1)^2 = (\sqrt{2})^2$$

The *center* is $(-4, 1)$ and the *radius* is $\sqrt{2}$.

7. Find the center and radius of the circle
   $$x^2 + y^2 - 14x + 4y - 11 = 0.$$

**TRY THIS**

## Exercise Set 14-2

▮ Find an equation of a circle with center and radius as given. (*See Example 2.*)

1. Center: $(0, 0)$
   Radius: 7

2. Center: $(0, 0)$
   Radius: $\pi$

3. Center: $(-2, 7)$
   Radius: $\sqrt{5}$

4. Center: $(5, 6)$
   Radius: $2\sqrt{3}$

▮▮ Find the center and radius of each circle. Then graph the circle. (*See Example 3.*)

5. $(x + 1)^2 + (y + 3)^2 = 4$

6. $(x - 2)^2 + (y + 3)^2 = 1$

Find the center and radius of each circle. (*See Examples 3 and 4.*)

7. $(x - 8)^2 + (y + 3)^2 = 40$

8. $(x + 5)^2 + (y - 1)^2 = 75$

9. $x^2 + y^2 = 2$

10. $x^2 + y^2 = 3$

11. $(x - 5)^2 + y^2 = \frac{1}{4}$

12. $x^2 + (y - 1)^2 = \frac{1}{25}$

13. $x^2 + y^2 + 8x - 6y - 15 = 0$

14. $x^2 + y^2 + 6x - 4y - 15 = 0$

15. $x^2 + y^2 - 8x + 2y + 13 = 0$

16. $x^2 + y^2 + 6x + 4y + 12 = 0$

17. $x^2 + y^2 - 4x = 0$

18. $x^2 + y^2 + 10y - 75 = 0$

---

### Calculator Exercises

Find the center and radius of each circle.

19. $x^2 + y^2 + 8.246x - 6.348y - 74.35 = 0$

20. $x^2 + y^2 + 25.074x + 10.004y + 12.054 = 0$

### Challenge Exercises

21. Use Theorem 14-4 to find an equation of a circle satisfying the given conditions.
    a) Center $(0, 0)$, passing through $(\frac{\sqrt{3}}{2}, \frac{1}{2})$
    b) Center $(3, -2)$, passing through $(11, -2)$
    c) Center $(2, 4)$ and tangent (touching at one point) to the *x*-axis

22. Find an equation of a circle such that:
    a) The endpoints of a diameter are $(5, -3)$ and $(-3, 7)$
    b) The endpoints of a diameter are $(7, 3)$ and $(-1, -3)$

23. Prove that $\angle ABC$ is a right angle. Assume point $B$ is on the circle whose radius is $a$ and whose center is at the origin. (*Hint:* Use slopes and an equation of the circle.)

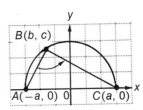

# 14-3 Ellipses

After finishing Lesson 14-3, you should be able to
▌ given an equation of an ellipse, find the center, vertices, and foci. Then graph the ellipse.

▌ An ellipse is defined as follows.

## DEFINITION

An ellipse is the set of all points $P$ in a plane such that the sum of the distances from $P$ to two fixed points $F_1$ and $F_2$ is constant. Each fixed point is called a *focus* (plural: *foci*) of the ellipse.

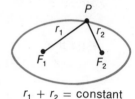

$r_1 + r_2 = $ constant

We first obtain an equation of an ellipse whose center is at the origin and whose foci lie on one of the coordinate axes.

## THEOREM 14-5

The equation (in standard form) of the ellipse centered at the origin with foci on the x-axis is $\dfrac{x^2}{a^2} + \dfrac{y^2}{b^2} = 1$.

From this equation, we see that the graph is symmetric with respect to both axes and the origin. The longer axis of symmetry $\overline{A'A}$ is called the *major axis*. The shorter axis of symmetry $\overline{B'B}$ is called the *minor axis*. The intersection of these axes is called the *center*. The points $A$, $A'$, $B$, and $B'$ are called *vertices*. The constant distance, $F_1P + F_2P$, is $2a$ and $c^2 = a^2 - b^2$.

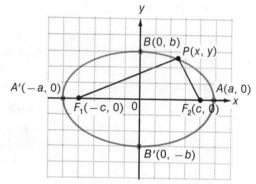

**Example 1.** For the ellipse $x^2 + 16y^2 = 16$, find the vertices and the foci. Then graph the ellipse.

a) We multiply by $\frac{1}{16}$ to get 1 on the right.

$$\frac{x^2}{16} + \frac{y^2}{1} = 1, \text{ or } \frac{x^2}{4^2} + \frac{y^2}{1^2} = 1$$

This is an equation of an ellipse centered at the origin. Thus, $a = 4$ and $b = 1$. Then two of the vertices are $(-4, 0)$ and $(4, 0)$. These are also x-intercepts. The other vertices are $(0, 1)$ and $(0, -1)$. These are also y-intercepts. Since $c^2 = a^2 - b^2$, $c^2 = 16 - 1$, so $c = \sqrt{15}$ and the foci are $(-\sqrt{15}, 0)$ and $(\sqrt{15}, 0)$.

b) The graph is at the right.

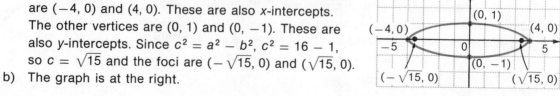

**TRY THIS** ➡️

> For this ellipse, find the vertices and foci. Then graph the ellipse.
>
> 1. $x^2 + 9y^2 = 9$

The foci of an ellipse can be on the *y*-axis.

## THEOREM 14-6

The equation (in standard form) of an ellipse centered at the origin, with foci on the *y*-axis is $\dfrac{x^2}{a^2} + \dfrac{y^2}{b^2} = 1$.

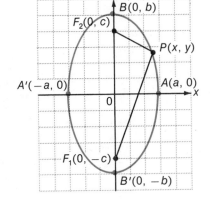

This is the same equation we have in Theorem 14-5. If $a > b$, the foci will be on the *x*-axis. If $b > a$, the foci will be on the *y*-axis.
In this case, the major axis is $\overline{B'B}$, and the minor axis is $\overline{A'A}$. The constant distance, $F_1P + F_2P$, is $2b$ and $c^2 = b^2 - a^2$.

**Example 2.** For the ellipse $9x^2 + 2y^2 = 18$, find the vertices and foci. Then graph the ellipse.

a) We first multiply by $\dfrac{1}{18}$.

$$\frac{x^2}{2} + \frac{y^2}{9} = 1 \text{ or } \frac{x^2}{(\sqrt{2})^2} + \frac{y^2}{3^2} = 1$$

Thus, $a = \sqrt{2}$ and $b = 3$. Then the vertices are $(-\sqrt{2}, 0)$, $(\sqrt{2}, 0)$, $(0, 3)$, and $(0, -3)$.

b) Since $b > a$ the foci are on the *y*-axis and the major axis lies along the *y*-axis. To find *c* in this case we proceed as follows.

$$
\begin{aligned}
c^2 &= b^2 - a^2 \\
&= 9 - 2 \\
&= 7 \\
c &= \sqrt{7}
\end{aligned}
$$

So, the foci are $(0, \sqrt{7})$ and $(0, -\sqrt{7})$.

c) The graph is at the right.

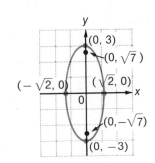

**TRY THIS** ➡

When an ellipse is translated so that its center is $(h, k)$, then by Theorems 8-7 and 8-8, we can find an equation for it by replacing $x$ by $x - h$ and $y$ by $y - k$.

For each ellipse find the vertices and foci. Then graph the ellipse.

2. $25x^2 + 9y^2 = 225$
3. $4x^2 + 2y^2 = 8$

**THEOREM 14-7**

The equation (in standard form) of an ellipse with center $(h, k)$ is $\dfrac{(x - h)^2}{a^2} + \dfrac{(y - k)^2}{b^2} = 1$.

**Example 3.** For the ellipse $16x^2 + 4y^2 + 96x - 8y + 84 = 0$, find the center, vertices, and foci. Then graph the ellipse.

a) We first complete the square to get standard form.

$$16(x^2 + 6x + \quad) + 4(y^2 - 2y + \quad) = -84$$
$$16(x^2 + 6x + 9) + 4(y^2 - 2y + 1) = -84 + 16 \cdot 9 + 4 \cdot 1$$
$$16(x + 3)^2 + 4(y - 1)^2 = 64$$
$$\frac{(x + 3)^2}{2^2} + \frac{(y - 1)^2}{4^2} = 1.$$

The center is $(-3, 1)$, $a = 2$, and $b = 4$.

b) We first find the vertices of the untranslated ellipse $\dfrac{x^2}{2^2} + \dfrac{y^2}{4^2} = 1$.

They are $(2, 0)$, $(-2, 0)$, $(0, 4)$, and $(0, -4)$, and since $c^2 = 16 - 4 = 12$, $c = 2\sqrt{3}$, and its foci are $(0, 2\sqrt{3})$ and $(0, -2\sqrt{3})$.

c) Then the vertices and foci of the translated ellipse are found by translation in the same way in which the center has been translated. The center was translated from $(0, 0)$ to $(-3, 1)$. So we subtract 3 from all $x$-coordinates and add 1 to all $y$-coordinates. The vertices are $(2 - 3, 0 + 1)$, $(-2 - 3, 0 + 1)$, $(0 - 3, 4 + 1)$, $(0 - 3, -4 + 1)$, or

$$(-1, 1), (-5, 1), (-3, 5), (-3, -3).$$

The foci are $(0 - 3, 2\sqrt{3} + 1)$ and $(0 - 3, -2\sqrt{3} + 1)$ or $(-3, 1 + 2\sqrt{3})$ and $(-3, 1 - 2\sqrt{3})$.

d) The graph is as follows.

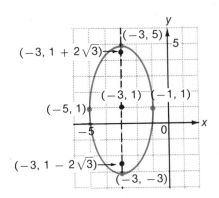

**TRY THIS**

For each ellipse find the center, vertices, and the foci. Then graph the ellipse.

4. $25x^2 + 9y^2 + 150x - 36y + 260 = 0$

5. $9x^2 + 25y^2 - 36x + 150y + 260 = 0$

## Exercise Set 14-3

▌For each ellipse find the center, vertices, and foci. Then graph the ellipse.
(*See Examples 1–3.*)

1. $\dfrac{x^2}{4} + \dfrac{y^2}{1} = 1$

2. $\dfrac{x^2}{1} + \dfrac{y^2}{4} = 1$

3. $\dfrac{(x-1)^2}{4} + \dfrac{(y-2)^2}{1} = 1$

4. $\dfrac{(x-1)^2}{1} + \dfrac{(y-2)^2}{4} = 1$

5. $\dfrac{(x+3)^2}{25} + \dfrac{(y-2)^2}{16} = 1$

6. $\dfrac{(x-2)^2}{25} + \dfrac{(y+3)^2}{16} = 1$

7. $16x^2 + 9y^2 = 144$

8. $9x^2 + 16y^2 = 144$

9. $3(x+2)^2 + 4(y-1)^2 = 192$

10. $4(x-5)^2 + 3(y-5)^2 = 192$

11. $2x^2 + 3y^2 = 6$

12. $5x^2 + 7y^2 = 35$

13. $4x^2 + 9y^2 = 1$

14. $25x^2 + 16y^2 = 1$

15. $4x^2 + 9y^2 - 16x + 18y - 11 = 0$

16. $x^2 + 2y^2 - 10x + 8y + 29 = 0$

17. $4x^2 + y^2 - 8x - 2y + 1 = 0$

18. $9x^2 + 4y^2 + 54x - 8y + 49 = 0$

### Challenge Exercises

19. Find the equation of the ellipse with the following vertices. (*Hint: Graph the vertices.*)
    a) $(2, 0), (-2, 0), (0, 3), (0, -3)$
    b) $(1, 1), (5, 1), (3, 6), (3, -4)$

20. Find an equation of an ellipse satisfying the given conditions.
    a) Center at $(-2, 3)$ with major axis of length 4 and parallel to the $y$-axis, minor axis of length 1.
    b) Vertices $(3, 0)$ and $(-3, 0)$ and containing the point $(2, \frac{22}{3})$.

# 14-4 Hyperbolas

After finishing Lesson 14-4, you should be able to
**I**   given an equation of a hyperbola, find the center, vertices, foci, and asymptotes. Then graph the hyperbola.
**II**  graph equations of hyperbolas of the type $xy = c$, $c \neq 0$.

## I Equations of Hyperbolas

We define a hyperbola as follows.

**DEFINITION**

A *hyperbola* is a set of all points $P$ in a plane such that the absolute value of the difference of the distances from $P$ to two fixed points $F_1$ and $F_2$ is constant. The fixed points $F_1$ and $F_2$ are called *foci*. The midpoint of the segment $F_1F_2$ is called the *center*.

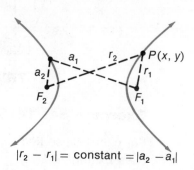

$|r_2 - r_1| = \text{constant} = |a_2 - a_1|$

We first obtain an equation of a hyperbola whose center is at the origin and whose foci lie on one of the coordinate axes.

**THEOREM 14-8**

The equation (in standard form) of a hyperbola centered at the origin with foci on the $x$-axis is $\dfrac{x^2}{a^2} - \dfrac{y^2}{b^2} = 1$.

The two parts of the hyperbola are called *branches*. Points $(a, 0)$ and $(-a, 0)$ are called the *vertices,* and the line segment joining them is called the *transverse axis*. The line segment from $(0, b)$ to $(0, -b)$ is called the *conjugate axis*. By looking at the equation, we can see that the hyperbola is symmetric with respect to the origin, and that the $x$- and $y$-axes are lines of symmetry.

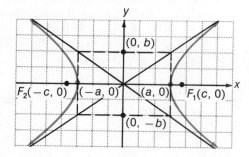

The lines $y = \left(\dfrac{b}{a}\right)x$ and $y = -\left(\dfrac{b}{a}\right)x$ are called *asymptotes*. They have slopes $\dfrac{b}{a}$ and $-\dfrac{b}{a}$.

The constant distance, $|PF_2 - PF_1|$, is $2a$ and $c^2 = a^2 + b^2$.

**Example 1.** For the hyperbola $9x^2 - 16y^2 = 144$, find the vertices, foci, and asymptotes. Then graph the hyperbola.

a)  We first multiply by $\dfrac{1}{144}$ to find the standard form: $\dfrac{x^2}{16} - \dfrac{y^2}{9} = 1$.

Thus $a = 4$ and $b = 3$. The vertices are $(4, 0)$ and $(-4, 0)$.
Since $c^2 = a^2 + b^2$, $c = \sqrt{a^2 + b^2} = \sqrt{4^2 + 3^2} = 5$. Thus
the foci are $(5, 0)$ and $(-5, 0)$. The asymptotes are $y = \frac{3}{4}x$
and $y = -\frac{3}{4}x$.

b) To graph the hyperbola it is helpful to first graph the asymptotes. An easy way to do this is to draw the rectangle shown in the figure. The asymptotes are found by extending the diagonals. Then draw the branches of the hyperbola outward from the vertices toward the asymptotes.

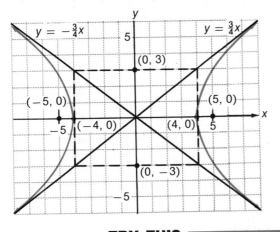

**TRY THIS** ➡

For each hyperbola find the vertices, foci, and asymptotes. Then graph.

1. $4x^2 - 9y^2 = 36$
2. $x^2 - y^2 = 16$

The foci of a hyperbola can be on the $y$-axis.

## THEOREM 14-9

The equation (in standard form) of a hyperbola centered at the origin with foci on the $y$-axis is $\dfrac{y^2}{b^2} - \dfrac{x^2}{a^2} = 1$.

In this case the slopes of the asymptotes are still $\pm\dfrac{b}{a}$ and it is still true that $c^2 = a^2 + b^2$. There are now $y$-intercepts and they are $(0, b)$ and $(0, -b)$. The constant distance, $|PF_2 - PF_1|$, is $2b$.

**Example 2.** For the hyperbola $25y^2 - 16x^2 = 400$, find the vertices, the foci, and the asymptotes. Then graph the hyperbola.

a) We first multiply by $\dfrac{1}{400}$ to find the standard form: $\dfrac{y^2}{16} - \dfrac{x^2}{25} = 1$.

Thus $a = 5$ and $b = 4$. The vertices are $(0, 4)$ and $(0, -4)$.
Since $c = \sqrt{4^2 + 5^2} = \sqrt{41}$, the foci are $(0, \sqrt{41})$ and
$(0, -\sqrt{41})$. The asymptotes are $y = \frac{4}{5}x$ and $y = -\frac{4}{5}x$.

b)  The graph is as follows.

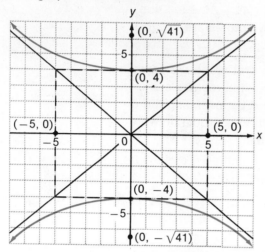

**TRY THIS** ➡

For each hyperbola find the vertices, foci, and asymptotes. Then graph the hyperbola.

3.  $9y^2 - 25x^2 = 225$
4.  $y^2 - x^2 = 25$

If the center of a hyperbola is not at the origin, but at some point $(h, k)$, then its equation is found by replacing $x$ by $x - h$ and $y$ by $y - k$.

**THEOREM 14-10**

The equation (in standard form) of a hyperbola with center $(h, k)$ is

$\dfrac{(x - h)^2}{a^2} - \dfrac{(y - k)^2}{b^2} = 1$ if the transverse axis is parallel to the $x$-axis, or

$\dfrac{(y - k)^2}{b^2} - \dfrac{(x - h)^2}{a^2} = 1$ if the transverse axis is parallel to the $y$-axis.

**Example 3.**  For the hyperbola $4x^2 - y^2 + 24x + 4y + 28 = 0$, find the center, the vertices, the foci, and the asymptotes. Then graph the hyperbola.

a)  We complete the square to find standard form.

$$4(x^2 + 6x + \quad) - (y^2 - 4y + \quad) = -28$$
$$4(x^2 + 6x + 9) - (y^2 - 4y + 4) = -28 + 4 \cdot 9 + (-1 \cdot 4)$$
$$4(x + 3)^2 - (y - 2)^2 = 4$$
$$\frac{(x + 3)^2}{1} - \frac{(y - 2)^2}{4} = 1$$

The center is $(-3, 2)$.

b) Consider the untranslated hyperbola $\dfrac{x^2}{1} - \dfrac{y^2}{4} = 1$. We have

$a = 1$ and $b = 2$. The vertices of this hyperbola are $(1, 0)$ and $(-1, 0)$. Also, $c = \sqrt{1^2 + 2^2} = \sqrt{5}$, so the foci are $(\sqrt{5}, 0)$ and $(-\sqrt{5}, 0)$. The asymptotes are $y = 2x$ and $y = -2x$.

c) The vertices, foci, and asymptotes of the translated hyperbola are found in the same way in which the center has been translated. The vertices are $(1 - 3, 0 + 2)$, $(-1 - 3, 0 + 2)$, or $(-2, 2)$, $(-4, 2)$. The foci are $(-3 + \sqrt{5}, 2)$ and $(-3 - \sqrt{5}, 2)$. The asymptotes are $y - 2 = 2(x + 3)$ and $y - 2 = -2(x + 3)$.

d) The graph is as follows.

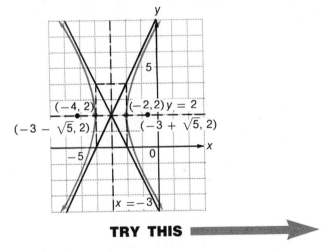

**TRY THIS**

For each hyperbola, find the center, vertices, foci, and asymptotes. Then graph the hyperbola.

5. $4x^2 - 25y^2 - 8x - 100y - 196 = 0$

6. $\dfrac{(y - 2)^2}{9} - \dfrac{(x + 1)^2}{16} = 1$

## ▪ Equations of the Type $xy = c$

Another type of equation whose graph is a hyperbola is the following.

$$xy = c \text{ or } y = \frac{c}{x}, \text{ where } c \neq 0.$$

The coordinate axes are asymptotes.

If $c$ is positive, the branches of the hyperbola lie in the first and third quadrants. If $c$ is negative, the branches lie in the second and fourth quadrants. In either case, the asymptotes are the $x$-axis and the $y$-axis.

**Example 4.** Graph $xy = 12$.

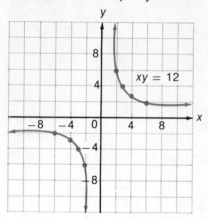

| $x$ | 1 | $-1$ | 2 | $-2$ | 3 | $-3$ | 4 | $-4$ | 6 | $-6$ | 12 | $-12$ |
|-----|---|------|---|------|---|------|---|------|---|------|----|-------|
| $y$ | 12 | $-12$ | 6 | $-6$ | 4 | $-4$ | 3 | $-3$ | 2 | $-2$ | 1 | $-1$ |

Graph.

7. $xy = 3$
8. $xy = -1$

**TRY THIS**

## Exercise Set 14-4

▌ For each hyperbola find the center, vertices, foci, and asymptotes. Then graph the hyperbola. (*See Examples 1–3.*)

1. $\dfrac{x^2}{9} - \dfrac{y^2}{1} = 1$

2. $\dfrac{x^2}{1} - \dfrac{y^2}{9} = 1$

3. $\dfrac{(x - 2)^2}{9} - \dfrac{(y + 5)^2}{1} = 1$

4. $\dfrac{(x - 2)^2}{1} - \dfrac{(y + 5)^2}{9} = 1$

5. $\dfrac{(y + 3)^2}{4} - \dfrac{(x + 1)^2}{16} = 1$

6. $\dfrac{(y + 3)^2}{25} - \dfrac{(x + 1)^2}{16} = 1$

7. $x^2 - 4y^2 = 4$

8. $4x^2 - y^2 = 4$

9. $x^2 - y^2 = 2$

10. $x^2 - y^2 = 3$

11. $x^2 - y^2 - 2x - 4y - 4 = 0$

12. $4x^2 - y^2 + 8x - 4y - 4 = 0$

13. $36x^2 - y^2 - 24x + 6y - 41 = 0$

14. $9x^2 - 4y^2 + 54x + 8y + 41 = 0$

▌▌ Graph. (*See Example 4.*)

15. $xy = 1$

16. $xy = -4$

17. $xy = -8$

18. $xy = 2$

---

### Challenge Exercises

19. Find an equation of a hyperbola having:
    a) Vertices at $(1, 0)$ and $(-1, 0)$; and foci at $(2, 0)$ and $(-2, 0)$.
    b) Asymptotes $y = \frac{3}{4}x$ and $y = -\frac{3}{4}x$ and one vertex $(4, 0)$.

# 14-5 The Parabola

After finishing Lesson 14-5, you should be able to
■ given an equation of a parabola, find the vertex, focus, and the directrix. Then graph the parabola.

■ We define a parabola as follows.

### DEFINITION

A *parabola* is a set of all points $P$ in a plane, equidistant
from a fixed line $l$, called the *directrix,* and a fixed point $F$,
called the *focus*.

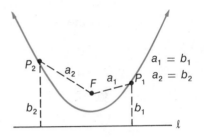

We first obtain an equation of a parabola with focus on the
$y$-axis, directrix parallel to the $x$-axis, and vertex at the origin.

### THEOREM 14-11

The equation (in standard form) of a parabola with focus at
$(0, p)$, directrix $y = -p$, vertex $(0, 0)$, and $y$-axis as the only line
of symmetry is $x^2 = 4py$.

If $p$ is negative in an equation $x^2 = 4py$, the graph is a reflection
across the $x$-axis, hence is still a parabola.

**Example 1.** For the parabola $y = x^2$, find the vertex, the
focus, and the directrix. Then graph.

We first write $x^2 = 4py$.

$$x^2 = 4(\tfrac{1}{4})y.$$

Vertex: $(0, 0)$
Focus: $(0, \tfrac{1}{4})$
Directrix: $y = -\tfrac{1}{4}$

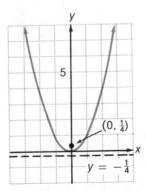

For each parabola find the
vertex, focus, and directrix.
Then graph the parabola.

1. $y = 2x^2$
2. $8y = x^2$
3. $y = -x^2$

**TRY THIS**

The next two theorems follow from Theorem 14-11 by transformations.

### THEOREM 14-12

The equation (in standard form) of a parabola with focus $(p, 0)$, directrix $x = -p$, vertex $(0, 0)$, and $x$-axis as the line of symmetry is $y^2 = 4px$.

**Example 2.** For the parabola $y^2 = -12x$, find the vertex, the focus, and the directrix. Then graph the parabola.

We first write $y^2 = 4px$.

$$y^2 = 4(-3)x$$

Vertex: $(0, 0)$
Focus: $(-3, 0)$
Directrix: $x = -(-3) = 3$

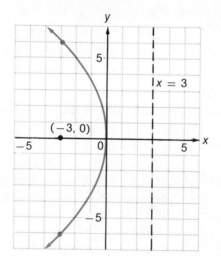

**TRY THIS**

> 4. For the parabola $y^2 = -6x$, find the vertex, focus, and directrix. Then graph the parabola.

### THEOREM 14-13

The equation (in standard form) of a parabola with vertex $(h, k)$, focus $(h, k + p)$, and directrix $y = k - p$, is

$$(x - h)^2 = 4p(y - k).$$

The equation (in standard form) of a parabola with vertex $(h, k)$, focus $(h + p, k)$, and directrix $x = h - p$, is

$$(y - k)^2 = 4p(x - h).$$

**Example 3.**  For the parabola $x^2 + 6x + 4y + 5 = 0$, find the vertex, the focus, and the directrix. Then graph the parabola.

We complete the square.

$$x^2 + 6x \quad = -4y - 5$$
$$x^2 + 6x + 9 = -4y - 5 + 9$$
$$(x + 3)^2 = -4y + 4$$
$$(x + 3)^2 = 4(-1)(y - 1).$$

Vertex: $(-3, 1)$
Focus: $(-3, 1 + (-1))$, or $(-3, 0)$
Directrix: $y = 2$

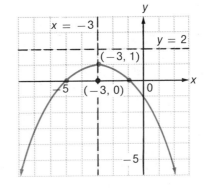

**Example 4.**  For the parabola $y^2 + 6y - 8x - 31 = 0$, find the vertex, the focus, and the directrix. Then graph the parabola.

We complete the square.

$$y^2 + 6y \quad = 8x + 31$$
$$y^2 + 6y + 9 = 8x + 31 + 9$$
$$(y + 3)^2 = 8x + 40$$
$$= 8(x + 5)$$
$$= 4(2)(x + 5)$$

Vertex: $(-5, -3)$
Focus: $(-5 + 2, -3)$, or $(-3, -3)$
Directrix: $x = -5 - 2$
$$x = -7$$

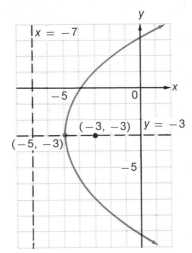

**TRY THIS** ➡

For each parabola, find the vertex, the focus, and the directrix, and graph the parabola.

5.  $x^2 + 2x - 8y - 3 = 0$
6.  $y^2 + 2y + 4x - 7 = 0$

## Exercise Set 14-5

❚ For each parabola find the vertex, focus, and directrix. Then graph the parabola. (*See Examples 1–4.*)

1. $x^2 = 8y$
2. $x^2 = 16y$
3. $y^2 = -6x$
4. $y^2 = -2x$
5. $x^2 - 4y = 0$
6. $y^2 + 4x = 0$
7. $y = 4x^2$
8. $y = \frac{1}{2}x^2$
9. $(x + 2)^2 = -6(y - 1)$
10. $(y - 3)^2 = -20(x + 2)$
11. $x^2 + 2x + 2y + 7 = 0$
12. $y^2 + 6y - x + 16 = 0$
13. $x^2 - y - 2 = 0$
14. $x^2 - 4x - 2y = 0$
15. $y = x^2 + 4x + 3$
16. $y = x^2 + 6x + 10$
17. $4y^2 - 4y - 4x + 24 = 0$
18. $4y^2 + 4y - 4x - 16 = 0$

### Calculator Exercises

For each parabola find the vertex, focus, and directrix.

19. $x^2 = 8056.25y$
20. $y^2 = -7645.88x$

### Challenge Exercises

21. Find an equation of a parabola satisfying the given conditions.
    a) Focus $(4, 0)$, directrix $x = -4$
    b) Focus $(0, \frac{1}{4})$, directrix $y = -\frac{1}{4}$
    c) Focus $(3, 2)$, directrix $x = -4$
    d) Focus $(-2, 3)$, directrix $y = -3$
22. Find equations of the following parabolas.
    a) Line of symmetry parallel to the $y$-axis, vertex $(-1, 2)$, and passing through $(-3, 1)$.
    b) Line of symmetry parallel to the $x$-axis, vertex $(2, 1)$, and passing through $(4, \frac{1}{3})$.

---

### HISTORICAL NOTE: Uses of the Abacus

The abacus is not just an Oriental device. It was used in ancient Greece and Rome. And it is still used in parts of Russia to add restaurant bills and do other calculations.

# 14-6 Systems of Equations

After finishing Lesson 14-6, you should be able to
**▮** solve systems of one first-degree and one second-degree equation algebraically.
**▮▮** solve problems involving systems of one first-degree and one second-degree equation.

## ▮ Algebraic Solutions

We consider systems of one first-degree and one second-degree equation. Let us consider the case in which the graphs are a circle and a line. The drawing shows the three ways in which the two graphs might intersect.

For $L_1$ there is no point of intersection, hence no real solution to the system. For $L_2$ there is one point of intersection, hence one real solution. For $L_3$ there are two points of intersection, hence two real solutions.

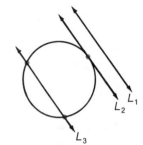

In solving systems where one equation is of first degree and one is of second degree, it is preferable to use the *substitution* method.

**Example 1.** Solve this system algebraically: 
$$x^2 + y^2 = 25 \qquad \textbf{(1)}$$
$$3x - 4y = 0 \qquad \textbf{(2)}$$

First solve the linear equation **(2)** for $x$.

$$x = \tfrac{4}{3}y$$

Then substitute $\tfrac{4}{3}y$ for $x$ in equation **(1)** and solve for $y$.

$$(\tfrac{4}{3}y)^2 + y^2 = 25$$
$$\tfrac{16}{9}y^2 + y^2 = 25$$
$$\tfrac{25}{9}y^2 = 25$$
$$y^2 = 9$$
$$y = \pm 3$$

Now substitute these numbers into the linear equation and solve for $x$.

$$x = \tfrac{4}{3}(3), \text{ or } 4$$
$$x = \tfrac{4}{3}(-3), \text{ or } -4$$

The pairs $(4, 3)$ and $(-4, -3)$ check, so they are solutions.

**TRY THIS** ➡

Solve these systems algebraically.

1. $x^2 + y^2 = 25$
   $y - x = -1$
2. $y = x^2 - 2x - 1$
   $y = x + 3$
3. $y = \dfrac{x^2}{4}$
   $x + 2y = 4$

**Example 2.** Solve the system: $y + 3 = 2x$ **(1)**

$$x^2 + 2xy = -1 \quad \textbf{(2)}$$

First solve the linear equation **(1)** for $y$.

$$y = 2x - 3$$

Then substitute $2x - 3$ for $y$ in equation **(2)** and solve for $x$.

$$x^2 + 2x(2x - 3) = -1$$
$$5x^2 - 6x + 1 = 0$$
$$(5x - 1)(x - 1) = 0 \quad \textit{Factoring}$$

$5x - 1 = 0 \qquad x - 1 = 0 \quad$ *Using the principle of zero products*
$\qquad x = \frac{1}{5} \quad$ or $\qquad x = 1$

Now substitute these numbers into the linear equation and solve for $y$.

$$y = 2(\tfrac{1}{5}) - 3, \text{ or } -\tfrac{13}{5}$$
$$y = 2(1) - 3, \text{ or } -1.$$

The pairs $(\frac{1}{5}, -\frac{13}{5})$ and $(1, -1)$ check, so they are solutions.

**TRY THIS** ➡️

> 4. Solve: $y + 3x = 1$
> $\qquad x^2 - 2xy = 5$

## ❚❚ Solving Problems

**Example 3.** The perimeter of a rectangular field is 204 m and the area is 2565 m². Find the dimensions of the field.

We first translate the conditions of the problem to equations, using $w$ for the width and $l$ for the length.

Perimeter: $2w + 2l = 204$
Area: $lw = 2565$

Now we solve the system

$$2w + 2l = 204$$
$$lw = 2565$$

and get the solution (45, 57). Now we check in the original problem: The perimeter is $2 \cdot 45 + 2 \cdot 57$, or 204. The area is $45 \cdot 57$, or 2565. The numbers check, so the answer is $l = 57$ m, $w = 45$ m.

**TRY THIS** ➡️

> 5. The difference of two numbers is 4 and the difference of their squares is 72. What are the numbers?
>
> 6. The perimeter of a rectangular field is 34 m and the length of a diagonal is 13 m. Find the dimensions of the field.

## Exercise Set 14-6

▮ Solve. (*See Examples 1 and 2.*)

1. $x^2 + y^2 = 25$
   $y - x = 1$

2. $x^2 + y^2 = 100$
   $y - x = 2$

3. $4x^2 + 9y^2 = 36$
   $3y + 2x = 6$

4. $9x^2 + 4y^2 = 36$
   $3x + 2y = 6$

5. $y^2 = x + 3$
   $2y = x + 4$

6. $y = x^2$
   $3x = y + 2$

7. $x^2 + 4y^2 = 25$
   $x + 2y = 7$

8. $y^2 - x^2 = 16$
   $2x - y = 1$

9. $x^2 - xy + 3y^2 = 27$
   $x - y = 2$

10. $2y^2 + xy + x^2 = 7$
    $x - 2y = 5$

11. $3x + y = 7$
    $4x^2 + 5y = 56$

12. $2y^2 + xy = 5$
    $4y + x = 7$

▮▮ (*See Example 3.*)

13. The sum of two numbers is 14 and the sum of their squares is 106. What are the numbers?

14. The sum of two numbers is 15 and the difference of their squares is also 15. What are the numbers?

15. A rectangle has perimeter 28 cm and the length of a diagonal is 10 cm. What are its dimensions?

16. A rectangle has perimeter 6 m and the length of a diagonal is $\sqrt{5}$ m. What are its dimensions?

17. A rectangle has area 20 m² and perimeter 18 m. Find its dimensions.

18. A rectangle has area 2 cm² and perimeter 6 cm. Find its dimensions.

---

### Challenge Exercises

19. Given the area $A$ and the perimeter $P$ of a rectangle, show that the length $L$ and the width $W$ are given by the formulas
    $L = \frac{1}{4}(P + \sqrt{P^2 - 16A})$,
    $W = \frac{1}{4}(P - \sqrt{P^2 - 16A})$.

20. Show that a hyperbola cannot intersect its asymptotes. That is, solve the system
    $$\frac{x^2}{a^2} - \frac{y^2}{b^2} = 1$$
    $$y = \frac{b}{a}x \left( \text{or, } y = -\frac{b}{a}x \right).$$

21. Find an equation of a circle that passes through the points (2, 4) and (3, 3) and whose center is on the line $3x - y = 3$.

---

# 14-7 Two Second-Degree Equations

After finishing Lesson 14-7, you should be able to
∎ solve systems of second-degree equations algebraically.
∎∎ solve problems involving systems of second-degree equations.

## ∎ Algebraic Solutions

We now consider systems of two second-degree equations. Let us consider the case in which the graphs are a circle and a hyperbola. The drawing shows the five ways in which the two graphs might intersect.

| 4 real solutions | 3 real solutions | 2 real solutions | 1 real solution | 0 real solutions |

To solve systems of two second-degree equations we can use either the substitution or the addition method.

**Example 1.** Solve this system: $2x^2 + 5y^2 = 22$ **(1)**
$3x^2 - y^2 = -1$ **(2)**

Here we use the addition method.

$$2x^2 + 5y^2 = 22$$
$$\underline{15x^2 - 5y^2 = -5} \quad \textit{Multiplying by 5 on both sides of \textbf{(2)}}$$
$$17x^2 = 17 \quad \textit{Adding}$$
$$x^2 = 1$$
$$x = \pm 1.$$

If $x = 1$, $x^2 = 1$, and if $x = -1$, $x^2 = 1$, so substituting 1 or $-1$ for $x$ in equation **(2)** we have

$$3 \cdot 1 - y^2 = -1$$
$$y^2 = 4$$
$$y = \pm 2.$$

Thus, if $x = 1$, $y = 2$ or $y = -2$, and if $x = -1$, $y = 2$ or $y = -2$. The possible solutions are $(1, 2)$, $(1, -2)$, $(-1, 2)$, $(-1, -2)$.

Check: Since $(2)^2 = 4$, $(-2)^2 = 4$, $(1)^2 = 1$, and $(-1)^2 = 1$, we
can check all four pairs at one time.

$$\frac{2x^2 + 5y^2 = 22}{\begin{array}{c|c} 2(\pm1)^2 + 5(\pm2)^2 & 22 \\ 2 + 20 & \\ 22 & \end{array}} \qquad \frac{3x^2 - y^2 = -1}{\begin{array}{c|c} 3(\pm1)^2 - (\pm2)^2 & -1 \\ 3 - 4 & \\ -1 & \end{array}}$$

**TRY THIS** ➡

Solve.

1.  $2y^2 - 3x^2 = 6$
    $5y^2 + 2x^2 = 53$

**Example 2.**  Solve the system: $x^2 + 4y^2 = 20$  **(1)**
$xy = 4$  **(2)**

Here we use the substitution method. First solve equation **(2)**
for $y$.

$$y = \frac{4}{x}$$

Then substitute $\frac{4}{x}$ for $y$ in equation **(1)** and solve for $x$.

$$x^2 + 4\left(\frac{4}{x}\right)^2 = 20$$

$$x^2 + \frac{64}{x^2} = 20$$

$$x^4 + 64 = 20x^2 \qquad \textit{Multiplying by } x^2$$

$$x^4 - 20x^2 + 64 = 0$$

$$u^2 - 20u + 64 = 0 \qquad \textit{Letting } u = x^2$$

Then $x = 4$ or $x = -4$ or $x = 2$ or $x = -2$.

Since $y = \frac{4}{x}$, if $x = 4$, $y = 1$; if $x = -4$, $y = -1$; if $x = 2$, $y = 2$;

if $x = -2$, $y = -2$.
The ordered pairs $(4, 1)$, $(-4, -1)$, $(2, 2)$, $(-2, -2)$ check.
They are the solutions.

**TRY THIS** ➡

Solve.

2.  $x^2 + xy + y^2 = 19$
    $xy = 6$

## ⅠⅠ Solving Problems

**Example 3.** The area of a rectangle is 300 m² and the length of a diagonal is 25 m. Find the dimensions.

First draw a picture.

We use *l* for the length and *w* for the width and translate to equations.

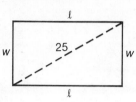

From the Pythagorean theorem: $l^2 + w^2 = 25^2$

Area: $\quad lw = 300$

Now we solve the system

$$l^2 + w^2 = 625$$
$$lw = 300$$

We get (15, 20) and (−15, −20). Now we check in the original problem: $15^2 + 20^2 = 25^2$ and $15 \cdot 20 = 300$, so (15, 20) is a solution of the problem. Lengths of sides cannot be negative so (−15, −20) is not a solution. The answer is $l = 20$ m and $w = 15$ m.

**TRY THIS**

> 3. The area of a rectangle is 2 cm² and the length of a diagonal is $\sqrt{5}$ cm. Find the dimensions of the rectangle.

## Exercise Set 14-7

Ⅰ Solve. (*See Examples 1 and 2.*)

1. $x^2 + y^2 = 25$
   $y^2 = x + 5$

2. $y = x^2$
   $x = y^2$

3. $x^2 + y^2 = 9$
   $x^2 - y^2 = 9$

4. $y^2 - 4x^2 = 4$
   $4x^2 + y^2 = 4$

5. $x^2 + y^2 = 4$
   $16x^2 + 9y^2 = 144$

6. $x^2 + y^2 = 25$
   $25x^2 + 16y^2 = 400$

7. $x^2 + y^2 = 16$
   $y^2 - 2x^2 = 10$

8. $x^2 + y^2 = 14$
   $x^2 - y^2 = 4$

9. $x^2 + y^2 = 5$
   $xy = 2$

10. $x^2 + y^2 = 20$
    $xy = 8$

11. $xy - y^2 = 2$
    $2xy - 3y^2 = 0$

12. $2xy + 3y^2 = 7$
    $3xy - 2y^2 = 4$

▌▌ (*See Example 3.*)

13. The product of two numbers is 156. The sum of their squares is 313. Find the numbers.

14. The product of two numbers is 60. The sum of their squares is 136. Find the numbers.

15. The area of a rectangle is $\sqrt{3}$ m² and the length of a diagonal is 2 m. Find the dimensions.

16. The area of a rectangle is $\sqrt{2}$ m² and the length of a diagonal is $\sqrt{3}$ m. Find the dimensions.

17. A garden contains two square peanut beds. The sum of their areas is 832 m², and the difference of their areas is 320 m². Find the length of each bed.

18. A certain amount of money saved for 1 year at a certain interest rate yielded $7.50. If the principal had been $25 more and the interest rate 1% less, the interest would have been the same. Find the principal and the rate of interest.

## Calculator Exercises

Solve.

19. $18.456x^2 + 788.723y^2 = 6408$
    $106.535x^2 - 788.723y^2 = 2692$

20. $0.319x^2 + 2688.7y^2 = 56{,}548$
    $0.306x^2 - 2688.7y^2 = 43{,}452$

## Challenge Exercises

21. Find an equation of the circle that passes through the points $(4, 6)$, $(-6, 2)$, and $(1, -3)$.

22. Find an equation of the circle that passes through the points $(2, 3)$, $(4, 5)$, and $(0, -3)$.

## SCIENCE NOTE: Halley's Comet

In 1985 you will have a chance to see a once-in-a-lifetime event, Halley's comet. It is named for Edmund Halley, an English astronomer. After the comet appeared in 1682, Halley used mathematics to predict that it would return once every 75 years or so. And it did.

Halley's comet follows a path through the solar system. The path is near the sun at one end and near the planet Pluto at the other.

## CHAPTER 14 REVIEW

Review the material in the chapter. Then see how you have done by trying these review exercises. If you miss an exercise, restudy the indicated lesson.

14-1    1. Find the distance between $(-3, 4)$ and $(7, 0)$.

14-1    2. Find the midpoint of the segment with endpoints $(-3, 4)$ and $(7, 0)$.

14-2    3. Find an equation of the circle with center $(-2, 6)$ and radius $\sqrt{13}$.

14-2    4. Find the center and radius of the circle $2x^2 + 2y^2 - 3x - 5y + 3 = 0$.

14-3    5. Find the center, vertices, and foci of the ellipse $16x^2 + 25y^2 - 64x + 50y - 311 = 0$. Then graph the ellipse.

14-4    6. Find the center, vertices, foci, and asymptotes of the hyperbola $x^2 - 2y^2 + 4x + y - \frac{1}{8} = 0$. Then graph the hyperbola.

14-5    7. Find the vertex, focus, and directrix of the parabola $y^2 = -12x$. Then graph the parabola.

14-6    8. Solve: $\dfrac{x^2}{16} + \dfrac{y^2}{9} = 1$

                  $3x + 4y = 12$

14-6    9. The sum of two numbers is 11 and the sum of their squares is 65. Find the numbers.

14-7   10. Solve: $x^2 + y^2 = 16$

                  $\dfrac{x^2}{16} + \dfrac{y^2}{9} = 1$

14-7   11. The sides of a triangle are 8, 10, and 14. Find the altitude to the longest side.

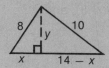

## CHAPTER 14 TEST

1. Find the distance between $(-3, 4)$ and $(7, 6)$.
2. Find the midpoint of the segment with endpoints $(-3, 4)$ and $(7, 6)$.
3. Find an equation of the circle with center $(4, -1)$ and radius 5.
4. Find the center and radius of the circle
   $x^2 + y^2 - 8x + 12y + 49 = 0$.
5. Find the center, vertices, and foci of the ellipse
   $9x^2 + 16y^2 + 36x - 32y - 92 = 0$. Then graph the ellipse.
6. Find the center, vertices, foci, and asymptotes of the hyperbola $8x^2 - 3y^2 = 48$. Then graph the hyperbola.
7. Find the vertex, focus, and directrix of the parabola
   $x^2 + 2x + 6y - 11 = 0$. Then graph the parabola.
8. Solve: $x^2 + y^2 = 74$
   $\phantom{Solve: } x - y = 2$
9. Two squares whose sides differ in length by 9 m have areas which differ by 153 m². Find the length of a side of each.
10. Solve: $3x^2 - 2y^2 = 30$
    $\phantom{Solve: } 2x^2 + 5y^2 = 77$
11. The area of a rectangle is 240 cm² and the length of a diagonal is 26 cm. Find the dimensions of the rectangle.

## Ready for Polynomial Functions?

11-3    1. Determine whether $1 + i$ is a solution of $x^2 - 2x + 1 = 0$.

7-2    2. Factor: $x^2 + x - 6$.

12-5    3. Find a quadratic equation whose solutions are $-5$ and $\frac{2}{3}$.

12-5    4. Find a quadratic equation whose solutions are $1 - \sqrt{2}$ and $1 + \sqrt{2}$.

11-3    5. Find an equation having $-2$, $i$, and $3i$ as solutions.

11-3    6. Show that $-1 - i$ is a square root of $2i$. Then find the other square root.

11-2    7. Find the conjugate of $-3 + 8i$.

11-2    8. Multiply: $(1 - 5i)(1 + 5i)$.

# Chapter 15
# Polynomial Functions

*Many things considered in aircraft design, such as
lift and drag, are given by polynomial functions.*

# 15-1 Polynomials and Polynomial Functions

After finishing Lesson 15-1, you should be able to
■ determine whether a number is a root of a polynomial.
■■ given a polynomial $P(x)$ and a divisor $d(x)$, find the quotient $Q(x)$ and the remainder $R(x)$. Then express $P(x)$ in the form $P(x) = d(x) \cdot Q(x) + R(x)$.

Recall the definition of a polynomial: A polynomial in $x$ is any expression equivalent to one of this form

$$a_n x^n + a_{n-1} x^{n-1} + a_{n-2} x^{n-2} + \cdots + a_1 x + a_0.$$

We will usually assume the coefficients are complex numbers, but in some cases will consider them to be real numbers, or rational numbers, or integers. The coefficient of the term of highest degree, $a_n$, is called the *leading coefficient*.

## ▮Roots of Polynomials

When a number is substituted for the variable in a polynomial, the result is some unique number. Thus every polynomial defines a function. We often refer to polynomials, therefore, using function notation $P(x)$.

**DEFINITION**

If a number $a$ makes a polynomial 0, then $a$ is called a *root*, or a *zero*, of the polynomial.

**Examples.** $P(x) = x^3 + 2x^2 - 5x - 6.$

**1.** Is 3 a root of $P(x)$?

We substitute 3 into the polynomial:

$$P(3) = 3^3 + 2(3)^2 - 5 \cdot 3 - 6 = 24.$$

Since $P(3) \neq 0$, 3 is not a root.

**2.** Is $-1$ a root of $P(x)$?

$$P(-1) = (-1)^3 + 2(-1)^2 - 5(-1) - 6 = 0.$$

Since $P(-1) = 0$, $-1$ is a root of the polynomial.

**TRY THIS** ▶

1. Determine whether the following numbers are roots of the polynomial $P(x) = x^2 - 4x - 21$.
   a) 7   b) 3
   c) $-3$

2. Determine whether the following numbers are roots of the polynomial $P(x) = x^4 - 16$.
   a) 2   b) $-2$
   c) $-1$   d) 0

3. Determine whether the following numbers are roots of the polynomial $P(x) = x^2 + 1$.
   a) 1   b) $-1$
   c) $1 + i$   d) $-i$

## ‖ Dividing Polynomials

When we divide one polynomial by another we obtain a quotient and a remainder. If the remainder is 0, then the divisor is a *factor* of the dividend.

**Example 3.**  Divide, to find whether $x^2 + 9$ is a factor of $x^4 - 81$.

$$
\begin{array}{r}
x^2 - 9 \\
x^2 + 9\overline{)x^4 \qquad\qquad - 81} \\
\underline{x^4 \qquad + 9x^2} \\
-9x^2 - 81 \\
\underline{-9x^2 - 81} \\
0
\end{array}
$$

*Spaces have been left for missing terms in the dividend.*

Since the remainder is 0, we know that $x^2 + 9$ is a factor.

**Example 4.**  Divide, to find whether $x^2 + 3x - 1$ is a factor of $x^4 - 81$.

$$
\begin{array}{r}
x^2 - 3x + 10 \\
x^2 + 3x - 1\overline{)x^4 \qquad\qquad\qquad -81} \\
\underline{x^4 + 3x^3 - \quad x^2} \\
-3x^3 + \quad x^2 \\
\underline{-3x^3 - \quad 9x^2 + \ 3x} \\
10x^2 - \ 3x - 81 \\
\underline{10x^2 + 30x - 10} \\
-33x - 71
\end{array}
$$

Since the remainder is not 0, we know that $x^2 + 3x - 1$ is not a factor of $x^4 - 81$.

**TRY THIS**

4. By division, determine whether the following polynomials are factors of the polynomial $x^4 - 16$.
   a) $x - 2$
   b) $x^2 + 3x - 1$
5. By division, determine whether the following polynomials are factors of the polynomial $x^3 + 2x^2 - 5x - 6$.
   a) $x - 3$
   b) $x + 1$
   c) $x^2 + 3x - 1$

When we divide a polynomial $P(x)$ by a divisor $d(x)$ we obtain a polynomial $Q(x)$ for a quotient and a polynomial $R(x)$ for a remainder. The remainder must either be 0 or have degree less than that of $d(x)$. To check we multiply the quotient by the divisor and add the remainder, to see if we get the dividend. Thus these polynomials are related as follows:

$$P(x) = d(x) \cdot Q(x) + R(x).$$

**Example 5.**  If $P(x) = x^4 - 81$ and $d(x) = x^2 + 9$, find $Q(x)$ and $R(x)$. (See Example 3.)

$$x^4 - 81 = (x^2 + 9) \cdot (x^2 - 9) + 0$$
$$P(x) = \quad d(x) \quad \cdot \quad Q(x) \quad + R(x)$$

**Example 6.**  $P(x) = x^4 - 81$ and $d(x) = x^2 + 3x - 1$. Find $Q(x)$ and $R(x)$. (See Example 4.)

$$x^4 - 81 = (x^2 + 3x - 1) \cdot (x^2 - 3x + 10) + (-33x - 71)$$
$$P(x) = \quad d(x) \quad \cdot \quad Q(x) \quad + \quad R(x)$$

**TRY THIS**

> 6.  Divide $x^3 + 2x^2 - 5x - 6$ by $x - 3$.
> Then express the dividend as $P(x) = d(x) \cdot Q(x) + R(x)$.

## Exercise Set 15-1

▌ Determine whether the given numbers are roots of the polynomial $P(x)$. (*See Examples 1 and 2.*)

1.  2, 3, −1;
    $P(x) = x^3 + 6x^2 - x - 30$
3.  0, −, $1 + i\sqrt{7}$, $1 - i\sqrt{7}$;
    $P(x) = x^3 - 2x^2 + 8x$

2.  2, 3, −1;
    $P(x) = 2x^3 - 3x^2 + x - 1$
4.  0, −2, $1 + i$, $1 - i$;
    $P(x) = x^3 - 2x^2 + 2x$

▌▌ By division, determine whether the polynomials are factors of the polynomial $P(x)$. (*See Examples 3 and 4.*)

5.  $P(x) = x^3 + 6x^2 - x - 30$
    a) $x - 2$    b) $x - 3$    c) $x + 1$
7.  $P(x) = x^4 - 81$
    a) $x - 3$    b) $x + 3$    c) $x + 9$

6.  $P(x) = 2x^3 - 3x^2 + x - 1$
    a) $x - 2$    b) $x - 3$    c) $x + 1$
8.  $P(x) = x^5 + 32$
    a) $x - 2$    b) $x + 2$    c) $x - 4$

In each of the following, a polynomial $P(x)$ and a divisor $d(x)$ are given. Find the quotient $Q(x)$ and the remainder $R(x)$ when $P(x)$ is divided by $d(x)$ and express $P(x)$ in the form $d(x) \cdot Q(x) + R(x)$. (*See Examples 5 and 6.*)

9.  $P(x) = x^3 + 6x^2 - x - 30$,
    $d(x) = x - 2$
11. $P(x)$ as in Exercise 9,
    $d(x) = x - 3$
13. $P(x) = x^3 - 8$,
    $d(x) = x + 2$
15. $P(x) = x^4 + 9x^2 + 20$,
    $d(x) = x^2 + 4$

10. $P(x) = 2x^3 - 3x^2 + x - 1$,
    $d(x) = x - 2$
12. $P(x)$ as in Exercise 10,
    $d(x) = x - 3$
14. $P(x) = x^3 + 27$,
    $d(x) = x + 1$
16. $P(x) = x^4 + x^2 + 2$,
    $d(x) = x^2 + x + 1$

# 15-2 The Remainder and Factor Theorems

After finishing Lesson 15-2, you should be able to

▮ use the Remainder Theorem to find the remainder $P(r)$ when a polynomial $P(x)$ is divided by $x - r$.

▮▮ determine whether $x - r$ is a factor of a polynomial $P(x)$ by determining whether $P(r) = 0$.

▮▮▮ use the Factor Theorem to find complete factorizations of polynomials.

## ▮ The Remainder Theorem

The next theorem states a remarkable fact about polynomials.

**THEOREM 15-1 (The Remainder Theorem)**

For a polynomial $P(x)$, the function value $P(r)$ is the remainder when $P(x)$ is divided by $x - r$.

In other words, if we divide a polynomial by $x - r$, the remainder would be the same as if we substituted $r$ in the polynomial and evaluated.

**Example 1.** If $P(x) = x^3 + 6x^2 - x - 30$, what is the remainder when $P(x)$ is divided by $x + 1$ or $[x - (-1)]$?

$$P(-1) = (-1)^3 + 6(-1)^2 - (-1) - 30$$
$$= -1 + 6 + 1 - 30$$
$$= -24$$

Thus, by the Remainder Theorem, when $P(x)$ is divided by $x + 1$, the remainder is $-24$.

**Example 2.** If $P(x)$, in Example 1, is divided by $x - 2$, what is the remainder?

$$P(2) = 2^3 + 6 \cdot 2^2 - 2 - 30$$
$$= 8 + 24 - 2 - 30$$
$$= 0$$

Thus, by the Remainder Theorem, when $P(x)$ is divided by $x - 2$, the remainder is 0. Note that this also tells us that $x - 2$ is a factor of $x^3 + 6x^2 - x - 30$.

**TRY THIS** ➡

1. If $P(x) = x^3 - x^2 + 1$ is divided by $x + 1$, what is the remainder?

2. If $P(x) = x^4 - 2x^3 + 5x - 7$ is divided by $x - 2$, what is the remainder?

3. If $P(x) = 2x^{15} + x^{12} + 1$ is divided by $x + 1$, what is the remainder?

## ❚❚ Determining Factors

The next theorem follows from the Remainder Theorem.

**THEOREM 15-2 (The Factor Theorem)**
For a polynomial $P(x)$, if $P(r) = 0$, then $x - r$ is a factor of $P(x)$.

Note that if $P(r)$ is 0, $r$ is a root, or zero, of $P(x)$.

**Example 3.**   Let $P(x) = x^3 + 2x^2 - 5x - 6$. Determine whether $x + 1$ is a factor of $P(x)$.

We think of $x + 1$ as $x - (-1)$. Thus we find $P(-1)$.
$$P(-1) = (-1)^3 + 2(-1)^2 - 5(-1) - 6 = 0.$$

Since $P(-1) = 0$, by the Factor Theorem we know that $x + 1$ is a factor of $P(x)$.

---

**A Proof of Theorem 15-2**

Consider dividing a polynomial $P(x)$ by $x - r$. From the Remainder Theorem we have

$$P(x) = (x - r) \cdot Q(x) + P(r).$$

Then if $P(r) = 0$, we have

$$P(x) = (x - r) \cdot Q(x),$$

so $x - r$ is a factor of $P(x)$.

---

**TRY THIS**

4.  Determine whether $x - \frac{1}{2}$ is a factor of
    $4x^4 + 2x^3 + 8x - 1$.
5.  Determine whether $x + 5$ is a factor of $x^4 + 625$.

## ❚❚❚ Factorizations

The Factor Theorem is helpful in factoring polynomials.

**Example 4.**   Consider the polynomial $P(x)$ in Example 3.

**a)**  Find another factor of $P(x)$.

We divide $P(x)$ by $x + 1$, obtaining for a quotient $x^2 + x - 6$.

**b)** Find a complete factorization of $P(x)$.

By part **a)** we know that
$P(x) = (x + 1)(x^2 + x - 6)$. The second
factor can be factored further giving the
complete factorization:

$$(x + 1)(x + 3)(x - 2).$$

**TRY THIS**

6. a) Let
$P(x) = x^3 + 6x^2 - x - 30.$
Determine whether $x - 2$
is a factor of $P(x)$.
b) Find another factor of $P(x)$.
c) Find a complete factorization of $P(x)$.

## Exercise Set 15-2

▮ What is the remainder when $P(x)$ is divided by the binomial? Use the Remainder Theorem. (*See Examples 1 and 2.*)

1. $P(x) = x^3 - 2x^2 + 5x - 4; x - 2$
2. $P(x) = x^3 - 2x^2 + 5x - 4; x + 2$
3. $P(x) = x^5 - 3x^2 + 2x - 1; x - 1$
4. $P(x) = x^5 - 3x^2 + 2x - 1; x + 1$
5. $P(x) = x^3 - 2x^2 + 5x - 4; x + 1$
6. $P(x) = x^3 - 2x^2 + 5x - 4; x - 1$
7. $P(x) = x^3 + 8; x + 2$
8. $P(x) = x^4 - 65; x - 4$
9. $P(x) = x^2 - 8x + 4; x - 3i$
10. $P(x) = x^2 + 8x - 4; x - 2i$
11. $P(x) = x^2 + 2x + 2; x - (1 + i)$
12. $P(x) = x^2 - 2x + 5; x - (1 + 2i)$

▮▮ Determine whether the expressions of the type $x - r$ are factors of the polynomial $P(x)$. Use the Factor Theorem. (*See Example 3.*)

13. $P(x) = x^3 - 3x^2 - 4x - 12; x + 2$
14. $P(x) = x^3 - 4x^2 + 3x + 8; x + 1$
15. $P(x) = 2x^2 + 2x + 1; x - (-\frac{1}{2} - \frac{1}{2}i)$
16. $P(x) = 9x^2 + 6x + 2; x - (\frac{1}{3} - \frac{1}{3}i)$
17. $P(x) = x^5 - 1; x - 1$
18. $P(x) = x^5 + 1; x + 1$
19. $P(x) = x^4 + x^3 - 13x^2 - x + 12;$
$x - 3, x + 4, x + 1, x - 1, x + 2$
20. $P(x) = x^3 - 2x^2 + 1; x - 3,$
$x - 2, x + 3, x + 2, x - 1$

▮▮▮ (*See Example 4.*)

21. a) Let $P(x) = x^3 + 2x^2 - x - 2$. Determine whether $x - 1$ is a factor of $P(x)$.
b) Find another factor of $P(x)$.
c) Find a complete factorization of $P(x)$.
22. a) Let $P(x) = x^3 + 4x^2 - x - 4$. Determine whether $x + 1$ is a factor of $P(x)$.
b) Find another factor of $P(x)$.
c) Find a complete factorization of $P(x)$.

## Challenge Exercises

23. Find $k$ so that $x - 1$ is a factor of $x^3 - 3x^2 + kx - 1$.
24. Use the Factor Theorem to prove that $x + a$ is a factor of $x^{2n} - a^{2n}$,
for any natural number $n$.

# 15-3 Synthetic Division

After finishing Lesson 15-3, you should be able to
**▌**    use synthetic division to find the quotient and remainder when a polynomial is divided by a binomial $x - r$.
**▌▌**   use synthetic division to find function values of a polynomial.
**▌▌▌**  use synthetic division to determine whether a number is a root of a polynomial.

## ▌Synthetic Division

To streamline division, we can arrange the work so that duplicate writing is avoided. Compare the following.

$$
\begin{array}{r}
4x^2 + 5x + 11 \\
\mathbf{A} \quad x - 2\overline{)4x^3 - 3x^2 + x + 7} \\
\underline{4x^3 - 8x^2} \\
5x^2 + x \\
\underline{5x^2 - 10x} \\
11x + 7 \\
\underline{11x - 22} \\
29
\end{array}
$$

remainder

$$
\begin{array}{r}
4 \quad 5 \quad 11 \\
\mathbf{B} \quad 1 - 2\overline{)4 - 3 + 1 + 7} \\
\underline{4 - 8} \\
5 + 1 \\
\underline{5 - 10} \\
11 + 7 \\
\underline{11 - 22} \\
29
\end{array}
$$

remainder

In **A** we performed a division. In **B** we performed the same division, but we wrote only the coefficients. If there had been any missing terms, we would have written 0's. Note that the numerals in color are duplicated. There would be no loss of understanding if we did not write them twice. Note also that when we subtract we add an additive inverse. We can accomplish this by using the additive inverse of $-2$, and then adding instead of subtracting.

**C  Synthetic Division**

$$
\begin{array}{r|l}
2 & \;\;4 - 3 + \;\;1 \;\; + \;\;7 \\
& \underline{\;\;+ 8 + 10 \;\; + 22} \\
& \;\;4 + 5 + 11 \,\big|\; + 29
\end{array}
$$

In **C,**

*Step 1.*   Write down the 2 of the divisor and the coefficients.

$$
\begin{array}{r|l}
2 & \;\;4 - 3 + 1 + 7
\end{array}
$$

*Step 2.* Bring down the first coefficient (4), then multiply it by the 2 and write the result under the next coefficient $(-3)$.

$$
\begin{array}{r|l}
2 & 4 - 3 + 1 + 7 \\
& \underline{+\ 8 \phantom{+++++}} \\
& 4
\end{array}
$$

*Step 3.* Add $-3$ and 8, multiply the sum (5) by the 2, and write the result under the next coefficient (1).

$$
\begin{array}{r|l}
2 & 4 - 3 +\ 1 + 7 \\
& \underline{+\ 8 + 10 \phantom{++}} \\
& 4 \quad 5
\end{array}
$$

*Step 4.* Add 1 and 10, multiply the sum (11) by 2, and write the result under the next coefficient (7). Then add.

$$
\begin{array}{r|l}
2 & 4 - 3 +\ 1 +\ 7 \\
& \underline{\phantom{44}8 \quad 10 \quad 22} \\
& 4 \quad 5 \quad 11 \quad 29
\end{array}
$$

$$\underbrace{4x^2 + 5x + 11}_{\text{quotient}} \quad \text{remainder}$$

**Example 1.** Use synthetic division to find the quotient and remainder: $(2x^3 + 7x^2 - 5) \div (x + 3)$.

First note that $x + 3 = x - (-3)$.

$$
\begin{array}{r|l}
-3 & 2 + 7 + 0 \quad -5 \\
& \underline{-6 - 3 \quad +9} \\
& 2 + 1 - 3 \ \big|\ +4
\end{array}
$$

The quotient is $2x^2 + 1x - 3$. The remainder is 4.

**TRY THIS** ➡

Use synthetic division to find the quotient and remainder.

1. $(x^3 + 6x^2 - x - 30) \div (x - 2)$
2. $(x^3 - 2x^2 + 5x - 4) \div (x + 2)$
3. $(y^3 + 1) \div (y + 1)$
4. $(x^5 - 1) \div (x - 1)$

## ॥ **Finding Function Values**

We can also use synthetic division to find function values, especially when large powers are involved.

**Example 2.** $P(x) = 2x^5 - 3x^4 + x^3 - 2x^2 + x - 8$. Find $P(10)$.

Recall that $P(10)$ is the remainder when $P(x)$ is divided by $x - 10$.

$$
\begin{array}{r|rrrrrr}
10 & 2 & -3 & +1 & -2 & +1 & -8 \\
   &   & 20 & 170 & 1710 & 17{,}080 & 170{,}810 \\
\hline
   & 2 & 17 & 171 & 1708 & 17{,}081 & \big|\ 170{,}802
\end{array}
$$

Thus $P(10) = 170{,}802$.

**TRY THIS** ⇒

> 5. Let $P(x) = x^5 - 2x^4 - 7x^3 + x^2 + 20$.
>    Use synthetic division to find
>    a) $P(10)$
>    b) $P(-8)$.

## ॥ **Roots**

We can use synthetic division to determine whether a number is a root of a polynomial.

**Example 3.** Let $P(x) = x^3 + 8x^2 + 8x - 32$. Determine whether $-4$ is a root of $P(x)$.

We must decide if $P(-4) = 0$. We find $P(-4)$ as the remainder, using synthetic division.

$$
\begin{array}{r|rrrr}
-4 & 1 & +8 & +8 & -32 \\
   &   & -4 & -16 & +32 \\
\hline
   & 1 & +4 & -8 & \big|\ 0
\end{array}
$$

Since $P(-4) = 0$, $-4$ is a root of $P(x)$.

**TRY THIS** ⇒

> 6. Let $P(x) = x^3 + 6x^2 - x - 30$. Using synthetic division, determine whether the given numbers are roots of $P(x)$.
>    a) 2
>    b) 5
>    c) $-3$

## Exercise Set 15-3

▌Use synthetic division to find the quotient and remainder. (*See Example 1.*)

1. $(x^3 - 7x^2 - 13x + 3) \div (x + 2)$
2. $(x^3 - 7x^2 + 13x + 3) \div (x - 2)$
3. $(2x^4 + 7x^3 + x - 12) \div (x - 3)$
4. $(2x^4 - 3x^2 + x - 7) \div (x + 4)$
5. $(x^3 - 2x^2 - 8) \div (x + 2)$
6. $(x^3 - 3x + 10) \div (x - 2)$
7. $(x^3 + 27) \div (x + 3)$
8. $(x^3 - 27) \div (x - 3)$
9. $(x^4 - 1) \div (x - 1)$
10. $(x^5 + 32) \div (x + 2)$
11. $(2x^4 + 3x^2 - 1) \div (x - \frac{1}{2})$
12. $(3x^4 - 2x^2 + 2) \div (x - \frac{1}{4})$
13. $(x^4 - 16) \div (x - 2)$
14. $(x^6 + 1) \div (x + 1)$
15. $(x^3 - 2ix^2 + ix + 5) \div (x - i)$
16. $(x^3 + 3ix^2 - 4ix - 2) \div (x + i)$

▌▌Use synthetic division to find the function values. (*See Example 2.*)

17. $P(x) = x^3 - 6x^2 + 11x - 6$;
    find $P(1)$, $P(-2)$, $P(3)$.
18. $P(x) = x^3 + 7x^2 - 12x - 3$;
    find $P(-3)$, $P(-2)$, $P(1)$.
19. $P(x) = 2x^5 - 3x^4 + 2x^3 - x + 8$;
    find $P(20)$, $P(-3)$.
20. $P(x) = x^5 - 10x^4 - 20x^3 - 5x - 100$;
    find $P(-10)$, $P(5)$.

▌▌▌Using synthetic division, determine whether the numbers are roots of the polynomials. (*See Example 3.*)

21. $-3, 2$; $P(x) = 3x^3 + 5x^2 - 6x + 18$
22. $-4, 2$; $P(x) = 3x^3 + 11x^2 - 2x + 8$
23. $-3, \frac{1}{2}$; $P(x) = x^3 - \frac{7}{2}x^2 + x - \frac{3}{2}$
24. $-6, \frac{1}{4}$; $P(x) = x^3 - \frac{7}{2}x^2 - 13x + 3$
25. $i, -i, -2$; $P(x) = x^3 + 2x^2 + x + 2$
26. $i, -i, 4$; $P(x) = x^3 - 4x^2 + x - 4$

---

## Calculator Exercises

27. Given that $f(x) = 2.13x^5 - 42.1x^3 + 17.5x^2 + 0.953x - 1.98$, find $f(3.21)$
    a) by synthetic division;
    b) by substitution.
28. Given that $f(x) = 0.673x^4 - 17.3x^2 + 923x - 1230$, find $f(-16.3)$
    a) by synthetic division;
    b) by substitution.

---

### COMPUTER NOTE: The Electronic Algebra Student

A computer has been programmed to solve problems in algebra. The computer translates each problem into algebraic terms. Then the computer solves the problem. If it has difficulty, it asks for more information. The program was written to provide knowledge of computer capabilities.

# 15-4 Theorems About Roots

After finishing Lesson 15-4, you should be able to
> **I** given a polynomial factored into linear factors, find the roots and state the multiplicities.
> **II** find a polynomial with roots of given multiplicities.
> **III** given that a polynomial of certain degree with real coefficients has given numbers as some of its roots, find the other roots.
> **IIII** given that a polynomial of certain degree with rational coefficients has given numbers as some of its roots, find the other roots.
> **IIIII** find a polynomial of lowest degree with rational coefficients which has given numbers as some of its roots.
> **IIIIII** given a polynomial and some of its roots, find the other roots.

## I The Fundamental Theorem of Algebra

By the fundamental theorem of algebra (Theorem 11-2), every polynomial of degree $n$ can be factored into $n$ linear factors. For example,

| **Polynomial** | **Roots** |
|---|---|
| $P_1(x) = x^4 + x^3 - 13x^2 - x + 12$ | |
| $\quad = (x - 3)(x + 4)(x + 1)(x - 1)$ | $3, -4, -1, 1$ |
| $P_2(x) = 3x^4 - 15x^3 + 18x^2 + 12x - 24$ | |
| $\quad = 3(x - 2)(x - 2)(x - 2)(x + 1)$ | |
| $\quad = 3(x - 2)^3(x + 1)$ | $2, -1$ |

Note that while the polynomial $P_2(x)$ has 4 linear factors, it has only 2 roots. We say that *2 is a root of multiplicity 3* and *−1 is a root of multiplicity 1*.

**TRY THIS**

Find the roots of each polynomial and state the multiplicity of each.

1. $P(x) = (x - 5)(x - 5)(x + 6)$
2. $P(x) = 4(x + 7)^2(x - 3)$
3. $P(x) = (x + 2)^3(x^2 - 9)$
4. $P(x) = (x^2 - 7x + 12)^2$
   (*Hint:* Factor first.)
5. $P(x) = 5x^2 - 5$

## ıı Finding Polynomials With *n* Given Roots

Given the roots of a polynomial, we can find the polynomial.

**Example 1.** Find a polynomial of degree three, having the roots $-2$, 1, and $3i$.

Such a polynomial has factors $x + 2$, $x - 1$, and $x - 3i$, so we have

$$P(x) = a_n(x + 2)(x - 1)(x - 3i).$$

The number $a_n$ can be any nonzero number. The simplest polynomial will be obtained if we let it be 1. If we then multiply the factors we obtain

$$P(x) = x^3 + (1 - 3i)x^2 + (-2 - 3i)x + 6i.$$

**Example 2.** Find a polynomial of degree 5 with $-1$ as a root of multiplicity 3, 4 as a root of multiplicity 1, and 0 as a root of multiplicity 1.

Proceeding as in Example 1, letting $a_n = 1$, we obtain

$$(x + 1)^3(x - 4)(x - 0).$$
$$x^5 - x^4 - 9x^3 - 11x^2 - 4x.$$

**TRY THIS** ⟹

6. Find a polynomial of degree 3 which has $-1$, 2, and 5 as roots.

7. Find a polynomial of degree 3 which has $-1$, 2, and $-5i$ as roots.

8. Find a polynomial of degree 5 with $-2$ as a root of multiplicity 3, and 0 as a root of multiplicity 2.

9. Find a polynomial of degree 4 with 1 as a root of multiplicity 3 and $-5$ as a root of multiplicity 1.

## ııı Roots of Polynomials With Real Coefficients

Consider the quadratic equation $x^2 - 2x + 2 = 0$, with real coefficients. Its roots are $1 + i$, and $1 - i$. Note that they are complex conjugates. This generalizes to any polynomial with real coefficients.

### THEOREM 15-3

If a complex number $z$ is a root of a polynomial $P(x)$ of degree greater than or equal to 1 with real coefficients, then its conjugate $\bar{z}$ is also a root. (Complex roots occur in conjugate pairs.)

It is essential that the coefficients be real numbers. This can be seen by considering Example 1. In that polynomial the root $3i$ occurs but its conjugate does not. This can happen because some of the coefficients of the polynomial are not real.

**Example 3.** Suppose a polynomial of degree 5 with real coefficients has 8, $-3 + i$, and $7 - 6i$ as some of its roots. Find the other roots.

By Theorem 15-3, the conjugates of $-3 + i$ and $7 - 6i$ must be roots. They are $-3 - i$ and $7 + 6i$. There are no other roots since the degree is 5. (Recall that by Theorem 11-3, every polynomial of degree $n$ with complex coefficients, $n \geq 1$, has at least one complex number root and at most $n$ complex number roots.)

**TRY THIS**

10. Suppose a polynomial of degree 5 with real coefficients has $-4$, $6 - 2i$, and $\sqrt{3} - i$ as some of its roots. Find the other roots.

11. Suppose a polynomial of degree 3 with real coefficients has 10 and $24 + 5i$ as some of its roots. Find the other roots.

## ⅠⅠⅠⅠ Rational Coefficients

When a polynomial has rational numbers for coefficients, certain irrational roots also occur in pairs, as described in the following theorem.

**THEOREM 15-4**

Suppose $P(x)$ is a polynomial with rational coefficients and of degree greater than or equal to 1. Then if either of the following is a root, so is the other: $a + c\sqrt{b}$, $a - c\sqrt{b}$.

**Example 4.** Suppose a polynomial of degree 6 with rational coefficients has $-2 + 5i$, $-i$, and $1 - \sqrt{3}$ as some of its roots. Find the other roots.

By Theorem 15-3, the conjugates of $-2 + 5i$ and $-i$ are roots. They are $-2 - 5i$ and $i$. By Theorem 15-4, since $1 - \sqrt{3}$ is a root, $1 + \sqrt{3}$ is also a root. There are no other roots since the degree is 6.

**TRY THIS**

12. Suppose a polynomial of degree 5 with rational coefficients has $-4$, $7 - 2i$, and $3 + \sqrt{5}$ as roots. Find the other roots.

## ▐▐▐▐▐ Finding Polynomials

**Example 5.**  Find a polynomial of lowest degree with rational coefficients which has $1 - \sqrt{2}$ and $1 + 2i$ as some of its roots.

By Theorem 15-3, $1 - 2i$ is a root. By Theorem 15-4, $1 + \sqrt{2}$ is a root. Thus the polynomial is

$$[x - (1 - \sqrt{2})][x - (1 + \sqrt{2})][x - (1 + 2i)][x - (1 - 2i)],$$

or

$$(x^2 - 2x - 1)(x^2 - 2x + 5),$$

or

$$x^4 - 4x^3 + 8x^2 - 8x - 5.$$

**TRY THIS**

13. Find a polynomial of lowest degree with rational coefficients which has $2 + \sqrt{3}$ and $1 - i$ as some of its roots.
14. Find a polynomial of lowest degree with real coefficients which has $2i$ and $2$ as some of its roots.

## ▐▐▐▐▐ Finding Roots

**Example 6.**  Let $P(x) = x^4 - 5x^3 + 10x^2 - 20x + 24$. Find the other roots of $P(x)$, given that $2i$ is a root.

Since $2i$ is a root, we know that $-2i$ is also a root. Thus

$$P(x) = (x - 2i)(x + 2i) \cdot Q(x)$$

for some $Q(x)$. Since $(x - 2i)(x + 2i) = x^2 + 4$, we know that

$$P(x) = (x^2 + 4) \cdot Q(x).$$

We find, using division, that $Q(x) = x^2 - 5x + 6$, and since we can factor $x^2 - 5x + 6$, we get

$$P(x) = (x^2 + 4)(x - 2)(x - 3).$$

Thus the other roots are $-2i$, $2$, and $3$.

**TRY THIS**

15. Find the other roots of $x^4 + x^3 - x^2 + x - 2$ given that $i$ is a root.

## Exercise Set 15-4

❚ Find the roots of each polynomial and state the multiplicity of each. (*See page 466.*)

1. $(x + 3)^2(x - 1)$
2. $-4(x + 2)(x - \pi)^5$
3. $-8(x - 3)^2(x + 4)^3x^4$
4. $x^3(x - 1)^2(x + 4)$
5. $(x^2 - 5x + 6)^2$
6. $(x^2 - x - 2)^2$

❚❚ Find a polynomial of degree 3 with the given numbers as roots. (*See Example 1.*)

7. $-2, 3, 5$
8. $3, 2, -1$
9. $2, i, -i$
10. $-3, 2i, -2i$
11. $2 + i, 2 - i, 3$
12. $1 + 4i, 1 - 4i, -1$
13. $\sqrt{2}, -\sqrt{2}, \sqrt{3}$. Are the coefficients rational?
14. $\sqrt{3}, -\sqrt{3}, \sqrt{2}$. Are the coefficients rational?

(*See Example 2.*)

15. Find a polynomial of degree 4 with 0 as a root of multiplicity 2 and 5 as a root of multiplicity 2.
16. Find a polynomial of degree 4 with 0 as a root of multiplicity 4.
17. Find a polynomial of degree 4 with $-2$ as a root of multiplicity 1, 3 as a root of multiplicity 2, and $-1$ as a root of multiplicity 1.
18. Find a polynomial of degree 5 with 4 as a root of multiplicity 3 and $-2$ as a root of multiplicity 2.

❚❚❚ Suppose a polynomial of degree 6 with real coefficients has the given roots. Find the other roots. (*See Example 3.*)

19. $-5, 6, 5 + i, -2i$
20. $8, 6, -3 - 2i, 4i$

❚❚❚❚ Suppose a polynomial of degree 5 with rational coefficients has the given roots. Find the other roots. (*See Example 4.*)

21. $6, -3 + 4i, 4 - \sqrt{5}$
22. $8, 6 - 7i, \frac{1}{2} + \sqrt{11}$
23. $-2, 3, 4, 1 - i$
24. $3, 4, -5, 7 + i$

❚❚❚❚❚ Find a polynomial of lowest degree with rational coefficients that has the given numbers as some of its roots. (*See Example 5.*)

25. $1 + i, 2$
26. $2 - i, -1$
27. $3i, -2$
28. $-4i, 5$
29. $2 - \sqrt{3}, 1 + i$
30. $3 + \sqrt{2}, 2 - i$
31. $\sqrt{5}, -3i$
32. $-\sqrt{2}, 4i$

❚❚❚❚❚❚ Given that the polynomial has the given root, find the other roots. (*See Example 6.*)

33. $x^4 - 5x^3 + 7x^2 - 5x + 6; -i$
34. $x^3 - 4x^2 + x - 4; -i$
35. $x^4 - 16; 2i$
36. $x^4 - 1; i$
37. $x^3 - x^2 - 7x + 15; -3$
38. $x^3 - 6x^2 + 13x - 20; 4$
39. $x^3 - 8; 2$
40. $x^3 + 8; -2$

# 15-5 *Rational Roots*

After finishing Lesson 15-5, you should be able to
▮ given a polynomial with integer coefficients, find the rational roots. Find
the other roots, if possible.

▮ Finding the roots of a polynomial is not always easy. However, if
a polynomial has integer coefficients, there is a procedure for
finding all of the rational roots.

### THEOREM 15-5 (Rational Roots Theorem)

Let $P(x) = a_n x^n + a_{n-1} x^{n-1} + \cdots + a_1 x + a_0$, where all the coefficients are integers. Consider a rational number denoted by $\dfrac{c}{d}$,
where $c$ and $d$ have no common factor besides 1 and $-1$. If $\dfrac{c}{d}$ is
a root of $P(x)$, then $c$ is a factor of $a_0$ and $d$ is a factor of $a_n$.

**Example 1.** Let $P(x) = 3x^4 - 11x^3 + 10x - 4$. Find the rational roots of $P(x)$. If possible, find the other roots.

By the rational roots theorem if $\dfrac{c}{d}$ is a root of $P(x)$, then $c$ must
be a factor of $-4$ and $d$ must be a factor of 3. Thus the possibilities for $c$ and $d$ are

$c$:  1, $-1$, 4, $-4$, 2, $-2$
$d$:  1, $-1$, 3, $-3$

Then the resulting possibilities for $\dfrac{c}{d}$ are

$$1, -1, 4, -4, \frac{1}{3}, -\frac{1}{3}, \frac{4}{3}, -\frac{4}{3}, \frac{2}{3}, -\frac{2}{3}, 2, -2.$$

Of these 12 possibilities, we know that at most 4 of them could
be roots because $P(x)$ is of degree 4. To find which are roots we
can use synthetic division.

We try 1:

$$
\begin{array}{r|rrrrr}
1 & 3 & -11 & 0 & 10 & -4 \\
  &   & 3 & -8 & -8 & 2 \\
\hline
  & 3 & -8 & -8 & 2 & -2 \\
\end{array}
$$

$P(1) = -2$, so 1 is not a root.

We try $-1$:

$$
\begin{array}{r|rrrrr}
-1 & 3 & -11 & 0 & 10 & -4 \\
   &   & -3 & 14 & -14 & 4 \\
\hline
   & 3 & -14 & 14 & -4 & 0
\end{array}
$$

$P(-1) = 0$, so $-1$ is a root, and

$$P(x) = (x + 1)(3x^3 - 14x^2 + 14x - 4).$$

We now use $3x^3 - 14x^2 + 14x - 4$ and check the other possible roots.

We try $\frac{2}{3}$:

$$
\begin{array}{r|rrrr}
\frac{2}{3} & 3 & -14 & 14 & -4 \\
   &   & 2 & -8 & 4 \\
\hline
   & 3 & -12 & 6 & 0
\end{array}
$$

$P(\frac{2}{3}) = 0$, so $\frac{2}{3}$ is a root. We now know that

$$P(x) = (x + 1)(x - \tfrac{2}{3})(3x^2 - 12x + 6).$$

Since the factor $3x^2 - 12x + 6$ is quadratic, we can use the quadratic formula to find the other roots. They are $2 + \sqrt{2}$ and $2 - \sqrt{2}$. Thus the rational roots are $-1$ and $\frac{2}{3}$.

**TRY THIS**

1. Let $P(x) = 2x^4 - 7x^3 - 35x^2 + 13x + 3$. If $\frac{c}{d}$ is a rational root of $P(x)$, then:
   a)  What are the possibilities for $c$?
   b)  What are the possibilities for $d$?
   c)  What are the possibilities for $\frac{c}{d}$?
   d)  Find the rational roots.
   e)  If possible, find the other roots.

**Example 2.** Let $P(x) = x^3 + 6x^2 + x + 6$. Find the rational roots of $P(x)$. If possible, find the other roots.

By the rational roots theorem if $\frac{c}{d}$ is a root of $P(x)$, then $c$ must be a factor of 6 and $d$ must be a factor of 1. Thus the possibilities for $c$ and $d$ are

$c$:  $1, -1, 2, -2, 3, -3, 6, -6$
$d$:  $1, -1$

Then the resulting possibilities for $\frac{c}{d}$ are

$1, -1, 2, -2, 3, -3, 6, -6.$

These are the same as the possibilities for $c$. Since the leading coefficient is 1, we need only check the factors of the last coefficient.

There is another aid in eliminating possibilities for rational roots. Note that all coefficients of $P(x)$ are positive. Thus when any positive number is substituted in $P(x)$, we get a positive value, never 0. Therefore no positive number can be a root. Thus the only possibilities for roots are

$$-1, -2, -3, -6.$$

We try $-6$:

$$
\begin{array}{r|rrrr}
-6 & 1 & 6 & 1 & 6 \\
   &   & -6 & 0 & -6 \\
\hline
   & 1 & 0 & 1 & 0
\end{array}
$$

$P(-6) = 0$, so $-6$ is a root. We now know that

$$P(x) = (x + 6)(x^2 + 1).$$

Now $x^2 + 1$ has no real roots, so the only rational root of $P(x)$ is $-6$. The other roots are $i$ and $-i$.

**TRY THIS** ➡

> 2. Let $P(x) = x^3 + 7x^2 + 4x + 28$.
>
>    If $\dfrac{c}{d}$ is a rational root of $P(x)$, then:
>
>    a) What are the possibilities for $c$?
>    b) What are the possibilities for $d$?
>    c) What are the possibilities for $\dfrac{c}{d}$?
>    d) How can you tell without substitution or synthetic division that there are no positive roots?
>    e) Find the rational roots of $P(x)$.
>    f) Find the other roots if they exist.

**Example 3.** Find the rational roots of $x^4 + 2x^3 + 2x^2 - 4x - 8$.

Since the leading coefficient is 1, the only possibilities for rational roots are the factors of the last coefficient, $-8$:

$$1, -1, 2, -2, 4, -4, 8, -8.$$

But, using substitution or synthetic division, we find that none of the possibilities is a root. Thus there are no rational roots.

**TRY THIS** ➡

> 3. Let $P(x) = x^4 + x^2 + 2x + 6$.
>    a) How do you know at the outset that this polynomial has no positive roots?
>    b) Find the rational roots of $P(x)$.
>
> 4. a) Find the rational roots of $x^2 + 3x + 3$.
>    b) Can you find the other roots of this polynomial? What are they? Why can you find them?

## Exercise Set 15-5

▌ Find the rational roots, if they exist, of each polynomial. If possible, find the other roots. (*See Examples 1–3.*)

1. $x^3 + 3x^2 - 2x - 6$
2. $x^3 - x^2 - 3x + 3$
3. $5x^4 - 4x^3 + 19x^2 - 16x - 4$
4. $3x^4 - 4x^3 + x^2 + 6x - 2$
5. $x^4 - 3x^3 - 20x^2 - 24x - 8$
6. $x^4 + 5x^3 - 27x^2 + 31x - 10$
7. $x^3 + 3x^2 - x - 3$
8. $x^3 + 5x^2 - x - 5$
9. $x^3 + 8$
10. $x^3 - 8$
11. $4x^3 - 3x^2 + 4x - 3$
12. $2x^3 - 3x^2 - x + 1$
13. $x^5 - 5x^4 + 5x^3 + 15x^2 - 36x + 20$
14. $x^5 - 3x^4 - 3x^3 + 9x^2 - 4x + 12$
15. $x^4 + 32$
16. $x^6 + 8$
17. $x^3 - x^2 - 4x + 3$
18. $2x^3 + 3x^2 + 2x + 3$
19. $x^4 + 2x^3 + 2x^2 - 4x - 8$
20. $x^4 + 6x^3 + 17x^2 + 36x + 66$

---

### Challenge Exercises

21. Rational Coefficients. The polynomial $P(x) = \frac{1}{12}x^3 - \frac{1}{12}x^2 - \frac{2}{3}x + 1$ does not have all integer coefficients, but all are rational. If we multiply by the LCM of the denominators, 12, we get a polynomial which does have all integer coefficients. Any rational root of $12P(x)$ is a rational root of $P(x)$, and conversely. Find the rational roots of each polynomial.

    a) $\frac{1}{12}x^3 - \frac{1}{12}x^2 - \frac{2}{3}x + 1$    b) $x^4 - \frac{1}{6}x^3 - \frac{4}{3}x^2 + \frac{1}{6}x + \frac{1}{3}$

22. The volume of a cube is 64 cm³. Find the length of a side. (*Hint:* Solve $x^3 - 64 = 0$.)

Graph.

23. $P(x) = x^3 + 3x^2 - 2x - 6$
24. $P(x) = x^3 - 3x + 1$
25. $P(x) = x^4 + x^2 + 1$
26. $P(x) = x^4 - 4x^2 + 5$

---

### CONSUMER NOTE: Car Costs

The costs of owning a car begin with the purchase price. They include sales tax, license fees, ownership fees, and insurance costs. They also include interest if the car is bought with borrowed money. Then there are the costs of gas, oil, and maintenance.

# COMPUTER ACTIVITY

## Approximating Roots of a Polynomial by the Bisection Method

**PROBLEM:** Find the roots of $F(X) = X^2 - 5X + 4$.

**Example using the flowchart:**

| 1 | | 2 | 3 | 4 |
|---|---|---|---|---|
| Input | | | | |
| A(**5**) | B(**6**) | X | F(X) | F(X) = 0? |
| 1 | 5 | $\dfrac{1+5}{2} = 3$ | $3^2 - 5(3) + 4 = -2$ | |
| 3 | 5 | $\dfrac{3+5}{2} = ④$ | $4^2 - 5(4) + 4 = 0$ | Stop |

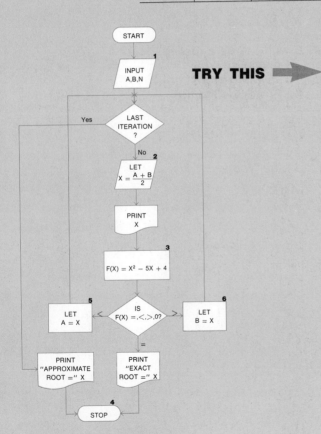

**TRY THIS** ➡

Find the roots of
$F(X) = X^2 + 3X + 1$. Use $A = -1$
and $B = 0$ for the larger root.
Then determine suitable values
for A and B and find a good
approximation for the smaller root.

\* A and B are estimates that are
larger and smaller than the exact
roots. N is the number of iterations.

BASIC PROGRAM (Optional)
```
*10   INPUT A,B,N
 20   DEF FNF(X) = X↑2 − 5*X + 4
 30   FOR I = 1 TO N
 40   LET X = (A + B)/2
 50   PRINT X
 60   IF FNF(X) = 0 THEN 140
 70   IF FNF(X) < 0 THEN 100
 80   LET B = X
 90   GO TO 110
100   LET A = X
110   NEXT I
120   PRINT "APPROXIMATE
         ROOT ="X
130   GO TO 150
140   PRINT "EXACT ROOT ="X
150   STOP
```

## CHAPTER 15 REVIEW

Review the material in the chapter. Then see how you have done by trying these review exercises. If you miss an exercise, restudy the indicated lesson.

15-1    1. Determine whether $2 + i$ is a root of $P(x) = x^2 - 4x + 5$.

15-2    2. What is the remainder when $-3x^3 + 6x^2 - x + 1$ is divided by $x + 2$?

15-2    3. Determine whether $x + i$ is a factor of $P(x) = x^4 - 1$.

15-3    4. Use synthetic division to find the quotient and remainder: $(5x^6 - 6x^4 + 1) \div (x + 1)$.

15-3    5. Use synthetic division to find $P(-4)$: $P(x) = -2x^4 - 8x^3 + 4x^2 - 2x + 1$.

15-4    6. Find a polynomial of degree 4 with roots $-1$, $1$, $i$, $-i$.

15-4    7. Find a polynomial of degree 3 with $-1$ as a root of multiplicity 1 and 1 as a root of multiplicity 2.

15-4    8. Suppose a polynomial of degree 5 with rational coefficients has roots $7$, $-3 + 4i$, $2 - \sqrt{5}$. Find the other roots.

15-4    9. Find the other roots of $x^4 - x^3 + 2x^2 - 4x - 8$ given that one root is $2i$.

15-5    10. Find the rational roots of $20x^3 - 30x^2 + 12x - 1$, if they exist. If possible, find the other roots.

## CHAPTER 15 TEST

1.  Determine whether $2i$ is a root of $P(x) = x^2 + 2$.
2.  What is the remainder when $x^4 + 3x^3 + 3x^2 + 2$ is divided by $x - 2$?
3.  Determine whether $x + 1$ is a factor of $P(x) = x^3 + 6x^2 + x + 30$.
4.  Use synthetic division to find the quotient and remainder: $(2x^4 - 6x^3 + 7x^2 - 5x + 1) \div (x + 2)$.
5.  Use synthetic division to find $P(3)$: $P(x) = 2x^4 - 3x^3 + x^2 - 3x + 7$.
6.  Find a polynomial of degree 3 with roots 0, 1, and $i$.
7.  Find a polynomial of degree 7 with 1 as a root of multiplicity 1, $-1$ as a root of multiplicity 1, 2 as a root of multiplicity 2, and $-3$ as a root with multiplicity 3.
8.  Suppose a polynomial of degree 4 with rational coefficients has roots $-8 - 7i$ and $10 + \sqrt{3}$. Find the other roots.
9.  Find the other roots of $x^3 - 1$ given that one of the roots is 1.
10. Find the rational roots of $x^3 - 7x^2 + 16x - 12$, if they exist. If possible, find the other roots.

## CUMULATIVE REVIEW FOR CHAPTERS 12–15

Solve.

| | | |
|---|---|---|
| 12-1 | 1. | $9x^2 - 2 = 0$ |
| 12-2 | 2. | $3x^2 = 4x$ |
| 12-2 | 3. | $2x^2 - 8x - 42 = 0$ |
| 12-3 | 4. | $x^2 - 3x - 9 = 0$ |

12-3   5.   Use the square root table, Table 1, in the back of the book to approximate solutions of $3x^2 + 7x - 1 = 0$ to the nearest tenth.

12-4   6.   Without solving, determine the nature of the solutions of $4x^2 - 3x + 7 = 0$.

12-5   7.   Without solving, find the sum and product of the solutions of $15x^2 - 7x - 2 = 0$.

12-5   8.   Find a quadratic equation whose solutions are $\frac{1}{2}$ and $-\frac{3}{4}$.

12-6   9.   Solve $v = \sqrt{\frac{4}{3}gh}$ for $h$.

12-7   10.   $2560 grows to $4000 in 2 years. What is the interest rate?

12-7   11.   From a height of 360 m, an object is thrown downward at an initial velocity of 12 m/sec. How long does it take to reach the ground? Round to the nearest tenth.

12-8   12.   Solve: $(3 + 2\sqrt{x})^2 + (3 + 2\sqrt{x}) - 20 = 0$.

13-1   13.   Graph: $f(x) = -\frac{1}{10}x^2$.

13-1   14.   Graph: $f(x) = 3(x - 2)^2$.

13-2   15.   Graph $f(x) = -4(x + 1)^2 - 2$. Then find the vertex, line of symmetry, and maximum or minimum value.

13-2   16.   Without graphing, find the vertex, line of symmetry, and maximum or minimum value of $f(x) = 6(x - \frac{1}{4})^2 + 19$.

13-3   17.   Find an equation of the type $f(x) = a(x - h)^2 + k$ for $f(x) = 3x^2 - 24x + 50$. Then find the vertex, line of symmetry, and the maximum or minimum value.

13-4   18.   Find the $x$-intercepts of $f(x) = x^2 + 2x - 3$.

13-5   19.   Find the quadratic function that fits the data points $(1, 4)$, $(-1, 6)$, $(-2, 16)$.

13-5   20.   A rocket is fired upward from ground level at a velocity of 147 m/s. Find a) its maximum height and when it is attained; and b) when it reaches the ground.

13-6   21.   The area of a cube varies directly as the square of the length of a side. If a cube has an area 168.54 m² when the length of a side is 5.3 m, what will the area be when the length of a side is 10.2 m?

14-1   22.   Find the distance between the points $(5, 6)$ and $(5, -2)$.

14-1   23.   Find the midpoint of the segment with endpoints $(4, 5)$ and $(6, -7)$.

| | | |
|---|---|---|
| 14-2 | 24. | Find an equation of a circle with center at $(-2, 7)$ and radius $\sqrt{5}$. |
| 14-2 | 25. | Find the center and radius of the circle $(x + 1)^2 + (y + 3)^2 = 4$. Then graph the circle. |
| 14-3 | 26. | Find the center, vertices, and foci for the ellipse $16x^2 + 9y^2 = 144$. Then graph the ellipse. |
| 14-4 | 27. | Find the vertices, foci, and asymptotes for the hyperbola $\dfrac{(y + 3)^2}{25} - \dfrac{(x + 1)^2}{16} = 1$. Graph the hyperbola. |
| 14-4 | 28. | Graph: $xy = -4$. |
| 14-5 | 29. | Find the vertex, focus, and directrix for the parabola $y^2 + 4x = 0$. Then graph the parabola. |
| 14-6 | 30. | Solve: $9x^2 + 4y^2 = 36$ <br> $\phantom{xxxx}3x + 2y = 6$ |
| 14-6 | 31. | A rectangle has perimeter 28 cm, and the length of a diagonal is 10 cm. What are its dimensions? |
| 14-7 | 32. | Solve: $x^2 + y^2 = 20$ <br> $\phantom{xxxxx}xy = 8$ |
| 14-7 | 33. | The product of two numbers is 60. The sum of their squares is 136. Find the numbers. |
| 15-1 | 34. | Is 2 a root of $p(x) = 2x^3 - 3x^2 + x - 1$? |
| 15-1 | 35. | Divide to find whether $x - 3$ is a factor of $x^4 - 81$. |
| 15-2 | 36. | Use the Remainder Theorem to find the remainder when $p(x) = x^3 - 2x^2 + 5x - 4$ is divided by $x + 2$. |
| 15-2 | 37. | Find a complete factorization of $P(x) = x^3 + 2x^2 - 2$. |
| 15-3 | 38. | Use synthetic division to find the quotient and remainder: $(x^3 - 27) \div (x - 3)$. |
| 15-3 | 39. | Let $P(x) = x^3 + 7x^2 - 12x - 3$. Find $P(-3)$ using synthetic division. |
| 15-3 | 40. | Let $P(x) = 3x^3 + 11x^2 - 2x + 8$. Use synthetic division to determine whether $-4$ is a root of $P(x)$. |
| 15-4 | 41. | Find the roots of the polynomial $P(x) = x^3(x - 1)^2(x + 4)$ and state the multiplicity of each. |
| 15-4 | 42. | Find a polynomial of degree 4 with 0 as a root of multiplicity 2 and 5 as a root of multiplicity 2. |
| 15-4 | 43. | Suppose a polynomial of degree 5 with rational coefficients has roots 8, $6 - 7i$, $\frac{1}{2} + \sqrt{11}$. Find the other roots. |
| 15-4 | 44. | Find a polynomial of lowest degree with rational coefficients which has $3 + \sqrt{2}$ and $2 - i$ as some of its roots. |
| 15-4 | 45. | Let $P(x) = x^3 - 4x^2 + x - 4$. Find the other roots of $P(x)$, given that $-i$ is a root. |
| 15-5 | 46. | Find the rational roots of $2x^3 - 3x^2 - x + 1$, if they exist. If possible, find the other roots. |

## Ready for Exponential and Logarithm Functions?

10-8    1.   Rewrite without fractional exponents: $x^{\frac{4}{5}}$.

1-7    Rename without using an exponent.
      2.   $5^1$
      3.   $8^0$

1-7    4.   Rename without using a negative exponent:   $8^{-4}$.

8-4    5.   Find an equation of the inverse of $y = x^3 + 4$.

10-9    6.   Solve:   $\sqrt{x} = 7$.

1-8    7.   Multiply and simplify:   $x^{-5} \cdot x^3$.

1-8    8.   Divide and simplify:   $\dfrac{x^{-3}}{x^4}$.

1-8    9.   Simplify:   $(x^{-3})^4$.

10-1    Convert to scientific notation.
      10.   5240
      11.   0.0845

10-1    Convert to decimal notation.
      12.   $4.335 \times 10^5$
      13.   $1.06 \times 10^{-3}$

2-2    14.   Solve:   $3x - 5 = 16$.

# Chapter 16
# Exponential and Logarithm Functions

*The loudness of an airplane during takeoff is measured using a logarithmic scale.*

# 16-1 Exponential Functions

After finishing Lesson 16-1, you should be able to
▮ graph exponential functions.

▮ In Chapter 10 we gave meaning to expressions with rational exponents such as

$$5^{\frac{1}{4}}, \; 5^{-\frac{3}{4}}, \; 7^{2.34}, \; 5^{1.73}.$$

For example, $5^{1.73}$ or $5^{\frac{173}{100}}$, means to raise 5 to the 173 power and take the 100th root. We shall now give meaning to expressions with irrational exponents such as

$$5^{\sqrt{2}}, \; 7^{\pi}, \; 9^{-\sqrt{5}}, \; 5^{\sqrt{3}}.$$

Let us think about $5^{\sqrt{3}}$. We consider $5^r$, where $r$ is rational. The exponent $\sqrt{3}$ is irrational, but we can let $r$ come very close to it. As this happens $5^r$ gets close to $5^{\sqrt{3}}$.

| $r$ | $5^r$ |
|---|---|
| $1 < \sqrt{3} < 2$ | $5^1 < p < 5^2$ |
| $1.7 < \sqrt{3} < 1.8$ | $5^{1.7} < p < 5^{1.8}$ |
| $1.73 < \sqrt{3} < 1.74$ | $5^{1.73} < p < 5^{1.74}$ |
| $1.732 < \sqrt{3} < 1.733$ | $5^{1.732} < p < 5^{1.733}$ |

As $r$ closes in on $\sqrt{3}$, $5^r$ closes in on exactly one real number $p$. We *define* $5^{\sqrt{3}}$ to be the number $p$.

   We can define any irrational exponent in a similar way. Thus any exponential expression $a^x$ now has meaning, whether $x$ is rational or irrational. The usual laws of exponents still hold, but we will not prove that here.

**DEFINITION**

The function $f(x) = a^x$, where $a$ is a positive constant, is called the *exponential function, base a.*

**Example 1.** Graph $y = 2^x$.

a)  First, we find some solutions (ordered pairs). To do this we choose numbers for $x$ and then find the corresponding $y$ values.

| $x$ | 0 | 1 | 2 | $-1$ | $-2$ | $-3$ |
|---|---|---|---|---|---|---|
| $y$ | 1 | 2 | 4 | $\frac{1}{2}$ | $\frac{1}{4}$ | $\frac{1}{8}$ |

b) Next, we plot these points and connect them with a smooth curve.

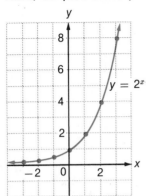

Note that as $x$ increases, the function values increase indefinitely. As $x$ decreases, the function values decrease toward 0.

**TRY THIS** ➡

1. Graph $y = 3^x$.
   a) Complete this table of solutions.

   | $x$ | 0 | 1 | 2 | $-1$ | $-2$ | $-3$ |
   |---|---|---|---|---|---|---|
   | $y$ | | | | | | |

   b) Plot the points from the table and connect them with a smooth curve.

**Example 2.** Graph $y = (\frac{1}{2})^x$.

We could plot points and connect them, but we note that $(\frac{1}{2})^x = (2^{-1})^x = 2^{-x}$. Thus the function we wish to graph is

   $y = 2^{-x}$.

Compare this with the graph of $y = 2^x$. The graph of $y = 2^{-x}$ is a reflection of it across the $y$-axis because we have replaced $x$ by $-x$. Knowing this allows us to graph $y = 2^{-x}$ at once.

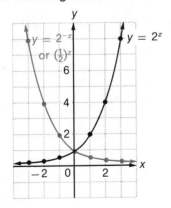

**TRY THIS** ➡

2. Graph $y = (\frac{1}{3})^x$.

The preceding examples and exercises illustrate exponential functions of various bases. If $a = 1$ the graph is the horizontal line $y = 1$. For other positive values of $a$, the graphs are more interesting. We can describe exponential functions as follows.

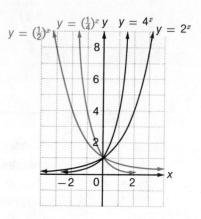

1. When $a > 1$, the function $f(x) = a^x$ is an increasing function. The greater the value of $a$, the faster the function increases.
2. When $a < 1$, the function $f(x) = a^x$ is a decreasing function. The greater the value of $a$, the more slowly the function decreases.

## Exercise Set 16-1

▌Graph. Where possible, use transformations. (*See Examples 1 and 2.*)

1. $y = 2^x$
2. $y = 3^x$
3. $y = 5^x$
4. $y = 6^x$
5. $y = (\frac{1}{4})^x$
6. $y = (\frac{1}{5})^x$
7. $y = (0.4)^x$
8. $y = (0.3)^x$
9. $y = 2^{x-1}$
10. $y = 3^{x+1}$
11. $y = 5^{x+2}$
12. $y = 6^{x-2}$

### Calculator Exercises

Graph.
13. $y = (2.34)^x$
14. $y = (0.568)^x$

### Challenge Exercises

Graph.
15. $y = 3^{|x|}$
16. $y = 2^{|x-1|}$
17. $y = 3^x + 3^{-x}$
18. $y = 2^x + 2^{-x}$

# 16-2 *Logarithmic Functions*

After finishing Lesson 16-2, you should be able to
**I**　graph logarithmic functions.
**II**　convert from exponential equations to logarithmic equations.
**III**　convert from logarithmic equations to exponential equations.
**IIII**　solve certain logarithmic equations.
**IIIII**　find simple logarithms.
**IIIIII**　simplify expressions like $a^{\log_a x}$ and $\log_a a^x$.

## I Logarithmic Functions

The inverse of an exponential function, for $a > 0$ and $a \neq 1$, is called a *logarithmic function,* or *logarithm function.* Thus one way to describe a logarithm function is to interchange variables in $y = a^x$:

$$x = a^y.$$

The most useful and interesting logarithmic functions are those for which $a > 1$. The graph of such a function is a reflection of $y = a^x$ across the line $y = x$. The domain of a logarithm function is the set of all positive real numbers.

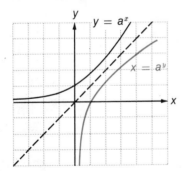

We use the symbol $\log_a x$ to denote the second coordinates of a logarithm function $x = a^y$. Thus a logarithm function can be described as $y = \log_a x$.

### DEFINITION
$y = \log_a x$ is defined to mean $x = a^y$, where $x > 0$, $a > 0$, $a \neq 1$.

$\text{Log}_a\, x$ represents the exponent in the equation $x = a^y$, so the logarithm, base $a$, of a number $x$ is the power to which $a$ is raised to get $x$.

Let us graph a logarithmic function.

**Example 1.**   Graph $y = \log_5 x$.

We graph $y = 5^x$ and reflect it across the line $y = x$.

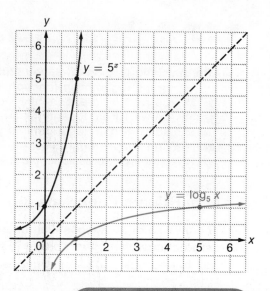

<br />

**TRY THIS**

> 1.   Graph $y = \log_4 x$.

For any base $a$, $\log_a a = 1$ and $\log_a 1 = 0$.

$\log_a a = 1$ follows from the exponential equation $a^1 = a$. Similarly, $\log_a 1 = 0$ follows from the exponential equation $a^0 = 1$.

**TRY THIS**

> Simplify.
>
> 2.   $\log_\pi \pi$
> 3.   $\log_9 1$
> 4.   $\log_e 1$
> 5.   $\log_{3.7} 3.7$

## ■ Converting from Exponential to Logarithmic Equations

We use the definition above to convert from exponential to logarithmic equations.

**Examples.**   Convert to logarithmic equations.

**2.**   $8 = 2^x \rightarrow x = \log_2 8$

**3.**   $y^{-1} = 4 \rightarrow -1 = \log_y 4$

**4.**   $a^b = c \rightarrow b = \log_a c$

*It helps, in such conversions, to remember that a logarithm is an exponent.*

**TRY THIS**

> Convert to logarithmic equations.
>
> 6.   $6^0 = 1$
> 7.   $10^{-3} = 0.001$
> 8.   $16^{0.25} = 2$
> 9.   $m^T = p$

## ɪɪɪ Converting from Logarithmic to Exponential Equations

We also use the definition to convert from logarithmic to exponential equations.

**Examples.** Convert to exponential equations.

**5.** $y = \log_3 5 \rightarrow 3^y = 5$

**6.** $-2 = \log_a 7 \rightarrow a^{-2} = 7$

**7.** $a = \log_b d \rightarrow b^a = d$

*Again, it helps to remember that a logarithm is an exponent.*

**TRY THIS** ▬▬▬▶

> Convert to exponential equations.
>
> 10. $\log_2 32 = 5$
> 11. $\log_{10} 1000 = 3$
> 12. $\log_a Q = 7$
> 13. $\log_t M = x$

## ɪɪɪɪ Solving Logarithmic Equations

Certain equations involving logarithms can be solved by first converting to exponential equations.

**Example 8.** Solve $\log_2 x = -3$.

$$2^{-3} = x \qquad \text{\textit{Converting to an exponential equation}}$$
$$x = \tfrac{1}{8}$$

**Example 9.** Solve $\log_x 4 = \tfrac{1}{2}$.

$$x^{\frac{1}{2}} = 4 \qquad \text{\textit{Converting to an exponential equation}}$$
$$(x^{\frac{1}{2}})^2 = 4^2 \qquad \text{\textit{Squaring both sides}}$$
$$x = 16$$

This checks, so the solution is 16.

**TRY THIS** ▬▬▬▶

> Solve.
>
> 14. $\log_{10} x = 4$
> 15. $\log_x 81 = 4$

## ɪɪɪɪɪ Finding Logarithms

We can find some logarithms by first converting to exponential notation.

**Example 10.** Find $\log_{10} 100$.

Let $x = \log_{10} 100$. Then

$$10^x = 100. \qquad \text{\textit{Converting to an exponential equation}}$$

Since we also know that

$$10^2 = 100,$$

we know that $x = 2$, so $\log_{10} 100 = 2$.

**Example 11.** Find $\log_{27} 3$.

Let $x = \log_{27} 3$. Then

$27^x = 3$.

Since we also know that

$27^{\frac{1}{3}} = 3$,

we know that $x = \frac{1}{3}$, so $\log_{27} 3 = \frac{1}{3}$.

**Example 12.** Find $\log_{10} 0.001$.

Let $x = \log_{10} 0.001$. Then

$10^x = 0.001$.

Since we also know that

$10^{-3} = 0.001$,

it follows that $x = -3$, so $\log_{10} 0.001 = -3$.

**TRY THIS**

Find.

16. $\log_{10} 1000$
17. $\log_2 16$
18. $\log_3 3$
19. $\log_{10} 0.01$
20. $\log_5 \frac{1}{25}$

## ⦚⦚⦚⦚⦚ Simplifying Expressions Like $a^{\log_a x}$ and $\log_a a^x$

Exponential and logarithm functions are inverses of each other. Let us also recall an important fact about functions and their inverses. If the domains are suitable, then for any $x$,

$$f(f^{-1}(x)) = x \quad \text{and} \quad f^{-1}(f(x)) = x.$$

When we apply this fact to exponential and logarithm functions, we get the following.

**THEOREM 16-1**

For any number $a$, suitable as a logarithm base,
1. $a^{\log_a x} = x$, for any positive number $x$; and
2. $\log_a a^x = x$, for any number $x$.

**Examples.** Simplify.

**13.** $2^{\log_2 5} = 5$
**14.** $10^{\log_{10} t} = t$
**15.** $\log_e e^{-3} = -3$
**16.** $\log_{10} 10^{5.6} = 5.6$

**TRY THIS**

Simplify.

21. $7^{\log_7 \pi}$
22. $\log_5 5^{97}$
23. $\log_e e^M$
24. $b^{\log_b 42}$

## Exercise Set 16-2

▮ Graph. Where possible, use transformations. (*See Example 1.*)

1. $y = \log_2 x$
2. $y = \log_3 x$
3. $y = \log_2 (x + 1)$
4. $y = \log_3 (x - 2)$

▮▮ Convert to logarithmic equations. (*See Examples 2–4.*)

5. $10^3 = 1000$
6. $10^2 = 100$
7. $5^{-3} = \frac{1}{125}$
8. $4^{-5} = \frac{1}{1024}$
9. $8^{\frac{1}{3}} = 2$
10. $16^{\frac{1}{4}} = 2$
11. $10^{0.3010} = 2$
12. $10^{0.4771} = 3$
13. $a^{-b} = c$
14. $P^t = M$

▮▮▮ Convert to exponential equations. (*See Examples 5–7.*)

15. $t = \log_3 8$
16. $h = \log_7 10$
17. $\log_5 25 = 2$
18. $\log_6 6 = 1$
19. $\log_{10} 0.1 = -1$
20. $\log_{10} 0.01 = -2$
21. $\log_{10} 7 = 0.845$
22. $\log_{10} 3 = 0.4771$
23. $\log_b M = N$
24. $\log_k A = c$

▮▮▮▮ Solve. (*See Examples 8 and 9.*)

25. $\log_3 x = 2$
26. $\log_4 x = 3$
27. $\log_x 16 = 2$
28. $\log_x 64 = 3$
29. $\log_2 x = -1$
30. $\log_3 x = -2$
31. $\log_8 x = \frac{1}{3}$
32. $\log_{32} x = \frac{1}{5}$

▮▮▮▮▮ Find. (*See Examples 10–12.*)

33. $\log_2 64$
34. $\log_4 64$
35. $\log_{10} 10^2$
36. $\log_3 3^4$
37. $\log_{10} 0.1$
38. $\log_{10} 10{,}000$
39. $\log_{10} 1$
40. $\log_{10} 10$

▮▮▮▮▮▮ Simplify. (*See Examples 13–16.*)

41. $3^{\log_3 4}$
42. $7^{\log_7 10}$
43. $\log_t t^9$
44. $\log_p p^a$
45. $\log_Q Q^{\sqrt{5}}$
46. $\log_m m^\pi$
47. $A^{\log_A 56}$
48. $Q^{\log_Q W}$

---

## Challenge Exercises

Graph.

49. $y = \log_2 |x|$
50. $y = \log_3 |x|$

# 16-3 Properties of Logarithmic Functions

After finishing Lesson 16-3, you should be able to

**I** express the logarithm of a product as a sum of logarithms, and conversely.

**II** express the logarithm of the $n$th power of a number, $\log_a (M^n)$, as a product $n \cdot \log_a M$, and conversely.

**III** express the logarithm of a quotient, $\log_a \dfrac{M}{N}$, as a difference of logarithms, $\log_a M - \log_a N$, and conversely.

**IIII** convert from logarithms of sums or differences to single logarithms, and convert from single logarithms to logarithms of sums or differences.

**IIIII** given logarithms of some numbers, find logarithms of other numbers, using properties of logarithms.

## ▮ Logarithms of Products

We now establish some basic properties of logarithms.

**THEOREM 16-2**

For any positive numbers $M$ and $N$,

$\log_a (M \cdot N) = \log_a M + \log_a N$,

where $a$ is any positive number different from 1.

Theorem 16-2 says that the logarithm of a product is the sum of logarithms.

**Example 1.** Express $\log_2 (4 \cdot 16)$ as a sum of logarithms.

$\log_2 (4 \cdot 16) = \log_2 4 + \log_2 16$    *By Theorem 16-2*

**TRY THIS**

Express as a sum of logarithms.

1. $\log_5 (25 \cdot 5)$
2. $\log_b PQ$

Express as a single logarithm.

3. $\log_3 7 + \log_3 5$
4. $\log_a C + \log_a A + \log_a B + \log_a I + \log_a N$

---

**A Proof of Theorem 16-2**

Let $\log_a M = x$ and $\log_a N = y$. Converting to exponential equations, we have $a^x = M$ and $a^y = N$.

Next we multiply, to obtain

$$M \cdot N = a^x \cdot a^y = a^{x+y}.$$

Now, converting back to a logarithmic equation, we get

$$\log_a (M \cdot N) = x + y, \text{ or}$$
$$\log_a (M \cdot N) = \log_a M + \log_a N,$$

which was to be shown.

## ▮▮ Logarithms of Powers

### THEOREM 16-3

For any positive number $M$ and any number $p$,

$$\log_a M^p = p \cdot \log_a M,$$

where $a$ is any positive number different from 1.

Theorem 16-3 says that the logarithm of a power of a number is the exponent times the logarithm of the number.

**Examples.**    Express as a product.

**2.**  $\log_b 9^{-5} = -5 \log_b 9$    *By Theorem 16-3*

**3.**  $\log_a \sqrt[4]{5} = \log_a 5^{\frac{1}{4}}$    *Writing exponential notation*

   $= \frac{1}{4}\log_a 5$    *By Theorem 16-3*

Express as a product.

5.  $\log_7 4^5$
6.  $\log_a \sqrt{5}$

**TRY THIS** ▬▬➤

### A Proof of Theorem 16-3

Let $x = \log_a M$. Then, converting to an exponential equation we get $a^x = M$. Raising both sides to the $p$th power, we get

$(a^x)^p = M^p$, or

$a^{xp} = M^p$.

Converting back to a logarithmic equation,

$\log_a M^p = xp$.

But $x = \log_a M$, so

$\log_a M^p = (\log_a M)p = p \cdot \log_a M,$

which was to be shown.

## ▮▮▮ Logarithms of Quotients

### THEOREM 16-4

For any positive numbers $M$ and $N$,

$$\log_a \frac{M}{N} = \log_a M - \log_a N,$$

where $a$ is any positive number different from 1.

Theorem 16-4 says that the logarithm of a quotient is the difference of the logarithms (the logarithm of the dividend minus the logarithm of the divisor).

**Example 4.** Express as a difference of logarithms.

$$\log_t \frac{6}{U} = \log_t 6 - \log_t U \qquad \text{By Theorem 16-4}$$

**TRY THIS** ➡️

Express as a difference.

7. $\log_b \frac{P}{Q}$

8. $\log_c \frac{1}{4}$

---

**A Proof of Theorem 16-4**

$\frac{M}{N} = M \cdot N^{-1}$, so $\log_a \frac{M}{N} = \log_a (M \cdot N^{-1})$.

By Theorem 16-2, $\log_a (M \cdot N^{-1}) = \log_a M + \log_a N^{-1}$
and by Theorem 16-3 $\log_a N^{-1} = -1 \cdot \log_a N$.
So we have

$$\log_a \frac{M}{N} = \log_a M - \log_a N,$$

which was to be shown.

---

## ▐▌▐▌ Using the Properties

**Example 5.** Express in terms of logarithms of $x$, $y$, and $z$.

$$\log_a \sqrt[4]{\frac{xy}{z^3}} = \log_a \left(\frac{xy}{z^3}\right)^{\frac{1}{4}} \qquad \text{\textit{Writing exponential notation}}$$

$$= \frac{1}{4} \cdot \log_a \frac{xy}{z^3} \qquad \text{\textit{Using Theorem 16-3}}$$

$$= \frac{1}{4}[\log_a xy - \log_a z^3] \qquad \text{\textit{Using Theorem 16-4}}$$

$$= \frac{1}{4}[\log_a x + \log_a y - 3 \log_a z] \qquad \text{\textit{Using Theorems 16-2 and 16-3}}$$

**TRY THIS** ➡️

Express in terms of logarithms of $x$, $y$, and $z$.

9. $\log_a \sqrt{\frac{z^3}{xy}}$

**Example 6.** Express as a single logarithm.

$$\tfrac{1}{2}\log_a x - 7 \log_a y + \log_a z = \log_a \sqrt{x} - \log_a y^7 + \log_a z \quad \textit{Using Theorem 16-3}$$

$$= \log_a \frac{\sqrt{x}}{y^7} + \log_a z \quad \textit{Using Theorem 16-4}$$

$$= \log_a \frac{z\sqrt{x}}{y^7} \quad \textit{Using Theorem 16-2}$$

**TRY THIS**

> Express as a single logarithm.
>
> 10.  $5 \log_a x - \log_a y + \tfrac{1}{4} \log_a z$

## ▌▌▌▌▌ Finding Logarithms

Given certain logarithms, we can find certain others using the properties we have developed.

**Examples.** Given that $\log_a 2 = 0.301$ and $\log_a 3 = 0.477$, find:

**7.** $\log_a 6 = \log_a (2 \cdot 3)$
$= \log_a 2 + \log_a 3 \quad \textit{Using Theorem 16-2}$
$= 0.301 + 0.477$
$= 0.778$

**8.** $\log_a \sqrt{3} = \log_a 3^{\frac{1}{2}}$
$= \tfrac{1}{2} \cdot \log_a 3$
$= \tfrac{1}{2} \cdot (0.477)$
$= 0.2385$

**9.** $\log_a \tfrac{2}{3} = \log_a 2 - \log_a 3 \quad \textit{Using Theorem 16-4}$
$= 0.301 - 0.477$
$= -0.176$

**10.** $\log_a 5$; *No way to find, using these properties.*
$(\log_a 5 \neq \log_a 2 + \log_a 3)$.

**11.** $\dfrac{\log_a 2}{\log_a 3} = \dfrac{0.301}{0.477} \approx 0.63$. Note that we could not use any of the properties; we simply divided.

**TRY THIS**

> Given that $\log_a 2 = 0.301$ and $\log_a 3 = 0.477$ find:
>
> 11.  $\log_a 9$
> 12.  $\log_a \sqrt{2}$
> 13.  $\log_a \sqrt[3]{2}$
> 14.  $\log_a \tfrac{3}{2}$
> 15.  $\dfrac{\log_a 3}{\log_a 2}$

## Exercise Set 16-3

▮ Express as a sum of logarithms. (*See Example 1.*)
1. $\log_2 (32 \cdot 8)$
2. $\log_3 (27 \cdot 81)$
3. $\log_4 (64 \cdot 16)$
4. $\log_5 (25 \cdot 125)$
5. $\log_c Bx$
6. $\log_t 5Y$

Express as a single logarithm. (*See Example 1.*)
7. $\log_a 6 + \log_a 70$
8. $\log_b 65 + \log_b 2$
9. $\log_c K + \log_c y$
10. $\log_t H + \log_t M$

▮▮ Express as a product. (*See Examples 2 and 3.*)
11. $\log_a x^3$
12. $\log_b t^5$

▮▮▮ Express as a difference of logarithms. (*See Example 4.*)
13. $\log_a \dfrac{67}{5}$
14. $\log_t \dfrac{T}{7}$

▮▮▮▮ Express in terms of logarithms of $x$, $y$, and $z$. (*See Example 5.*)
15. $\log_a x^2 y^3 z$
16. $\log_a 5xy^4 z^3$
17. $\log_b \dfrac{xy^2}{z^3}$
18. $\log_c \sqrt[3]{\dfrac{x^4}{y^3 z^2}}$

Express as a single logarithm and simplify if possible. (*See Example 6.*)
19. $\frac{2}{3}\log_a x - \frac{1}{2}\log_a y$
20. $\frac{1}{2}\log_a x + 3\log_a y - 2\log_a x$
21. $\log_a 2x + 3(\log_a x - \log_a y)$
22. $\log_a x^2 - 2\log_a \sqrt{x}$
23. $\log_a \dfrac{a}{\sqrt{x}} - \log_a \sqrt{ax}$
24. $\log_a (x^2 - 4) - \log_a (x - 2)$

▮▮▮▮▮ Given $\log_{10} 2 = 0.301$, $\log_{10} 3 = 0.477$, and $\log_{10} 10 = 1$, find the following. (*See Examples 7–11.*)
25. $\log_{10} 4$
26. $\log_{10} 5$ (*Hint:* $5 = \frac{10}{2}$)
27. $\log_{10} 50$ (*Hint:* $50 = \frac{100}{2}$)
28. $\log_{10} 12$
29. $\log_{10} 60$
30. $\log_{10} \frac{1}{3}$
31. $\log_{10} \sqrt{\frac{2}{3}}$
32. $\log_{10} \sqrt[5]{12}$
33. $\log_{10} 90$
34. $\log_{10} \frac{9}{8}$
35. $\log_{10} \frac{1}{4}$
36. $\log_{10} \frac{9}{10}$

---

## Challenge Exercises

37. If $\log_a x = 2$, what is $\log_a \left(\dfrac{1}{x}\right)$?
38. If $\log_a x = 2$, what is $\log_{\frac{1}{a}} x$?

# 16-4 Common Logarithms

After finishing Lesson 16-4, you should be able to
**I**  use Table 2 to find logarithms and antilogarithms.
**II**  use Table 2 and scientific notation to find logarithms of numbers not in the table.
**III**  reverse the process above to find antilogarithms.

Base ten logarithms are known as *common logarithms*. Table 2 in the back of the book contains common logarithms of numbers from 1 to 10.

## I Logarithms in Computation

Before calculators and computers became so readily available, common logarithms were used extensively to do calculations. In fact, this is why logarithms were developed. Today, computations with logarithms are mainly of historical interest, but logarithm functions are still of substantial importance. The study of logarithms in computation does help one become more familiar with the properties of logarithm functions.

The following is a short table of powers of 10, or logarithms base 10.

$$1 = 10^{0.0000}, \quad \text{or} \quad \log_{10} 1 \ = 0.0000$$
$$2 \approx 10^{0.3010}, \quad \text{or} \quad \log_{10} 2 \ \approx 0.3010$$
$$3 \approx 10^{0.4771}, \quad \text{or} \quad \log_{10} 3 \ \approx 0.4771$$
$$4 \approx 10^{0.6021}, \quad \text{or} \quad \log_{10} 4 \ \approx 0.6021$$
$$5 \approx 10^{0.6990}, \quad \text{or} \quad \log_{10} 5 \ \approx 0.6990$$
$$6 \approx 10^{0.7782}, \quad \text{or} \quad \log_{10} 6 \ \approx 0.7782$$
$$7 \approx 10^{0.8451}, \quad \text{or} \quad \log_{10} 7 \ \approx 0.8451$$
$$8 \approx 10^{0.9031}, \quad \text{or} \quad \log_{10} 8 \ \approx 0.9031$$
$$9 \approx 10^{0.9542}, \quad \text{or} \quad \log_{10} 9 \ \approx 0.9542$$
$$10 = 10^{1.0000}, \quad \text{or} \quad \log_{10} 10 = 1.0000$$
$$11 \approx 10^{1.0414}, \quad \text{or} \quad \log_{10} 11 \approx 1.0414$$
$$12 \approx 10^{1.0792}, \quad \text{or} \quad \log_{10} 12 \approx 1.0792$$
$$13 \approx 10^{1.1139}, \quad \text{or} \quad \log_{10} 13 \approx 1.1139$$
$$14 \approx 10^{1.1461}, \quad \text{or} \quad \log_{10} 14 \approx 1.1461$$
$$15 \approx 10^{1.1761}, \quad \text{or} \quad \log_{10} 15 \approx 1.1761$$
$$16 \approx 10^{1.2041}, \quad \text{or} \quad \log_{10} 16 \approx 1.2041$$

The exponents are approximate, but accurate to four decimal places. To illustrate how logarithms can be used for computation we will use the above table and do some easy calculations.

**Example 1.**   Find $3 \times 4$ using the table of exponents.

$$3 \times 4 \approx 10^{0.4771} \times 10^{0.6021}$$
$$\approx 10^{1.0792} \quad \textit{Adding exponents}$$

From the table we see that $10^{1.0792} \approx 12$, so $3 \times 4 \approx 12$.

**TRY THIS** ➤

1. Find $2 \times 8$ using the table.

Note in Example 1 that we can find a product by adding the logarithms of the factors and then finding the number having the result as its logarithm. That is, we found the number $10^{1.0792}$. This number is often referred to as the *antilogarithm* of 1.0792. To state this another way, if

$$f(x) = \log_{10} x,$$

then   $f^{-1}(x) = \text{antilog}_{10} x = 10^x.$

In other words, an antilogarithm function is simply an exponential function. It is the inverse of a logarithm function.

**Example 2.**   Find $\frac{14}{2}$ using base 10 logarithms.

$$\log_{10} \frac{14}{2} = \log_{10} 14 - \log_{10} 2 \quad \textit{Using Theorem 16-4}$$
$$\approx 1.1461 - 0.3010 \quad \textit{Finding the logs from the table}$$
$$\log_{10} \frac{14}{2} \approx 0.8451 \quad \textit{Subtracting}$$
$$\frac{14}{2} \approx \text{antilog}_{10} 0.8451 \approx 7 \quad \textit{Using the table in reverse}$$

**Example 3.**   Find $\sqrt[4]{16}$ using base 10 logarithms.

$$\log_{10} \sqrt[4]{16} = \log_{10} 16^{\frac{1}{4}}$$
$$= \frac{1}{4} \cdot \log_{10} 16 \quad \textit{Using Theorem 16-3}$$
$$\approx \frac{1}{4} \cdot 1.2041$$
$$\log_{10} \sqrt[4]{16} \approx 0.3010 \quad \textit{Rounding to four decimal places}$$
$$\sqrt[4]{16} \approx \text{antilog}_{10} 0.3010 \approx 2$$

**Example 4.**   Find $2^3$ using base 10 logarithms.

$$\log_{10} 2^3 = 3 \cdot \log_{10} 2 \quad \textit{Using Theorem 16-3}$$
$$\approx 3 \cdot 0.3010 \approx 0.9030$$
$$\log_{10} 2^3 \approx 0.9030$$
$$2^3 \approx \text{antilog}_{10} 0.9030 \approx 8$$

**TRY THIS** ➤

Using base 10 logarithms and the table, find:

2. $4 \times 2$
3. $\frac{15}{3}$
4. $\sqrt[3]{8}$
5. $3^2$

## ▪▪ Using a Logarithm Table

We will often omit the base, 10, when working with common logarithms. That is,

log $M$ will be agreed to mean $\log_{10} M$.

Table 2 contains logarithms of numbers from 1 to 10. Part of that table is as follows.

| $x$ | 0 | 1 | 2 | 3 | 4 | 5 | 6 | 7 | 8 | 9 |
|-----|------|------|------|------|------|------|------|------|------|------|
| 5.0 | 0.6990 | 0.6998 | 0.7007 | 0.7016 | 0.7024 | 0.7033 | 0.7042 | 0.7050 | 0.7059 | 0.7067 |
| 5.1 | 0.7076 | 0.7084 | 0.7093 | 0.7101 | 0.7110 | 0.7118 | 0.7126 | 0.7135 | 0.7143 | 0.7152 |
| 5.2 | 0.7160 | 0.7168 | 0.7177 | 0.7185 | 0.7193 | 0.7202 | 0.7210 | 0.7218 | 0.7226 | 0.7235 |
| 5.3 | 0.7234 | 0.7251 | 0.7259 | 0.7267 | 0.7275 | 0.7284 | 0.7292 | 0.7300 | 0.7308 | 0.7316 |
| 5.4 | 0.7324 | 0.7332 | 0.7340 | 0.7348 | 0.7356 | 0.7364 | 0.7372 | 0.7380 | 0.7388 | 0.7396 |

To illustrate the use of the table, let us find log 5.24. We locate the row headed 5.2, then move across to the column headed 4. We find log 5.24 (the red entry in the table).

We can find antilogarithms by reversing this process. For example, antilog $0.7193 = 10^{0.7193} \approx 5.24$. Similarly, antilog $0.7292 \approx 5.36$.

**TRY THIS** ➡

Using Table 2 and scientific notation we can find logarithms of numbers that are not between 1 and 10. First recall the following:

$\log_a a^k = k$ for any number $k$.

Thus

$\log_{10} 10^k = k$ for any number $k$.

Use Table 2 to find each logarithm.

6. log 3.14
7. log 9.99
8. log 4.00

Use Table 2 to find each antilogarithm.

9. antilog 0.7589
10. antilog 0.0000
11. antilog 0.5587

### Examples

**5.** log 52.4 $= \log(5.24 \times 10^1)$    *Writing scientific notation for 52.4*
$= \log 5.24 + \log 10^1$    *Using Theorem 16-2*
$\approx \mathbf{0.7193} + 1$    *Using log table*

**6.** log 52,400 $= \log(5.24 \times 10^4)$
$= \log 5.24 + \log 10^4$
$\approx \mathbf{0.7193} + 4$

**7.** log 0.00524 = log(5.24 × 10⁻³)

$$= \log 5.24 + \log 10^{-3}$$

$$\approx \mathbf{0.7193} + (-3)$$

**TRY THIS** ➤

Use scientific notation and Table 2 to find each logarithm.

12. log 289
13. log 0.000289

In all of the examples above 0.7193 is the fractional part of the logarithm. It is called a *mantissa*. The integer part varies and is known as the *characteristic*. Table 2 contains only mantissas. Characteristics must be supplied. The characteristic is the exponent used in writing scientific notation.

$$\log 5240 \approx 0.7193 + 3$$

*mantissa*          *characteristic*

The preceding examples illustrate the importance of using the base 10. It allows great economy in the printing of tables. If we know the logarithms of numbers from 1 to 10 we can find the logarithm of any number. For any base other than 10 this would not be the case.

**Example 8.** Find log 0.0538, indicating the characteristic and mantissa.

We first write scientific notation:

$$5.38 \times 10^{-2}.$$

Then we find log 5.38, the mantissa:

$$\log 5.38 \approx 0.7308.$$

The characteristic is the exponent −2.
Now log 0.0538 ≈ 0.7308 + (−2), or −1.2692.

When negative characteristics occur, it is helpful to name the logarithm in such a way that the characteristic and mantissa are preserved. In the preceding example, we have

$$\log 0.0538 \approx -1.2692.$$

This notation displays neither the characteristic nor the mantissa. We can rename the characteristic −2 as 8 − 10 and then add the mantissa to obtain

$$8.7308 - 10.$$

This preserves both mantissa and characteristic.

**Example 9.** Find log 0.00687.

We write scientific notation (or at least visualize it):

$$0.00687 = 6.87 \times 10^{-3}.$$

The characteristic is −3, or 7 − 10. The mantissa from the table is 0.8370. Thus log 0.00687 ≈ 7.8370 − 10.

**TRY THIS**

Find the following. Use Table 2 and try to write only the answers. Where appropriate, name the answers so that positive mantissas are preserved.

14. log 67,800
15. log 892,000
16. log 45.9
17. log 609,000,000
18. log 0.0782
19. log 0.000111
20. log 0.0079

## ⅠⅠⅠ Antilogarithms

To find antilogarithms, we reverse the procedure for finding logarithms.

**Example 10.** Find antilog 2.6085.

$$\text{antilog } 2.6085 = 10^{2.6085} = 10^{(2+0.6085)}$$
$$= 10^2 \cdot 10^{0.6085}$$

From the table we can find $10^{0.6085}$, or antilog 0.6085. It is 4.06. Hence we have

$$\text{antilog } 2.6085 \approx 10^2 \times 4.06, \text{ or } 406.$$

In this example, we in effect separate the number 2.6085 into an integer and a number between 0 and 1. We use the latter with the table, after which we have scientific notation for our answer.

**Example 11.** Find antilog 3.7118.

From the table we find antilog 0.7118 ≈ 5.15. Thus

$$\text{antilog } 3.7118 \approx 5.15 \times 10^3 \qquad \textit{Note that 3 is the}$$
$$\approx 5150. \qquad\qquad \textit{characteristic.}$$

**Example 12.** Find antilog (7.7143 − 10).

The characteristic is −3 and the mantissa is 0.7143. From the table we find that antilog 0.7143 ≈ 5.18. Thus

$$\text{antilog } (7.7143 - 10) \approx 5.18 \times 10^{-3}$$
$$\approx 0.00518.$$

**TRY THIS**

Find the following. Use Table 2. Try to write only the answers.

21. antilog 4.8069
22. $10^{4.8069}$
23. $10^{3.9325}$
24. antilog 6.6284 − 10
25. $10^{8.2014-10}$

## Exercise Set 16-4

▍▎ Use Table 2 to find each of the following. (*See page 497.*)

1. log 2.46
2. log 7.65
3. log 5.31
4. log 8.57
5. log 3.72
6. log 9.04
7. log 1.07
8. log 4.60
9. antilog 0.8657
10. antilog 0.3502
11. antilog 0.6803
12. antilog 0.1399
13. antilog 0.7574
14. antilog 0.9191
15. $10^{0.5551}$
16. $10^{0.8021}$
17. $10^{0.5911}$
18. $10^{0.9609}$
19. $10^{0.3502}$
20. $10^{0.8657}$

Find these logarithms using Table 2. Try to write only the answers. Where appropriate, name the answers so that positive mantissas are preserved. (*See Examples 8 and 9.*)

21. log 347
22. log 8720
23. log 52.5
24. log 20.6
25. log 834
26. log 92.4
27. log 3870
28. log 624,000
29. log 0.00134
30. log 0.0702
31. log 0.64
32. log 0.000216
33. log 0.173
34. log 0.00347
35. log 0.0000404
36. log 0.00006

▍▍▍ Find these antilogarithms using Table 2. Try to write only the answers. (*See Examples 10–12.*)

37. antilog 3.3674
38. antilog 4.9222
39. antilog 1.2553
40. antilog 2.6294
41. antilog 9.7875 − 10
42. antilog 8.9881 − 10
43. antilog 7.5391 − 10
44. antilog 7.7774 − 10
45. $10^{1.4014}$
46. $10^{2.5391}$
47. $10^{7.9881-10}$
48. $10^{8.5391-10}$
49. $10^{6.7875-10}$
50. $10^{4.6294-10}$

### Challenge Exercises

Find *x*.

51. log *x* = 0.8021
52. log *x* = 4.1903
53. log *x* = 9.7875 − 10
54. $10^x = 2.67$
55. $10^x = 345$
56. $10^x = 5670$

# 16-5 Calculations With Logarithms

After finishing Lesson 16-5, you should be able to
▌ use logarithms for certain calculations.

▌The kinds of calculations in which logarithms may be helpful are multiplication, division, taking powers, and taking roots.

**Example 1.** Find $\dfrac{0.0578 \times 32.7}{8460}$.

We write a *plan* for the use of logarithms, then look up all of the mantissas at one time.

Let

$$N = \frac{0.0578 \times 32.7}{8460}.$$

Then

$$\log N = \log 0.0578 + \log 32.7 - \log 8460.$$

This gives us the plan.
We use a straight line to indicate addition and a wavy line to indicate subtraction.

Completion of plan:

$$\log 0.0578 \approx 8.7619 - 10$$
$$\log 32.7 \approx 1.5145$$

---

$$\log \text{numerator} \approx 10.2764 - 10$$
$$\log 8460 \approx 3.9274$$

~~~~~~~~

$$\log \text{fraction} \approx 6.3490 - 10$$
$$\text{fraction} \approx 0.0002234 \qquad \textit{Taking antilog}$$

This answer was found from the table. We sometimes need to estimate the fourth digit.

**Example 2.** Use logarithms to find $(92.8)^3 \times \sqrt[5]{0.986}$.

Let $N = (92.8)^3 \times \sqrt[5]{0.986}$.

Then $\log N = \log (92.8)^3 + \log \sqrt[5]{0.986} = 3 \log 92.8 + \frac{1}{5} \log 0.986$. Note that powers and roots are involved. In such cases it is easier to first find the following logs:

$$\log 92.8 \approx 1.9675$$
$$\log 0.986 \approx 9.9939 - 10$$

Consider $9.9939 - 10$. We are going to multiply this number by $\frac{1}{5}$. Now in order to obtain $-10$ as a term in the result, we rename this number as follows.

$$\log 0.986 \approx 49.9939 - 50$$

Now we will obtain $-10$ as a term when we multiply by $\frac{1}{5}$. Thus

| | |
|---|---|
| $\log (92.8)^3 \approx 5.9025$ | $\log 92.8 \approx 1.9675$ |
| $\log \sqrt[5]{0.986} \approx 9.9988 - 10$ | $\log 0.986 \approx 49.9939 - 50$ |

$$\log N \approx 15.9013 - 10$$
$$\approx 5.9013$$
$$N \approx 796{,}700 \quad \text{\textit{Taking antilog; we estimated the}}$$
$$\text{\textit{fourth digit}}$$

**TRY THIS** ➡

Use logarithms to calculate.

1. $\dfrac{78.6 \times 0.00642}{9.45}$

2. $\sqrt[4]{0.325} \times (4.23)^2$

## Exercise Set 16-5

▌Use logarithms to calculate. (*See Examples 1 and 2.*)

1. $3.14 \times 60.4$
2. $541 \times 0.0152$
3. $286 \div 1.05$
4. $12.8 \div 81.6$
5. $\sqrt{76.9}$
6. $\sqrt{678}$
7. $\sqrt[3]{56.9}$
8. $\sqrt[4]{2600}$
9. $(1.36)^{4.2}$
10. $(0.727)^{3.6}$
11. $\sqrt[3]{\dfrac{3.24 \times (3.16)^2}{78.4 \times 24.6}}$
12. $\dfrac{70.7 \times (10.6)^2}{18.6 \times \sqrt{276}}$

# 16-6 Interpolation

After finishing Lesson 16-6, you should be able to
▌ use linear interpolation to find logarithms with four-digit precision.
▌▌ use linear interpolation to find antilogarithms with four-digit precision.

## ▌ Logarithms

In Lesson 16-4 we developed procedures for using Table 2 with three-digit precision. By a procedure called *interpolation* we can find values between those listed in the table, obtaining four-digit precision. Interpolation can be done in various ways, the simplest and most common being *linear* interpolation. What we say applies to a table for any continuous function.

Let us consider how a table of values for any function is made. We select numbers of the domain $x_1$, $x_2$, $x_3$, and so on. Then we compute or somehow determine the corresponding function values (outputs), $f(x_1)$, $f(x_2)$, $f(x_3)$, and so on. Then we tabulate the results. We might also graph the results.

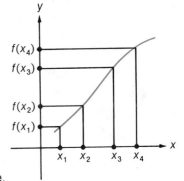

| $x$ | $x_1$ | $x_2$ | $x_3$ | $x_4$ | $\cdots$ |
|---|---|---|---|---|---|
| $f(x)$ | $f(x_1)$ | $f(x_2)$ | $f(x_3)$ | $f(x_4)$ | $\cdots$ |

Suppose we want to find an output $f(x)$ for an $x$ not in the table. If $x$ is halfway between $x_1$ and $x_2$, then we can take the number halfway between $f(x_1)$ and $f(x_2)$ as an approximation to $f(x)$. If $x$ is one-fifth of the way between $x_2$ and $x_3$, we can take the number that is one-fifth of the way between $f(x_2)$ and $f(x_3)$ as an approximation to $f(x)$. What we do is divide the length from $x_2$ to $x_3$ in a certain ratio, and then divide the length from $f(x_2)$ to $f(x_3)$ in the same ratio. This is *linear interpolation.*

We can show this geometrically. The length from $x_1$ to $x_2$ is divided in a certain ratio by $x$. The length from $f(x_1)$ to $f(x_2)$ is divided in the same ratio by $y$. The number $y$ approximates $f(x)$ with the noted error.

Note the slanted line in the figure. The approximation $y$ comes from this line. This explains the use of the term *linear interpolation.* Let us apply linear interpolation to Table 2 of common logarithms.

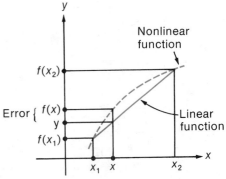

**Example 1.**   Find log 34870.

a)   Find the characteristic. Since $34870 = 3.487 \times 10^4$, the characteristic is 4.

b)   Find the mantissa. From Table 2 we have:

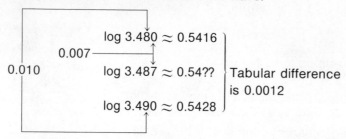

$$\begin{array}{l} \log 3.480 \approx 0.5416 \\ \log 3.487 \approx 0.54?? \\ \log 3.490 \approx 0.5428 \end{array}$$ Tabular difference is 0.0012

The tabular difference (difference between consecutive values in the table) is 0.0012. Now 3.487 is $\frac{7}{10}$ of the way from 3.480 to 3.490. So we take 0.7 of 0.0012, which is 0.00084, and round it to 0.0008. We add this to 0.5416. The mantissa is 0.5424.

c)   Add the characteristic and mantissa:
log 34870 ≈ 4.5424.

With practice you will take 0.7 of 12, forgetting the zeros, but adding in the same way.

**TRY THIS** ➡️

1.   Find log 4562.

**Example 2.**   Find log 0.009543.

a)   Find the characteristic. Since $0.009543 = 9.543 \times 10^{-3}$, the characteristic is −3, or 7 − 10.

b)   Find the mantissa. From Table 2 we have:

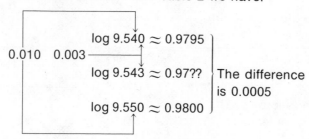

$$\begin{array}{l} \log 9.540 \approx 0.9795 \\ \log 9.543 \approx 0.97?? \\ \log 9.550 \approx 0.9800 \end{array}$$ The difference is 0.0005

Now 9.543 is $\frac{3}{10}$ of the way from 9.540 to 9.550, so we take 0.3 of 0.0005, which is 0.00015, and round it to 0.0002. We add this to 0.9795. The mantissa that results is 0.9797.

c)  Add the characteristic and the mantissa:

log 0.009543 ≈ 7.9797 − 10.

**TRY THIS** ➡️

2.  Find log 0.02387.

## ‖ Antilogarithms

We interpolate when finding antilogarithms, using the table in reverse.

**Example 3.**  Find antilog 4.9164.

a)  The characteristic is 4. The mantissa is 0.9164.

b)  Find the antilog of the mantissa, 0.9164. From Table 2 we have:

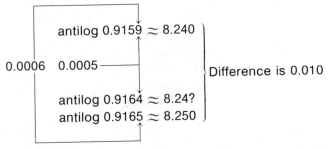

$$0.0006 \quad 0.0005 \left. \begin{array}{l} \text{antilog } 0.9159 \approx 8.240 \\ \\ \\ \text{antilog } 0.9164 \approx 8.24? \\ \text{antilog } 0.9165 \approx 8.250 \end{array} \right\} \text{Difference is } 0.010$$

The difference between 0.9159 and 0.9165 is 0.0006. Thus 0.9164 is $\frac{0.0005}{0.0006}$, or $\frac{5}{6}$, of the way between 0.9159 and 0.9165. Then antilog 0.9164 is $\frac{5}{6}$ of the way between 8.240 and 8.250, so we take $\frac{5}{6}$ (0.010), which is 0.00833. . . , and round it to 0.008. Thus the antilog of the mantissa is 8.248.

Thus antilog $4.9164 \approx 8.248 \times 10^4 = 82,480.$

**TRY THIS** ➡️

3.  Find antilog 3.7749.

**Example 4.**  Find antilog (7.4122 − 10).

a)  The characteristic is −3. The mantissa is 0.4122.

b)  Find the antilog of the mantissa, 0.4122. From Table 2 we have:

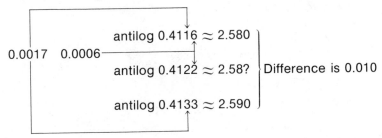

$$0.0017 \quad 0.0006 \left. \begin{array}{l} \text{antilog } 0.4116 \approx 2.580 \\ \\ \text{antilog } 0.4122 \approx 2.58? \\ \\ \text{antilog } 0.4133 \approx 2.590 \end{array} \right\} \text{Difference is } 0.010$$

The difference between 0.4116 and 0.4133 is 0.0017. Thus 0.4122 is $\frac{0.0006}{0.0017}$, or $\frac{6}{17}$, of the way between 0.4116 and 0.4133. Then antilog 0.4122 is $\frac{6}{17}$ of the way between 2.580 and 2.590, so we take $\frac{6}{17}$ (0.010), which is 0.0035 to four places. We round it to 0.004. Thus the antilog of the mantissa is 2.584.

So antilog $(7.4122 - 10) \approx 2.584 \times 10^{-3} = 0.002584$.

**TRY THIS** ➡

> 4. Find antilog $6.4557 - 10$.

## Exercise Set 16-6

❚ Find each of the following logarithms using interpolation. (*See Examples 1 and 2.*)

1. log 41.63
3. log 2.944
5. log 650.2
7. log 0.1425
9. log 0.004257
11. log 0.1776
13. log 600.6

2. log 472.1
4. log 21.76
6. log 37.37
8. log 0.09045
10. log 4518
12. log 0.08356
14. log 800.1

❚❚ Find each of the following antilogarithms using interpolation. (*See Examples 3 and 4.*)

15. antilog 1.6350
17. antilog 0.6478
19. antilog 0.0342
21. antilog $9.8564 - 10$
23. antilog $7.4128 - 10$
25. antilog $8.2010 - 10$

16. antilog 2.3512
18. antilog 1.1624
20. antilog 4.8453
22. antilog $8.9659 - 10$
24. antilog $9.7278 - 10$
26. antilog $7.8630 - 10$

### Challenge Exercises

Use logarithms and interpolation to do the following calculations. Use four-digit precision. Answers may be checked using a calculator.

27. $\dfrac{35.24 \times (16.77)^3}{12.93 \times \sqrt{276.2}}$

28. $\sqrt[5]{\dfrac{16.79 \times (4.234)^3}{18.81 \times 175.3}}$

Find.

29. $\log (\log 3)$

30. $\log (\log 5)$

# 16-7 Exponential and Logarithmic Equations

After finishing Lesson 16-7, you should be able to
**▌** solve exponential equations.
**▌▌** solve logarithmic equations.

## ▌Exponential Equations

Equations with variables in exponents, such as $3^{2x-1} = 4$, are called *exponential equations*. We can often solve such equations by taking the logarithm on both sides and then using Theorem 16-3.

**Example 1.** Solve $2^{3x-5} = 16$.

*Method 1.* 
$$\log 2^{3x-5} = \log 16 \qquad \textit{Taking log on both sides}$$
$$(3x - 5)\log 2 = \log 16 \qquad \textit{Using Theorem 16-3}$$
$$3x - 5 = \frac{\log 16}{\log 2}$$
$$x = \frac{\dfrac{\log 16}{\log 2} + 5}{3} \qquad \textit{Solving for x}$$
$$x \approx \frac{\dfrac{1.2041}{0.3010} + 5}{3} \qquad \textit{Finding logs}$$
$$x \approx 3.0001 \qquad \textit{Calculating}$$

The answer is approximate because the logarithms are approximate.

*Method 2.* Note that $16 = 2^4$. Then we have

$$2^{3x-5} = 2^4.$$

Since the base is the same, 2, on both sides, the exponents must be the same. Thus

$$3x - 5 = 4.$$

We solve this equation to get

$$x = 3.$$

This answer is exact.

**TRY THIS** ➞

1. Solve $4^{2x-3} = 64$.
   a) Use a method like Method 1 of Example 1.
   b) Use a method like Method 2 of Example 1. Note that $4^3 = 64$.

## ‖ Logarithmic Equations

Equations that contain logarithmic expressions are called *logarithmic equations*. To solve such equations we try to obtain a single logarithmic expression on one side of the equation and then take the antilogarithm on both sides.

**Example 2.** Solve $\log x + \log (x - 3) = 1$.

$$\log x(x - 3) = 1 \qquad \textit{Using Theorem 16-1 to obtain a single logarithm}$$
$$x(x - 3) = 10^1 \qquad \textit{Taking the antilog on both sides}$$
$$x^2 - 3x - 10 = 0$$
$$(x + 2)(x - 5) = 0 \qquad \textit{Factoring and principle of zero products}$$

$$x = -2 \text{ or } x = 5$$

Check: $\log x + \log (x - 3) = 1$

$$\frac{\log (-2) + \log (-2 - 3) \mid 1}{}$$

$$\frac{\log x + \log (x - 3) = 1}{\log 5 + \log (5 - 3) \mid 1}$$
$$\log 5 + \log 2$$
$$\log 10$$
$$1$$

The number $-2$ is not a solution because negative numbers do not have logarithms.

The solution is 5.

**TRY THIS** ⟹

2. Solve.
   $\log x + \log (x + 3) = 1$.

## Exercise Set 16-7

‖ Solve. (*See Example 1.*)

1. $2^x = 8$
3. $2^x = 10$
5. $5^{4x-7} = 125$
7. $3^{x^2+4x} = \frac{1}{27}$
9. $4^x = 7$
11. $2^x = 3^{x-1}$
13. $(2.8)^x = 41$

2. $2^x = 32$
4. $2^x = 33$
6. $4^{3x+5} = 16$
8. $3^{5x} \cdot 9^{x^2} = 27$
10. $8^x = 10$
12. $3^{x+2} = 5^{x-1}$
14. $(1.7)^x = 20$

‖‖ Solve. (*See Example 2.*)

15. $\log x + \log(x - 9) = 1$
17. $\log x - \log(x + 3) = -1$
19. $\log_4 (x + 3) + \log_4 (x - 3) = 2$
21. $\log \sqrt[3]{x} = \sqrt{\log x}$
23. $\log_5 \sqrt{x^2 + 1} = 1$

16. $\log x + \log(x + 9) = 1$
18. $\log(x + 9) - \log x = 1$
20. $\log_5 (x + 4) + \log_5 (x - 4) = 2$
22. $\log \sqrt[4]{x} = \sqrt{\log x}$
24. $\log \sqrt[3]{x^2} + \log \sqrt[3]{x^4} = \log 2^{-3}$

# 16-8 Applications

After finishing Lesson 16-8, you should be able to
∎ solve problems involving exponential and logarithmic functions and equations.

∎ Exponential and logarithmic functions and equations have many applications.

**Example 1.** (*Compound Interest*) The amount $A$ that principal $P$ will be worth after $t$ years at interest rate $r$, compounded annually, is given by the formula

$$A = P(1 + r)^t.$$

Suppose $4000 principal is invested at 6% interest and yields $5353. How many years was it invested?

Using the formula $A = P(1 + r)^t$, we have

$$5353 = 4000(1 + 0.06)^t, \text{ or } 5353 = 4000(1.06)^t.$$

Solving for $t$, we have

$$\log 5353 = \log 4000(1.06)^t$$
$$\log 5353 = \log 4000 + t \log 1.06$$
$$\frac{\log 5353 - \log 4000}{\log 1.06} = t$$
$$\frac{3.7286 - 3.6021}{0.0253} \approx t$$
$$5 \approx t.$$

The money was invested for 5 years.

**TRY THIS** ➡

1. Suppose $5000 principal is invested at 8% interest and yields $8569. How many years was it invested?

**Example 2.** (*Loudness of Sound*) The sensation of loudness of sound is not proportional to the energy intensity, but rather is a logarithmic function. *Loudness* in bels (after Alexander Graham Bell) of a sound of intensity $I$ is defined to be

$$L = \log \frac{I}{I_0},$$

where $I_0$ is the minimum intensity detectable by the human ear (such as the tick of a watch at 6 meters under quiet conditions).

When a sound is 10 times as intense as another, its loudness is 1 bel greater. If a sound is 100 times as intense as another, it is louder by 2 bels, and so on. The bel is a large unit, so a subunit one tenth as large (a *decibel*) is usually used. For $L$ in decibels, the formula is as follows:

$$L = 10 \log \frac{I}{I_0}.$$

**a)** Find the loudness in decibels of the background noise in a radio studio, for which the intensity $I$ is 199 times $I_0$.

We substitute into the formula and calculate, using Table 2.

$$L = 10 \log \frac{199 \cdot I_0}{I_0}$$
$$= 10 \log 199$$
$$\approx 10(2.2989)$$
$$\approx 23 \text{ decibels}$$

**b)** Find the loudness of the sound of a heavy truck, for which the intensity is $10^9$ times $I_0$.

$$L = 10 \log \frac{10^9 \cdot I_0}{I_0}$$
$$= 10 \log 10^9$$
$$= 10 \cdot 9$$
$$= 90 \text{ decibels}$$

**TRY THIS** ⟹

2. Find the loudness in decibels of the sound in a library, for which the intensity $I$ is 2510 times $I_0$.
3. Find the loudness in decibels of conversational speech, for which the intensity is $10^6$ times $I_0$.

**Example 3.** (*Earthquake Magnitude*) The magnitude $R$ (on the Richter scale) of an earthquake of intensity $I$ is defined as follows:

$$R = \log \frac{I}{I_0},$$

where $I_0$ is a minimum intensity used for comparison.

An earthquake has an intensity $10^{8.6}$ times $I_0$. What is its magnitude on the Richter scale?

We substitute into the formula:

$$R = \log \frac{10^{8.6} \cdot I_0}{I_0}$$
$$= \log 10^{8.6}$$
$$= 8.6$$

**TRY THIS**

4.  The earthquake in Anchorage, Alaska on March 27, 1964 had an intensity $10^{8.4}$ times $I_0$. What was its magnitude on the Richter scale?

**Example 4.** (*Forgetting*) A group of people take a test and make an average score of $S$. After a time $t$ they take an equivalent form of the same test. At that time the average score is $S(t)$. According to one theory, $S(t)$ is given by the following function.

$$S(t) = A - B \log (t + 1),$$

where $t$ is in months and the constants $A$ and $B$ are determined by experiment.

Students in a zoology class took an exam. They took equivalent forms of the test at monthly intervals thereafter. The average scores were found to be given by the function

$$S(t) = 78 - 15 \log (t + 1).$$

What was the average score **a)** when they took the test originally? **b)** after 4 months?

We substitute into the equation defining the function.

**a)** $S(0) = 78 - 15 \log(0 + 1)$
$\phantom{S(0)} = 78 - 15 \log 1$
$\phantom{S(0)} = 78 - 0$
$\phantom{S(0)} = 78$

**b)** $S(4) = 78 - 15 \log (4 + 1)$
$\phantom{S(4)} = 78 - 15 \log 5$
$\phantom{S(4)} \approx 78 - 15 \cdot 0.6990$
$\phantom{S(4)} \approx 78 - 10.49$
$\phantom{S(4)} \approx 67.51.$

**TRY THIS**

5.  Students in an accounting course take an exam and are then retested at monthly intervals. The forgetting function is given by $S(t) = 68 - 14 \log (t + 1)$. What was the average score
    a)  when they took the exam originally?
    b)  after 5 months?

## Exercise Set 16-8

▌(*See Examples 1–4.*)

1. (*Doubling time*) How many years will it take an investment of $1000 to double itself when interest is compounded annually at 6%?

2. (*Tripling time*) How many years will it take an investment of $1000 to triple itself when interest is compounded annually at 5%?

3. Find the loudness in decibels of the sound of an automobile having an intensity 3,100,000 times $I_0$.

4. Find the loudness in decibels of the sound of a dishwasher having an intensity 2,500,000 times $I_0$.

5. Find the loudness in decibels of the threshold of sound pain, for which the intensity is $10^{14}$ times $I_0$.

6. Find the loudness in decibels of a jet aircraft having an intensity $10^{12}$ times $I_0$.

7. The Los Angeles earthquake of 1971 had an intensity $10^{6.7}$ times $I_0$. What was its magnitude on the Richter scale?

8. The San Francisco earthquake of 1906 had an intensity $10^{8.25}$ times $I_0$. What was its magnitude on the Richter scale?

9. An earthquake has a magnitude of 5 on the Richter scale. What is its intensity?

10. An earthquake has a magnitude of 7 on the Richter scale. What is its intensity?

11. Students in an industrial mathematics course take an exam and are then retested at monthly intervals. The forgetting function is given by $S(t) = 82 - 18 \log (t + 1)$.
    a) What was the average score on the original exam?
    b) What was the average score after 5 months had elapsed?

12. Students graduating from a cosmetology curriculum take an exam and are then retested at monthly intervals. The forgetting function is given by $S(t) = 75 - 20 \log (t + 1)$.
    a) What was the average score on the original exam?
    b) What was the average score after 6 months had elapsed?

13. Refer to Exercise 11. How much time will elapse before the average score has decreased to 64?

14. Refer to Exercise 12. How much time will elapse before the average score has decreased to 61?

In chemistry, pH is defined as follows:

$$pH = -\log [H^+],$$

where $[H^+]$ is the hydrogen ion concentration in moles per liter. For example, the hydrogen ion concentration in milk is $4 \times 10^{-7}$ moles per liter, so $pH = -\log (4 \times 10^{-7}) = -[\log 4 + (-7)] \approx 6.4$.

15. For tomatoes, $[H^+]$ is about $6.3 \times 10^{-5}$. Find the pH.

16. For eggs, $[H^+]$ is about $1.6 \times 10^{-8}$. Find the pH.

**Challenge Exercises**

The average walking speed $V$ of a person in a city of population $p$, in thousands, is given by

$$V(p) = 0.26 \log p + 0.015,$$

where $V$ is in meters per second.

17. The population of Seattle, Washington is 531,000. What is the average walking speed of a person in Seattle? (Let $p = 531$.)

18. The population of New York City is 7,900,000. What is the average walking speed of a person in New York? (Let $p = 7900$.)

19. What is the population of your city? What is the average walking speed of a person in your city?

20. The population of a small town is 2000. What is the average walking speed of a person in that town?

21. Solve $R = \log \dfrac{I}{I_0}$ for $I$.

22. Solve $A = P(1 + r)^t$ for $t$.

---

**BIOGRAPHICAL NOTE: Hypatia**

Hypatia was a woman of outstanding abilities in mathematics. Luckily, she was born in circumstances that allowed her abilities to flourish.

She was born about A.D. 370. Her father, Theon, was a professor of mathematics at the University of Alexandria in Egypt. He encouraged her interest in mathematics, astronomy, and other areas of learning. Eventually she became a teacher of mathematics and philosophy at the university. She lectured on the algebra of first- and second-degree equations and on other subjects. Her lectures were very popular. They attracted students from Africa, Asia, and Europe.

Her popularity did not protect Hypatia from the cruelty of power struggles in Alexandria. In 415 she was murdered by extremists there.

## CHAPTER 16 REVIEW

Review the material in the chapter. Then see how you have done by trying these review exercises. If you miss an exercise, restudy the indicated lesson.

16-1    1.   Graph $y = 5^x$.

16-1    2.   Graph $y = \log_5 x$.

16-2    3.   Convert to a logarithmic equation: $7^{2.3} = x$.

16-2    4.   Convert to an exponential equation: $\log_8 M = t$.

16-2    5.   Solve $\log_x 64 = 3$.

16-2    6.   Solve $\log_{16} 4 = x$.

16-2    7.   Simplify $\log_h h^3$.

16-3    8.   Express as a single logarithm:
$\frac{1}{2} \log_b a + \frac{3}{2} \log_b c - 4 \log_b d$.

16-3    9.   Express in terms of logarithms of $M$ and $N$: $\log \sqrt[3]{\dfrac{M^2}{N}}$.

16-3    Given that $\log_a 2 = 0.301$, $\log_a 3 = 0.477$, and $\log_a 7 = 0.845$, find:

        10.   $\log_a 18$

        11.   $\log_a \frac{7}{2}$

        12.   $\log_a \frac{1}{4}$

        13.   $\log_a \sqrt{3}$

16-4    Use Table 2 to find each of the following.

        14.   log 26.2

        15.   log 0.00806

        16.   $10^{1.8686}$

16-5    17.   Use logarithms to calculate $(0.0524)^2 \cdot \sqrt{0.0638}$.

16-6    Use Table 2 to find each of the following.

        18.   log 2904

        19.   antilog 8.4414 − 10

        20.   Solve $3^{1-x} = 9^{2x}$.

16-7    21.   Solve $\log (x^2 - 1) - \log (x - 1) = 1$.

16-8    22.   How many years will it take an investment of $1000 to double itself if interest is compounded annually at 5%?

16-8    23.   What is the loudness in decibels of a sound which is 1000 times $I_0$?

## CHAPTER 16 TEST

1. Graph $y = 3^x$.
2. Graph $y = \log_3 x$.
3. Convert to a logarithmic equation: $3^x = 25$.
4. Convert to an exponential equation: $\log_3 9 = 2$.
5. Solve $\log_x 125 = 3$.
6. Solve $\log_{25} 5 = x$.
7. Simplify $14^{\log_{14} 7t}$.
8. Express as a single logarithm: $2 \log_a b - 3 \log_a c + \frac{1}{2} \log_a d$.

9. Express in terms of logarithms of $x$ and $y$: $\log_a \sqrt[3]{\dfrac{x}{y^2}}$.

Given $\log_a 3 = 0.451$, $\log_a 4 = 0.510$, and $\log_a 5 = 0.565$, find:
10. $\log_a 9$
11. $\log_a 20$
12. $\log_a \frac{4}{3}$
13. $\log_a 2$

Use Table 2 to find each of the following.
14. $\log 14.3$
15. $\log 0.00324$
16. antilog $7.5340 - 10$

17. Use logarithms to calculate $3^{20}$.

Use Table 2 to find each of the following.
18. $\log 456.1$
19. $10^{3.6409}$
20. Solve $2^{x-1} = 32$.

21. Solve $\log 4x + \log x = 2$.
22. How many years will it take an investment of $1000 to triple itself when interest is compounded annually at 8%?
23. The forgetting function for a certain test is $S(t) = 80 - 5 \log (t + 1)$. What was the average score after 9 months?

Technical writers for telephone companies assist communication within the companies. The writers describe new methods or products so other workers can understand them.

Supervisors in telephone company business offices coordinate the work of company representatives. They help to handle the requests and complaints of customers.

Pilots for large companies fly executives from place to place on business trips. The routes and schedules they follow depend on company needs.

Material handlers for trucking firms work in warehouses. Handlers may work alone or in a group to load and unload goods with handtrucks and other devices.

# CAREERS IN TRANSPORTATION, COMMUNICATION, AND PUBLIC UTILITIES

Careers in transportation involve movement of goods or people by various means, including pipelines, trucks, trains, planes, buses, and cabs. Careers in communication involve movement of information. The means are telephone, telegraph, radio, and television systems. Careers in public utilities involve movement of water, electricity, gas, or waste materials by conduits or other means.

Some subdivisions of transportation careers are listed in the table below. It gives percentages of workers in transportation, communication, and public utilities.

| | Percentages of workers in mid-1960s | Percentages of workers in mid-1970s |
|---|---|---|
| Trucking and warehousing | 24% | 25% |
| Railroads | 19 | 12.5 |
| Local and interurban lines | 7 | 6 |
| Airlines | 5.5 | 8 |
| Other transportation | 9 | 7.5 |
| Total transportation | 63.5% | 59.0% |
| Communication | 21 | 25 |
| Public utilities | 15.5 | 16 |

**Percentages of Workers in Transportation, Communication, and Public Utilities**

rain signal-department workers are responsible for train signals and control systems. Workers may install ew signal equipment or inspect nd maintain existing equipment.

Taxicab drivers provide individual transportation service. Drivers may respond to calls from radio dispatchers or to signals from people on the street.

Local truck drivers transport goods from terminals or warehouses to local stores, factories, or homes. Drivers may also pick up goods on the way.

Meter readers for electric companies go to customers' homes or businesses. Readers note how much electricity has been used so customers can be billed correctly.

In the 10 years from the mid-1960s to the mid-1970s, the total of all these careers grew 18%. To increase its share of the total, a career area had to grow *more* than 18%. The area of communication careers, for example, grew 41%. It raised its share of the total from 21% to 25%. Airline careers grew 71% in the 10 years. Local and interurban lines, which include subways and local buses, did not grow at all. Only one area shrank. Railroad careers decreased 23%. (Even so, a number of workers were hired by railroads to replace some of those who retired, died, or transferred to other areas of work.)

A few of the people who work in transportation, communication, and public utilities are pictured here. The projected place of these careers in the United States labor force is shown in the circle graph.

Information about many different career trends is given in *Occupational Outlook Handbook*. It is compiled by the United States Bureau of Labor Statistics. The *Handbook* describes more than 250 occupations, and it gives facts about the labor force. It is available at many libraries.

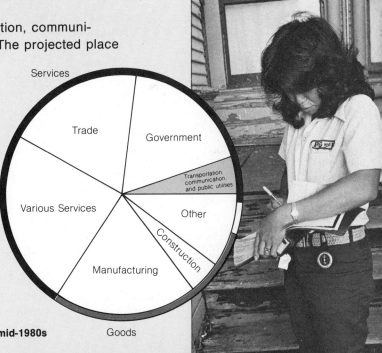

Services
Trade
Government
Various Services
Transportation, communication, and public utilities
Other
Construction
Manufacturing
Goods

**Projected United States Labor Force in the mid-1980s**

**Ready for Sequences and Series?**

8-5    1. Given a function $f$ described by $f(x) = 3x + 2$, find $f(1)$, $f(2)$, and $f(3)$.

8-5    2. Given a function $f$ described by $f(x) = 3x^2 - 1$, find $f(1)$, $f(2)$, and $f(3)$.

8-5    3. Given a function $f$ described by $f(x) = 3^x$, find $f(1)$, $f(2)$, and $f(3)$.

Simplify.

10-2    4. $\sqrt{1}$

10-2    5. $\sqrt{4}$

10-3    6. $\sqrt{56}$

4-2    7. Solve: $\begin{aligned} x + 15y &= 47 \\ x + 2y &= 8 \end{aligned}$

1-1    8. Find decimal notation for $\frac{3}{11}$.

# Chapter 17
# Sequences and Series

*The arrangement of the seeds on this sunflower
is given by a certain kind of sequence.*

# 17-1 Sequences

After finishing Lesson 17-1, you should be able to
- I given a formula for the general term of a sequence, find the $n$th term.
- II given a sequence, look for a pattern, and try to guess a rule for the general term.

## I Sequences

**DEFINITION**

A *sequence* is an ordered set of numbers.

Here is an example of a sequence.

$$3, 5, 7, 9, \ldots$$

The dots mean that there are more numbers in the sequence. A sequence that does not end is called *infinite*.

Each number is called a *term* of the sequence. The first term is 3, the second term is 5, the third term is 7, and so on. We can think of a sequence as a function $a$ whose domain is a set of consecutive natural numbers.

Some sequences have a rule which describes the $n$th term. The above sequence could be described $3, 5, 7, 9, \ldots, 2n + 1, \ldots$ where the $n$th term is $2n + 1$. We also say $a(n) = 2n + 1$.

We can find the terms of the sequence by consecutively substituting the numbers $1, 2, 3, \ldots, n$, and so on. Thus

$$a(1) = 2 \cdot 1 + 1, \text{ or } 3$$
$$a(2) = 2 \cdot 2 + 1, \text{ or } 5$$
$$a(3) = 2 \cdot 3 + 1, \text{ or } 7$$
$$\vdots \qquad \vdots$$

The $n$th term is also called the *general term*. It is customary to use $a_n$, instead of $a(n)$ for the general term of a sequence. The letter $k$ is often used instead of $n$.

**Example 1.** Find the first two terms of the sequence whose general term is given by $a_n = \dfrac{(-1)^n}{n + 1}$.

$$a_1 = \frac{(-1)^1}{1 + 1} = \frac{-1}{2} = -\frac{1}{2} \qquad a_2 = \frac{(-1)^2}{2 + 1} = \frac{(-1)^2}{3} = \frac{1}{3}$$

**TRY THIS** ➡

1. A sequence is given by $a_n = 2n - 1$.
   a) Find the first three terms.
   b) Find the 34th term.
2. A sequence is given by $a_n = 2^n$. Find the first four terms.
3. A sequence is given by $a_n = (-1)^n n^2$. Find the first four terms.

## ▋▋ Finding General Terms

We may know the first few terms of a sequence, but not the general term. In such a case we cannot know for sure what the general term is, but we can make a guess by looking for a pattern.

**Examples.** For each sequence, make a guess at the general term.

**2.** 1, 4, 9, 16, 25, . . .
These are squares of numbers, so the general term may be $n^2$.

**3.** $\sqrt{1}$, $\sqrt{2}$, $\sqrt{3}$, $\sqrt{4}$, . . .
These are square roots of numbers, so the general term may be $\sqrt{n}$.

**4.** $-1$, 2, $-4$, 8, $-16$, . . .
These are powers of 2 with alternating signs, so the general term may be $(-1)^n 2^{n-1}$.

**TRY THIS**

For each sequence try to find a rule for finding the general term or the $n$th term.

4. 2, 4, 6, 8, 10, . . .
5. 1, 2, 3, 4, 5, 6, . . .
6. 1, 8, 27, 64, 125, . . .
7. $x, \dfrac{x^2}{2}, \dfrac{x^3}{3}, \dfrac{x^4}{4}, \dfrac{x^5}{5}, \ldots$
8. 1, 2, 4, 8, 16, 32, . . .

## Exercise Set 17-1

▋ In each of the following the $n$th term of a sequence is given. In each case find the first four terms, the 10th term, and the 15th term. (*See Example 1.*)

1. $a_n = 3n + 1$

2. $a_n = 3n - 1$

3. $a_n = \dfrac{n}{n + 1}$

4. $a_n = n^2 + 1$

5. $a_n = n^2 - 2n + 1$

6. $a_n = \dfrac{n^2 - 1}{n^2 + 1}$

7. $a_n = n + \dfrac{1}{n}$

8. $a_n = n + \dfrac{(-1)^n}{n}$

9. $a_n = \left(-\dfrac{1}{2}\right)^{n-1}$

10. $a_n = 2^n$

▋▋ For each of the following sequences find a rule for finding the general term or $n$th term. (*See Examples 2–4.*)

11. 1, 3, 5, 7, 9, . . .

12. 3, 9, 27, 81, 243, . . .

13. $\frac{2}{3}, \frac{3}{4}, \frac{4}{5}, \frac{5}{6}, \frac{6}{7}, \ldots$

14. $\sqrt{2}$, $\sqrt{4}$, $\sqrt{6}$, $\sqrt{8}$, $\sqrt{10}$, . . .

15. $\sqrt{3}$, 3, $3\sqrt{3}$, 9, $9\sqrt{3}$, . . .

16. $1 \cdot 2$, $2 \cdot 3$, $3 \cdot 4$, $4 \cdot 5$, . . .

17. $-1$, $-4$, $-7$, $-10$, $-13$, . . .

18. $\frac{1}{10}, \frac{2}{100}, \frac{3}{1000}, \ldots$

# 17-2 Series

After finishing Lesson 17-2, you should be able to
∎ name a series with or without sigma notation.

**DEFINITION**

A series is the sum of the terms in a sequence.

With any sequence there is an associated *series*. For example,
associated with the sequence

$$3, 5, 7, 9, \ldots, 2n + 1$$

is the series

$$3 + 5 + 7 + 9 + \cdots + (2n + 1).$$

This is the sum of the first $n$ terms of the sequence.

**TRY THIS** ⟶

> For each sequence find the associated series.
>
> 1. $2, 4, 8, 16, 25, 36$
> 2. $-2, 4, -6, 8, -10$
> 3. $x, x^2, x^3, x^4, \ldots, x^n$

## ∎ Sigma Notation

The Greek letter $\Sigma$ (sigma) can be used to simplify notation when a series
has a formula for the general term. The series above can be named

$$\sum_{k=1}^{n} (2k + 1).$$

This is read "the sum as $k$ goes from 1 to $n$, of $(2k + 1)$."

**Example 1.** Name $\displaystyle\sum_{k=1}^{4} (2^k + k)$ without using sigma notation.

To find the terms we replace $k$ successively by each of the numbers 1 through 4.

For $k = 1$: $2^1 + 1 = 3$
For $k = 2$: $2^2 + 2 = 6$
For $k = 3$: $2^3 + 3 = 11$
For $k = 4$: $2^4 + 4 = 20$

Then $\displaystyle\sum_{k=1}^{4} (2^k + k) = 3 + 6 + 11 + 20.$

We can try to find sigma notation for a series by guessing a rule
for the $n$th term. Answers can vary, of course.

**Examples.** Write sigma notation for each series.

**2.** $1 + 4 + 9 + 16 + 25$; These are sums of squares, so the general term is $k^2$. Sigma notation is $\displaystyle\sum_{k=1}^{5} k^2$.

**3.** $-1 + 3 - 5 + 7$; These are odd integers with alternating signs. The general term is $(-1)^k(2k - 1)$ or $(-1)^{k+1}(2k + 1)$, depending upon where $k$ begins. Sigma notation is

$$\sum_{k=1}^{4} (-1)^k(2k - 1) \text{ or } \sum_{k=0}^{3} (-1)^{k+1}(2k + 1).$$

**4.** $\sqrt{1} + \sqrt{2} + \sqrt{3} + \cdots \sqrt{n}$; The general term is $\sqrt{k}$. Sigma notation is $\displaystyle\sum_{k=1}^{n} \sqrt{k}$.

**TRY THIS**

> Write sigma notation for each series.
>
> **4.** $2 + 4 + 6 + 8 + 10$
> **5.** $1 + 8 + 27 + 64 + \cdots + n^3$
> **6.** $x + \dfrac{x^2}{2} + \dfrac{x^3}{3} + \dfrac{x^4}{4} + \dfrac{x^5}{5} + \dfrac{x^6}{6}$
> **7.** $2 + 3 + 4 + 5 + \cdots + n$

## Exercise Set 17-2

▌Name each series without using $\Sigma$. *(See Example 1.)*

**1.** $\displaystyle\sum_{k=1}^{5} \dfrac{1}{2k}$

**2.** $\displaystyle\sum_{k=1}^{6} \dfrac{1}{2k + 1}$

**3.** $\displaystyle\sum_{k=0}^{5} 2^k$

**4.** $\displaystyle\sum_{k=4}^{7} \sqrt{2k - 1}$

**5.** $\displaystyle\sum_{k=7}^{10} \log k$

**6.** $\displaystyle\sum_{k=0}^{4} \pi k$

**7.** $\displaystyle\sum_{k=1}^{5} k^3$

**8.** $\displaystyle\sum_{k=1}^{4} t^k$

Write sigma notation. *(See Examples 2–4.)*

**9.** $\frac{1}{2} + \frac{2}{3} + \frac{3}{4} + \frac{4}{5} + \frac{5}{6} + \frac{6}{7}$

**10.** $3 + 6 + 9 + 12 + 15$

**11.** $-2 + 4 - 8 + 16 - 32 + 64$

**12.** $\dfrac{1}{1^2} + \dfrac{1}{2^2} + \dfrac{1}{3^2} + \dfrac{1}{4^2} + \dfrac{1}{5^2}$

**13.** $1 + 2 + 4 + 8 + 16 + 32$

**14.** $\frac{1}{3} + \frac{1}{9} + \frac{1}{27} + \frac{1}{81}$

**15.** $-1 - 2 - 3 - 4 - 5 - 6 - 7$

**16.** $1 + \dfrac{1}{\sqrt{2}} + \dfrac{1}{\sqrt{3}} + \dfrac{1}{2}$

**17.** $4 + 5 + 6 + 7 + 8 + \cdots + n$

**18.** $8 + 9 + 10 + \cdots + n$

**19.** $4 - 9 + 16 - 25 + \cdots (-1)^n n^2$

**20.** $9 - 16 + 25 + \cdots + (-1)^{n+1} n^2$

# 17-3 Arithmetic Sequences

After finishing Lesson 17-3, you should be able to

**▌** identify the first term and the common difference of an arithmetic sequence.

**▌▌** given any three of the numbers $a_1$, $a_n$, $d$, or $n$, associated with an arithmetic sequence, solve for the fourth using $a_n = a_1 + (n - 1)d$.

**▌▌▌** given any two terms of an arithmetic sequence and their places in the sequence, find $a_1$ and $d$.

## ▌Arithmetic Sequences

Look at the sequence

2, 5, 8, 11, 14, . . .

Note that 3 can be added to each term to get the next term.

**DEFINITION**

A sequence in which a constant $d$ can be added to each term to get the next is called an *arithmetic sequence*. The constant $d$ is called the *common difference*.

The following notation is used with arithmetic sequences.

$a_1$ is the first term.
$a_2$ is the second term.
$a_n$ is the $n$th term.
$n$ is the number of terms from $a_1$ up to and including $a_n$.

To find the common difference, subtract any term from the one that follows it.

**Examples.** The following are arithmetic sequences. Identify the first term and the common difference.

| Sequence | First term | Common difference |
|---|---|---|
| **1.** 4, 9, 14, 19, 24, . . . | 4 | 5 |
| **2.** 34, 27, 20, 13, 6, −1, −8, . . . | 34 | −7 |
| **3.** 2, $2\frac{1}{2}$, 3, $3\frac{1}{2}$, 4, $4\frac{1}{2}$, . . . | 2 | $\frac{1}{2}$ |

**TRY THIS** ➡

Identify the first term and the common difference of each arithmetic sequence.

1. 2, 3, 4, 5, 6, . . .
2. 1, 4, 7, 10, 13, . . .
3. 19, 14, 9, 4, −1, −6, . . .
4. 10, 20, 30, 40, . . .
5. 5, $5\frac{1}{4}$, $5\frac{1}{2}$, $5\frac{3}{4}$, 6, $6\frac{1}{4}$, . . .
6. 10, $9\frac{1}{2}$, 9, $8\frac{1}{2}$, 8, $7\frac{1}{2}$, . . .

## ▪ The *n*th Term

The first term of an arithmetic sequence is $a_1$. We add $d$ to get the next term, $a_1 + d$. We add $d$ again to get the next term, $(a_1 + d) + d$, and so on. There is a pattern.

$$a_1$$
$$a_2 = a_1 + d$$
$$a_3 = (a_1 + d) + d = a_1 + 2d$$
$$a_4 = (a_1 + d) + d + d = a_1 + 3d$$
$$\vdots$$
$$a_n = a_1 + (n - 1)d$$

We have a theorem.

**THEOREM 17-1**

The *n*th term of an arithmetic sequence is given by
$a_n = a_1 + (n - 1)d$.

**Example 4.** Find the 14th term of the arithmetic sequence 4, 7, 10, 13, . . . .

First note that $a_1 = 4$, $d = 3$, and $n = 14$. Then using the formula of Theorem 17-1 we have

$$a_{14} = 4 + (14 - 1)3$$
$$= 4 + 39$$
$$a_{14} = 43.$$

**Example 5.** In the sequence of Example 4, which term is 301? That is, what is $n$ if $a_n = 301$?

$$a_n = a_1 + (n - 1)d \qquad \textit{Theorem 17-1}$$
$$301 = 4 + (n - 1)3 \qquad \textit{Substituting}$$
$$301 = 4 + 3n - 3$$
$$300 = 3n$$
$$100 = n$$

Thus the 100th term is 301.

In a similar manner we can find $a_1$ if we know $n$, $a_n$, and $d$. Also, we can find $d$ if we know $a_1$, $n$, and $a_n$.

**TRY THIS** ⟹

7. Find the 13th term of the sequence 2, 6, 10, 14, . . .
8. In the sequence of Exercise 7, what term is 298? That is, what is $n$ if $a_n = 298$?
9. Find $a_7$ when $a_1 = 5$ and $d = 2$.
10. Find $a_1$ when $d = \frac{1}{2}$, $n = 7$, and $a_n = 16$.

## ⅲ Constructing Sequences

Given two terms and their places in a sequence, we can find $a_1$ and $d$ and then construct the sequence.

**Example 6.** The 3rd term of an arithmetic sequence is 8 and the 16th term is 47. Find $a_1$ and $d$. Construct the sequence.

Using the formula $a_n = a_1 + (n - 1)d$, where $a_3 = 8$, we have

$$8 = a_1 + (3 - 1)d \qquad \text{or} \qquad 8 = a_1 + 2d.$$

Using the same formula where $a_{16} = 47$, we have

$$47 = a_1 + (16 - 1)d \qquad \text{or} \qquad 47 = a_1 + 15d.$$

Now we solve the system of equations.

$$a_1 + 15d = 47$$
$$a_1 + 2d = 8$$

$$
\begin{aligned}
a_1 + 15d &= 47 \\
-a_1 - \ 2d &= -8 \qquad \textit{Multiplying by } -1 \\
\hline
13d &= 39 \qquad \textit{Adding} \\
d &= 3
\end{aligned}
$$

$$a_1 + 2 \cdot 3 = 8$$
$$a_1 = 2$$

Thus $a_1$ is 2, $d$ is 3, and the sequence is 2, 5, 8, 11, 14, . . .

**TRY THIS** ➡

11. The 7th term of an arithmetic sequence is 79 and the 13th term is 151. Find $a_1$ and $d$. Construct the sequence.

We can use sequence construction to insert *arithmetic means* between two numbers.

**Example 7.** Insert three arithmetic means between 8 and 16.

Let 8 be the 1st term. Then 16 will be the 5th term. Using the formula $a_n = a_1 + (n - 1)d$ we have

$$16 = 8 + (5 - 1)d \text{ or } d = 2.$$

So we have 8, 10, 12, 14, 16.

## Exercise Set 17-3

▌For each of the following arithmetic sequences find the first term and the common difference. (*See Examples 1–3.*)

1. 2, 7, 12, 17, . . .
2. 1.06, 1.12, 1.18, 1.24, . . .
3. 7, 3, −1, −5, . . .
4. −9, −6, −3, 0, . . .
5. $\frac{3}{2}, \frac{9}{4}, 3, \frac{15}{4}, \ldots$
6. $\frac{3}{5}, \frac{1}{10}, -\frac{2}{5}, \ldots$

▌▌(*See Example 4.*)

7. Find the 12th term of the arithmetic sequence 2, 6, 10, . . .
8. Find the 11th term of the arithmetic sequence 0.07, 0.12, 0.17, . . .
9. Find the 17th term of the arithmetic sequence 7, 4, 1, . . .
10. Find the 14th term of the arithmetic sequence 3, $\frac{7}{3}$, $\frac{5}{3}$, . . .

(*See Example 5.*)

11. In the sequence of Exercise 7, what term is 106?
12. In the sequence of Exercise 8, what term is 1.67?
13. In the sequence of Exercise 9, what term is −296?
14. In the sequence of Exercise 10, what term is −27?
15. Find $a_{17}$ when $a_1 = 5$ and $d = 6$.
16. Find $a_{20}$ when $a_1 = 14$ and $d = -3$.
17. Find $a_1$ when $d = 4$ and $a_8 = 33$.
18. Find $d$ when $a_1 = 8$ and $a_{11} = 26$.
19. Find $n$ when $a_1 = 5$, $d = -3$, and $a_n = -76$.
20. Find $n$ when $a_1 = 25$, $d = -14$, and $a_n = -507$.

▌▌▌(*See Example 6.*)

21. In an arithmetic sequence $a_{17} = -40$ and $a_{28} = -73$. Find $a_1$ and $d$. Write the first 5 terms of the sequence.
22. In an arithmetic sequence $a_{17} = \frac{25}{3}$ and $a_{32} = \frac{95}{6}$. Find $a_1$ and $d$. Write the first 5 terms of the sequence.

(*See Example 7.*)

23. Insert three arithmetic means between 2 and 22.
24. Insert four arithmetic means between 8 and 23.

## Challenge Exercises

25. Smalltown, whose population was 18,395 ten years ago, has lost 270 inhabitants each year since then. What is the present population of Smalltown?
26. Find the first term and the common difference for the arithmetic sequence $3x + 2y$, $4x + y$, $5x$, $6x - y$, . . .
27. Find the first term and the common difference for the arithmetic sequence where $a_2 = 4p - 3q$ and $a_4 = 10p + q$.

# 17-4 Arithmetic Series

After finishing Lesson 17-4, you should be able to

▮ given an arithmetic sequence or series determine $a_1$, $a_n$, and $n$, and use the formula $S_n = \frac{n}{2}(a_1 + a_n)$ to find the sum of the first $n$ terms. Or, determine $a_1$, $n$, and $d$, and use the formula $S_n = \frac{n}{2}[2a_1 + (n-1)d]$ to find the sum of the first $n$ terms.

▮ An arithmetic series is a series associated with an arithmetic sequence. Two theorems give useful formulas for finding the sum of the first $n$ terms.

**THEOREM 17-2**

The sum of the first $n$ terms of an arithmetic series is given by

$S_n = \frac{n}{2}(a_1 + a_n)$.

This formula is useful when we know $a_1$ and $a_n$.

**THEOREM 17-3**

The sum of the first $n$ terms of an arithmetic series is given by

$S_n = \frac{n}{2}[2a_1 + (n-1)d]$.

This formula is useful when we do not know $a_n$.

**Example 1.** Find the sum of the first 100 natural numbers.

The sum of the first 100 natural number is $1 + 2 + 3 + \cdots + 100$. This is an arithmetic series.
$a_1 = 1$, $a_n = 100$, and $n = 100$. We use Theorem 17-2.

$$S_n = \frac{n}{2}(a_1 + a_n)$$

Substituting, we get

$$S_{100} = \tfrac{100}{2}(1 + 100)$$

$$= 50(101), \text{ or } 5050.$$

**TRY THIS** ➡

1. Find the sum of the first 200 natural numbers.

**A Proof of Theorem 17-2**

Let us write out the sum of the first $n$ terms of an arithmetic sequence in two different ways.

$$S_n = a_1 + (a_1 + d) + (a_1 + 2d) + \cdots + (a_n - 2d) + (a_n - d) + a_n.$$
$$S_n = a_n + (a_n - d) + (a_n - 2d) + \cdots + (a_1 + 2d) + (a_1 + d) + a_1.$$

We now add, obtaining

$$2S_n = (a_1 + a_n) + (a_1 + a_n) + \cdots + (a_1 + a_n), \; n \text{ summands.}$$

Thus $2S_n = n(a_1 + a_n)$, and $S_n = \dfrac{n}{2}(a_1 + a_n)$.

**Example 2.** Find the sum of the first 14 terms of the arithmetic series $2 + 5 + 8 + 11 + 14 + 17 + \cdots$

Note that $a_1 = 2$, $d = 3$, and $n = 14$. We use Theorem 17-3.

$$S_n = \frac{n}{2}[2a_1 + (n - 1)d]$$
$$S_{14} = \tfrac{14}{2} \cdot [2 \cdot 2 + (14 - 1)3]$$
$$= 7 \cdot [4 + 13 \cdot 3]$$
$$= 7 \cdot 43$$
$$S_{14} = 301$$

**TRY THIS**

2. Find the sum of the first 15 terms of the arithmetic series
$$1 + 3 + 5 + 7 + 9 + \cdots$$

**Example 3.** Find the sum of the series $\displaystyle\sum_{k=1}^{13} (4k + 5)$.

First find a few terms.

$$9 + 13 + 17 + \cdots$$

We see that this is an arithmetic series with $a_1 = 9$, $d = 4$, and $n = 13$. We use Theorem 17-3.

$$S_n = \frac{n}{2}[2a_1 + (n - 1)d]$$
$$S_{13} = \tfrac{13}{2}[2 \cdot 9 + (13 - 1)4]$$
$$= \tfrac{13}{2}[18 + 12 \cdot 4]$$
$$= \tfrac{13}{2} \cdot 66$$
$$S_{13} = 429.$$

**TRY THIS**

3. Find the sum of the series
$$\sum_{k=1}^{10} (9k - 4).$$

**Example 4.** Money is saved in an arithmetic sequence. $500 is saved one year, $600 the next, $700 the next, and so on, for 10 years. How much is saved?

We have the arithmetic series $500 + 600 + 700 + \cdots$
Thus $a_1 = 500$, $n = 10$, and $d = 100$. We use Theorem 17-3.

$$S_n = \frac{n}{2}[2a_1 + (n-1)d]$$

Substituting, we get

$$S_{10} = \frac{10}{2}[2 \cdot 500 + (10-1)100]$$
$$S_{10} = 9500.$$

$9500 is saved.

**TRY THIS**

> 4. A cheerleader pyramid has 15 students on the bottom row, 14 on the next row, and so on until there is 1 student on top. How many cheerleaders are in the pyramid? (How would you like being on the bottom?)

## Exercise Set 17-4

(*See Examples 1 and 2.*)

1. Find the sum of the first 20 terms of the series $5 + 8 + 11 + 14 + \cdots$
2. Find the sum of the first 14 terms of the series $11 + 7 + 3 + \cdots$
3. Find the sum of the first 15 terms of the series $5 + \frac{55}{7} + \frac{75}{7} + \frac{95}{7} + \cdots$
4. Find the sum of the first 16 terms of the series $\frac{3}{4} + \frac{5}{4} + \frac{7}{4} + \cdots$
5. Find the sum of the even numbers from 2 to 100, inclusive.
6. Find the sum of the odd numbers from 1 to 99, inclusive.
7. If an arithmetic series has $a_1 = 2$, $d = 5$, and $n = 20$, find $S_n$.
8. If an arithmetic series has $a_1 = 7$, $d = -3$, and $n = 32$, find $S_n$.

Find the sum of each series. (*See Example 3.*)

9. $\displaystyle\sum_{k=1}^{12} (6k - 3)$
10. $\displaystyle\sum_{k=1}^{16} (7k - 76)$

11. $\displaystyle\sum_{k=1}^{18} 5k$
12. $\displaystyle\sum_{k=1}^{20} 3k$

(*See Example 4.*)

13. How many poles will be in a pile of telephone poles if there are 30 in the first layer, 29 in the second, and so on until there is one in the last layer?
14. If 10¢ is saved on October 1, 20¢ on October 2, 30¢ on October 3, and so on, how much is saved during October? (October has 31 days).

# 17-5 Geometric Sequences

After finishing Lesson 17-5, you should be able to
**I**  find the common ratio of a geometric sequence.
**II**  given a geometric sequence, determine $a_1$ and $r$; and find the $n$th term using the formula $a_n = a_1 r^{n-1}$.

## I Geometric Sequences

The following sequence is not arithmetic.

$$3, 6, 12, 24, 48, 96, \ldots$$

If we multiply each term by 2 we get the next term.

**DEFINITION**
A sequence in which a constant $r$ can be multiplied by each term to get the next is called a *geometric sequence*. The constant $r$ is called the *common ratio*.

To find the common ratio, divide any term by the one before it.

**Examples.**  Each of the following are geometric sequences. Identify the common ratio.

| Sequence | Common ratio |
|---|---|
| **1.**  3, 6, 12, 24, . . . | 2 |
| **2.**  3, −6, 12, −24, . . . | −2 |
| **3.**  $1, \frac{1}{2}, \frac{1}{4}, \frac{1}{8}, \ldots$ | $\frac{1}{2}$ |

**TRY THIS**

Identify the common ratio of each geometric sequence.

1.  $1, 5, 25, 125, \ldots$
2.  $3, -9, 27, -81, \ldots$
3.  $48, -12, 3, \ldots$

## II The $n$th Term

If we let $a_1$ be the first term and $r$ be the common ratio, then $a_1 r$ is the second term, $a_1 r^2$ is the third term, and so on. Generalizing, we have the following.

**THEOREM 17-4**
In a geometric sequence, the $n$th term is given by $a_n = a_1 r^{n-1}$.

Note that the exponent is one less than the number of the term.

**Example 4.** Find the 11th term of the geometric sequence 64, −32, 16, −8, . . .

Note that $a_1 = 64$, $n = 11$, and $r = \frac{-32}{64}$, or $-\frac{1}{2}$. We use Theorem 17-4.

$$a_n = a_1 r^{n-1}$$
$$a_{11} = 64 \cdot \left(-\frac{1}{2}\right)^{11-1}$$
$$= 64 \cdot \left(-\frac{1}{2}\right)^{10}$$
$$= 2^6 \cdot \frac{1}{2^{10}} = 2^{-4}, \text{ or } \frac{1}{16}.$$

**TRY THIS**

> 4. Find the 6th term of the geometric sequence
> 3, −15, 75, . . .

We can use the $n$th term to insert geometric means between two numbers. The two numbers and their geometric means are terms of a geometric sequence.

**Example 5.** Insert two geometric means between 3 and 24.

3 is the 1st term and 24 is the 4th term.
$$24 = 3(r)^{4-1}$$
$$8 = r^3$$
$$2 = r$$

So we have 3, 6, 12, 24.

**TRY THIS**

> 5. Insert one geometric mean between 5 and 20.

**Example 6.** A college student borrows $600 at 7% interest compounded annually. The student pays off the loan at the end of 3 years. How much does the student pay?

For any principal $P$, at 7% interest, the student will owe $P + 0.07P$ at the end of 1 year, or $1.07P$. Then $1.07P$ is the principal for the second year. So at the end of the second year the student owes $1.07(1.07P)$. Then the principal at the beginning of consecutive years is

$$P, 1.07P, 1.07(1.07P), \ldots$$

This is a geometric sequence with $a_1 = 600$, $n = 4$, $r = 1.07$. We use Theorem 17-4.

$$a_n = a_1 r^{n-1}$$
$$a_4 = 600 \cdot (1.07)^{4-1}$$
$$= 600 \cdot 1.225043 \approx 735.03$$

Thus the student pays $735.03.

**TRY THIS**

> 6. A college student borrows $400 at 6% interest compounded annually. The loan is paid in full at the end of 3 years. How much has the student paid?

## Exercise Set 17-5

▌For each geometric sequence find the common ratio. (*See Examples 1–3.*)

1. 4, 8, 16, 32, . . .

2. 2, 1, $\frac{1}{2}$, $\frac{1}{4}$, $\frac{1}{8}$, . . .

3. 12, $-4$, $\frac{4}{3}$, $-\frac{4}{9}$, . . .

4. 5, 15, 45, 135, . . .

5. 1, $-1$, 1, $-1$, 1, . . .

6. $-5$, $-0.5$, $-0.05$, $-0.005$, . . .

7. $\frac{1}{x}$, $\frac{1}{x^2}$, $\frac{1}{x^3}$, . . .

8. 5, $\frac{5m}{2}$, $\frac{5m^2}{4}$, $\frac{5m^3}{8}$, . . .

▐▌(*See Example 4.*)

9. Find the 6th term of the geometric sequence 1, 3, 9, . . .

10. Find the 10th term of the geometric sequence $\frac{8}{243}$, $\frac{4}{81}$, $\frac{2}{27}$, . . .

11. Find the 5th term of the geometric sequence 2, $-10$, 50, . . .

12. Find the 9th term of the geometric sequence 2, $2\sqrt{3}$, 6, . . .

(*See Example 5.*)

13. Insert one geometric mean between 3 and 48.

14. Insert two geometric means between 4 and 32.

15. A college student borrows $800 at 8% interest compounded annually. The loan is paid in full at the end of 2 years. How much has the student paid?

16. A college student borrows $1000 at 8% interest compounded annually. The loan is paid in full at the end of 4 years. How much has the student paid?

## Challenge Exercises

17. A ping-pong ball is dropped from a height of 16 cm and always rebounds $\frac{1}{4}$ of the distance of the previous fall. What distance does it rebound the 6th time?

18. The population of a town is $P$ and is growing at the rate of 24% each year. What will its population be in $k$ years?

# 17-6 Geometric Series

After finishing Lesson 17-6, you should be able to
▪ find the sum of the first $n$ terms of a geometric series by identifying $a_1$ and $r$ and using the formula $S_n = \dfrac{a_1 - a_1 r^n}{1 - r}$.

▪ A geometric series is a series associated with a geometric sequence. The next theorem gives a formula for the first $n$ terms of a geometric series.

**THEOREM 17-5**

The sum of the first $n$ terms of a geometric series is given by

$$S_n = \frac{a_1 - a_1 r^n}{1 - r}.$$

**Example 1.** Find the sum of the first 6 terms of the geometric series $3 + 6 + 12 + 24 + \cdots$

$a_1 = 3$, $n = 6$, and $r = \frac{6}{3}$, or 2.

$$S_n = \frac{a_1 - a_1 r^n}{1 - r} \qquad \textit{Using Theorem 17-5}$$

$$S_6 = \frac{3 - 3 \cdot 2^6}{1 - 2}$$

$$= \frac{3 - 192}{-1}, \text{ or } 189.$$

**TRY THIS**

1. Find the sum of the first 6 terms of the geometric series $3 + 15 + 75 + 375 + \cdots$
2. Find the sum of the first 10 terms of the geometric series $2 - 1 + \frac{1}{2} - \frac{1}{4} + \cdots$

---

### A Proof of Theorem 17-5

Let us describe the sum of a geometric series as follows.

$$S_n = a_1 + a_1 r + a_1 r^2 + \cdots + a_1 r^{n-2} + a_1 r^{n-1}.$$

We multiply on both sides by $-r$. This gives us

$$-r S_n = -a_1 r - a_1 r^2 - \cdots - a_1 r^{n-1} - a_1 r^n.$$

Next, we add the two equations and solve for $S_n$.

$$S_n - r S_n = a_1 - a_1 r + a_1 r + a_1 r^2 - a_1 r^2 + \cdots - a_1 r^n$$
$$= a_1 - a_1 r^n$$
$$S_n = \frac{a_1 - a_1 r^n}{1 - r}$$

**Example 2.** Find the sum of the series $\sum\limits_{k=1}^{5} (\tfrac{1}{2})^{k+1}$.

First find a few terms.

$$(\tfrac{1}{2})^2 + (\tfrac{1}{2})^3 + (\tfrac{1}{2})^4 + \cdots$$

We see that this is a geometric series with $a_1 = \tfrac{1}{4}$, $n = 5$, and $r = \tfrac{1}{2}$.

$$S_n = \frac{a_1 - a_1 r^n}{1 - r} \qquad \textit{Using Theorem 17-5}$$

$$S_5 = \frac{\tfrac{1}{4} - \tfrac{1}{4} \cdot (\tfrac{1}{2})^5}{1 - \tfrac{1}{2}}$$

$$= \tfrac{31}{64}.$$

> 3. Find the sum of the geo-
>    metric series
>
>    $$\sum_{k=1}^{5} 3^k.$$

**TRY THIS**

## Exercise Set 17-6

▌ (*See Example 1.*)

1. Find the sum of the first 7 terms of the geometric series
   $$6 + 12 + 24 + \cdots$$
3. Find the sum of the first 8 terms of the geometric series
   $$5 + 10 + 20 + \cdots$$
5. Find the sum of the first 7 terms of the geometric series $\tfrac{1}{18} - \tfrac{1}{6} + \tfrac{1}{2} - \cdots$

7. Find the sum of the first 8 terms of the series $1 + x + x^2 + x^3 + \cdots$

2. Find the sum of the first 6 terms of the geometric series
   $$16 - 8 + 4 - \cdots$$
4. Find the sum of the first 6 terms of the geometric series
   $$24 + 12 + 6 + \cdots$$
6. Find the sum of the first 5 terms of the geometric series
   $$6 + 0.6 + 0.06 + \cdots$$
8. Find the sum of the first 10 terms of the series $1 + x^2 + x^4 + x^6 + \cdots$

Find the sum of each geometric series. (*See Example 2.*)

9. $\sum\limits_{k=1}^{6} (\tfrac{1}{2})^{k-1}$

10. $\sum\limits_{k=1}^{8} 2^k$

11. $\sum\limits_{k=1}^{7} 4^k$

12. $\sum\limits_{k=1}^{5} (\tfrac{1}{3})^{k-1}$

### Challenge Exercises

13. Find the sum of $-8 + 4 - 2 + \cdots - \tfrac{1}{32}$.
14. Find the sum of the first $n$ terms of $1 + x + x^2 + x^3 + \cdots$

# 17-7 Infinite Geometric Series

After finishing Lesson 17-7, you should be able to
**I** determine whether an infinite geometric series has a sum.
**II** find the sum of an infinite geometric series when $|r| < 1$.
**III** convert from repeating decimal notation for a number to fractional notation.

## I Sums of Infinite Geometric Series

By an *infinite* series we mean one that is unending. Let us consider two different infinite geometric series.

$$2 + 4 + 8 + 16 + 32 + 64 + \cdots + 2^n + \cdots$$

As we take $n$ larger and larger, the sum of the first $n$ terms gets large without bound. The next example, however, is different.

$$\frac{1}{2} + \frac{1}{4} + \frac{1}{8} + \frac{1}{16} + \cdots + \frac{1}{2^n} + \cdots$$

Let us look at the sum of the first $n$ terms for some values of $n$.

$$S_1 = \frac{1}{2}$$

$$S_2 = \frac{1}{2} + \frac{1}{4} = \frac{3}{4}$$

$$S_3 = \frac{1}{2} + \frac{1}{4} + \frac{1}{8} = \frac{7}{8}$$

$$S_4 = \frac{1}{2} + \frac{1}{4} + \frac{1}{8} + \frac{1}{16} = \frac{15}{16}$$

We see a pattern, which we can describe as follows.

$$S_n = \frac{2^n - 1}{2^n}.$$

We can see that as $n$ gets very very large, $S_n$ gets very very close to 1. We say that $S_n$ approaches a *limit* of 1. We *define* the sum of the infinite series to be 1.

**DEFINITION**

If, in an infinite series, $S_n$ approaches some limit as $n$ becomes very large, that limit is defined to be the *sum* of the series.

**TRY THIS** ➡️

1. Consider the infinite geometric series
$1 - \frac{1}{2} + \frac{1}{4} - \frac{1}{8} + \cdots$
$+ (-1)^{n-1}(\frac{1}{2})^{n-1} + \cdots$
a) Find $S_1$, $S_2$, $S_3$, $S_4$, and $S_5$.
b) What appears to be the sum of the series?

Some infinite series have sums and some do not.

**THEOREM 17-6**
An infinite geometric series has a sum if and only if $|r| < 1$. (The absolute value of the common ratio is less than 1.)

**Examples.** Determine which series have sums.

1. $1 - \frac{1}{2} + \frac{1}{4} - \frac{1}{8} + \frac{1}{16} + \cdots$
   $r = -\frac{1}{2}, |r| < 1$
   Series has a sum, by Theorem 17-6.

2. $1 + 5 + 25 + 125 + \cdots$
   $r = 5, |r| > 1$
   Series does not have a sum.

3. $1 + (-1) + 1 + (-1) + \cdots$
   $r = -1, |r| = 1$
   Series does not have a sum.

**TRY THIS**

Decide which geometric series have sums.

2. $4 + 16 + 64 + \cdots$
3. $5 - 30 + 180 - \cdots$
4. $1 + \frac{1}{3} + \frac{1}{9} + \frac{1}{27} + \cdots$

## ▌Finding Sums

**THEOREM 17-7**
The sum of an infinite geometric series, with $|r| < 1$, is given by

$$S = \frac{a_1}{1 - r}.$$

**Example 4.** Find the sum of the infinite geometric series
$5 + \frac{5}{2} + \frac{5}{4} + \frac{5}{8} + \cdots$

Note that $a_1 = 5$ and $r = \frac{1}{2}$. We use Theorem 17-7.

$$S = \frac{a_1}{1 - r}$$

Substituting, we get

$$S = \frac{5}{1 - \frac{1}{2}}$$
$$S = 10$$

**TRY THIS**

Find the sum of each geometric series.

5. $1 + \frac{1}{3} + \frac{1}{9} + \frac{1}{27} + \cdots$
6. $4 - 1 + \frac{1}{4} - \frac{1}{16} + \cdots$

---

**A Proof of Theorem 17-7**

We look at the sum of the first $n$ terms of an infinite geometric series.

$$S_n = \frac{a_1 - a_1 r^n}{1 - r}$$

As $n$ gets very large, we look at $r^n$, and see that, since $|r| < 1$, $r^n$ gets very small, approaching 0. Thus the numerator approaches $a_1$. The limit of $S_n$ as $n$ gets very large is therefore $\frac{a_1}{1 - r}$, and we have $S = \frac{a_1}{1 - r}$.

---

## ⁐ Repeating Decimals

The *repeating decimal* $0.66666666\ldots$, represents an infinite geometric series,

$$0.6 + 0.06 + 0.006 + 0.0006 + \cdots$$

Thus $a_1 = 0.6$ and $r = 0.1$. So $|r| < 1$ and we can use Theorem 17-7.

$$S = \frac{a_1}{1 - r}$$
$$S = \frac{0.6}{1 - 0.1}$$
$$= \frac{0.6}{0.9}$$
$$= \frac{2}{3}.$$

Thus $0.666\ldots = \frac{2}{3}$.

We can use a bar to indicate the repeating cycle, as follows: $0.66\overline{6}$.

**Example 5.** Find fractional notation for $0.27\overline{27}$.

Note that $a_1 = 0.27$ and $r = 0.01$ so

$$S = \frac{a_1}{1 - r} \qquad \textit{Using Theorem 17-7}$$
$$= \frac{0.27}{1 - 0.01}$$
$$= \frac{0.27}{0.99}$$
$$= \frac{3}{11}$$

Thus $0.27\overline{27} = \frac{3}{11}$.

This can be checked by doing the division $3 \div 11$.

**TRY THIS** ➤

## Exercise Set 17-7

Find fractional notation for each number.

7. $0.45\overline{45}$
8. $5.36\overline{36}$

▌ In each geometric series find $r$ and determine which series have sums. (*See Examples 1–3.*)

1. $5 + 10 + 20 + 40 + \cdots$
2. $16 + 8 + 4 + 2 + \cdots$
3. $6 + 2 + \frac{2}{3} + \frac{3}{9} + \cdots$
4. $2 - 4 + 8 - 16 + 32 - \cdots$
5. $1 + 0.1 + 0.01 + 0.001 + \cdots$
6. $-\frac{5}{3} - \frac{10}{9} - \frac{20}{27} - \frac{40}{81} - \cdots$
7. $1 - \frac{1}{5} + \frac{1}{25} - \frac{1}{125} + \cdots$
8. $6 + \frac{42}{5} + \frac{294}{25} + \cdots$

▌▌ Find the sum of each geometric series. (*See Example 4.*)

9. $4 + 2 + 1 + \cdots$
10. $7 + 3 + \frac{9}{7} + \cdots$
11. $25 - 20 + 16 - \cdots$
12. $12 - 9 + \frac{27}{4} - \cdots$
13. $1 + \frac{1}{2} + \frac{1}{4} + \cdots$
14. $\frac{8}{3} + \frac{4}{3} + \frac{2}{3} + \cdots$
15. $16 + 1.6 + 0.16 + \cdots$
16. $4 + 2.4 + 1.44 + \cdots$

▌▌▌ Find fractional notation for each number. (*See Example 5.*)

17. $0.77\overline{7}$
18. $0.33\overline{3}$
19. $0.2121\overline{21}$
20. $0.6363\overline{63}$
21. $5.1515\overline{15}$
22. $4.125\overline{125}$

---

### Challenge Exercises

23. The infinite series

$$2 + \frac{1}{2} + \frac{1}{2 \cdot 3} + \frac{1}{2 \cdot 3 \cdot 4} + \frac{1}{2 \cdot 3 \cdot 4 \cdot 5} + \frac{1}{2 \cdot 3 \cdot 4 \cdot 5 \cdot 6} + \cdots \text{ is not}$$

geometric, but does have a sum. Find values of $S_1$, $S_2$, $S_3$, $S_4$, $S_5$, and $S_6$. Make a conjecture about the value of $S$.

24. How far up and down will a ball travel before stopping if it is dropped from a height of 12 m, and each rebound is $\frac{1}{3}$ of the previous distance? (*Hint:* Use an infinite geometric series.)

25. The sides of a square are each 16 cm long. A second square is inscribed by joining the midpoints of the sides, successively. In the second square we repeat the process, inscribing a third square. If this process is continued indefinitely, what is the sum of all of the squares? (*Hint:* Use an infinite geometric series.)

## COMPUTER ACTIVITY

### Generating Terms in the Fibonacci Sequence

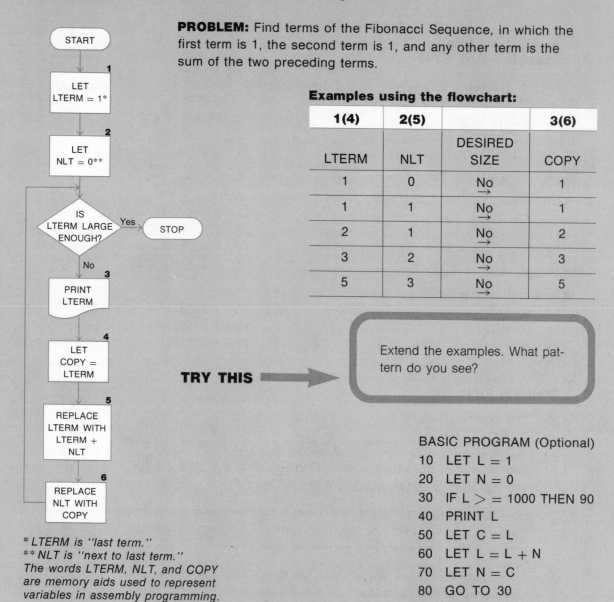

**PROBLEM:** Find terms of the Fibonacci Sequence, in which the first term is 1, the second term is 1, and any other term is the sum of the two preceding terms.

**Examples using the flowchart:**

| 1(4) | 2(5) | | 3(6) |
|---|---|---|---|
| LTERM | NLT | DESIRED SIZE | COPY |
| 1 | 0 | No → | 1 |
| 1 | 1 | No → | 1 |
| 2 | 1 | No → | 2 |
| 3 | 2 | No → | 3 |
| 5 | 3 | No → | 5 |

**TRY THIS** →

Extend the examples. What pattern do you see?

*LTERM is "last term."*
**NLT is "next to last term."*
*The words LTERM, NLT, and COPY are memory aids used to represent variables in assembly programming.*

BASIC PROGRAM (Optional)
```
10   LET L = 1
20   LET N = 0
30   IF L > = 1000 THEN 90
40   PRINT L
50   LET C = L
60   LET L = L + N
70   LET N = C
80   GO TO 30
90   STOP
```

## CHAPTER 17 REVIEW

Review the material in the chapter. Then see how you have done by trying these review exercises. If you miss an exercise, restudy the indicated lesson.

17-1  1.  Find the first four terms of the sequence given by $a_n = \dfrac{n-1}{n+1}$.

17-2  2.  Write sigma notation for this series: $4^2 + 4^3 + 4^4 + 4^5 + 4^6$.

17-3  3.  In an arithmetic sequence, find $d$ when $a_1 = 5$ and $a_{17} = 53$.

      4.  Insert two arithmetic means between 7 and 25.

17-4  5.  Find the sum of the first 30 positive integers.

17-5  6.  In a geometric sequence, $a_1 = 0.27$ and $r = 0.1$. Find the fifth term.

      7.  Insert one geometric mean between 8 and 72.

      8.  The present population of a city is 30,000. Its population is supposed to double every 10 years. If it does, what will its population be at the end of 80 years?

17-6  9.  Find the sum of the first 9 terms of the geometric series
$$5 - 10 + 20 - 40 + \cdots$$

17-7  10.  Find the sum of the infinite geometric series $8 - 2 + 0.5 - \cdots$

     11.  Find fractional notation for $0.\overline{59}$.

## CHAPTER 17 TEST

1.  Find the first four terms of the sequence given by $a_n = (-1)^n 3^n$.

2.  Write sigma notation for this series: $\dfrac{5}{3} + \dfrac{5}{3^2} + \dfrac{5}{3^3} + \dfrac{5}{3^4} + \dfrac{5}{3^5} + \dfrac{5}{3^6}$.

3.  Find the 6th term in the arithmetic sequence $a - b, a, a + b, \ldots$

4.  Insert three arithmetic means between 4 and 24.

5.  Deposits are made as follows: $10 for the first week, $13 the second week, $16 the third week, and so on, for 52 deposits. What is the sum of the deposits?

6.  For this geometric sequence find the common ratio: $24, 16, 10\frac{2}{3}, \ldots$

7.  Insert one geometric mean between 4 and 16.

8.  Find the 6th term of the geometric sequence $-2, -4, -8, \ldots$

9.  Find the sum of the first 9 terms of the geometric series
$$1 + x^3 + x^6 + x^9 + x^{12} + \cdots$$

10.  Find the sum of the infinite geometric series $64 - 8 + 1 - 0.125 +$

11.  Find fractional notation for $0.\overline{24}$.

## Ready for Matrices and Determinants?

4-1    1.  Determine whether $(-2, 4)$ is a solution of the system:
$$x + y = -3$$
$$2x - y = -8$$

4-2    Solve.

   2.  $x + y = 6$
       $x - y = 4$

   3.  $5x + 3y = 7$
       $3x - 5y = -23$

4-4    4.  Determine whether $(-1, 2, 1)$ is a solution of the system:
$$x + y + z = 2$$
$$x - y - z = 4$$
$$x - y + z = -5$$

4-4    5.  Solve:   $2x - y + 4z = -3$
                    $x\quad\ \ - 4z = \quad 5$
                    $6x - y + 2z = 10$

1-5    6.  Evaluate and simplify:   $-2(5) - (-3)(-4)$.

1-5    7.  Evaluate $x(y + z)$ when $x = -2$, $y = 3$, and $z = 8$.

1-5    8.  Evaluate $xy + xz$ when $x = -2$, $y = 3$, and $z = 8$.

1-2    9.  Name the additive inverse of $-12$.

1-3    10. Subtract:   $-2 - 8$.

# Chapter 18
# Matrices and Determinants

This mathematician is using matrices in her work
with computers.

# 18-1 Systems of Equations in Two Variables

After finishing Lesson 18-1, you should be able to

▌ solve systems of two linear equations in two variables using matrices.

▌In solving systems of equations, we work with the constants. The
variables play no essential role in the process. We can simplify
the writing by omitting the variables. For example, the system

$$5x + 3y = \phantom{-2}7$$
$$3x - 5y = -23$$

simplifies to

$$\begin{array}{ccc} 5 & 3 & 7 \\ 3 & -5 & -23 \end{array}$$

We have written a rectangular array of numbers called a *matrix*
(plural *matrices*). We ordinarily write brackets around matrices.
The following are matrices.

$$\begin{bmatrix} 4 & 1 & 3 & 5 \\ 1 & 0 & 1 & 2 \\ 6 & 3 & -2 & 0 \end{bmatrix}, \begin{bmatrix} 6 & 2 & 1 & 4 & 7 \\ 1 & 2 & 1 & 3 & 1 \\ 4 & 0 & -2 & 0 & -3 \end{bmatrix}, \begin{bmatrix} 1 & 2 \\ 145 & 0 \\ -7 & 9 \\ 8 & 1 \\ 0 & 0 \end{bmatrix}$$

The *rows* of a matrix are horizontal, and the *columns* are vertical.

$$\begin{bmatrix} 5 & -2 & 2 \\ 1 & 0 & 1 \\ 0 & 1 & 2 \end{bmatrix} \begin{array}{l} \leftarrow row\ 1 \\ \leftarrow row\ 2 \\ \leftarrow row\ 3 \end{array}$$

*column 1   column 2   column 3*

Let us now use matrices to solve systems of linear equations.

**Example.** Solve: $5x + 3y = \phantom{-2}7$
$\phantom{Solve: }3x - 5y = -23$

We first write a matrix, using only the constants.

$$\begin{bmatrix} 5 & 3 & 7 \\ 3 & -5 & -23 \end{bmatrix}$$

We do about the same calculations as if we wrote the entire
equations, but we are going to use a procedure that is a bit new.

The first thing we do is make the first number in the row 1. We multiply the first row by $\frac{1}{5}$.

$$\begin{bmatrix} 1 & \frac{3}{5} & \frac{7}{5} \\ 3 & -5 & -23 \end{bmatrix}$$   *This corresponds to multiplying the first equation by $\frac{1}{5}$.*

Now we multiply the first row by $-3$ (this gives $-3 \quad -\frac{9}{5} \quad -\frac{21}{5}$) and add it to the second row.

$$\begin{bmatrix} 1 & \frac{3}{5} & \frac{7}{5} \\ 0 & -\frac{34}{5} & -\frac{136}{5} \end{bmatrix}$$   *This corresponds to multiplying the first equation by $-3$ and adding to the second. (We retain the row in which the first number is 1.)*

Our goal was to get a 1 in the first row, first column, and a 0 in the second row, first column. Next we want to get a 1 in the second row, second column. To do this we multiply by $-\frac{5}{34}$.

$$\begin{bmatrix} 1 & \frac{3}{5} & \frac{7}{5} \\ 0 & 1 & 4 \end{bmatrix}$$   *This corresponds to multiplying the second equation by $-\frac{5}{34}$.*

We now work back up. We want to get a 0 in the first row, second column. We multiply the second row by $-\frac{3}{5}$, (this gives $0 \quad -\frac{3}{5} \quad -\frac{12}{5}$) and add to the first row.

$$\begin{bmatrix} 1 & 0 & -1 \\ 0 & 1 & 4 \end{bmatrix}$$

If we now put the variables back we have

$$\begin{aligned} x &= -1 \\ y &= 4 \end{aligned}$$

The solution is $(-1, 4)$.

Notice that we reduced the matrix to the form

$$\begin{bmatrix} 1 & 0 & p \\ 0 & 1 & q \end{bmatrix}$$

If the equations are not arranged in the form of the Example, we must first arrange them that way.

**TRY THIS** ➡

Solve, using matrices.

1. $5x - 2y = -3$
   $2x + 5y = -24$
2. $3y + 11 = 2x$
   $5y + 17 - 4x = 0$

There are some shortcuts when using the matrices. One is to interchange two rows before beginning. For example, in the matrix

$$\begin{bmatrix} 3 & -5 & 17 \\ 1 & 2 & 4 \end{bmatrix}$$

we can interchange the two rows to get a 1 in the first row, first column:

$$\begin{bmatrix} 1 & 2 & 4 \\ 3 & -5 & 17 \end{bmatrix}$$

This corresponds to interchanging equations. Another shortcut consists of multiplying one or more rows by a power of 10 before beginning in order to eliminate decimal points.

In the procedure we are developing, it is important not to use any shortcuts other than these two.

**TRY THIS**

Solve, using matrices.

3. $5x - 2y = 1$
   $x + 3y = 7$
4. $0.2x + 0.3y = 0.1$
   $0.3x - 0.1y = 0.7$

## Exercise Set 18-1

▌Solve, using matrices. (*See the Example.*)

1. $4x + 2y = 11$
   $3x - y = 2$
2. $3x - 3y = 11$
   $9x - 2y = 5$
3. $5x + 2 = 3y$
   $4x + 2y - 5 = 0$
4. $3x + 3y - 7 = 0$
   $2y = 10 + 5x$
5. $3x + y = 7$
   $x + y = 1$
6. $2x + y = 7$
   $x - 5y = 4$
7. $0.3x + 0.2y = -0.9$
   $0.2x - 0.3y = -0.6$
8. $0.2x - 0.3y = 0.3$
   $0.4x + 0.6y = -0.2$

---

### Challenge Exercises

9. A grocer mixes candy worth $0.80 per kg with nuts worth $0.70 per kg to get a 20-kg mixture worth $0.77 per kg. How many kg of candy and how many kg of nuts were used?

10. One year some money was invested at $5\frac{1}{2}\%$ and another amount invested at $5\frac{3}{4}\%$. The income from the investments was $1355. The income from the $5\frac{1}{2}\%$ investment was $255 less than from the $5\frac{3}{4}\%$ investment. How much as invested at each rate? (Recall the formula $I = Prt$, for simple interest.)

# 18-2 Systems of Equations in Three Variables

After finishing Lesson 18-2, you should be able to
▪ solve systems of three linear equations in three variables using matrices.

▪**Example.** Solve: 
$$2x - y + 4z = -3$$
$$x \qquad - 4z = 5$$
$$6x - y + 2z = 10$$

We first write a matrix. We write a 0 for the missing term in the second equation.

$$\begin{bmatrix} 2 & -1 & 4 & -3 \\ 1 & 0 & -4 & 5 \\ 6 & -1 & 2 & 10 \end{bmatrix}$$

To make the first number in the first row 1, we interchange the first and second rows.

$$\begin{bmatrix} 1 & 0 & -4 & 5 \\ 2 & -1 & 4 & -3 \\ 6 & -1 & 2 & 10 \end{bmatrix}$$ 
*This corresponds to interchanging the first and second equations.*

Next, we multiply the first row by $-2$ and add it to the second row.

$$\begin{bmatrix} 1 & 0 & -4 & 5 \\ 0 & -1 & 12 & -13 \\ 6 & -1 & 2 & 10 \end{bmatrix}$$ 
*This corresponds to multiplying the first equation by $-2$ and adding it to the second equation.*

Now we multiply the first row by $-6$ and add it to the third row.

$$\begin{bmatrix} 1 & 0 & -4 & 5 \\ 0 & -1 & 12 & -13 \\ 0 & -1 & 26 & -20 \end{bmatrix}$$ 
*This corresponds to multiplying the first equation by $-6$ and adding it to the third equation.*

Next we multiply row 2 by $-1$.

$$\begin{bmatrix} 1 & 0 & -4 & 5 \\ 0 & 1 & -12 & 13 \\ 0 & -1 & 26 & -20 \end{bmatrix}$$ 
*This corresponds to multiplying the second equation by $-1$ to make the y-coefficient 1.*

Now we add row 2 to row 3.

$$\begin{bmatrix} 1 & 0 & -4 & 5 \\ 0 & 1 & -12 & 13 \\ 0 & 0 & 14 & -7 \end{bmatrix}$$

Then we multiply row 3 by $\frac{1}{14}$.

$$\begin{bmatrix} 1 & 0 & -4 & 5 \\ 0 & 1 & -12 & 13 \\ 0 & 0 & 1 & -\frac{1}{2} \end{bmatrix}$$ *This corresponds to making the z-coefficient 1.*

Now we work back up. We multiply the third row by 12 and add it to the second row.

$$\begin{bmatrix} 1 & 0 & -4 & 5 \\ 0 & 1 & 0 & 7 \\ 0 & 0 & 1 & -\frac{1}{2} \end{bmatrix}$$

We multiply the third row by 4 and add it to the first row.

$$\begin{bmatrix} 1 & 0 & 0 & 3 \\ 0 & 1 & 0 & 7 \\ 0 & 0 & 1 & -\frac{1}{2} \end{bmatrix}$$

If we now put the variables back we have

$$\begin{aligned} x & = 3 \\ y & = 7 \\ z & = -\tfrac{1}{2}. \end{aligned}$$

The solution is $(3, 7, -\frac{1}{2})$.

Notice that in this case, we found a matrix of the form

$$\begin{bmatrix} 1 & 0 & 0 & p \\ 0 & 1 & 0 & q \\ 0 & 0 & 1 & r \end{bmatrix}$$

**TRY THIS** ➡

> 1. Solve, using matrices.
>
> $x - 2y + 3z = 4$
> $2x - y + z = -1$
> $4x + y + 2z = 4$

## Exercise Set 18-2

Solve, using matrices. (*See the Example.*)

1. $x + 2y - 3z = 9$
   $2x - y + 2z = -8$
   $3x - y - 4z = 3$

2. $x - y + 2z = 0$
   $x - 2y + 3z = -1$
   $2x - 2y + z = -3$

3. $4x - y - 3z = 1$
   $8x + y - z = 5$
   $2x + y + 2z = 5$

4. $3x + 2y + 2z = 3$
   $x + 2y - z = 5$
   $2x - 4y + z = 0$

5. $p + q + r = 1$
   $p + 2q + 3r = 4$
   $p + 3q + 7r = 13$

6. $m + n + t = 9$
   $m - n - t = -15$
   $m + n - t = -5$

# 18-3 Determinants and Two Equations

After finishing Lesson 18-3, you should be able to
▮ evaluate determinants of second order.
▮▮ solve systems of two equations in two variables, using Cramer's Rule.

## ▮ Determinants of Second Order

A matrix with the same number of rows as columns is called a *square* matrix. With every square matrix is associated a number called its *determinant*.

**DEFINITION**

The determinant of a matrix $\begin{bmatrix} a & c \\ b & d \end{bmatrix}$ is denoted $\begin{vmatrix} a & c \\ b & d \end{vmatrix}$ and is defined as follows: $\begin{vmatrix} a & c \\ b & d \end{vmatrix} = ad - bc$.

The determinant of a 2 × 2 matrix is said to be of *second order;* the determinant of a 3 × 3 matrix is said to be of *third order;* and so on.

**Examples.** Evaluate.

**1.** $\begin{vmatrix} 2 & 5 \\ 6 & 7 \end{vmatrix} = 2 \cdot 7 - 6 \cdot 5 = -16$    *The arrows indicate the way we multiply.*

**2.** $\begin{vmatrix} -2 & -4 \\ -3 & 5 \end{vmatrix} = -2 \cdot 5 - (-3)(-4) = -10 - 12 = -22$

**TRY THIS** ➡

Evaluate.

1. $\begin{vmatrix} 2 & 3 \\ 7 & 8 \end{vmatrix}$

2. $\begin{vmatrix} -2 & \frac{1}{2} \\ 6 & 1 \end{vmatrix}$

3. $\begin{vmatrix} 4 & -2 \\ -\frac{1}{4} & 10 \end{vmatrix}$

4. $\begin{vmatrix} -3 & -6 \\ -4 & -5 \end{vmatrix}$

## ▮▮ Solving by Determinants

Determinants can be used to solve equations.

**THEOREM 18-1**   **(Cramer's Rule)**

If the system $a_1 x + b_1 y = c_1$
$\qquad\qquad a_2 x + b_2 y = c_2$

has exactly one solution, it is given by

$$x = \frac{\begin{vmatrix} c_1 & b_1 \\ c_2 & b_2 \end{vmatrix}}{\begin{vmatrix} a_1 & b_1 \\ a_2 & b_2 \end{vmatrix}} \quad \text{and} \quad y = \frac{\begin{vmatrix} a_1 & c_1 \\ a_2 & c_2 \end{vmatrix}}{\begin{vmatrix} a_1 & b_1 \\ a_2 & b_2 \end{vmatrix}}$$

Compare the values of *x* and *y* in Cramer's Rule. The same determinant

$$\begin{vmatrix} a_1 & b_1 \\ a_2 & b_2 \end{vmatrix},$$ which we call *D*,

occurs as the denominator of both *x* and *y*. The determinant

$$\begin{vmatrix} a_1 & c_1 \\ a_2 & c_2 \end{vmatrix},$$ which we call $D_y$,

is the numerator of *y* and is obtained from the determinant *D* by replacing the *y*-coefficients by $c_1$ and $c_2$. The determinant

$$\begin{vmatrix} c_1 & b_1 \\ c_2 & b_2 \end{vmatrix},$$ which we call $D_x$,

is the numerator of *x* and is obtained from *D* by replacing the *x*-coefficients by $c_1$ and $c_2$.

**Example 3.** Solve, using Cramer's Rule: 
$$3x - 2y = 7$$
$$3x + 2y = 9$$

$$D = \begin{vmatrix} 3 & -2 \\ 3 & 2 \end{vmatrix} = 3 \cdot 2 - 3(-2) = 6 + 6 = 12$$

$$D_x = \begin{vmatrix} 7 & -2 \\ 9 & 2 \end{vmatrix} = 7 \cdot 2 - 9(-2) = 14 + 18 = 32$$

$$D_y = \begin{vmatrix} 3 & 7 \\ 3 & 9 \end{vmatrix} = 3 \cdot 9 - 3 \cdot 7 = 27 - 21 = 6$$

Then

$$x = \frac{D_x}{D} = \frac{32}{12}, \text{ or } \frac{8}{3} \qquad y = \frac{D_y}{D} = \frac{6}{12}, \text{ or } \frac{1}{2}$$

The solution is $\left( \frac{8}{3}, \frac{1}{2} \right)$.

**TRY THIS**

Solve, using Cramer's Rule.

5. $20x - 15y = 75$
   $x + 3y = 0$

The quotients in Cramer's Rule make sense only if the denominator determinant *D* is not 0. If $D = 0$, then one of two things happens.
1.  If $D = 0$, and $D_x$ and $D_y$ are also 0, then the system is dependent (has many solutions).
2.  If $D = 0$, and at least one of $D_x$ or $D_y$ is not 0, then the system is inconsistent (has no solution).

**TRY THIS** ━━━━▶

Solve, using Cramer's Rule.

6. $2x - y = 6$
   $3x + 4y = 4$

## Exercise Set 18-3

▮ Evaluate. (*See Examples 1 and 2.*)

1. $\begin{vmatrix} 2 & 7 \\ 1 & 5 \end{vmatrix}$

2. $\begin{vmatrix} 3 & 2 \\ 2 & -3 \end{vmatrix}$

3. $\begin{vmatrix} 6 & -9 \\ 2 & 3 \end{vmatrix}$

4. $\begin{vmatrix} 3 & 2 \\ -7 & 5 \end{vmatrix}$

5. $\begin{vmatrix} 1.3 & 2.7 \\ 4.2 & 0.8 \end{vmatrix}$

6. $\begin{vmatrix} 2.4 & 1.6 \\ 0.9 & 1.8 \end{vmatrix}$

7. $\begin{vmatrix} -7 & -7 \\ 3 & 3 \end{vmatrix}$

8. $\begin{vmatrix} 8 & -1 \\ 8 & -1 \end{vmatrix}$

▮▮ Solve, using Cramer's Rule. (*See Example 3.*)

9. $-2x + 4y = 3$
   $3x - 7y = 1$

10. $5x - 4y = -3$
    $7x + 2y = 6$

11. $3x - 4y = 6$
    $5x + 9y = 10$

12. $5x + 8y = 1$
    $3x + 7y = 5$

13. $2x - 2y = 2$
    $6x - 5y = 1$

14. $5x - 6y = 8$
    $2x - 5y = -2$

---

### Calculator Exercises

Solve, using Cramer's Rule.

15. $2.35x - 3.18y = 4.82$
    $1.92x + 6.77y = -3.87$

16. $0.0375x + 0.912y = -1.003$
    $463x - 801y = 946$

### Challenge Exercises

17. Evaluate: $\begin{vmatrix} x & 4 \\ x & x^2 \end{vmatrix}$

18. Solve: $\sqrt{3}x + \pi y = -5$
    $\pi x - 3y = 4$

# 18-4 Determinants and Three Equations

After finishing Lesson 18-4, you should be able to
∎ evaluate determinants of third order.
∎∎ solve systems of three equations in three variables using Cramer's Rule.

## ∎ Determinants of Third Order

We now define third order determinants.

**DEFINITION**

The *determinant* of a matrix with three rows and three columns is defined as follows:

$$\begin{vmatrix} a_1 & b_1 & c_1 \\ a_2 & b_2 & c_2 \\ a_3 & b_3 & c_3 \end{vmatrix} = a_1 \cdot \begin{vmatrix} b_2 & c_2 \\ b_3 & c_3 \end{vmatrix} - a_2 \cdot \begin{vmatrix} b_1 & c_1 \\ b_3 & c_3 \end{vmatrix} + a_3 \cdot \begin{vmatrix} b_1 & c_1 \\ b_2 & c_2 \end{vmatrix}$$

The second order determinants on the right can be found by crossing out the row and column in which the *a*-coefficient occurs. Thus for $a_2$, we cross out the rows and columns shown:

$$\begin{vmatrix} a_1 & b_1 & c_1 \\ a_2 & b_2 & c_2 \\ a_3 & b_3 & c_3 \end{vmatrix}$$

**Example 1.** Evaluate.

$$\begin{vmatrix} -1 & 0 & 1 \\ -5 & 1 & -1 \\ 4 & 8 & 1 \end{vmatrix} = -1 \cdot \begin{vmatrix} 1 & -1 \\ 8 & 1 \end{vmatrix} - (-5) \cdot \begin{vmatrix} 0 & 1 \\ 8 & 1 \end{vmatrix} + 4 \cdot \begin{vmatrix} 0 & 1 \\ 1 & -1 \end{vmatrix}$$

$$= -1(1 + 8) + 5(-8) + 4(-1)$$
$$= -9 - 40 - 4$$
$$= -53$$

**TRY THIS** ➡

Evaluate.

1. $\begin{vmatrix} 2 & -1 & 1 \\ 1 & 2 & -1 \\ 3 & 4 & -3 \end{vmatrix}$

2. $\begin{vmatrix} 3 & 2 & 2 \\ -2 & 1 & 4 \\ 4 & -3 & 3 \end{vmatrix}$

3. $\begin{vmatrix} 2 & 0 & 2 \\ 0 & 2 & 0 \\ 1 & 0 & 2 \end{vmatrix}$

## ▮ Solving by Determinants

**THEOREM 18-2   (Cramer's Rule)**

If the system $a_1x + b_1y + c_1z = d_1$
$$a_2x + b_2y + c_2z = d_2$$
$$a_3x + b_3y + c_3z = d_3$$

has exactly one solution, it is given by

$$x = \frac{D_x}{D}, \ y = \frac{D_y}{D}, \ z = \frac{D_z}{D},$$

where

$$D = \begin{vmatrix} a_1 & b_1 & c_1 \\ a_2 & b_2 & c_2 \\ a_3 & b_3 & c_3 \end{vmatrix}, \ D_x = \begin{vmatrix} d_1 & b_1 & c_1 \\ d_2 & b_2 & c_2 \\ d_3 & b_3 & c_3 \end{vmatrix}, \ D_y = \begin{vmatrix} a_1 & d_1 & c_1 \\ a_2 & d_2 & c_2 \\ a_3 & d_3 & c_3 \end{vmatrix}, \ D_z = \begin{vmatrix} a_1 & b_1 & d_1 \\ a_2 & b_2 & d_2 \\ a_3 & b_3 & d_3 \end{vmatrix}.$$

We obtain the determinant $D_x$ in the numerator of $x$ from $D$ by replacing the $x$ coefficients by $d_1$, $d_2$, and $d_3$. A similar thing happens with $D_y$ and $D_z$. We have thus extended *Cramer's Rule* to solve systems of three equations in three variables. As before, when $D = 0$, Cramer's rule cannot be used. If $D = 0$, and $D_x$, $D_y$, and $D_z$ are 0, the system is dependent (has an infinite number of solutions). If $D = 0$ and one of $D_x$, $D_y$, or $D_z$, is not zero, then the system is inconsistent (has no solution).

**Example 2.**   Solve, using Cramer's rule: $x - 3y + 7z = 13$
$$x + y + z = 1$$
$$x - 2y + 3z = 4$$

We find the appropriate determinants and evaluate.

$$D = \begin{vmatrix} 1 & -3 & 7 \\ 1 & 1 & 1 \\ 1 & -2 & 3 \end{vmatrix} = -10, \ D_x = \begin{vmatrix} 13 & -3 & 7 \\ 1 & 1 & 1 \\ 4 & -2 & 3 \end{vmatrix} = 20,$$

$$D_y = \begin{vmatrix} 1 & 13 & 7 \\ 1 & 1 & 1 \\ 1 & 4 & 3 \end{vmatrix} = -6, \ D_z = \begin{vmatrix} 1 & -3 & 13 \\ 1 & 1 & 1 \\ 1 & -2 & 4 \end{vmatrix} = -24.$$

Then

$$x = \frac{D_x}{D} = \frac{20}{-10} = -2, \ y = \frac{D_y}{D} = \frac{-6}{-10} = \frac{3}{5}, \ z = \frac{D_z}{D} = \frac{-24}{-10} = \frac{12}{5}.$$

The solution is $(-2, \frac{3}{5}, \frac{12}{5})$.

In practice it is actually not necessary to evaluate $D_z$, since, if we have the solutions for $x$ and $y$, we could substitute in one of the equations and find $z$. We know $x = -2$ and $y = \frac{3}{5}$ in Example 2; so by using the second equation $-2 + \frac{3}{5} + z = 1$, we find $z = \frac{12}{5}$.

**TRY THIS**

4.  Solve, using Cramer's Rule.

$$x - 3y - 7z = 6$$
$$2x + 3y + z = 9$$
$$4x + y = 7$$

## Exercise Set 18-4

▌Evaluate. (*See Example 1.*)

1.  $\begin{vmatrix} 0 & 2 & 0 \\ 3 & -1 & 1 \\ 1 & -2 & 2 \end{vmatrix}$

2.  $\begin{vmatrix} 3 & 0 & -2 \\ 5 & 1 & 2 \\ 2 & 0 & -1 \end{vmatrix}$

3.  $\begin{vmatrix} -1 & -2 & -3 \\ 3 & 4 & 2 \\ 0 & 1 & 2 \end{vmatrix}$

4.  $\begin{vmatrix} 1 & 2 & 2 \\ 2 & 1 & 0 \\ 3 & 3 & 1 \end{vmatrix}$

5.  $\begin{vmatrix} 3 & 2 & 2 \\ -2 & 1 & 4 \\ 4 & -3 & 3 \end{vmatrix}$

6.  $\begin{vmatrix} 2 & -1 & 1 \\ 1 & 2 & -1 \\ 3 & 4 & -3 \end{vmatrix}$

▌▌Solve, using Cramer's Rule. (*See Example 2.*)

7.  $3x + 2y - z = 4$
    $3x - 2y + z = 5$
    $4x - 5y - z = -1$

8.  $3x - y + 2z = 1$
    $x - y + 2z = 3$
    $-2x + 3y + z = 1$

9.  $2x - 3y + 5z = 27$
    $x + 2y - z = -4$
    $5x - y + 4z = 27$

10. $x - y + 2z = -3$
    $x + 2y + 3z = 4$
    $2x + y + z = -3$

11. $r - 2s + 3t = 6$
    $2r - s - t = -3$
    $r + s + t = 6$

12. $a - 3c = 6$
    $b + 2c = 2$
    $7a - 3b - 5c = 14$

## Challenge Exercises

13. Evaluate: $\begin{vmatrix} 1 & x & y \\ 1 & x & y \\ 1 & 1 & 1 \end{vmatrix}$

14. Verify: $\begin{vmatrix} 1 & x & x^2 \\ 1 & y & y^2 \\ 1 & z & z^2 \end{vmatrix} = (x - y)(y - z)(z - x)$

# 18-5 Operations on Matrices

After finishing Lesson 18-5, you should be able to
  **I**   find the dimensions of a matrix.
  **II**  add matrices of the same dimensions.
  **III** add a matrix and a zero matrix of the same dimensions.
  **IIII** subtract matrices of the same dimensions.
  **IIIII** find the additive inverse of a matrix, and subtract matrices by adding an additive inverse.

## I Dimensions of a Matrix

A matrix of *m* rows and *n* columns is called a matrix with *dimensions m × n* (read "*m* by *n*").

**Examples.** Find the dimensions of each matrix.

**1.** $\begin{bmatrix} 2 & -3 & 4 \\ -1 & \frac{1}{2} & \pi \end{bmatrix}$  **2.** $\begin{bmatrix} -3 & 8 & 9 \\ \pi & -2 & 5 \\ -6 & 7 & 8 \end{bmatrix}$  **3.** $\begin{bmatrix} 10 \\ -7 \end{bmatrix}$  **4.** $[-3 \quad 4]$

   2 × 3 matrix         3 × 3 matrix            2 × 1 matrix         1 × 2 matrix

**TRY THIS**

## II Matrix Addition

### DEFINITION

To *add* matrices, we add the corresponding members. The matrices must have the same dimensions.

**Examples.** Add.

**5.** $\begin{bmatrix} -5 & 0 \\ 4 & \frac{1}{2} \end{bmatrix} + \begin{bmatrix} 6 & -3 \\ 2 & 3 \end{bmatrix} = \begin{bmatrix} -5+6 & 0-3 \\ 4+2 & \frac{1}{2}+3 \end{bmatrix} = \begin{bmatrix} 1 & -3 \\ 6 & 3\frac{1}{2} \end{bmatrix}.$

**6.** $\begin{bmatrix} 1 & 3 & 2 \\ -1 & 5 & 4 \\ 6 & 0 & 1 \end{bmatrix} + \begin{bmatrix} -1 & -2 & 1 \\ 1 & -2 & 2 \\ -3 & 1 & 0 \end{bmatrix} = \begin{bmatrix} 0 & 1 & 3 \\ 0 & 3 & 6 \\ 3 & 1 & 1 \end{bmatrix}$

Addition of matrices is both commutative and associative.

### THEOREM 18-3

For any matrices of the same dimensions, **A**, **B**, and **C**,
**A** + **B** = **B** + **A**, **A** + (**B** + **C**) = (**A** + **B**) + **C**.

Find the dimensions of each matrix.

1. $\begin{bmatrix} -3 & 5 \\ 4 & \frac{1}{4} \\ -\pi & 0 \end{bmatrix}$

2. $\begin{bmatrix} -3 & 0 \\ 0 & 3 \end{bmatrix}$

3. $\begin{bmatrix} 1 & 2 & 3 \\ 0 & 1 & 8 \\ 0 & 0 & 1 \end{bmatrix}$

4. $[\pi \quad \sqrt{2}]$

5. $\begin{bmatrix} -5 \\ \pi \end{bmatrix}$

6. $[-3]$

**TRY THIS** ➡️

7. Let $\mathbf{A} = \begin{bmatrix} 4 & -1 \\ 6 & -3 \end{bmatrix}$ and $\mathbf{B} = \begin{bmatrix} -6 & -5 \\ 7 & 3 \end{bmatrix}$

   a) Find $\mathbf{A} + \mathbf{B}$.
   b) Find $\mathbf{B} + \mathbf{A}$.

### ⅠⅠⅠ Zero Matrices

**DEFINITION**

A *zero matrix* is a matrix all of whose elements are 0.

**Example 7.** Add.

$$\begin{bmatrix} 2 & -1 & 3 \\ 1 & 0 & -1 \end{bmatrix} + \begin{bmatrix} 0 & 0 & 0 \\ 0 & 0 & 0 \end{bmatrix} = \begin{bmatrix} 2 & -1 & 3 \\ 1 & 0 & -1 \end{bmatrix}$$

A zero matrix is denoted by $\mathbf{O}$.

8. Let $\mathbf{A} = \begin{bmatrix} 4 & -3 \\ 5 & 8 \end{bmatrix}$

   and $\mathbf{O} = \begin{bmatrix} 0 & 0 \\ 0 & 0 \end{bmatrix}$

   a) Find $\mathbf{A} + \mathbf{O}$.
   b) Find $\mathbf{O} + \mathbf{A}$.

**TRY THIS** ➡️

It follows that a zero matrix is an additive identity.

**THEOREM 18-4**

For any matrices $\mathbf{A}$ and $\mathbf{O}$ of the same dimensions, $\mathbf{A} + \mathbf{O} = \mathbf{A}$

### ⅠⅠⅠⅠ Subtraction

The definition of subtraction is the same for matrices as it is for numbers.

**DEFINITION**

The matrix $\mathbf{A} - \mathbf{B}$ is the matrix which when added to $\mathbf{B}$ gives $\mathbf{A}$.

**THEOREM 18-5**

To subtract matrices of the same dimensions we can subtract the corresponding elements.

**Example 8.** Subtract.

$$\begin{bmatrix} 1 & 2 \\ -2 & 0 \\ -3 & -1 \end{bmatrix} - \begin{bmatrix} 1 & -1 \\ 1 & 3 \\ 2 & 3 \end{bmatrix} = \begin{bmatrix} 0 & 3 \\ -3 & -3 \\ -5 & -4 \end{bmatrix}$$

Subtract.

9. $\begin{bmatrix} 1 & 3 & -2 \\ 4 & 0 & 5 \end{bmatrix} - \begin{bmatrix} 2 & -1 & 5 \\ 6 & 4 & -3 \end{bmatrix}$

10. $\begin{bmatrix} 1 & 2 \\ 4 & 1 \\ -5 & 4 \end{bmatrix} - \begin{bmatrix} 7 & -4 \\ 3 & 5 \\ 2 & -1 \end{bmatrix}$

**TRY THIS** ➡️

## ▮▮▮▮▮ **Additive Inverses and Subtraction**

Additive inverses are defined for matrices the same way as for numbers.

### DEFINITION
Two matrices are additive inverses of each other if their sum is a zero matrix.

### THEOREM 18-6
The additive inverse of a matrix can be found by replacing each element by its additive inverse.

**Example 9.** Find the additive inverse of $\begin{bmatrix} -3 & 4 & 0 \\ 2 & 6 & 4 \\ -1 & 5 & -5 \end{bmatrix}$.

The additive inverse is $\begin{bmatrix} 3 & -4 & 0 \\ -2 & -6 & -4 \\ 1 & -5 & 5 \end{bmatrix}$.

**TRY THIS**

> Find the additive inverse.
>
> 11. $\begin{bmatrix} 2 & -1 & 5 \\ 6 & 4 & -3 \end{bmatrix}$

The additive inverse of **A** is denoted $-$**A**.

With numbers, we can subtract by adding an additive inverse. This is also true of matrices.

### THEOREM 18-7
For any matrices **A** and **B** of the same dimensions,
$$\mathbf{A} - \mathbf{B} = \mathbf{A} + (-\mathbf{B}).$$

**Example 10.** Subtract, by adding an additive inverse.

$$\begin{bmatrix} 3 & -1 \\ -2 & 4 \end{bmatrix} - \begin{bmatrix} 2 & 1 \\ 3 & -2 \end{bmatrix} = \begin{bmatrix} 3 & -1 \\ -2 & 4 \end{bmatrix} + \begin{bmatrix} -2 & -1 \\ -3 & 2 \end{bmatrix}$$

$$\quad\;\; \mathbf{A} \quad\; - \quad\; \mathbf{B} \quad = \quad\;\; \mathbf{A} \quad + \quad (-\mathbf{B})$$

$$= \begin{bmatrix} 1 & -2 \\ -5 & 6 \end{bmatrix}$$

**TRY THIS**

> 12. Let $\mathbf{A} = \begin{bmatrix} 1 & 2 \\ 4 & 1 \\ -5 & 4 \end{bmatrix}$
>
> and $\mathbf{B} = \begin{bmatrix} 7 & -4 \\ 3 & 5 \\ 2 & -1 \end{bmatrix}$.
>
> Subtract, by adding an additive inverse.
>
> a) $\mathbf{A} - \mathbf{B}$
>
> b) $\mathbf{B} - \mathbf{A}$

## Exercise Set 18-5

For Exercises 1–36, let

$$A = \begin{bmatrix} 1 & 2 \\ 4 & -3 \end{bmatrix}, B = \begin{bmatrix} -3 & -5 \\ 2 & -1 \end{bmatrix}, C = \begin{bmatrix} 1 & -1 \\ -1 & 1 \end{bmatrix}, D = \begin{bmatrix} 1 & 1 \\ 1 & 1 \end{bmatrix}, E = \begin{bmatrix} 1 & 3 \\ 2 & 6 \end{bmatrix},$$

$$F = \begin{bmatrix} 3 & 3 \\ -1 & -1 \end{bmatrix}, G = \begin{bmatrix} 1 & 0 & -2 \\ 0 & -1 & 3 \\ 3 & -2 & 4 \end{bmatrix}, H = \begin{bmatrix} -1 & -2 & 5 \\ 1 & 0 & -1 \\ -2 & -3 & 1 \end{bmatrix}, M = \begin{bmatrix} -4 & 5 & -2 \\ 1 & 0 & -4 \\ -2 & -3 & -5 \end{bmatrix},$$

$$O = \begin{bmatrix} 0 & 0 \\ 0 & 0 \end{bmatrix}, P = \begin{bmatrix} -2 & 3 & 4 \\ 8 & 0 & -1 \end{bmatrix}, Q = \begin{bmatrix} -3 & -3 & 7 \\ -5 & 2 & 1 \end{bmatrix}, R = \begin{bmatrix} -1 & 0 & 0 \\ 0 & 2 & 0 \end{bmatrix}.$$

▌Find the dimensions of each matrix. (*See Examples 1–4.*)

1. **A**
2. **G**
3. **Q**
4. **O**

▌▌Add. (*See Examples 5 and 6.*)

5. **A + B**
6. **B + C**
7. **D + F**
8. **E + F**
9. **P + Q**
10. **R + P**
11. **H + G**
12. **M + H**

▌▌▌Add. (*See Example 7.*)

13. **A + O**
14. **O + B**
15. **O + C**
16. **D + C**

▌▌▌▌Subtract. (*See Example 8.*)

17. **A − B**
18. **C − B**
19. **F − D**
20. **E − F**
21. **H − M**
22. **G − H**
23. **Q − P**
24. **R − Q**

▌▌▌▌▌Find the additive inverse of each matrix. (*See Example 9.*)

25. **−D**
26. **−Q**
27. **−E**
28. **−M**

Subtract by adding an additive inverse. (*See Example 10.*)

29. **D − C**
30. **C − E**
31. **M − H**
32. **H − G**
33. **P − Q**
34. **R − P**
35. **O − F**
36. **O − A**

# 18-6 Multiplying Matrices and Numbers

After finishing Lesson 18-6, you should be able to
**I** find the scalar product of a number $k$ and a matrix **A**.
**II** find the product of a row matrix and a column matrix.
**III** find the product **AB** of a matrix **A** and a matrix **B**, where the number of columns in **A** is the same as the number of rows in **B**.

## I Scalar Products

We define a kind of product of a matrix and a number.

**DEFINITION**
The (*scalar*) product of a number $k$ and a matrix **A** is the matrix, denoted $k$**A**, obtained by multiplying each number in **A** by the number $k$.

**Examples.** Let $\mathbf{A} = \begin{bmatrix} -3 & 0 \\ 4 & x \end{bmatrix}$. Find these scalar products.

**1.** $3\mathbf{A} = 3\begin{bmatrix} -3 & 0 \\ 4 & x \end{bmatrix} = \begin{bmatrix} -9 & 0 \\ 12 & 3x \end{bmatrix}$

**2.** $(-1)\mathbf{A} = -1\begin{bmatrix} -3 & 0 \\ 4 & x \end{bmatrix} = \begin{bmatrix} 3 & 0 \\ -4 & -x \end{bmatrix}$

**TRY THIS** ➡️

Find these scalar products.

1. $5\begin{bmatrix} 1 & -2 & x \\ 4 & y & 1 \\ 0 & -5 & x^2 \end{bmatrix}$

2. $t\begin{bmatrix} 1 & -1 & 4 & x \\ y & 3 & -2 & y \\ 1 & 4 & -5 & t \end{bmatrix}$

## II Product of a Row Matrix and a Column Matrix

We do not multiply two matrices by multiplying their corresponding members. The motivation for defining matrix products comes from equations. Let us begin by considering one equation,

$$3x + 2y - 2z = 4.$$

We will write the coefficients on the left side in a $1 \times 3$ matrix (a *row* matrix) and the variables in a $3 \times 1$ matrix (a *column* matrix). The 4 on the right is written in a $1 \times 1$ matrix.

$$[3 \quad 2 \quad -2]\begin{bmatrix} x \\ y \\ z \end{bmatrix} = [4]$$

We can return to our original equation by multiplying the members of the row matrix by those of the column matrix, and adding.

$$[3 \quad 2 \quad -2]\begin{bmatrix} x \\ y \\ z \end{bmatrix} = [3x + 2y - 2z] = [4]$$

We define multiplication accordingly.

**DEFINITION**

The *product* **AB** of a row matrix **A**, $[a_1 \, a_2 \cdots a_n]$, and a column matrix **B**, $\begin{bmatrix} b_1 \\ b_2 \\ \vdots \\ b_n \end{bmatrix}$, is a $1 \times 1$ matrix whose member is $[a_1 b_1 + a_2 b_2 + \cdots + a_n b_n]$.

**Example 3.** Multiply.

$$[3 \quad 2 \quad -1]\begin{bmatrix} 1 \\ -2 \\ 3 \end{bmatrix} = [3 \cdot 1 + 2 \cdot (-2) + (-1) \cdot 3]$$

$$= [-4]$$

**TRY THIS**

Multiply.

3. $[4 \quad -2 \quad 3]\begin{bmatrix} 2 \\ 3 \\ -5 \end{bmatrix}$

4. $[-2 \quad 1]\begin{bmatrix} x \\ y \end{bmatrix}$

## ꀸ Products of Matrices

In the following example, we multiply each row of the matrix on the left by the column matrix.

**Example 4.** Multiply.

$$\begin{bmatrix} 3 & 1 & -1 \\ 1 & 2 & 2 \\ -1 & 0 & 5 \\ 4 & 1 & 2 \end{bmatrix}\begin{bmatrix} 1 \\ 2 \\ 4 \end{bmatrix} = \begin{bmatrix} 3 \cdot 1 + 1 \cdot 2 + (-1) \cdot 4 \\ 1 \cdot 1 + 2 \cdot 2 + 2 \cdot 4 \\ -1 \cdot 1 + 0 \cdot 2 + 5 \cdot 4 \\ 4 \cdot 1 + 1 \cdot 2 + 2 \cdot 4 \end{bmatrix} = \begin{bmatrix} 1 \\ 13 \\ 19 \\ 14 \end{bmatrix}$$

**TRY THIS**

5. Multiply.

$$\begin{bmatrix} 1 & 4 & 2 \\ -1 & 6 & 3 \\ 3 & 2 & -1 \\ 5 & 0 & 2 \end{bmatrix}\begin{bmatrix} 2 \\ 1 \\ 3 \end{bmatrix}$$

In all of the examples so far, the second matrix had only one column. If the second matrix has more than one column, we treat it in the same way when multiplying that we treated the single column. The product matrix will have as many columns as the second matrix.

**Example 5.**  Multiply (compare with Example 4).

$$\begin{bmatrix} 3 & 1 & -1 \\ 1 & 2 & 2 \\ -1 & 0 & 5 \\ 4 & 1 & 2 \end{bmatrix}\begin{bmatrix} 1 & 0 \\ 2 & 1 \\ 4 & 3 \end{bmatrix} = \begin{bmatrix} 3\cdot 1 + 1\cdot 2 + (-1)\cdot 4 \\ 1\cdot 1 + 2\cdot 2 + \quad 2\cdot 4 \\ -1\cdot 1 + 0\cdot 2 + \quad 5\cdot 4 \\ 4\cdot 1 + 1\cdot 2 + \quad 2\cdot 4 \end{bmatrix} \quad \begin{matrix} 3\cdot 0 + 1\cdot 1 + (-1)3 \\ 1\cdot 0 + 2\cdot 1 + \quad 2\cdot 3 \\ -1\cdot 0 + 0\cdot 1 + \quad 5\cdot 3 \\ 4\cdot 0 + 1\cdot 1 + \quad 2\cdot 3 \end{matrix} = \begin{bmatrix} 1 & -2 \\ 13 & 8 \\ 19 & 15 \\ 14 & 7 \end{bmatrix}$$

      **A**        **B**           Same as in                    The rows of **A**
                             Example 4                    multiplied by the
                                                              second column of **B**

**TRY THIS** ➡

If matrix **A** has *n* columns and matrix **B** has *n* rows, then we can compute the product **AB**, regardless of the other dimensions. The product will have as many rows as **A** and as many columns as **B**.

> 6.  Multiply.
>
> $$\begin{bmatrix} 1 & 4 & 2 \\ -1 & 6 & 3 \\ 3 & 2 & -1 \\ 5 & 0 & 2 \end{bmatrix}\begin{bmatrix} 2 & -4 \\ 1 & 0 \\ 3 & 5 \end{bmatrix}$$

## Exercise Set 18-6

For Exercises 1–28, let $\mathbf{A} = \begin{bmatrix} 1 & 2 \\ 4 & 3 \end{bmatrix}$, $\mathbf{B} = \begin{bmatrix} -3 & 5 \\ 2 & -1 \end{bmatrix}$,

$\mathbf{C} = \begin{bmatrix} 1 & -1 \\ -1 & 1 \end{bmatrix}$, $\mathbf{D} = \begin{bmatrix} 1 & 1 \\ 1 & 1 \end{bmatrix}$, $\mathbf{E} = \begin{bmatrix} 1 & 3 \\ 2 & 6 \end{bmatrix}$, $\mathbf{F} = \begin{bmatrix} 3 & 3 \\ -1 & -1 \end{bmatrix}$, $\mathbf{I} = \begin{bmatrix} 1 & 0 \\ 0 & 1 \end{bmatrix}$,

$\mathbf{G} = \begin{bmatrix} 1 & 0 & -2 \\ 0 & -1 & 3 \\ 3 & 2 & 4 \end{bmatrix}$, $\mathbf{H} = \begin{bmatrix} -1 & -2 & 5 \\ 1 & 0 & -1 \\ 2 & -3 & 1 \end{bmatrix}$, $\mathbf{Z} = \begin{bmatrix} -2 & 9 & 6 \\ -3 & 3 & 4 \\ 2 & -2 & 1 \end{bmatrix}$,

$\mathbf{J} = [-2 \quad 3 \quad -4]$, $\mathbf{K} = [8 \quad -1]$, $\mathbf{L} = [-1 \quad -2 \quad -3 \quad 4]$,

$\mathbf{M} = \begin{bmatrix} -2 \\ -4 \\ 7 \end{bmatrix}$, $\mathbf{N} = \begin{bmatrix} 8 \\ -6 \\ \frac{1}{2} \end{bmatrix}$, $\mathbf{P} = \begin{bmatrix} -3 \\ -2 \end{bmatrix}$, $\mathbf{Q} = \begin{bmatrix} 10 \\ -4 \\ 5 \\ 2 \end{bmatrix}$

▌Multiply. (*See Examples 1 and 2.*)

1.  $(-2)\mathbf{A}$

2.  $(-5)\mathbf{B}$

3.  $14\mathbf{C}$

4.  $12\mathbf{D}$

5.  $t\mathbf{E}$

6.  $p\mathbf{F}$

7.  $(-1)\mathbf{Z}$

8.  $(-1)\mathbf{H}$

▌▌Multiply. (*See Example 3.*)

9.  **KP**

10.  **JM**

11.  **JN**

12.  **LQ**

▌▌▌Multiply, if possible. (*See Examples 4 and 5.*)

| | | |
|---|---|---|
| 13. **AB** | | 14. **BC** |
| 15. **CD** | | 16. **EF** |
| 17. **JG** | | 18. **KF** |
| 19. **JZ** | | 20. **FP** |
| 21. **FI** | | 22. **IB** |
| 23. **GH** | | 24. **HG** |
| 25. **AP** | | 26. **KC** |
| 27. **HA** | | 28. **CG** |

### Challenge Exercises

29.  Let $\mathbf{A} = \begin{bmatrix} -1 & 0 \\ 2 & 1 \end{bmatrix}$ and $\mathbf{B} = \begin{bmatrix} 1 & -1 \\ 0 & 2 \end{bmatrix}$.

   a)  Show that $(\mathbf{A} + \mathbf{B})(\mathbf{A} - \mathbf{B}) \neq \mathbf{A}^2 - \mathbf{B}^2$, where $\mathbf{A}^2 = \mathbf{AA}$ and $\mathbf{B}^2 = \mathbf{BB}$.

   b)  Show that $(\mathbf{A} + \mathbf{B})(\mathbf{A} + \mathbf{B}) \neq \mathbf{A}^2 + 2\mathbf{AB} + \mathbf{B}^2$.

Let $\mathbf{A} = \begin{bmatrix} a & c \\ b & d \end{bmatrix}$, $\mathbf{B} = \begin{bmatrix} e & g \\ f & h \end{bmatrix}$, and $\mathbf{I} = \begin{bmatrix} 1 & 0 \\ 0 & 1 \end{bmatrix}$.

Prove.

30.  $k(\mathbf{A} + \mathbf{B}) = k\mathbf{A} + k\mathbf{B}$

31.  $(-1)\mathbf{A} = -\mathbf{A}$

32.  $(k + m)\mathbf{A} = k\mathbf{A} + m\mathbf{A}$

33.  Find **AI** and **IA**.

34.  What can you conclude about matrix **I**?

### CONSUMER NOTE: Interest on Savings

The formula $A = P(1 + r)^t$ applies when interest is compounded once a year. Usually, interest is compounded more often. It may be paid semi-annually, quarterly, or monthly.

   The more often interest is compounded, the faster savings grow. Once interest is compounded, it is added to the savings. Then interest is paid on both the original savings and the interest.

   Interest on savings is compounded at different rates. Savings institutions often advertise their interest rates. A consumer may shop for interest by asking several questions. How much interest will a certain amount of savings earn in a certain time? When does the interest period start? When may withdrawals be made without losing interest?

## CHAPTER 18 REVIEW

Review the material in the chapter. Then see how you have done by trying these review exercises. If you miss an exercise, restudy the indicated lesson.

Solve, using matrices.

18-1  1.  $x - 3y = 0$
          $5x - y = -14$

18-2  2.  $x + 5y + 3z = 4$
          $3x - 2y + 4z = 21$
          $2x + 3y - z = -13$

18-3  3.  Evaluate: $\begin{vmatrix} 2 & -3 \\ 2 & 5 \end{vmatrix}$

18-3  4.  Solve, using Cramer's Rule.
          $5x - 2y = 19$
          $7x + 3y = 15$

18-4  5.  Evaluate: $\begin{vmatrix} 2 & -1 & 1 \\ 1 & -2 & 3 \\ 4 & 1 & 2 \end{vmatrix}$

18-4  6.  Solve, using Cramer's Rule.
          $2x - y + z = -1$
          $x - 2y + 3z = 4$
          $4x + y + 2z = 4$

Let $\mathbf{A} = \begin{bmatrix} 1 & 2 & -1 \\ 2 & 0 & 1 \\ -2 & 1 & 0 \end{bmatrix}$

and $\mathbf{B} = \begin{bmatrix} 0 & 4 & 2 \\ -1 & 2 & 0 \\ 0 & 2 & 1 \end{bmatrix}$.

Find.

18-5  7.  $\mathbf{A} + \mathbf{B}$      8.  $\mathbf{A} - \mathbf{B}$
18-6  9.  $3\mathbf{B}$      10.  $\mathbf{AB}$

## CHAPTER 18 TEST

Solve, using matrices.

1.  $x + 2y = 5$
    $2x - 5y = -8$

2.  $3x + 4y + 2z = 3$
    $5x - 2y - 13z = 3$
    $4x + 3y - 3z = 6$

3.  Evaluate: $\begin{vmatrix} 1 & 2 \\ 2 & -5 \end{vmatrix}$

4.  Solve, using Cramer's Rule.
    $2x + 3y = 2$
    $5x - y = -29$

5.  Evaluate: $\begin{vmatrix} 3 & 4 & 2 \\ 5 & -2 & 0 \\ 4 & 3 & -3 \end{vmatrix}$

6.  Solve, using Cramer's Rule.
    $3x + 2y + 2z = 3$
    $2x - 4y + z = 0$
    $x + 2y - z = 5$

Let $\mathbf{A} = \begin{bmatrix} 1 & 1 & 3 \\ 0 & 2 & -1 \\ 2 & -1 & 0 \end{bmatrix}$

and $\mathbf{B} = \begin{bmatrix} -1 & 0 & 2 \\ 1 & -2 & 0 \\ 0 & 1 & -3 \end{bmatrix}$.

Find.

7.  $\mathbf{B} + \mathbf{A}$      8.  $\mathbf{A} - \mathbf{B}$
9.  $-2\mathbf{B}$      10.  $\mathbf{AB}$

## Ready for Combinatorial Algebra and Probability?

1-7 1. Evaluate $n^r$ when $n = 5$ and $r = 3$.

1-7 2. Evaluate $n(n - 1)(n - 2)$ when $n = 5$.

6-4 3. Multiply: $(a + b)^2$.

6-3 4. Multiply $a + b$ and $a^2 + 2ab + b^2$.

1-8 5. Simplify: $(5x)^3$.

1-8 6. Simplify: $(-2y)^4$.

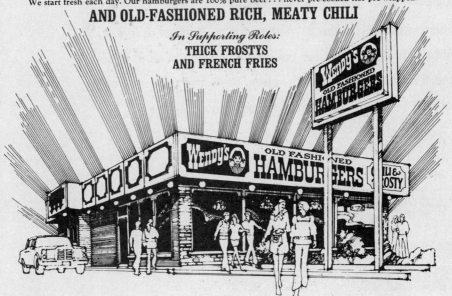

*How did they figure out how many ways they can fix hamburgers?*

# 19-1 Combinatorial Algebra: Permutations

After finishing Lesson 19-1, you should be able to

**I**  use the Fundamental Counting Principle to determine the total number of ways a compound event may occur.

**II**  find the total number of permutations of a set of $n$ objects, by applying the formula $_nP_n = n!$

**III**  express a factorial as a product and evaluate.

## I The Fundamental Counting Principle

We shall develop means of determining the number of ways a set of objects can be arranged or combined, the number of ways certain objects can be chosen, or the number of ways a succession of events can occur. The study of such things is called *combinatorial algebra*.

**Example 1.**  How many 3-letter code symbols can be formed with the letters *A*, *B*, and *C* without repetition?

Consider placing letters in these frames ☐☐☐

We can select any of the ⬚3⬚ letters for the first letter in the symbol. Once this letter has been selected, the second is selected from the remaining ⬚2⬚ letters. Then the third is already determined since there is only ⬚1⬚ letter left.

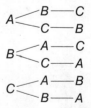

There are $3 \cdot 2 \cdot 1$ possibilities. Thus the symbols are

*ABC, ACB, BAC,*
*BCA, CAB, CBA.*

In the preceding example, a selection was made. Let us call this an *event*. When several of them occur we say that the event is *compound*. The following principle concerns compound events.

## THEOREM 19-1 (Fundamental Counting Principle)

In a compound event in which the first event may occur independently in $n_1$ ways, the second may occur independently in $n_2$ ways, and so on, and the $k$th event may occur independently in $n_k$ ways, the total number of ways the compound event may occur is $n_1 \cdot n_2 \cdot n_3 \cdots n_k$.

**Example 2.** How many 3-letter code symbols can be formed with the letters $A$, $B$, and $C$ with repetition?

There are 3 choices for the first letter, and since we allow repetition, 3 choices for the second, and 3 for the third. Thus by the Fundamental Counting Principle there are $3 \cdot 3 \cdot 3$, or 27, choices.

**Example 3.** A family is redecorating their living room. They will choose one of 3 paint colors, one of 4 carpets, and one of 2 drapery fabrics. How many possible arrangements can they make for the living room?

There are 3 choices for the paint, 4 choices for the carpet, and 2 choices for the drapes. Thus, by the Fundamental Counting Principle, there are $3 \cdot 4 \cdot 2$, or 24, choices.

**TRY THIS**

1. How many 3-digit numbers can be named using all the digits 5, 6, 7 without repetition? with repetition?
2. A man is planning a date. He will first put on one of 4 suits, then call one of 2 girl friends, and then select one of 5 restaurants. How many possible arrangements can he make for his date (assuming the girls will accept)?
3. In how many ways can 5 different cars be parked in a row in a parking lot?

## ıı Permutations

A *permutation* of a set of $n$ objects is an ordered arrangement of the objects. Consider, for example, a set of 4 objects $\{A, B, C, D\}$. Here are some ordered arrangements of these objects.

> ABDC DBAC ADBC
> BACD CBDA DCAB

To find the number of ordered arrangements of the set we select a first one; there are 4 choices. Then we select a second one; there are 3 choices. Then we select a third one; there are 2 choices. Finally there is 1 choice for the last selection. Thus by the Fundamental Counting Principle, there are $4 \cdot 3 \cdot 2 \cdot 1$, or 24 permutations of a set of 4 objects.

**TRY THIS** ━━━▶

We can generalize this to a set of $n$ objects. We have $n$ choices for the first selection, $n - 1$ for the second, $n - 2$ for the third, and so on. For the $n$th selection there is only one choice.

> 4. How many permutations are there of a set of 5 objects? Consider a set $\{A, B, C, D, E\}$.

**THEOREM 19-2**

The total number of permutations of a set of $n$ objects, denoted $_nP_n$, is given by $_nP_n = n(n - 1)(n - 2) \cdots 3 \cdot 2 \cdot 1$.

**Examples.** Find the following.

**4.** $_4P_4 = 4 \cdot 3 \cdot 2 \cdot 1 = 24$

**5.** $_7P_7 = 7 \cdot 6 \cdot 5 \cdot 4 \cdot 3 \cdot 2 \cdot 1 = 5040$

**TRY THIS** ━━━▶

> Evaluate.
>
> 5. $_3P_3$
> 6. $_5P_5$
> 7. $_6P_6$

**Example 6.** How many different ways can 5 paintings be lined up on the wall of an art gallery?

By Theorem 19-2, there are $_5P_5$ ways.

$$_5P_5 = 5 \cdot 4 \cdot 3 \cdot 2 \cdot 1$$
$$= 120$$

**TRY THIS** ━━━▶

**⊪Factorial Notation**

Products such as $5 \cdot 4 \cdot 3 \cdot 2 \cdot 1$ are used so often that it is convenient to adopt a notation for them. For the product $5 \cdot 4 \cdot 3 \cdot 2 \cdot 1$ we write 5!, read "5-factorial."

> 8. In how many different ways can 4 horses be lined up for a race?
> 9. In how many different ways can 6 people line up at a ticket window?
> 10. In how many ways can the 9 players of a baseball team be put into batting order, if the pitcher bats last?

**DEFINITION**

$n! = n(n - 1)(n - 2) \cdots 3 \cdot 2 \cdot 1$.

**Examples.**

**7.** $7! = 7 \cdot 6 \cdot 5 \cdot 4 \cdot 3 \cdot 2 \cdot 1 = 5040$

**8.** $3! = \qquad 3 \cdot 2 \cdot 1 = \quad 6$

**9.** $1! = \qquad\qquad 1 = \quad 1$

TRY THIS

Evaluate.

11. 9!

12. 4!

We also define 0! to be 1. We do this so that certain formulas and theorems can be stated concisely.

We can now simplify the formula of Theorem 19-2.

$$_nP_n = n!$$

13. Using factorial notation only, represent the number of permutations of 18 objects.

TRY THIS

Note that $8! = 8 \cdot 7!$ We can see this as follows.

$$8! = 8 \cdot 7 \cdot 6 \cdot 5 \cdot 4 \cdot 3 \cdot 2 \cdot 1 = 8 \cdot (7 \cdot 6 \cdot 5 \cdot 4 \cdot 3 \cdot 2 \cdot 1)$$
$$= 8 \cdot 7!$$

Generalizing gives us the following theorem.

**THEOREM 19-3**

For any natural number $n$,

$$n! = n(n - 1)!$$

Represent each in the form $n(n - 1)!$

14. 10!

15. 20!

TRY THIS

By using Theorem 19-3 repeatedly, we can further manipulate factorial notation.

**Example 10.** Rewrite 7! with a factor of 5!

$$7! = 7 \cdot 6 \cdot 5!$$

**Example 11.** Rewrite 12! with a factor of 7!

$$12! = 12 \cdot 11 \cdot 10 \cdot 9 \cdot 8 \cdot 7!$$

16. Rewrite 11! with a factor of 8!

17. Rewrite 17! with a factor of 12!

TRY THIS

## Exercise Set 19-1

▌(*See Examples 1–3.*)

1. How many 4-letter code symbols can be formed with the letters *P, D, Q, X* without repetition? with repetition?

2. How many 5-digit numbers can be formed using all the digits 0, 1, 2, 3, 4 without repetition? with repetition?

3. How many ways can 6 bicycles be parked in a row?

4. How many ways can 7 different cards be laid out on a table in a row?

5. A woman is going out for the evening. She will put on one of 6 pantsuits, one pair out of 8 pairs of shoes, and go to one of 7 restaurants. In how many ways can this be done?

6. A man is going out for the evening. He will put on one of 7 suits, one pair out of 4 pairs of shoes, and go to one of 10 restaurants. In how many ways can this be done?

▌▌Evaluate. (*See Examples 4 and 5.*)

7. $_6P_6$

8. $_5P_5$

9. $_4P_4$

10. $_2P_2$

(*See Example 6.*)

11. How many ways can 7 people line up in a row?

12. How many ways can 8 motorcycles be parked in a row?

13. How many permutations are there of the set $\{R, S, T, U, V, W\}$?

14. How many permutations are there of the set $\{M, N, O, P, Q, R, S\}$?

15. The owner of a business hires 8 secretaries, one for each of 8 department managers. How many different assignments of the secretaries are possible?

16. An ice cream store has 9 different flavors of ice cream and room under the counter for 9 cartons of ice cream lined up in a row. How many different ways can the ice cream be arranged under the counter?

▌▌▌Evaluate. (*See Examples 7–9.*)

17. 5!

18. 6!

19. 1!

20. 0!

Represent each in the form $n(n-1)!$ (*See page 569.*)

21. 9!

22. 13!

23. *a*!

24. *m*!

(*See Examples 10 and 11.*)

25. Rewrite 27! with a factor of 22!

26. Rewrite 13! with a factor of 5!

# 19-2 Permutations, n Objects r at a Time

After finishing Lesson 19-2, you should be able to

▪ apply the formula $_nP_r = \dfrac{n!}{(n-r)!}$ to find the number of permutations of $n$ objects taken $r$ at a time.

▪▪ apply the expression $n^r$ to find the number of distinct arrangements of $n$ objects taken $r$ at a time with replacement, or with repetition.

## ▪ Permutations of *n* Objects Taken *r* at a Time

Consider a set of 6 objects. In how many ways can we construct an ordered subset having three members? We can select the first object in 6 ways. There are then 5 choices for the second and then 4 choices for the third. By the Fundamental Counting Principle, there are then $6 \cdot 5 \cdot 4$ ways to construct the subset. In other words, there are $6 \cdot 5 \cdot 4$ permutations of a set of 6 objects taken three at a time. Note that $6 \cdot 5 \cdot 4$ is equal to $\dfrac{6 \cdot 5 \cdot 4 \cdot 3!}{3!}$, or $\dfrac{6!}{3!}$. We adopt the following notation.

$_nP_r$ denotes the number of permutations of a set of $n$ objects, taken $r$ at a time.

Generalizing the above result gives us a theorem.

**THEOREM 19-4**

The number of permutations of a set of $n$ objects taken $r$ at a time is given by

$$_nP_r = \frac{n!}{(n-r)!}.$$

**Examples.** Compute.

**1.** $_6P_4 = \dfrac{6!}{(6-4)!}$  *By Theorem 19-4*

$= \dfrac{6!}{2!}$

$= \dfrac{6 \cdot 5 \cdot 4 \cdot 3 \cdot 2!}{2!}$  *By Theorem 19-3*

$= 6 \cdot 5 \cdot 4 \cdot 3$  *Simplifying*

$= 360$  *Multiplying*

**2.** $_5P_2 = \dfrac{5!}{(5-2)!}$  *By Theorem 19-4*

$= \dfrac{5!}{3!}$

$= \dfrac{5 \cdot 4 \cdot 3!}{3!}$  *By Theorem 19-3*

$= 5 \cdot 4$

$= 20$

**TRY THIS** ➡

**Example 3.** How many ways can letters of the set $\{A, B, C, D, E, F, G\}$ be arranged to form code symbols of **a)** 7 letters? **b)** 5 letters? **c)** 2 letters?

**a)** $_7P_7 = 7 \cdot 6 \cdot 5 \cdot 4 \cdot 3 \cdot 2 \cdot 1 = 5040$

**b)** $_7P_5 = 7 \cdot 6 \cdot 5 \cdot 4 \cdot 3 \qquad = 2520$

**c)** $_7P_2 = 7 \cdot 6 \qquad\qquad\qquad = \quad 42$

**Example 4.** A baseball manager arranges the batting order as follows: The 4 infielders will bat first, then the outfielders, catcher, and pitcher will follow, not necessarily in that order. How many batting orders are possible?

The infielders can bat in 4! different ways; the rest in 5! different ways. Then by the Fundamental Counting Principle we have $_4P_4 \cdot {_5P_5} = 4! \cdot 5!$, or 2880, possible batting orders.

**TRY THIS** ➡

## ▮ Repeated Use of the Same Object

For an arrangement of objects to be a permutation, we can't repeat any of the objects. Sometimes we want to be able to repeat, so we have another theorem.

**Example 5.** How many 5-letter code symbols can be formed with the letters $A$, $B$, $C$, and $D$ if we allow repeated use of the same letter? We have five spaces: ▢▢▢▢▢

We can select the first in 4 ways, the second in 4 ways, and so on. Thus there are $4^5$, or 1024, arrangements. Generalizing gives us a theorem.

**THEOREM 19-5**

The number of arrangements of $n$ objects taken $r$ at a time, with repetition, is $n^r$.

**TRY THIS** ➡

---

Compute.

1. $_7P_3$  2. $_{10}P_4$

3. $_8P_2$  4. $_{11}P_5$

---

5. In how many ways can a 5-player starting unit be selected from a basketball squad of 12 members and arranged in a straight line?

6. A teacher wants to write a 6-item test from a pool of 10 questions. In how many ways can this be done?

7. How many 7-digit numbers can be named, without repetition, using the digits 2, 3, 4, 5, 6, 7, and 8 if the even digits come first?

---

8. How many 5-letter code symbols can be formed by repeated use of the letters of the alphabet? Just find an expression. Do not evaluate.

**Example 6.** A standard deck of cards has 52 different cards. How many 3-card ordered arrangements can be made by selecting the 3 cards **a)** without replacement? **b)** with replacement?

**a)** The case 'without replacement' is the number of permutations of 52 things taken 3 at a time.

$$_{52}P_3 = 52 \cdot 51 \cdot 50 = 132,600 \qquad \textit{By Theorem 19-4}$$

**b)** The case 'with replacement' is the number of arrangements of 52 objects taken 3 at a time, with repetition.

$$52 \cdot 52 \cdot 52 = 52^3 = 140,608 \qquad \textit{By Theorem 19-5}$$

Thus there are 140,608 possible ordered arrangements.

**TRY THIS**

9. How many 2-card ordered arrangements can be made by selecting 2 cards from a deck of 52
   a) without replacement?
   b) with replacement?

## Exercise Set 19-2

❚ Evaluate. (*See Examples 1 and 2.*)

1. $_4P_3$
2. $_7P_5$
3. $_{10}P_7$
4. $_{10}P_3$
5. $_{20}P_2$
6. $_{30}P_2$
7. $_8P_3$
8. $_7P_4$

(*See Examples 3 and 4.*)

9. How many ways can the letters of the set $\{M, N, O, P, Q\}$ be arranged to form code symbols of 4 letters? 3 letters?

10. How many ways can the letters of the set $\{P, D, Q, W, T, Z\}$ be arranged to form code symbols of 3 letters? 5 letters?

11. How many ways can 4 people be assigned to 6 offices?

12. How many ways can 3 people be assigned to 5 offices?

❚❚ (*See Examples 5 and 6.*)

13. How many 4-number license plates can be made using the digits 0, 1, 2, 3, 4, 5 if repetitions are allowed? not allowed?

14. How many 5-number license plates can be made using the digits 1, 2, 3, 4, 5, 6, 7 if repetitions are allowed? not allowed?

15. A teacher wants to write a 4-item test from a pool of 12 questions. In how many ways can this be done?

16. A teacher wants to write a 5-item test from a pool of 8 questions. In how many ways can this be done?

17. As in Exercise 13, but the even digits must come first.

18. As in Exercise 14, but the odd digits must come first.

19. As in Exercise 13, but the license number must be even.

20. As in Exercise 14, but the license number must be odd.

# 19-3 *Combinatorial Algebra: Combinations*

After finishing Lesson 19-3, you should be able to

▌ apply the formula $_nC_r = \dbinom{n}{r}$ to find the number of combinations of a set of $n$ objects taken $r$ at a time.

▌Permutations of a set are ordered subsets. Unordered subsets are called *combinations*.

**Example 1.** How many combinations are there of the set $\{A, B, C, D\}$ taken 3 at a time?

The combinations are the subsets

$\{A, B, C\}$   $\{B, C, D\}$   $\{A, C, D\}$   $\{A, B, D\}$

Note that the set $\{A, B, C\}$ is the same as the set $\{B, A, C\}$ since they contain the same objects.

**TRY THIS** ▆▆▆▆▆▆▆▆▆▆▆▆➤

1. Consider the set $\{A, B, C, D\}$. How many combinations are there taken
   a) 4 at a time?
   b) 3 at a time?
   c) 2 at a time?
   d) 1 at a time?
   e) 0 at a time?

**DEFINITION**

The number of combinations of a set of $n$ objects taken $r$ at a time, denoted $_nC_r$, is the number of subsets that contain $r$ objects.

A general formula for $_nC_r$ is given in the next theorem. First we define some convenient symbolism.

**DEFINITION**

$\dbinom{n}{r}$ is defined to mean $\dfrac{n!}{r!(n-r)!}$.

The notation $\dbinom{n}{r}$ is read "*n* over *r*," or (for reasons we see later) "binomial coefficient *n* over *r*."

**Examples.** Evaluate.

2. $\dbinom{5}{2} = \dfrac{5!}{2!(5-2)!}$   *By definition of* $\dbinom{5}{2}$

$= \dfrac{5!}{2!3!}$

$= \dfrac{5 \cdot 4 \cdot 3!}{2!3!}$   *By Theorem 19-3*

$= 10$

**3.** $\dbinom{7}{4} = \dfrac{7!}{4!(7-4)!} = \dfrac{7!}{4!3!} = \dfrac{7 \cdot 6 \cdot 5 \cdot 4!}{3!4!} = \dfrac{7 \cdot 6 \cdot 5}{3 \cdot 2 \cdot 1} = 35$

**TRY THIS** ➤

Evaluate.

2. $\dbinom{10}{8}$

3. $\dbinom{10}{2}$

**THEOREM 19-6**

The number of combinations of a set of $n$ objects taken $r$ at a time is given by $_nC_r = \dbinom{n}{r}$.

**TRY THIS** ➤

Evaluate.

4. $_7C_5$
5. $_7C_2$

**Example 4.** For a sociological study 4 people are chosen at random from a group of 10 people. How many ways can this be done?

No order is implied here so the number of ways 4 people can be selected is $_{10}C_4$.

$$_{10}C_4 = \dbinom{10}{4} \quad \textit{By Theorem 19-6}$$
$$= \dfrac{10!}{4!6!}$$
$$= \dfrac{10 \cdot 9 \cdot 8 \cdot 7 \cdot 6!}{4!6!}$$
$$= \dfrac{10 \cdot 9 \cdot 8 \cdot 7}{4 \cdot 3 \cdot 2 \cdot 1}$$
$$= 210$$

6. How many ways can a 5-player starting unit be selected from a 12-member basketball squad?

**TRY THIS** ➤

**Example 5.** How many committees can be formed from a set of 5 governors and 7 senators if each committee contains 3 governors and 4 senators?

The 3 governors can be selected in $_5C_3$ ways and the 4 senators can be selected in $_7C_4$ ways. Using the Fundamental Counting Principle, it follows that the number of committees will be

$$_5C_3 \cdot {_7C_4} = 10 \cdot 35 = 350.$$

**TRY THIS** ➡

**Example 6.** *Wendy's Hamburgers,* a national firm, advertises "We Fix Hamburgers 256 Ways!" This is accomplished using various *combinations* of catsup, onion, mustard, pickle, mayonnaise, relish, tomato, or lettuce. Of course, one can also have a plain hamburger. Use combination notation to show the number of possible hamburgers. Do not evaluate. (We will show an easy way in Lesson 19-4.)

There are 8 basic seasonings. Each way of fixing a hamburger is a combination, or subset, of these seasonings. There are $\binom{8}{0}$ subsets with 0 seasonings, $\binom{8}{1}$ subsets with 1 seasoning, $\binom{8}{2}$ subsets with 2 seasonings, and so on, up to $\binom{8}{8}$ subsets with 8 seasonings. Thus the total number of combinations, or subsets, is

$$\binom{8}{0} + \binom{8}{1} + \binom{8}{2} + \cdots + \binom{8}{8}.$$

**TRY THIS** ➡

7. A committee is to be chosen from 12 men and 8 women and is to consist of 3 men and 2 women. How many ways can this committee be formed?

8. Wendy's excludes cheese from the possibilities. Including cheese as a possibility, use combination notation to show the number of ways Wendy's could fix hamburgers.

## Exercise Set 19-3

▌Evaluate. (*See Examples 2 and 3.*)

1. $_9C_5$

2. $_{14}C_2$

3. $\binom{50}{2}$

4. $\binom{40}{3}$

5. $\binom{12}{8}$

6. $\binom{14}{9}$

7. $_nC_3$

8. $_nC_2$

(*See Examples 4–6.*)

9. There are 23 students in a club. How many ways can 4 officers be selected?

10. On a test a student is to select 6 out of 10 questions, without regard to order. How many ways can this be done?

11. How many basketball games can be played in a 9-team league if each team plays all other teams twice?

12. How many basketball games can be played in a 10-team league if each team plays all other teams twice?

13. How many lines are determined by 8 points, no three of which are collinear? How many triangles are determined by the same points if no four are coplanar?

14. How many lines are determined by 7 points, no three of which are collinear? How many triangles are determine by the same points if no four are coplanar?

15. Of the first 10 questions on a test, a student must answer 7. On the second 5 questions, 3 must be answered. In how many ways can this be done?

16. Of the first 8 questions on a test, a student must answer 6. On the second 4 questions, 3 must be answered. In how many ways can this be done?

17. Suppose the Senate of the United States consisted of 58 Democrats and 42 Republicans. How many committees consisting of 6 Democrats and 4 Republicans could be formed? You do not need to simplify the expression.

18. Suppose the Senate of the United States consisted of 63 Republicans and 37 Democrats. How many committees consisting of 8 Republicans and 12 Democrats could be formed? You need not simplify the expression.

19. How many 5-card poker hands consisting of 3 aces and 2 cards that are not aces are possible with a 52-card deck? See p. 583 for a description of a 52-card deck.

20. How many 5-card poker hands consisting of 2 kings and 3 cards that are not kings are possible with a 52-card deck?

---

**Challenge Exercises**

21. How many line segments are determined by the 5 vertices of a pentagon? Of these, how many are diagonals?

22. How many line segments are determined by the $n$ vertices of an $n$-agon? Of these, how many are diagonals?

Solve for $n$.

23. $\dbinom{n + 1}{3} = 2 \cdot \dbinom{n}{2}$    24. $\dbinom{n}{n - 2} = 6$

25. $\dbinom{n + 2}{4} = 6 \cdot \dbinom{n}{2}$    26. $\dbinom{n}{3} = 2 \cdot \dbinom{n - 1}{2}$

27. Prove that $\dbinom{n}{r} = \dbinom{n}{n - r}$.

28. How many ways can 2 people be chosen from 3 men and 4 women such that at least one is a woman?

# 19-4 The Binomial Theorem

After finishing Lesson 19-4, you should be able to
- **I**   find the *r*th term of the binomial expansion of $(a + b)^n$.
- **II**   use the Binomial Theorem to expand expressions like $(x^2 + 3y)^9$.
- **III**   determine the number of subsets of a finite set.

Consider the following expanded powers of $(a + b)^n$, where $a + b$ is any binomial. Look for patterns.

$$(a + b)^0 = \qquad\qquad 1$$
$$(a + b)^1 = \qquad\qquad a + b$$
$$(a + b)^2 = \qquad\qquad a^2 + 2ab + b^2$$
$$(a + b)^3 = \qquad\quad a^3 + 3a^2b + 3ab^2 + b^3$$
$$(a + b)^4 = \quad\; a^4 + 4a^3b + 6a^2b^2 + 4ab^3 + b^4$$
$$(a + b)^5 = a^5 + 5a^4b + 10a^3b^2 + 10a^2b^3 + 5ab^4 + b^5$$

Note that each expansion is a polynomial. It is also a series, though not arithmetic or geometric. There are some patterns to be noted.

1. In each term, the sum of the exponents is *n*.
2. The exponents of *a* start with *n* and decrease. The last term has no factor of *a*. The first term has no factor of *b*. The exponents of *b* start in the second term with 1 and increase to *n*.
3. There is one more term than the degree of the polynomial.
4. If *a* and *b* are positive, all the terms are positive. If *b* is negative, its odd powers are negative, so the terms would alternate from positive to negative.

All that remains is finding a way to determine the coefficients. The next theorem shows how to do this.

### THEOREM 19-7   (The Binomial Theorem)
For any binomial $(a + b)$ and any natural number *n*,

$$(a + b)^n = \binom{n}{0}a^n + \binom{n}{1}a^{n-1}b + \binom{n}{2}a^{n-2}b^2 + \cdots + \binom{n}{n}b^n.$$

The statement of Theorem 19-7 in sigma notation is as follows.

$$(a + b)^n = \sum_{r=0}^{n} \binom{n}{r}a^{n-r}b^r$$

Because of this theorem $\binom{n}{r}$ is called a *binomial coefficient*.

## ▮ Finding the *r*th Term

Look at the theorem. We see that the $(r + 1)$st term is $\binom{n}{r}a^{n-r}b^r$.

That is, the 1st term is $\binom{n}{0}a^{n-0}b^0$, the 2nd term is $\binom{n}{1}a^{n-1}b^1$, the

3rd term is $\binom{n}{2}a^{n-2}b^2$, the 8th term is $\binom{n}{7}a^{n-7}b^7$, and so on.

**Example 1.**  Find the 7th term of $(4x - y^2)^9$.

We let $r = 6$, $n = 9$, $a = 4x$, and $b = -y^2$ in the formula

$\binom{n}{r}a^{n-r}b^r$. Then

$$\binom{9}{6}(4x)^3(-y^2)^6 = \frac{9!}{6!3!}(4x)^3(-y^2)^6$$

$$= \frac{9 \cdot 8 \cdot 7 \cdot 6!}{3! \cdot 6!}(64x^3y^{12})$$

$$= 5376x^3y^{12}.$$

**TRY THIS** ⟹

1.  Find the 4th term of $(x - 3)^8$.
2.  Find the 6th term of $(y^2 + 2)^{10}$.

## ▮ Binomial Expansion

Let us now find an expansion.

**Example 2.**  Expand $(x^2 - 2y)^5$.

Note that $a = x^2$, $b = -2y$, and $n = 5$. Then using the binomial theorem we have

$$(x^2 - 2y)^5 = \binom{5}{0}(x^2)^5 + \binom{5}{1}(x^2)^4(-2y) + \binom{5}{2}(x^2)^3(-2y)^2 +$$

$$\binom{5}{3}(x^2)^2(-2y)^3 + \binom{5}{4}x^2(-2y)^4 + \binom{5}{5}(-2y)^5$$

$$= \frac{5!}{0!5!}x^{10} + \frac{5!}{1!4!}x^8(-2y) + \frac{5!}{2!3!}x^6(-2y)^2 +$$

$$\frac{5!}{3!2!}x^4(-2y)^3 + \frac{5!}{4!1!}x^2(-2y)^4 + \frac{5!}{5!0!}(-2y)^5$$

$$= x^{10} - 10x^8y + 40x^6y^2 - 80x^4y^3 + 80x^2y^4 - 32y^5.$$

**TRY THIS** ⟹

Expand.

3.  $(x^2 - 1)^5$
4.  $\left(2x + \dfrac{1}{y}\right)^4$

**A Proof of Theorem 19-7**

Consider the $n$th power of a binomial $(a + b)$

$$(a + b)^n = \underbrace{(a + b)(a + b)(a + b)(a + b) \cdots (a + b)}_{n \text{ factors}}$$

When we multiply, we will find all possible products of $a$'s and $b$'s. For example, when we multiply all the first terms we will get $n$ factors of $a$, or $a^n$. Thus the first term in the expansion is $a^n$. The binomial coefficient $\binom{n}{0}$ is 1; this establishes that the first term mentioned in the theorem is correct.

To get a term such as the $a^{n-r}b^r$ term, we will take $a$'s from $n - r$ factors and $b$'s from $r$ factors. Thus we take $n$ objects, $n - r$ of them $a$'s and $r$ of them $b$'s. The number of ways we can do this is

$$\frac{n!}{(n - r)!r!}.$$

This is $\binom{n}{r}$. Thus the $a^{n-r}b^r$ term in the expansion has the coefficient $\binom{n}{r}$.

## ⅢⅢ Subsets

Suppose a set has $n$ objects. The number of subsets containing $r$ members is $\binom{n}{r}$, by Theorem 19-6. The total number of subsets of a set is the number with 0 elements, plus the number with 1 element, plus the number with two elements, and so on. The total number of subsets of a set with $n$ members is

$$\binom{n}{0} + \binom{n}{1} + \binom{n}{2} + \cdots + \binom{n}{n}.$$

Now let us expand $(1 + 1)^n$.

$$(1 + 1)^n = \binom{n}{0} + \binom{n}{1} + \binom{n}{2} + \cdots + \binom{n}{n}$$

Thus the total number of subsets is $(1 + 1)^n$ or $2^n$. We have proved the following theorem.

## THEOREM 19-8

The total number of subsets of a set with *n* members is $2^n$.

**Example 3.** How many subsets are in the set $\{A, B, C, D, E\}$?

The set has 5 members, so the number of subsets is $2^5$, or 32.

**Example 4.** *Wendy's Hamburgers* makes hamburgers 256 ways using combinations of 8 seasonings. Show why.

The total number of combinations is

$$\binom{8}{0} + \binom{8}{1} + \cdots + \binom{8}{8} = 2^8$$
$$= 256.$$

**TRY THIS**

5. How many subsets are there of the set of all states of the United States?

6. Including cheese as a possibility, Wendy's makes hamburgers using combinations of 9 seasonings. How many different ways is this?

## Exercise Set 19-4

I Find the indicated term of the binomial expression. (*See Example 1.*)
1. 3rd, $(a + b)^6$
2. 6th, $(x + y)^7$
3. 12th, $(a - 2)^{14}$
4. 11th, $(x - 3)^{12}$
5. 5th, $(2x^3 - \sqrt{y})^8$
6. 4th, $\left(\dfrac{1}{b^2} + \dfrac{b}{3}\right)^7$
7. Middle, $(2u - 3v^2)^{10}$
8. Middle two, $(\sqrt{x} + \sqrt{3})^5$

II Expand. (*See Example 2.*)
9. $(m + n)^5$
10. $(a - b)^4$
11. $(x^2 - 3y)^5$
12. $(3c - d)^6$
13. $(x^{-2} + x^2)^4$
14. $\left(\dfrac{1}{\sqrt{x}} - \sqrt{x}\right)^6$
15. $(1 - 1)^n$
16. $(1 + 3)^n$
17. $(\sqrt{2} + 1)^6 - (\sqrt{2} - 1)^6$
18. $(1 - \sqrt{2})^4 + (1 + \sqrt{2})^4$
19. $(\sqrt{2} - i)^4$, where $i^2 = -1$
20. $(1 + i)^6$, where $i^2 = -1$

III Determine the number of subsets. (*See Examples 3 and 4.*)
21. Of a set of 7 members
22. Of a set of 6 members
23. Of the set of letters of the English alphabet, which contains 26 letters
24. Of the set of letters of the Greek alphabet, which contains 24 letters

# 19-5 Probability

After finishing Lesson 19-5, you should be able to

▮ compute the probability of a simple event, using Principle *P*.

We say that when a coin is tossed the chances that it will fall heads are 1 out of 2, or that the *probability* that it will fall heads is $\frac{1}{2}$. Of course this does not mean that if a coin is tossed ten times it will fall heads exactly five times. If the coin is tossed a great number of times, however, it will fall heads very nearly half of them.

## ▮ Experimental and Theoretical Probability

If we toss a coin a large number of times, say 1000, and count the number of heads, we can determine the probability. If there are 503 heads we would calculate the probability to be

$$\frac{503}{1000} \text{ or } 0.503.$$

This is an *experimental* determination of the probability.

If we consider a coin and reason that it is just as likely to fall heads as tails we would calculate the probability to be $\frac{1}{2}$. This is a *theoretical* determination of probability.

You might ask "What is the *true* probability?" In fact there is none. Experimentally we can determine probabilities within certain limits. These may or may not agree with what we obtain theoretically. In this chapter we consider only theoretically determined probability, and will make a definition accordingly. We use the notation $P(E)$ for the probability of an event $E$.

### DEFINITION (Principle *P*)
The probability of an event $E$ that can occur $m$ ways out of $n$ equally likely outcomes is given by $P(E) = \dfrac{m}{n}$.

**Example 1.** A die (plural, dice) is a cube with 6 faces, each containing a number of dots from 1 to 6. What is the probability of rolling a 3?

The *event* is rolling a 3. It can occur in only one way. The number of possible outcomes is 6. By Principle *P*,

$$P(3) = \frac{1}{6}.$$

**Example 2.** What is the probability of rolling an even number on a die?

The event $P$(even) can occur in 3 ways (getting a 2, 4, or 6). The number of possible outcomes is 6. By Principle $P$,

$$P(\text{even}) = \frac{3}{6}$$

$$= \frac{1}{2}.$$

**TRY THIS** ➡

1. What is the probability of rolling a prime number on a die?

Many examples involve a standard deck of playing cards, described as follows:

**Example 3.** What is the probability of drawing an ace from a well-shuffled deck of 52 cards?

An ace can be drawn in 4 ways. There are 52 equally likely outcomes (cards in the deck). By Principle $P$,

$$P(\text{drawing an ace}) = \frac{4}{52}, \text{ or } \frac{1}{13}.$$

**Example 4.** Suppose we select, without looking, one marble from a bag containing 3 red marbles and 4 green marbles. What is the probability of selecting a red marble?

A red marble can be selected in 3 ways. There are 7 equally likely ways of selecting a marble. By Principle *P*, *P*(selecting a red marble) $= \frac{3}{7}$.

## TRY THIS ▌▆▶

2. Suppose we draw a card from a well-shuffled deck of 52 cards. What is the probability of drawing
   a) a king?
   b) a spade?
   c) a black card?
   d) a jack or a queen?
3. Suppose we select, without looking, one marble from a bag containing 5 red marbles and 6 green marbles. What is the probability of selecting a green marble?

We can use Principle *P* only when outcomes are equally likely. We could reason that the probability that a thumbtack will land point up is $\frac{1}{2}$ because there are just two ways for it to land: 🖈 🖈. But these are not equally likely. If the point of the tack is very long, like a nail, it would almost always land on its side. If the point is short, so that it looks like a coin, it should land point up about half the time. The next theorem follows at once from Principle *P*.

**THEOREM 19-9**
The probability of any event is a number from 0 to 1. If an event cannot occur its probability is 0. If an event is certain to occur its probability is 1.

**Example 5.** Suppose 2 cards are drawn from a well-shuffled deck of 52 cards. What is the probability that both of them are spades?

13 of the 52 cards are spades, so the number *m* of ways of drawing 2 spades is $_{13}C_2$. By Principle *P*,

$$P(\text{getting 2 spades}) = \frac{m}{n} = \frac{_{13}C_2}{_{52}C_2} = \frac{78}{1326} = \frac{1}{17}.$$

**Example 6.** Suppose 2 people are selected at random from a group that consists of 6 men and 4 women. What is the probability that both of them are women?

The number of ways of selecting 2 women from a group of 4 is $_4C_2$. The number of ways of selecting 2 people from a group of 10 is $_{10}C_2$. Thus the probability of selecting 2 women from the group of 10 is *P*, where $P = \frac{_4C_2}{_{10}C_2} = \frac{6}{45} = \frac{2}{15}.$

**Example 7.** Suppose 3 people are selected at random from a group that consists of 6 men and 4 women. What is the probability that 1 man and 2 women are selected?

One man can be selected in $_6C_1$ ways, and 2 women can be selected in $_4C_2$ ways. By the Fundamental Counting Principle the number of ways of selecting 1 man and 2 women is $_6C_1 \cdot {_4C_2}$. The number of ways of selecting 3 people from a group of 10 is $_{10}C_3$. Thus the probability is

$$\frac{_6C_1 \cdot {_4C_2}}{_{10}C_3}, \text{ or } \frac{3}{10}.$$

**TRY THIS** ➡

**Example 8.** What is the probability of getting a total of 8 on a roll of a pair of dice? (Assume the dice are different, say one red and one green.)

On each die there are 6 possible outcomes. There are $6 \cdot 6$, or 36, possible outcomes for the pair. The outcome set (the set of all possible outcomes) is shown below.

Red die

| | | | | | | |
|---|---|---|---|---|---|---|
| 6 | (1, 6) | (2, 6) | (3, 6) | (4, 6) | (5, 6) | (6, 6) |
| 5 | (1, 5) | (2, 5) | (3, 5) | (4, 5) | (5, 5) | (6, 5) |
| 4 | (1, 4) | (2, 4) | (3, 4) | (4, 4) | (5, 4) | (6, 4) |
| 3 | (1, 3) | (2, 3) | (3, 3) | (4, 3) | (5, 3) | (6, 3) |
| 2 | (1, 2) | (2, 2) | (3, 2) | (4, 2) | (5, 2) | (6, 2) |
| 1 | (1, 1) | (2, 1) | (3, 1) | (4, 1) | (5, 1) | (6, 1) |
| | 1 | 2 | 3 | 4 | 5 | 6 Green die |

The pairs that total 8 are as shown. There are 5 ways of getting a total of 8, so the probability is $\frac{5}{36}$.

**TRY THIS** ➡

4. Suppose 3 cards are drawn from a well-shuffled deck of 52 cards. What is the probability that all three of them are spades?

5. Suppose 2 people are selected at random from a group which consists of 8 men and 6 women. What is the probability that both of them are women?

6. Suppose 3 people are selected at random from a group which consists of 8 men and 6 women. What is the probability that 2 men and 1 woman are selected?

7. What is the probability of getting a total of 7 on a roll of a pair of dice?

## Exercise Set 19-5

▌Suppose we draw a card from a well-shuffled deck of 52 cards. (*See Examples 1–3.*) What is the probability of drawing

1. a heart?
2. a queen?
3. a 4?
4. a club?
5. a black card?
6. a red card?
7. a 9 or a king?
8. an ace or a deuce?

Suppose we select, without looking, one marble from a bag containing 4 red marbles and 10 green marbles. (*See Example 4.*) What is the probability of selecting

9. a red marble?
10. a green marble?
11. a purple marble?
12. a white marble?

Suppose 4 cards are drawn from a well-shuffled deck of 52 cards. (*See Example 5.*) What is the probability that

13. all 4 are spades?
14. all 4 are hearts?

(*See Examples 6–8.*)

15. If marbles are drawn at random all at once from a bag containing 8 white marbles and 6 black marbles, what is the probability that 2 will be white and 2 will be black?

16. From a group of 8 men and 7 women, a committee of 4 is chosen. What is the probability that 2 men and 2 women will be chosen?

17. What is the probability of getting a total of 6 on a roll of a pair of dice?

18. What is the probability of getting a total of 3 on a roll of a pair of dice?

19. What is the probability of getting snake eyes (a total of 2) on a roll of a pair of dice?

20. What is the probability of getting box-cars (a total of 12) on a roll of a pair of dice?

21. From a bag containing 5 nickels, 8 dimes, and 7 quarters, 5 coins are drawn at random all at once. What is the probability of getting 2 nickels, 2 dimes, and 1 quarter?

22. From a bag containing 6 nickels, 10 dimes, and 4 quarters, 6 coins are drawn at random all at once. What is the probability of getting 3 nickels, 2 dimes, and 1 quarter?

### COMPUTER NOTE: Computers Go into Business

Beginning in the 1950s, electronic computers entered the world of business. Now they are an established part of that world. They prepare paychecks, keep track of sales and inventory, and calculate costs and profits.

## CHAPTER 19 REVIEW

Review the material in the chapter. Then see how you have done by trying these review exercises. If you miss an exercise, restudy the indicated lesson.

19-1  1. Evaluate 8!

19-1  2. How many different displays are possible using 9 signal flags in a row?

19-2  3. Evaluate $_6P_3$.

19-2  4. The Greek alphabet contains 24 letters. How many different 3-letter code names can be formed, without repetition?

19-3  5. Evaluate $\binom{10}{3}$.

19-3  6. How many different 3-card hands are possible from a 52-card deck? (Do not consider order.)

19-4  7. Find the 12th term of $(a + x)^{18}$. Do *not* multiply out the factorials in the binomial coefficient.

19-4  8. Expand: $(m + n)^7$.

19-5  9. A bag contains 4 white balls, 3 blue balls, and 7 red balls. A ball is drawn at random. What is the probability that it is red?

## CHAPTER 19 TEST

1. Evaluate $_5P_5$.
2. How many ways can 6 books be arranged on a shelf?
3. Evaluate $_4P_2$.
4. How many ways can the letters of the set $\{D, E, F, G, H\}$ be arranged to form code symbols of 3 letters, without repetition?
5. Evaluate $_8C_3$.
6. The winner of a contest can choose any 8 of 15 prizes. How many different selections can he make?
7. Find the 4th term of $(a + x)^{12}$.
8. Expand: $(x^2 + 3y)^4$.
9. From a deck of 52 cards 1 card is drawn. What is the probability that it is a club?

## CUMULATIVE REVIEW FOR CHAPTERS 16–19

16-1    1.  Graph:   $y = (\frac{1}{5})^x$.

16-2    2.  Graph:   $y = \log_2(x + 1)$.

16-2    3.  Convert $10^{0.4771} = 3$ to a logarithmic equation.

16-2    4.  Convert $\log_5 25 = 2$ to an exponential equation.

16-2    Solve.

      5.  $\log_4 x = 3$     6.  $\log_x 64 = 3$     7.  $\log_{10} 10{,}000 = x$

16-2    Simplify.

      8.  $7^{\log_7 10}$     9.  $\log_p p^a$

16-3    10.  Express $\frac{1}{2} \log_a x + 3 \log_a y - 2 \log x$ as a single logarithm.

16-3    11.  Given $\log_{10} 3 = 0.477$ and $\log_{10} 10 = 1$, find $\log_{10} 90$.

Use Table 2 to find each of the following.

16-4    12.  log 0.00134

16-4    13.  antilog 2.6294

16-5    14.  Use logarithms to calculate: $\dfrac{70.7 \times (10.6)^2}{18.6 \times \sqrt{276}}$.

16-6    15.  Find log 4518 using interpolation.

Solve.

16-7    16.  $4^{3x+5} = 16$

16-7    17.  $\log(x + 9) - \log x = 1$

16-8    18.  An earthquake has a magnitude of 7 on the Richter scale. What is its intensity?

17-1    19.  Find the first four terms, the 10th term, and the 15th term for the sequence $a_n = n + \dfrac{1}{n}$.

17-2    20.  Write sigma notation for $\frac{1}{3} + \frac{1}{9} + \frac{1}{27} + \frac{1}{81}$.

17-3    21.  Find the 17th term of the arithmetic sequence 7, 4, 1, . . .

17-4    22.  Find the sum of the odd numbers from 1 to 99, inclusive.

17-5    23.  Find the common ratio for the geometric sequence 12, $-4$, $\frac{4}{3}$, $-\frac{4}{9}$, . . .

17-5    24.  Find the 5th term of the geometric sequence 2, $-10$, 50, . . .

17-6    25.  Find the sum of the geometric series $\displaystyle\sum_{k=1}^{7} 4^k$.

17-7    26.  Find the sum of the geometric series $\frac{8}{3} + \frac{4}{3} + \frac{2}{3} + \cdots$

17-7    27.  Find fractional notation for $5.15\overline{15}$.

Solve, using matrices.

18-1   28.  $2x + y = 7$
            $x - 5y = 4$

18-2   29.  $p + q + r = 1$
            $p + 2q + 3r = 4$
            $p + 3q + 7r = 13$

18-3   30.  Evaluate: $\begin{vmatrix} 3 & 2 \\ -7 & 5 \end{vmatrix}$.

18-3   31.  Solve, using Cramer's Rule:  $2x - 2y = 2$
                                          $6x - 5y = 1$

18-4   32.  Evaluate: $\begin{vmatrix} -1 & -2 & -3 \\ 3 & 4 & 2 \\ 0 & 1 & 2 \end{vmatrix}$.

18-4   33.  Solve, using Cramer's Rule:  $3x - y + 2z = 1$
                                          $x - y + 2z = 3$
                                          $-2x + 3y + z = 1$

18-5   34.  Add: $\begin{bmatrix} 1 & 3 \\ 2 & 6 \end{bmatrix} + \begin{bmatrix} 3 & 3 \\ -1 & -1 \end{bmatrix}$.

18-5   35.  Subtract: $\begin{bmatrix} -1 & 0 & 0 \\ 0 & 2 & 0 \end{bmatrix} - \begin{bmatrix} -3 & -3 & 7 \\ -5 & 2 & 1 \end{bmatrix}$.

Multiply, if possible.

18-6   36.  $-5 \begin{bmatrix} -3 & 5 \\ 2 & -1 \end{bmatrix}$      37.  $[8 \quad -1] \begin{bmatrix} 3 & 3 \\ -1 & -1 \end{bmatrix}$

       38.  $\begin{bmatrix} 3 & 3 \\ -1 & -1 \end{bmatrix} \begin{bmatrix} -3 \\ -2 \end{bmatrix}$

19-1   39.  In how many ways can 8 motorcycles be parked in a row?

19-1   40.  Evaluate 6!.

19-2   41.  Evaluate $_8P_3$.

19-2   42.  How many 5-digit license plates can be made using the digits 1, 2, 3, 4, 5, 6, 7 if repetitions are allowed? not allowed?

19-3   43.  There are 23 students in a club. How many ways can 4 officers be selected?

19-4   44.  Expand: $(x^2 - 3y)^5$.

19-4   45.  Determine the number of subsets of a set of 6 members.

19-5   46.  What is the probability of getting a total of 6 on a roll of a pair of dice?

## TABLE 1: *SQUARES AND SQUARE ROOTS*

| N | N² | √N | N | N² | √N |
|---|---|---|---|---|---|
| 1 | 1 | 1 | 51 | 2,601 | 7.141 |
| 2 | 4 | 1.414 | 52 | 2,704 | 7.211 |
| 3 | 9 | 1.732 | 53 | 2,809 | 7.280 |
| 4 | 16 | 2 | 54 | 2,916 | 7.348 |
| 5 | 25 | 2.236 | 55 | 3,025 | 7.416 |
| 6 | 36 | 2.449 | 56 | 3,136 | 7.483 |
| 7 | 49 | 2.646 | 57 | 3,249 | 7.550 |
| 8 | 64 | 2.828 | 58 | 3,364 | 7.616 |
| 9 | 81 | 3 | 59 | 3,481 | 7.681 |
| 10 | 100 | 3.162 | 60 | 3,600 | 7.746 |
| 11 | 121 | 3.317 | 61 | 3,721 | 7.810 |
| 12 | 144 | 3.464 | 62 | 3,844 | 7.874 |
| 13 | 169 | 3.606 | 63 | 3,969 | 7.937 |
| 14 | 196 | 3.742 | 64 | 4,096 | 8 |
| 15 | 225 | 3.873 | 65 | 4,225 | 8.062 |
| 16 | 256 | 4 | 66 | 4,356 | 8.124 |
| 17 | 289 | 4.123 | 67 | 4,489 | 8.185 |
| 18 | 324 | 4.243 | 68 | 4,624 | 8.246 |
| 19 | 361 | 4.359 | 69 | 4,761 | 8.307 |
| 20 | 400 | 4.472 | 70 | 4,900 | 8.367 |
| 21 | 441 | 4.583 | 71 | 5,041 | 8.426 |
| 22 | 484 | 4.690 | 72 | 5,184 | 8.485 |
| 23 | 529 | 4.796 | 73 | 5,329 | 8.544 |
| 24 | 576 | 4.899 | 74 | 5,476 | 8.602 |
| 25 | 625 | 5 | 75 | 5,625 | 8.660 |
| 26 | 676 | 5.099 | 76 | 5,776 | 8.718 |
| 27 | 729 | 5.196 | 77 | 5,929 | 8.775 |
| 28 | 784 | 5.292 | 78 | 6,084 | 8.832 |
| 29 | 841 | 5.385 | 79 | 6,241 | 8.888 |
| 30 | 900 | 5.477 | 80 | 6,400 | 8.944 |
| 31 | 961 | 5.568 | 81 | 6,561 | 9 |
| 32 | 1,024 | 5.657 | 82 | 6,724 | 9.055 |
| 33 | 1,089 | 5.745 | 83 | 6,889 | 9.110 |
| 34 | 1,156 | 5.831 | 84 | 7,056 | 9.165 |
| 35 | 1,225 | 5.916 | 85 | 7,225 | 9.220 |
| 36 | 1,296 | 6 | 86 | 7,396 | 9.274 |
| 37 | 1,369 | 6.083 | 87 | 7,569 | 9.327 |
| 38 | 1,444 | 6.164 | 88 | 7,744 | 9.381 |
| 39 | 1,521 | 6.245 | 89 | 7,921 | 9.434 |
| 40 | 1,600 | 6.325 | 90 | 8,100 | 9.487 |
| 41 | 1,681 | 6.403 | 91 | 8,281 | 9.539 |
| 42 | 1,764 | 6.481 | 92 | 8,464 | 9.592 |
| 43 | 1,849 | 6.557 | 93 | 8,649 | 9.644 |
| 44 | 1,936 | 6.633 | 94 | 8,836 | 9.695 |
| 45 | 2,025 | 6.708 | 95 | 9,025 | 9.747 |
| 46 | 2,116 | 6.782 | 96 | 9,216 | 9.798 |
| 47 | 2,209 | 6.856 | 97 | 9,409 | 9.849 |
| 48 | 2,304 | 6.928 | 98 | 9,604 | 9.899 |
| 49 | 2,401 | 7 | 99 | 9,801 | 9.950 |
| 50 | 2,500 | 7.071 | 100 | 10,000 | 10 |

**TABLE 2:** *COMMON LOGARITHMS*

| x | 0 | 1 | 2 | 3 | 4 | 5 | 6 | 7 | 8 | 9 |
|---|---|---|---|---|---|---|---|---|---|---|
| 1.0 | .0000 | .0043 | .0086 | .0128 | .0170 | .0212 | .0253 | .0294 | .0334 | .0374 |
| 1.1 | .0414 | .0453 | .0492 | .0531 | .0569 | .0607 | .0645 | .0682 | .0719 | .0755 |
| 1.2 | .0792 | .0828 | .0864 | .0899 | .0934 | .0969 | .1004 | .1038 | .1072 | .1106 |
| 1.3 | .1139 | .1173 | .1206 | .1239 | .1271 | .1303 | .1335 | .1367 | .1399 | .1430 |
| 1.4 | .1461 | .1492 | .1523 | .1553 | .1584 | .1614 | .1644 | .1673 | .1703 | .1732 |
| 1.5 | .1761 | .1790 | .1818 | .1847 | .1875 | .1903 | .1931 | .1959 | .1987 | .2014 |
| 1.6 | .2041 | .2068 | .2095 | .2122 | .2148 | .2175 | .2201 | .2227 | .2253 | .2279 |
| 1.7 | .2304 | .2330 | .2355 | .2380 | .2405 | .2430 | .2455 | .2480 | .2504 | .2529 |
| 1.8 | .2553 | .2577 | .2601 | .2625 | .2648 | .2672 | .2695 | .2718 | .2742 | .2765 |
| 1.9 | .2788 | .2810 | .2833 | .2856 | .2878 | .2900 | .2923 | .2945 | .2967 | .2989 |
| 2.0 | .3010 | .3032 | .3054 | .3075 | .3096 | .3118 | .3139 | .3160 | .3181 | .3201 |
| 2.1 | .3222 | .3243 | .3263 | .3284 | .3304 | .3324 | .3345 | .3365 | .3385 | .3404 |
| 2.2 | .3424 | .3444 | .3464 | .3483 | .3502 | .3522 | .3541 | .3560 | .3579 | .3598 |
| 2.3 | .3617 | .3636 | .3655 | .3674 | .3692 | .3711 | .3729 | .3747 | .3766 | .3784 |
| 2.4 | .3802 | .3820 | .3838 | .3856 | .3874 | .3892 | .3909 | .3927 | .3945 | .3962 |
| 2.5 | .3979 | .3997 | .4014 | .4031 | .4048 | .4065 | .4082 | .4099 | .4116 | .4133 |
| 2.6 | .4150 | .4166 | .4183 | .4200 | .4216 | .4232 | .4249 | .4265 | .4281 | .4298 |
| 2.7 | .4314 | .4330 | .4346 | .4362 | .4378 | .4393 | .4409 | .4425 | .4440 | .4456 |
| 2.8 | .4472 | .4487 | .4502 | .4518 | .4533 | .4548 | .4564 | .4579 | .4594 | .4609 |
| 2.9 | .4624 | .4639 | .4654 | .4669 | .4683 | .4698 | .4713 | .4728 | .4742 | .4757 |
| 3.0 | .4771 | .4786 | .4800 | .4814 | .4829 | .4843 | .4857 | .4871 | .4886 | .4900 |
| 3.1 | .4914 | .4928 | .4942 | .4955 | .4969 | .4983 | .4997 | .5011 | .5024 | .5038 |
| 3.2 | .5051 | .5065 | .5079 | .5092 | .5105 | .5119 | .5132 | .5145 | .5159 | .5172 |
| 3.3 | .5185 | .5198 | .5211 | .5224 | .5237 | .5250 | .5263 | .5276 | .5289 | .5307 |
| 3.4 | .5315 | .5328 | .5340 | .5353 | .5366 | .5378 | .5391 | .5403 | .5416 | .5428 |
| 3.5 | .5441 | .5453 | .5465 | .5478 | .5490 | .5502 | .5514 | .5527 | .5539 | .5551 |
| 3.6 | .5563 | .5575 | .5587 | .5599 | .5611 | .5623 | .5635 | .5647 | .5658 | .5670 |
| 3.7 | .5682 | .5694 | .5705 | .5717 | .5729 | .5740 | .5752 | .5763 | .5775 | .5786 |
| 3.8 | .5798 | .5809 | .5821 | .5832 | .5843 | .5855 | .5866 | .5877 | .5888 | .5899 |
| 3.9 | .5911 | .5922 | .5933 | .5944 | .5955 | .5966 | .5977 | .5988 | .5999 | .6010 |
| 4.0 | .6021 | .6031 | .6042 | .6053 | .6064 | .6075 | .6085 | .6096 | .6107 | .6117 |
| 4.1 | .6128 | .6138 | .6149 | .6160 | .6170 | .6180 | .6191 | .6201 | .6212 | .6222 |
| 4.2 | .6232 | .6243 | .6253 | .6263 | .6274 | .6284 | .6294 | .6304 | .6314 | .6325 |
| 4.3 | .6335 | .6345 | .6355 | .6365 | .6375 | .6385 | .6395 | .6405 | .6415 | .6425 |
| 4.4 | .6435 | .6444 | .6454 | .6464 | .6474 | .6484 | .6493 | .6503 | .6513 | .6522 |
| 4.5 | .6532 | .6542 | .6551 | .6561 | .6571 | .6580 | .6590 | .6599 | .6609 | .6618 |
| 4.6 | .6628 | .6637 | .6646 | .6656 | .6665 | .6675 | .6684 | .6693 | .6702 | .6712 |
| 4.7 | .6721 | .6730 | .6739 | .6749 | .6758 | .6767 | .6776 | .6785 | .6794 | .6803 |
| 4.8 | .6812 | .6821 | .6830 | .6839 | .6848 | .6857 | .6866 | .6875 | .6884 | .6893 |
| 4.9 | .6902 | .6911 | .6920 | .6928 | .6937 | .6946 | .6955 | .6964 | .6972 | .6981 |
| 5.0 | .6990 | .6998 | .7007 | .7016 | .7024 | .7033 | .7042 | .7050 | .7059 | .7067 |
| 5.1 | .7076 | .7084 | .7093 | .7101 | .7110 | .7118 | .7126 | .7135 | .7143 | .7152 |
| 5.2 | .7160 | .7168 | .7177 | .7185 | .7193 | .7202 | .7210 | .7218 | .7226 | .7235 |
| 5.3 | .7243 | .7251 | .7259 | .7267 | .7275 | .7284 | .7292 | .7300 | .7308 | .7316 |
| 5.4 | .7324 | .7332 | .7340 | .7348 | .7356 | .7364 | .7372 | .7380 | .7388 | .7396 |

| x | 0 | 1 | 2 | 3 | 4 | 5 | 6 | 7 | 8 | 9 |
|---|---|---|---|---|---|---|---|---|---|---|
| 5.5 | .7404 | .7412 | .7419 | .7427 | .7435 | .7443 | .7451 | .7459 | .7466 | .7474 |
| 5.6 | .7482 | .7490 | .7497 | .7505 | .7513 | .7520 | .7528 | .7536 | .7543 | .7551 |
| 5.7 | .7559 | .7566 | .7574 | .7582 | .7589 | .7597 | .7604 | .7612 | .7619 | .7627 |
| 5.8 | .7634 | .7642 | .7649 | .7657 | .7664 | .7672 | .7679 | .7686 | .7694 | .7701 |
| 5.9 | .7709 | .7716 | .7723 | .7731 | .7738 | .7745 | .7752 | .7760 | .7767 | .7774 |
| 6.0 | .7782 | .7789 | .7796 | .7803 | .7810 | .7818 | .7825 | .7832 | .7839 | .7846 |
| 6.1 | .7853 | .7860 | .7868 | .7875 | .7882 | .7889 | .7896 | .7903 | .7910 | .7917 |
| 6.2 | .7924 | .7931 | .7938 | .7945 | .7952 | .7959 | .7966 | .7973 | .7980 | .7987 |
| 6.3 | .7993 | .8000 | .8007 | .8014 | .8021 | .8028 | .8035 | .8041 | .8048 | .8055 |
| 6.4 | .8062 | .8069 | .8075 | .8082 | .8089 | .8096 | .8102 | .8109 | .8116 | .8122 |
| 6.5 | .8129 | .8136 | .8142 | .8149 | .8156 | .8162 | .8169 | .8176 | .8182 | .8189 |
| 6.6 | .8195 | .8202 | .8209 | .8215 | .8222 | .8228 | .8235 | .8241 | .8248 | .8254 |
| 6.7 | .8261 | .8267 | .8274 | .8280 | .8287 | .8293 | .8299 | .8306 | .8312 | .8319 |
| 6.8 | .8325 | .8331 | .8338 | .8344 | .8351 | .8357 | .8363 | .8370 | .8376 | .8382 |
| 6.9 | .8388 | .8395 | .8401 | .8407 | .8414 | .8420 | .8426 | .8432 | .8439 | .8445 |
| 7.0 | .8451 | .8457 | .8463 | .8470 | .8476 | .8482 | .8488 | .8494 | .8500 | .8506 |
| 7.1 | .8513 | .8519 | .8525 | .8531 | .8537 | .8543 | .8549 | .8555 | .8561 | .8567 |
| 7.2 | .8573 | .8579 | .8585 | .8591 | .8597 | .8603 | .8609 | .8615 | .8621 | .8627 |
| 7.3 | .8633 | .8639 | .8645 | .8651 | .8657 | .8663 | .8669 | .8675 | .8681 | .8686 |
| 7.4 | .8692 | .8698 | .8704 | .8710 | .8716 | .8722 | .8727 | .8733 | .8739 | .8745 |
| 7.5 | .8751 | .8756 | .8762 | .8768 | .8774 | .8779 | .8785 | .8791 | .8797 | .8802 |
| 7.6 | .8808 | .8814 | .8820 | .8825 | .8831 | .8837 | .8842 | .8848 | .8854 | .8859 |
| 7.7 | .8865 | .8871 | .8876 | .8882 | .8887 | .8893 | .8899 | .8904 | .8910 | .8915 |
| 7.8 | .8921 | .8927 | .8932 | .8938 | .8943 | .8949 | .8954 | .8960 | .8965 | .8971 |
| 7.9 | .8976 | .8982 | .8987 | .8993 | .8998 | .9004 | .9009 | .9015 | .9020 | .9025 |
| 8.0 | .9031 | .9036 | .9042 | .9047 | .9053 | .9058 | .9063 | .9069 | .9074 | .9079 |
| 8.1 | .9085 | .9090 | .9096 | .9101 | .9106 | .9112 | .9117 | .9122 | .9128 | .9133 |
| 8.2 | .9138 | .9143 | .9149 | .9154 | .9159 | .9165 | .9170 | .9175 | .9180 | .9186 |
| 8.3 | .9191 | .9196 | .9201 | .9206 | .9212 | .9217 | .9222 | .9227 | .9232 | .9238 |
| 8.4 | .9243 | .9248 | .9253 | .9258 | .9263 | .9269 | .9274 | .9279 | .9284 | .9289 |
| 8.5 | .9294 | .9299 | .9304 | .9309 | .9315 | .9320 | .9325 | .9330 | .9335 | .9340 |
| 8.6 | .9345 | .9350 | .9555 | .9360 | .9365 | .9370 | .9375 | .9380 | .9385 | .9390 |
| 8.7 | .9395 | .9400 | .9405 | .9410 | .9415 | .9420 | .9425 | .9430 | .9435 | .9440 |
| 8.8 | .9445 | .9450 | .9455 | .9460 | .9465 | .9469 | .9474 | .9479 | .9484 | .9489 |
| 8.9 | .9494 | .9499 | .9504 | .9509 | .9513 | .9518 | .9523 | .9528 | .9533 | .9538 |
| 9.0 | .9542 | .9547 | .9552 | .9557 | .9562 | .9566 | .9571 | .9576 | .9581 | .9586 |
| 9.1 | .9590 | .9595 | .9600 | .9605 | .9609 | .9614 | .9619 | .9624 | .9628 | .9633 |
| 9.2 | .9638 | .9643 | .9647 | .9652 | .9657 | .9661 | .9666 | .9671 | .9675 | .9680 |
| 9.3 | .9685 | .9689 | .9694 | .9699 | .9703 | .9708 | .9713 | .9717 | .9722 | .9727 |
| 9.4 | .9731 | .9736 | .9741 | .9745 | .9750 | .9754 | .9759 | .9763 | .9768 | .9773 |
| 9.5 | .9777 | .9782 | .9786 | .9791 | .9795 | .9800 | .9805 | .9809 | .9814 | .9818 |
| 9.6 | .9823 | .9827 | .9832 | .9836 | .9841 | .9845 | .9850 | .9854 | .9859 | .9863 |
| 9.7 | .9868 | .9872 | .9877 | .9881 | .9886 | .9890 | .9894 | .9899 | .9903 | .9908 |
| 9.8 | .9912 | .9917 | .9921 | .9926 | .9930 | .9934 | .9939 | .9943 | .9948 | .9952 |
| 9.9 | .9956 | .9961 | .9965 | .9969 | .9974 | .9978 | .9983 | .9987 | .9991 | .9996 |

# *Glossary*

**absolute value** The absolute value of a number is its distance from 0 on the number line.

**addition principle** For equations: If an equation $a = b$ is true, then $a + c = b + c$ is true for any number $c$. For inequalities: If any number is added on both sides of a true inequality we get another true inequality.

**additive identity** Zero is the additive identity for addition.

**additive inverse** If the sum of two numbers is 0, they are additive inverses of each other.

**antilogarithm** As a function, the inverse of a logarithm function. $\text{Antilog}_b x = b^x$

**arithmetic sequence** A sequence is arithmetic if each term can be obtained from the preceeding one by adding a constant, or the difference between successive terms is a constant.

**associative laws** Addition: For any numbers $a$, $b$, and $c$, $a + (b + c) = (a + b) + c$. Multiplication: $(a \cdot b) \cdot c = a \cdot (b \cdot c)$.

**asymptote** A line is an asymptote to a curve if the curve gets very close to the line as the distance from the origin increases.

**base** In exponential notation $n^x$, $n$ is the base. In logarithmic notation, $\log_b x$, $b$ is the base.

**binomial** A polynomial with just two terms.

**binomial coefficient** The binomial coefficient $\binom{n}{a}$ means $\dfrac{n!}{a!(n - a)!}$.

**binomial theorem** A theorem that tells how to expand a power of a binomial.

**branches of hyperbola** The two parts of a hyperbola are called branches.

**cartesian coordinates** When axes are placed on a plane at right angles so that ordered pairs of numbers are matched with the points of the plane we say we have a cartesian coordinate system.

**cartesian product (of sets)** The cartesian product of sets $A$ and $B$, denoted $A \times B$, is the set of all ordered pairs with first member from $A$ and second member from $B$.

**characteristic (of logarithm)** The integer part of a base 10 logarithm.

**coefficient** In any term, the coefficient is the number that is multiplied by the variable.

**combination** A combination of $r$ objects of a set is a subset containing $r$ objects.

**common factor** A factor that is common to all the terms in an expression.

**common logarithm** A base 10 logarithm.

**commutative laws** Addition: For any numbers $a$ and $b$, $a + b = b + a$. Multiplication: $a \cdot b = b \cdot a$.

**completing the square** Adding one or more terms to an expression to make it the square of a binomial.

**complex fractional expression** A fractional expression that has fractional expressions within it.

**complex number** The sum of a real and an imaginary number.

**compound event** An event that is considered to be made up of two or more events.

**conditional sentence** An if-then sentence.

**conjugate** The conjugate of the complex number $a + bi$ is $a - bi$.

**conjunction** An expression formed by connecting two or more sentences with the word *and*.

**consistent system** A system of equations or inequalities having a solution.

**constant term** A term with no variable.

**constant of variation** Whenever a situation gives rise to a relation $y = kx$, where $x$ and $y$ are variables, $k$ is the constant of variation.

**converse** The converse of a sentence "if $a$, then $b$," is "if $b$, then $a$."

**coordinates** The numbers associated with a point on a number line or in a plane.

**Cramer's rule** A rule for solving systems of equations using determinants.

**degree** The degree of a term is its exponent (or the number of times a variable occurs as a factor). The degree of a polynomial is the greatest degree of any of its terms.

**dependent system** A system of *n* equations is dependent if it is equivalent to a system of fewer than *n* of them.

**direct variation** A relation between variables *x* and *y* in which their relationship can be expressed by an equation $y = kx$, where *k* is a constant.

**discriminant** For a quadratic equation $ax^2 + bx + c = 0$, the expression $b^2 - 4ac$ is called the discriminant.

**disjunction** An expression formed by connecting two or more sentences with the word *or*.

**distance formula** A formula giving the distance between any two points.

**distributive laws** Multiplication over addition: For any numbers *a*, *b*, and *c*, $(a + b) \cdot c = a \cdot c + b \cdot c$. Multiplication over subtraction: For any numbers *a*, *b*, and *c*, $(a - b) \cdot c = a \cdot c - b \cdot c$.

**domain** SEE *function*.

**ellipse** A set of all points *P* in a plane such that the sum of the distances from *P* to two fixed points $F_1$ and $F_2$ is constant.

**equivalent expressions** Expressions that represent the same number for all sensible replacements of the variables.

**even function** If $f(a) = f(-a)$ for all *a* in the domain of a function, then that function is even.

**exponent** In exponential notation $n^x$, *x* is the exponent.

**factor** When two or more numbers (or expressions) are multiplied, each of the numbers is a factor of the product.

**factor theorem** If a number *a*, when substituted into a polynomial, makes the expression zero, then $x - a$ is a factor of the polynomial.

**focus** Ellipses, hyperbolas, and parabolas have associated with them a point called a focus or points called *foci* (plural).

**function** A correspondence or rule that assigns to each member of one set (called the *domain*) exactly one member of some set (called the *range*).

**fundamental counting principle** If an event can occur in $n_1$ ways, another in $n_2$ ways, then the combined event can occur in $n_1 \cdot n_2$ ways.

**fundamental theorem of algebra** Any polynomial of degree *n* greater than 1, with complex number coefficients, can be factored into *n* linear factors.

**geometric sequence** A sequence in which successive terms have a common ratio.

**hyperbola** A set of all points *P* in a plane such that the absolute value of the difference of the distances from *P* to two fixed points $F_1$ and $F_2$ is constant.

**identity** An equation which is true for all sensible replacements of the variables.

**image** Under a transformation, the point corresponding to a given point.

**imaginary number** The square root of a negative number.

**inconsistent system** A system of equations or inequalities having no solution.

**inequality** A sentence formed by placing $>$, $<$, $\geq$, $\leq$, or $\neq$ between two expressions.

**infinite sequence** A sequence that does not end.

**integer** Any natural number, the additive inverse of a natural number, or zero.

**intercept** In the graph of an equation in two variables, the point where the graph crosses an axis.

**inverse of a function** The relation obtained by interchanging the first and second members of all ordered pairs in the relation.

**inverse variation** A relation between two variables, *x* and *y*, in which $y = \dfrac{k}{x}$, $x \neq 0$, and *k* is a constant.

**irrational number** A number that cannot be named by fractional notation $\dfrac{a}{b}$, where *a* and *b* are integers.

**line of symmetry** In any figure, a line that divides the figure so that if it is folded on the line the two halves will match.

**linear equation** An equation in which the variables occur to the first power only.

**linear function** A function that can be described by a linear equation.

**linear programming** A kind of mathematics in which maximum and minimum values of certain functions can be found.

**logarithmic function** The inverse of an exponential function.

**mantissa** The portion of a base 10 logarithm between 0 and 1.

**matrix** A rectangular array.

**monomial** A polynomial with just one term.

**multiplication principle** For equations: If an equation $a = b$ is true, then $a \cdot c = b \cdot c$ is true for any number $c$. For inequalities: If we multiply on both sides of a true inequality by a positive number, we get another true inequality. If we multiply by a negative number, the inequality sign must be reversed to get another true inequality.

**multiplicative identity** The number 1 is the multiplicative identity.

**multiplicative inverse** SEE *reciprocal*.

**nonsensible replacement** A replacement for a variable for which an expression does not name any number.

**odd function** If $f(a) = -f(-a)$ for all $a$ in the domain of a function, then that function is odd.

**parabola** A set of all points in a plane equidistant from a fixed line and a fixed point.

**permutation** A permutation of a set is an ordered arrangement of that set, without repetition.

**polynomial** An expression
$$a_n x^n + a_{n-1} x^{n-1} + \cdots a_1 x + a_0.$$

**principle of powers** If an equation $a = b$ is true, then the equation $a^n = b^n$ is true.

**principle of zero products** An equation with 0 on one side and with a factorization on the other can be solved by finding those numbers that make the factors 0.

**quadrant** The $x$ and $y$ axes divide the plane into four regions, called quadrants.

**quadratic equation** An equation in which the term of highest degree has degree two.

**quadratic formula** A formula for finding the solutions of a quadratic equation.

**quadratic function** A function that can be described by a quadratic equation.

**radical** The symbol $\sqrt{\phantom{x}}$ is called a radical.

**radicand** The expression under a radical.

**range** SEE *function*.

**rational number** Any number of ordinary arithmetic or the additive inverse of any number of ordinary arithmetic.

**rationalizing a denominator** Simplifying a radical expression so that there are no radicals in the denominator and only whole numbers or variables in the radicand.

**real number** There is a real number for every point of the number line.

**reciprocal** Two expressions are reciprocals if their product is 1. A reciprocal is also called a *multiplicative inverse*.

**reflection** A transformation in which points are reflected across a line.

**relation** Any set of ordered pairs.

**root of a polynomial** Any number which makes the polynomial zero.

**slope of a line** A number that tells how steeply the line slants.

**synthetic division** A method of division of a polynomial by a binomial $x - a$, in which the variables are not written.

**transformation** A function from a set to itself.

**translation** A geometric transformation in which all points are moved in the same direction, the same distance.

**trinomial square** An expression with three terms that is the square of a binomial.

**variable** A letter (or other symbol) used to stand for one or several numbers.

**zero (of a polynomial)** A number, which when substituted into a polynomial, makes it zero.

# Index

# Selected Answers

## CHAPTER 1

### Answers for TRY THIS

**1–1** 1.–4. Answers may vary. 5. 0.875 6. $0.\overline{63}$
7. $1.1\overline{3}$ 8. Rational 9. Rational 10. Rational 11. Rational 12. Irrational 13. Irrational

**1–2** 1. 2 2. $\sqrt{3}$ 3. 0 4. $\frac{1}{4}$ 5. –9 6. 23 7. 14
8. 0 9. 9 10. 7 11. 0 12. –8.4 13. $\frac{1}{2}$ 14. 9.8
15. –2 16. 5 17. –5 18. –14 19. –18 20. –17
21. –29 22. –18.6 23. $-\frac{29}{5}$ 24. –3 25. 12
26. –3.3 27. $-\frac{7}{3}$ 28. $-\frac{11}{24}$ 29. 0 30. 0 31. 0
32. –4 33. 14 34. 8.6 35. 0

**1–3** 1. 53 2. 144 3. –2 4. –2 5. a) –5; –5 b) –14;
–14 c) –9.9; –9.9 6. a) 16; 16 b) –11; –11 c) 18.3;
18.3 7. Associative law, addition 8. Commutative law,
addition 9. Associative law, addition 10. –5 11. –3
12. 3 13. 17 14. –16 15. –29.6 16. $\frac{59}{48}$

**1–4** 1. –24 2. –72 3. –74 4. –2 5. 72 6. 5
7. 128 8. $\frac{10}{3}$ 9. Commutative law, addition 10. Associative law, multiplication 11. Commutative law, multiplication 12. Associative law, addition 13. –3 14. –25
15. 3 16. 2 17. $\frac{8}{3}$ 18. $\frac{1}{18}$ 19. $-\frac{234}{112}$ 20. $-\frac{1}{43}$
21. $-\frac{15}{28}$ 22. $\frac{88}{35}$ 23. No 24. 0 25. No

**1–5** 1. $a \cdot b \cdot c$ 2. $b \cdot b \cdot b$ 3. $8 \cdot a \cdot b$ 4. 58
5. –100 6. 30 7. –50 8. 20 9. 20 10. 72 11. 72
12. $9(x + y)$ 13. $a(c - y)$ 14. $6(x + 2)$ 15. $4(y - 4)$
16. $b(s + t - w)$ 17. $5(7x - 5y + 3)$ 18. $5x - 45$ 19. $8y$
$+ 80$ 20. $ax + ay - az$ 21. $-2x$ 22. $17x$ 23. $6y$
24. $-6t$ 25. $36x - 19y$

**1–6** 1. –24 2. 0 3. 10 4. $-9x$ 5. $24t$ 6. $y - 7$
7. $y - x$ 8. $-9x - 6y - 11$ 9. $-23x + 7y + 2$ 10. $2x +$
$5z - 24$ 11. $t$ 12. $-5x, -7y, 67t$, and $-\frac{4}{5}$ 13. $-9a$,
$-4b, 17c$, and $-24$ 14. $3x - 8$ 15. $4y + 1$ 16. $-2x -$
$9y - 6$ 17. $-31$ 18. $-13$ 19. $-2$ 20. 8 21. $8x - 12$
22. $24y + 89$ 23. $-26x - 21y + 148$

**1–7** 1. $8^4$ 2. $m^3$ 3. $(4y)^5$ 4. $3 \circ 3 \cdot 3 \circ 3$ or 81 5. $y$
$\circ y$ 6. $5x \cdot 5x \cdot 5x \cdot 5x$ 7. $25y^2$ 8. $-8x^3$ 9. 8 10. 31
11. –7.89 12. $23\frac{1}{4}$ 13. 1 14. 1 15. 1 16. 1 17. $\frac{1}{10^4}$
18. $\frac{1}{12^7}$ 19. $4^{-3}$ 20. $9^{-8}$ 21. $4^{-3} = \frac{1}{4^3} = \frac{1}{4 \cdot 4 \cdot 4} = \frac{1}{64}$

**1–8** 1. $8^{13}$ 2. $7^2$ 3. $7^5$ 4. $x^{-10}$ 5. $10x^{-12}y^2$
6. $-60y$ 7. $4^3$ 8. $5^6$ 9. $10^{-14}$ 10. $9^{-6}$ 11. $y^{11}$
12. $5y^{-1}$ 13. $-2y^{10}x^{-4}$ 14. $5^{24}$ 15. $8^{-8}$ 16. $9^{15}$
17. $8x^3y^3$ 18. $16x^{-4}y^{14}$ 19. $-243x^{20}y^{10}$ 20. $1000x^{-12}y^{21}z^{-6}$

**1–9** 1. False 2. True 3. False 4. True 5. True
6. False 7. 19 8. 9 9. 15 10. $7|x|$ 11. $x^8$

12. $5a^2|b|$ 13. $\frac{7|a|}{b^2}$ 14. $9|x|$

### Exercise Set 1–1, page 5

1.–5. Answers may vary. 7. 0.625 9. $0.\overline{428571}$
11. 0.5625 13. $0.41\overline{6}$ 15. $0.\overline{63}$ 17. Rational 19. Rational 21. Rational 23. Irrational 25. Irrational 27. Irrational 29. Rational

### Exercise Set 1–2, page 9

1. 4 3. 9 5. $\sqrt{5}$ 7. $\frac{1}{9}$ 9. 0 11. 19 13. 4.7 15. –12
17. 31 19. –5 21. $\frac{1}{6}$ 23. 7.6 25. –9.03 27. 8
29. –5 31. 7.5 33. 0 35. 1 37. –18 39. –28
41. –16 43. 5 45. 4 47. –7 49. –24 51. 1.2
53. –8.86 55. $\frac{1}{7}$ 57. $-\frac{4}{3}$ 59. $-\frac{23}{12}$ 61. –8 63. 18
65. $\sqrt{11}$ 67. $-\frac{5}{6}$

### Exercise Set 1–3, page 14

1. 49 3. 93 5. 135 7. 0 9. Commutative law, addition
11. Associative law, addition 13. Associative law, addition
15. Commutative law, addition 17. –2 19. –12 21. 5
23. 15 25. –11.6 27. –29.25 29. $-\frac{7}{4}$

### Exercise Set 1–4, page 18

1. –21 3. –8 5. 16 7. 126 9. 34.2 11. 26.46
13. 2 15. 60 17. 24 19. Associative law, addition
21. Commutative law, addition 23. –2 25. –7 27. 7
29. 0.3 31. $\frac{4}{3}$ 33. $-\frac{8}{7}$ 35. $\frac{1}{26}$ 37. $-\frac{1}{56}$ 39. $-\frac{6}{77}$
41. 25 43. Not possible 45. 0 47. Not possible

### Exercise Set 1–5, page 24

1. $x \cdot y \cdot z$ 3. $x \cdot x \cdot x$ 5. $9 \cdot x \cdot y$ 7. 45 9. –28
11. –29 13. –8 15. –4 17. –18 19. 16 21. 96
23. $8(x + y)$ 25. $9(p - q)$ 27. $7(x - 3)$ 29. $x(y + z)$
31. $2(x - y + z)$ 33. $3(x + 2y - 3z)$ 35. $a(b + c - d)$
37. $P(1 + rt)$ 39. $\pi r(r + s)$ 41. $3a + 6$ 43. $4x - 4y$
45. $-10a - 15b$ 47. $2ab - 2ac + 2ad$ 49. $2\pi rh + 2\pi rr$
51. $\frac{1}{2}ha + \frac{1}{2}hb$ 53. $9a$ 55. $-3b$ 57. $15y$ 59. $11a$
61. $-8t$ 63. $10x$ 65. $8x - 8y$ 67. $2c + 10d$

### Exercise Set 1–6, page 29

1. –5 3. 19 5. $4b$ 7. $-a - 2$ 9. $-b + 3$ 11. $-t + y$
13. $-a - b - c$ 15. $-8x + 6y - 13$ 17. $-m + n + s$
19. $2c - 5d + 3e - 4f$ 21. $4a, -5b, 6$ 23. $8m, -5n, \frac{1}{2}p$
25. $\sqrt{2}x, -\sqrt{3}y, -2z$ 27. $3a + 5$ 29. –2 31. $m + 1$
33. $5d - 12$ 35. 0 37. $-a + b$ 39. $-7x + 14$ 41. $-10x$
$+ 19$ 43. $44a - 22$ 45. –215 47. $17x + 14y + 129$
49. $-42x - 360z - 276$ 51. $-490,990a + 855,484b$
53. $0.008733x - 0.000784y$ 55. –10

## Exercise Set 1–7, page 34

1. $4^5$  3. $5^6$  5. $m^4$  7. $(3a)^4$  9. $5^2c^3d^4$  11. $2 \cdot 2 \cdot 2 \cdot 2 \cdot 2$ or 32  13. $-3 \cdot (-3) \cdot (-3) \cdot (-3)$ or 81  15. $x \cdot x \cdot x \cdot x$  17. $4b \cdot 4b \cdot 4b$  19. $ab \cdot ab \cdot ab \cdot ab$  21. 5
23. $\frac{7}{8}$  25. 1  27. 1  29. $\frac{1}{6^3}$  31. $\frac{1}{9^5}$  33. $\frac{1}{11^1}$
35. $3^{-4}$  37. $10^{-3}$  39. $16^{-2}$

## Exercise Set 1–8, page 38

1. $5^9$  3. $8^{-4}$  5. $8^{-6}$  7. $b^{-3}$  9. $a^3$  11. $72x^5$
13. $-28m^5n^5$  15. $6^5$  17. $4^5$  19. $10^{-9}$  21. $9^2$  23. $a^5$
25. 1  27. $4^6$  29. $8^{-12}$  31. $6^{12}$  33. $3^3x^6y^6$ or $27x^6y^6$
35. $(-2)^{-2}x^{-6}y^8$ or $\frac{1}{4}x^{-6}y^8$  37. $(-6)^{-2}a^4b^{-6}c^{-2}$ or $\frac{1}{36}a^4b^{-6}c^{-2}$

## Exercise Set 1–9, page 42

1. False  3. True  5. False  7. True  9. True  11. True
13. False  15. $3|x|$  17. $x^6$  19. $7x^2y^2|y|$  21. $\frac{a^2}{|b|}$
23. $4|t|$  25. $5a^4|b|$  27. $t^2|t|$  29. $a^8$

# CHAPTER 2

## Answers for TRY THIS

**2–1**  1.–3. Answers may vary.  4. The equation, $89 + 2 = 3 + 4$, says that $89 + 2$ and $3 + 4$ name the same number.
5. The equation, $6 - 7 + \frac{1}{2} = 14$, says that $6 - 7 + \frac{1}{2}$ and 14 name the same number.  6. Answers may vary.  7. 4
8. $-7$  9. 38  10. $-1$  11. 140.3  12. $\frac{5}{4}$  13. $-16$
14. $\frac{2}{7}$  15. $-3$
**2–2**  1. $\frac{4}{3}$  2. 4  3. 3  4. $-\frac{29}{5}$  5. $-2$  6. $-\frac{19}{8}$  7. 19,
$-5$  8. $0, \frac{17}{3}$  9. $-\frac{2}{9}, \frac{1}{2}$
**2–3**  1. 9 cm; 3 cm.  2. 1.645 min.  3. $1.92  4. $124
5. $725
**2–4**  1. $Q = \frac{T}{1 + iy}$  2. $b = \frac{2A}{h}$  3. $m = \frac{H - 2r}{3}$

## Exercise Set 2–1, page 51

1. The equation, $91 + 4 = 7 - 9$, says that $91 + 4$ and $7 - 9$ name the same number  3. Answers may vary.  5. 6  7. 9
9. $-3$  11. 40  13. 21  15. $-15$  17. $-41$  19. 2
21. $-14$  23. 23  25. $\frac{6}{5}$  27. $-\frac{17}{12}$  29. $-\frac{1}{12}$  31. $-7.06$
33. 113.5  35. 4  37. 8  39. $-9$  41. 8  43. 40  45. $\frac{81}{2}$
47. $\frac{2}{3}$  49. $\frac{2}{5}$  51. 3  53. 8  55. 0.007  57. 0.0022596

## Exercise Set 2–2, page 56

1. 18  3. 5  5. 24  7. 11  9. $-12$  11. 8  13. 7  15. 2
17. 8  19. 21  21. $-5$  23. 2  25. $-12$  27. 2  29. $-1$
31. $\frac{18}{5}$  33. 0  35. $\frac{4}{5}$  37. 2  39. 2  41. 7  43. 5
45. $-\frac{3}{2}$  47. 5  49. 2  51. $-2, 5$  53. 8, 9  55. $\frac{3}{2}, \frac{2}{3}$
57. 0, 8  59. $-4, 3$  61. 0, 1, $-2$

## Exercise Set 2–3, page 59

1. 8 cm; 4 cm  3. $1\frac{3}{5}$ m; $2\frac{2}{5}$ m  5. $14.75  7. $59.50
9. 4  11. 5  13. $45  15. $650  17. $32°, 96°, 52°$
19. Length is 31 m; width is 17 m

## Exercise Set 2–4, page 61

1. $I = \frac{A}{w}$  3. $I = \frac{W}{E}$  5. $m = \frac{F}{a}$  7. $t = \frac{I}{pr}$  9. $m = \frac{E}{c^2}$
11. $I = \frac{1}{2}(P - 2w)$  13. $a^2 = C^2 - b^2$  15. $r^2 = \frac{A}{\pi}$  17. $h = \frac{2}{11}W + 40$  19. $r^3 = \frac{3V}{4\pi}$  21. $h = \frac{2A}{a + b}$  23. $V_1 = \frac{T_1 P_2 V_2}{P_1 T_2}$

# CHAPTER 3

## Answers for TRY THIS

**3–1**  6. $B(-3, 4)$, $C(-4, -3)$, $D(6, -2)$, $E(1, 4)$, $F(-2, 0)$, $G(0, 2)$  7. Both coordinates are negative.  8. The first coordinate is positive and the second negative.  9. No  10. No
11. Yes  12. Line through $(0, -1)$ and $(2, 3)$  13. Line through $(2, -1)$ and $(-1, 2)$
**3–2**  1. Yes  2. Yes  3. No  4. No  5. No  6. Yes
7. $-5x + 5y - \frac{1}{2} = 0$  8. $0x + 3y - 10 = 0$  9. Line through $(2, 1)$ and $(-4, -1)$  10. Line through $(3, 0)$ and $(0, -2)$
11. Line through $(3, 0)$ and $(0, -2)$  12. Line through $(7, 0)$ and $(0, 4)$  13. Line through $(2, 0)$ and $(0, 9)$  14. Vertical line through $(4, 0)$  15. Horizontal line through $(0, -3)$
16. x-axis
**3–3**  1. $\frac{13}{11}$  2. 1  3. $-1$  4. $-\frac{1}{3}$  5. 0  6. No slope
7. $y = -3x - 2$  8. $y = \frac{1}{4}x - 9$  9. $y = -\frac{1}{2}x + \frac{5}{2}$
**3–4**  1. $y = -3x + 7$  2. $y = -\frac{10}{3}x + 4$  3. $m = -7$, $b = 11$
4. $m = 0$, $b = -4$  5. a) $y = \frac{2}{3}x + 2$  b) $m = \frac{2}{3}$, $b = 2$
**3–5**  1. Yes  2. No  3. Yes  4. $y = -4x - 12$  5. a) $-\frac{1}{2}$
b) 4  c) $-\frac{6}{7}$  d) $\frac{5}{2}$  6. a) Yes  b) No  7. $y = -\frac{8}{7}x + \frac{6}{7}$
8. $y = \frac{1}{2}x + \frac{5}{2}$
**3–6**  1. a) $R = -0.01t + 10.43$  b) 9.83; 9.73  c) 2063

## Exercise Set 3–1, page 70

17. $A(3, 2)$, $B(-5, -3)$, $C(-3, 4)$, $D(5, -2)$, $E(0, -4)$
19. Yes  21. No  23. Yes  25. Yes  27. Yes  29. No
31. Line through $(3, 3)$ and $(-3, -3)$  33. Line through $(1, -3)$ and $(-1, 3)$  35. Line through $(0, 2)$ and $(-2, 0)$
37. Line through $(1, -3)$ and $(-1, -2)$  39. Line through $(1, -3)$ and $(0, 1)$  41. Line through $(3, 4)$ and $(-1, -2)$
43. Line through $(5, 0)$ and $(0, 2)$  45. Line through $(2, 0)$ and $(0, -3)$  47. Line through $(0, 2)$ and $(-4, 0)$  49. Yes

## Exercise Set 3–2, page 75

1. Yes  3. No, second degree term  5. Yes  7. Yes  9. Yes
11. $4x - y - 8 = 0$  13. $-2x + y - 3 = 0$  15. $-4x + y - 1 = 0$  17. $x + 0y - 6 = 0$  19. $-3x + \sqrt{2}y + 0 = 0$  21. Line through $(4, 0)$ and $(0, 2)$  23. Line through $(-8, 0)$ and

(0, 2)   25. Line through (2, 0) and (0, 8)   27. Line through (1, 3) and (−1, −1)   29. Line through (1, 3) and (−1, −3)   31. Line through (6, 0) and (0, 3)   33. (0, −2), (2, 0)   35. (0, −1), $(\frac{1}{3}, 0)$   37. (0, −5), (4, 0)   39. (0, −5), (−1, 0)   41. (0, 2), (7, 0)   53. Vertical line through (2, 0)   55. Horizontal line through (0, −6)   57. Vertical line through (−5, 0)   59. Horizontal line through (0, 7)

### Exercise Set 3–3, page 81

1. 8   3. −1   5. $-\frac{1}{2}$   7. 2   9. $\frac{3}{7}$   11. $\frac{1}{2}$   13. $\frac{2}{5}$   15. No slope   17. 0   19. No slope   21. 0   23. y = 4x − 10   25. y = −x − 7   27. y = $\frac{1}{2}$x + 7   29. y = −7

### Exercise Set 3–4, page 84

1. y = $\frac{1}{2}$x + $\frac{7}{2}$   3. y = x   5. y = $\frac{5}{2}$x + 5   7. y = $\frac{1}{4}$x + $\frac{17}{4}$   9. y = $\frac{2}{5}$x   11. y = 3x + 5   13. m = 2, b = 3   15. m = −4, b = 9   17. m = −1, b = 6   19. m = −3, b = 5   21. m = $\frac{3}{4}$, b = −3   23. m = −3, b = 4   25. m = $-\frac{7}{3}$, b = −3   27. m = 0, b = 7   29. m = 0, b = $-\frac{10}{3}$

### Exercise Set 3–5, page 89

1. Yes   3. No   5. Yes   7. y = $-\frac{1}{2}$x + $\frac{17}{2}$   9. y = $\frac{5}{7}$x − $\frac{17}{7}$   11. y = $\frac{1}{3}$x + 4   13. y = $\frac{1}{2}$x + 4   15. y = $\frac{4}{3}$x − 6   17. y = $\frac{5}{2}$x + 9

### Exercise Set 3–6, page 92

1. a) E = 0.15t + 72   b) 76.5; 77.25   3. a) H = $\frac{50}{49}$W + $\frac{5000}{49}$ or H = $\frac{50W + 5000}{49}$   b) 56.8 kg   5. a) R = −0.0075t + 3.85   b) 3.475; 3.445   c) 2004

## CHAPTER 4

### Answers for TRY THIS

**4–1**   1. Yes   2. No   3. Line through (0, 1) and (−2, −3); line through (0, 1) and (1, −2)   4. Line through (3, 3) and (0, 0); line through (3, 3) and (4, 0)

**4–2**   1. (2, 4)   2. (5, 2)   3. (−3, 2)   4. (13, 16)   5. (1, 4)   6. $(\frac{1}{3}, \frac{1}{2})$   7. (2, 3)   8. (5, 3)

**4–3**   1. Yes   2. Yes

**4–4**   1. a) No   b) Yes   2. (2, 1, −1)   3. (2, −2, $\frac{1}{2}$)   4. (20, 30, 50)

**4–5**   1. 35 and 140   2. 22 white ones and 8 red ones   3. 30 *l* of 5% and 70 *l* of 15%   4. 7%: $1800; 9%: $1900

**4–6**   1. 280 km   2. 126 km/h   3. 4

### Exercise Set 4–1, page 101

1. No   3. No   5. Yes   7. No   9. Line through (3, 1) and (0, 4); line through (3, 1) and (0, −2)   11. Line through

(3, 2) and (0, −4); line through (3, 2) and (2, −3)   13. Line through (1, −5) and (3, 3); line through (1, −5) and (4, −4)   15. Line through (2, 1) and (0, −1); line through (2, 1) and (0, 5)   17. Line through $(\frac{5}{2}, -2)$ and (0, 3); line through $(\frac{5}{2}, -2)$ and (5, 3)   19. Line through (3, −2) and (−3, 0); line through (3, −2) and (0, −6)

### Exercise Set 4–2, page 106

1. (−4, 3)   3. (−3, −15)   5. (2, −2)   7. (−2, 1)   9. (1, 2)   11. (3, 0)   13. (−1, 2)   15. $(\frac{128}{31}, -\frac{17}{31})$   17. (6, 2)   19. $(\frac{140}{13}, -\frac{50}{13})$   21. (4, 6)

### Exercise Set 4–3, page 108

1. Inconsistent   3. Dependent   5. Inconsistent   7. Inconsistent   9. Dependent

### Exercise Set 4–4, page 112

1. Yes   3. (1, 2, 3)   5. (−1, 5, −2)   7. (3, 1, 2)   9. (−3, −4, 2)   11. (2, 4, 1)   13. (−3, 0, 4)   15. (2, 2, 4)   17. $(\frac{1}{2}, 4, -6)$   19. $(\frac{1}{2}, \frac{1}{3}, \frac{1}{6})$

### Exercise Set 4–5, page 117

1. 5 and −47   3. 24 and 8   5. Length is 160 m; width is 154 m   7. 8 white, 22 yellow   9. 150 lbs of soybean meal; 200 lbs of corn meal   11. $4100 at 7%, $4700 at 8%   13. $30,000 at 5%, $40,000 at 6%   15. Ann 40, son 20   17. $4000   19. Length is 31.2075 cm; width is 11.8975 cm

### Exercise Set 4–6, page 121

1. 375 km   3. 3 hours   5. $1\frac{3}{4}$ hours   7. Plane $1017\frac{1}{2}$ km/h, wind $92\frac{1}{2}$ km/h   9. 4 km   11. 11.196246 km/h

## CHAPTER 5

### Answers for TRY THIS

**5–1**   1. a) Yes   b) No   c) Yes   d) Yes   2. a) No   b) Yes   c) Yes   d) Yes   3. All points left of −2   4. All points left of, and including, −2   5. All points right of 3   6. All points left of, and including, 3   7. x > −6   8. y ⩾ −1   9. x > $\frac{19}{12}$

**5–2**   1. All points between −1 and 4, including −1   2. All points between −1 and 4, including 4   3. All points between and including, −1 and 4   4. −6 < x < 3   5. 2 < x < 15   6. All points left of, and including −2 and all points right of 2   7. All points left of −2 and all points right of, and including, 2   8. All points left of, and including, −2 and all points right of, and including, 2   9. x < 1 or x > 7   10. x < −7 or x > −1   11. y ⩽ $\frac{3}{10}$   12. y < $-\frac{5}{12}$   13. y ⩽ $-\frac{1}{5}$   14. x < $\frac{1}{2}$   15. y ⩾ $\frac{22}{13}$   16. 3 ⩽ x < 4

**5–3**   1. 28   2. 5   3. |a|   4. −6, 6   5. $-\frac{1}{2}, \frac{1}{2}$   6. −6 < x < 6   7. $-\frac{1}{2} \leqslant x \leqslant \frac{1}{2}$   8. x ⩽ −6 or x ⩾ 6   9. x < $-\frac{1}{2}$

or $x > \frac{1}{2}$   10. $-4 < x < 10$   11. $x \leqslant -7$ or $x \geqslant 1$   12. $-8 \leqslant x \leqslant 3$   13. $x < -\frac{5}{4}$ or $x > \frac{1}{4}$

**5–4**   1. Yes   2. All points above line through (3, 3) and (0, 0)   3. All points left of, and including line through (2, 1) and (0, −5)   4. All points above line through (5, 0) and (0, −2)   5. All points below line through (2, 0) and (0, −3)   6. All points below, and including, line through (3, 0) and (0, 2)   7. All points left of, and including, vertical line through (−1, 0)   8. All points right of vertical line through (2, 0)   9. All points above horizontal line through (0, −2)   10. All points above horizontal line through (0, 1) and horizontal line through (0, 3), including both lines   11. All points between vertical line through (−4, 0) and vertical line through (1, 0), including line through (−4, 0)

**5–5**   1. All points above line through (3, 3) and (0, 0) and also below line through (2, −3) and (0, 1)   2. All points above horizontal line through (0, 3) and also right of vertical line through (−3, 0)   3. All points inside, and including, polygon with vertices $(\frac{1}{2}, 3)$, (5, 3), (5, 1), (3, 1), (0, 2)

**5–6**   1. Max of F is 120 when x = 3 and y = 3; min of F is 34 when x = 1 and y = 0   2. Max of G is 45 when x = 6 and y = 0; min of G is 12 when x = 0 and y = 3   3. The snack bar will make a maximum profit of $23.70 by selling 40 hamburgers and 50 hot dogs.

### Exercise Set 5–1, page 133

1. All points left of, and including, 4   3. All points right of 5   5. All points left of 10   7. All points right of, and including, −5   9. All points left of 0   11. $x > -5$   13. $y < 6$   15. $a \leqslant -21$   17. $t \geqslant -5$   19. $x \leqslant 19$   21. $y > -6$   23. $x \leqslant 9$   25. $y \leqslant \frac{3}{8}$   27. $x \geqslant -\frac{1}{12}$   29. $x \leqslant 2.7$   31. $x > 8$   33. $x > -4$   35. $x \geqslant -14$   37. $x \leqslant -\frac{37}{24}$

### Exercise Set 5–2, page 138

1. All points between −2 and 4   3. All points between −2 and 4, including −2   5. All points between 1 and 6   7. All points between, and including, −7 and −3   9. $-4 < x < 6$   11. $-3 \leqslant y \leqslant 4$   13. $-13 < x < 4$   15. $-5 \leqslant x \leqslant 4$   17. All points left of −1 and all points right of 2   19. All points left of, and including, −3 and all points right of 1   21. All points left of −8 and right of −2   23. All points left of 1 and all points right of, and including, 5   25. $x < -9$ or $x > -5$   27. $x \leqslant 5$ or $x \geqslant 11$   29. $x < 4$ or $x > 15$   31. $x < 6$   33. $x \leqslant -2$   35. $x \leqslant 9$   37. $y \geqslant -\frac{3}{5}$   39. $y > \frac{1}{72}$   41. $x \leqslant \frac{5}{6}$   43. $x \leqslant 6$   45. $x > 7$   47. $y \leqslant -3$   49. $y > \frac{2}{3}$   51. $x \leqslant \frac{5}{4}$   53. $2 < x < 4$   55. $\frac{3}{5} \leqslant x \leqslant \frac{11}{2}$

### Exercise Set 5–3, page 142

1. 34   3. 11   5. 9   7. 33   9. $\frac{1}{4}$   11. $|h|$   13. −3, 3   15. −9, 9   17. $-3 < x < 3$   19. $-6 \leqslant y \leqslant 6$   21. $x < -2$ or $x > 2$   23. $y \leqslant -4$ or $y \geqslant 4$   25. $-9 < x < 15$   27. −24 $\leqslant x \leqslant 14$   29. $-\frac{7}{2} \leqslant x \leqslant \frac{1}{2}$   31. $\frac{1}{4} < x < \frac{17}{4}$   33. $y < 1$ or $y > 6$   35. $x \leqslant -\frac{5}{4}$ or $x \geqslant \frac{23}{4}$   37. $-1 \leqslant x \leqslant 2$

### Exercise Set 5–4, page 147

1. All points above line through (1, 2) and (−1, −2)   3. All points below and including line through (2, 3) and (−2, −1)   5. All points above line through (0, 2) and (−2, 0)   7. All points below and including line through (2, 0) and (0, −2)   9. All points above line through (3, 2) and (0, −1)   11. All points below line through (4, 0) and (0, 4)   13. All points below line through (8, 0) and (0, −8)   15. All points below and including line through (4, 0) and (0, 3)   17. All points below line through (3, 0) and (0, 7)   19. All points above line through (−3, 0) and (0, 3)   21. All points left of vertical line through (−4, 0)   23. All points above and including horizontal line through (0, 5)   25. All points right of and including y-axis   27. All points between horizontal line through (0, −1) and horizontal line through (0, −4)   29. All points between vertical line through (3, 0) and vertical line through (−3, 0), including both lines

### Exercise Set 5–5, page 150

1. All points above line through (3, 0) and (0, 3) and also below line through (3, 3) and (0, 0)   3. All points above, and including, line through (3, 3) and (0, 0) and also below line through (4, 0) and (0, 4)   5. All points above, and including, horizontal line through (0, 2) and also right of vertical line through (1, 0)   7. All points above, and including, line through (2, −4) and (0, 2) and also left of vertical line through (3, 0)   9. All points above, and including, line through (−3, 0) and (0, 3) and also above, and including, horizontal line through (0, −2)   11. All points above, and including, line through (2, 0) and (0, −2) and also below, and including, line through (3, −2) and (0, 1)   13. All points between line through (1, 3) and (−1, −1) and line through (0, 3) and (−2, −1)   15. All points above, and including, line through (1, 2) and (0, −1) and also below, and including line through (0, 1) and (−2, 0)   17. All points inside, and including, quadrilateral with vertices (0, 0), (0, 6), (4, 4), (6, 0)   19. All points inside, and including, parallelogram with vertices $(1, \frac{9}{4})$, $(1, \frac{25}{6})$, $(3, \frac{5}{2})$, $(3, \frac{3}{4})$

### Exercise Set 5–6, page 153

1. Max of F is 168 when x = 0 and y = 6; min of F is 0 when x = 0 and y = 0   3. Max of P is 152 when x = 7 and y = 0; min of P is 32 when x = 0 and y = 4   5. 8 of A and 10 of B to maximize score at 102   7. $7000 at Bank X and $15,000 at Bank Y to maximize income at $1395

## CHAPTER 6

### Answers for TRY THIS

**6–1**   1. $9xy + (-5x^3) + (-y) + 4$   2. $8pq + (-7pqr^2) + (-34xyz^6)$   3. $9xy, -5x^3, -y, 10$   4. $-92x^5, -8x^4, x^2, \frac{1}{4}$   5. 5, −4, −2, 1, −1, −7   6. $x^3, x^2, x$   7. $x^2, x$   8. $y^3, y^2, y, y^0$   9. 1, 0, 1, 7, 3; 7   10. $3x^2$   11. $-x^3 + x^4$   12. $3x^2 + 2x^4$   13. $-2x^2y + 6xy^2 + 2xy$   14. $-5pq + 11pqr^3 - 1$   15. $-6x^7 + 3x^5 - 7x^4 + 6x^3 - 5x^2 + x$

16. $9 + 4y^2 - 2y^3 - 5y^4 - 7y^5$   17. $7xy^4 - 2xy^3 - 8xy^2$ $+ 3xy$   18. $-4 + 5xy^2 + 4x^2yz + 5x^3yz^2$   19. None of these   20. Monomial   21. Trinomial   22. Binomial

**6–2**   1. $-4x^3 + 2x^2 - 4x + 2$   2. $10y^5 - 4y^4 + 5$ 3. $5p^2q^4 - 2p^2q^2 - 6pq^2 + 3p^2q - 3q + 5$   4. $-4x^3 +$ $5x^2 - \frac{1}{4}x + 10$   5. $-8xy^2 + 4x^3y^2 + 9x + \frac{1}{5}$   6. $9y^5 +$ $8y^4 - \frac{1}{2}y^3 + y^2 - y + 1$   7. $3x^2 + 5$   8. $14y^3 - 2y + 4$ 9. $p^2 - 6p - 2$   10. $3y^5 - 3y^4 + 5y^3 - 2y^2 - 3$ 11. $9p^4q - 10p^3q^2 + 4p^2q^3 + 9q^4$   12. $y^3 - y^2 + \frac{4}{3}y + 0.1$

**6–3**   1. $-18y^3$   2. $24x^8y^3$   3. $-90x^4y^9z^{12}$   4. $-6y^2 -$ $18y$   5. $8xy^3 - 10xy$   6. $5x^3 + 15x^2 - 4x - 12$   7. $6y^2$ $- y - 12$   8. $p^4 + p^3 - 12p^2 - 5p + 15$   9. $2x^4 - 8x^3 +$ $4x^2 - 21x + 20$   10. $8x^5 + 12x^4 - 20x^3 + 4x^2 - 15x + 6$

**6–4**   1. $y^2 + 6y - 40$   2. $2p^2 + 7pq - 15q^2$   3. $x^3y^3 +$ $x^2y^3 + 2x^2y^2 + 2xy^2$   4. $x^2 - 16x + 64$   5. $9x^2 + 42x +$ $49$   6. $16x^2 + 40xy + 25y^2$   7. $4y^4 - 24x^2y^3 + 36x^4y^2$

**6–5**   1. $x^2 - 64$   2. $16y^2 - 49$   3. $9x^4y^2 - 4y^2$   4. $4x^2$ $+ 12x + 9 - 25y^2$   5. $25t^2 - 4x^6y^4$   6. $x^2 - 16x + 64$ 7. $4x^2 + 12x + 9$   8. $4x^2 - 1$   9. $-15x^2y^5 + 10xy^4 -$ $45y^2$   10. $p^2 - 3pq - 28q^2$

**6–6**   1. $800   2. $561.80   3. $1169.86

## Exercise Set 6–1, page 164

1. $8x^2 + (-2x) + (-5)$   3. $18xy + (-8x^3) + (-y) + 50$ 5. $4xy + (-5xy^2) + 6x^2y + (-7x^2y^2)$   7. $2x^5 + (-7x^4) +$ $(-6x^3) + 3x^2 + (-8x) + (-9)$   9. $5x^3, 7x^2, -3x, -9; 5, 7,$ $-3, -9$   11. $-3xyz, 7x^2y^2, -5xy^2z, 4xyz^2; -3, 7, -5, 4$ 13. $x^2, x$   15. $y^3, y^2, y$   17. 2, 5, 7, 0; 7   19. 5, 6, 2, 1, 0; 6   21. $2x^2$   23. $3x + y$   25. $a + 6$   27. $-2x - 6y + 3z$ 29. $-6a^2b - 2b^2$   31. $9x^2 + 2xy + 15y^2$   33. $4y^2 - z^2$ 34. $-3x^4 + 3x^3 - 5x^2 - 2x + 1$   35. $x^3 - 3x^2 + x + 1$ 37. $5a^5 - a^3 + 6a^2 + a - 9$   39. $-7 - y + 3y^2 + 2y^3 + y^4$ 41. $-x + x^2 - 9x^3 + 18x^4 + 5x^5$   43. $-xy^3 + x^2y^2 + x^3y$ $+ 1$   45. $3xy^3 + x^2y^2 - 9x^3y + 2x^4$   47. Binomial 49. Trinomial   51. Monomial   53. None of these 55. $0.81125x^2y^2 - 0.07111x^3y$

## Exercise Set 6–2, page 168

1. $5x^2 + 2y^2 + 5$   3. $6a + b + c$   5. $-4a^2 - b^2 + 3c^2$ 7. $-2x^2 + x - xy - 1$   9. $5x^2y - 4xy^2 + 5xy$   11. $9r^2 +$ $9r - 9$   13. $4x + 2y - 2z - 3$   15. $0.05x^3 + 0.1x^2 +$ $1.84x + 0.04$   17. $9.46y^4 + 2.5y^3 - 11.8y - 3.1$ 19. $-\frac{1}{2}x^4 + \frac{1}{3}x^3 + \frac{1}{2}x^2 - 3$   21. $-5x^3 + 7x^2 - 3x + 6$ 23. $4y^4 - 7y^2 + 2y + 1$   25. $13x - 6$   27. $-4x^2 - 3x +$ $13$   29. $2a - 4b + 3c$   31. $-2x^2 + 6x$   33. $-4a^2 + 8ab -$ $5b^2$   35. $-2x^2 - 17x + 5$   37. $6y^3 - 7y^2 + 8y - 2$ 39. $6a - 5b - 2c + 4d$   41. $-0.01x^3 - 0.11x^2 + 0.02x + 5$ 43. $x^4 - x^2 - 1$   45. $414.9944x^3 - 27.01313x - 0.0484$

## Exercise Set 6–3, page 172

1. $10y^3$   3. $-12xy^3$   5. $-20x^3y$   7. $-6a^3b^3$ 9. $-10x^5y^6$   11. $15x^2 - 6x$   13. $-8t^2 + 36t$   15. $-6x +$ $2x^2 + 2x^3$   17. $3a^2b + 3ab^2 - 6ab$   19. $a^2 - a^3 + 2a^4 -$ $5a^5$   21. $x^2 + 7x + 12$   23. $x^2 - 7x + 10$   25. $2x^2 + 11x$

$+ 12$   27. $6x^2 + 7x - 20$   29. $s^2 - 9t^2$   31. $x^2 - 2xy +$ $y^2$   33. $2y^2 + 9xy - 56x^2$   35. $x^4 - x^2y - 2y^2$   37. $a^4$ $- 5a^2b^2 + 6b^4$   39. $x^3 - 64$   41. $y^3 + 27$   43. $x^4 - x^3$ $+ x^2 - 3x + 2$   45. $-6x^5 + 12x^4 - 7x^3 - 22x^2 + 39x -$ $27$   47. $x^3 + y^3$   49. $3a^4 + 12a^3 - 16a^2 - 4a + 5$ 51. $2m^5 + 10m^4 - 14m^3 - 3m^2 - 15m + 21$   53. $8x^3 +$ $26x^2y + 37xy^2 + 28y^3$

## Exercise Set 6–4, page 174

1. $a^2 + 5a + 6$   3. $y^2 + y - 6$   5. $y^2 + 3y - 28$   7. $b^2 -$ $12b + 35$   9. $2x^2 + 13x + 18$   11. $4a^2 - a - 3$   13. $3y^2$ $- 11y + 6$   15. $6b^2 + b - 40$   17. $6x^2 - 29x + 35$ 19. $8x^2 + 22xy + 15y^2$   21. $a^4 - a^2b - 2b^2$   23. $2m^4 +$ $5m^2n^2 - 3n^4$   25. $8x^4 + 2x^2y^2 - 15y^4$   27. $21m^4 -$ $59m^2n^2 + 40n^4$   29. $x^2 + 6x + 9$   31. $y^2 - 10y + 25$ 33. $4s^2 + 12st + 9t^2$   35. $25x^2 - 90xy + 81y^2$   37. $9a^4$ $+ 12a^2 + 4$   39. $49x^4 - 28x^2 + 4$   41. $4x^2 - 12xy^2 +$ $9y^4$   43. $a^4b^4 + 2a^3b^4 + a^2b^4$

## Exercise Set 6–5, page 176

1. $c^2 - 4$   3. $x^2 - y^2$   5. $4a^2 - 1$   7. $9 - 4x^2$   9. $9m^2$ $- 4n^2$   11. $x^4 - 81$   13. $25a^4 - 4b^2$   15. $9c^4 - 4d^4$ 17. $y^2 + 8y + 15$   19. $4x^2 - 49$   21. $16x^2 + 16xy + 4y^2$ 23. $81x^2 - 90xy + 25y^2$   25. $20x^5y^2 + 16x^4y - 36x^3$ 27. $25x^2 + 30x + 9$   29. $10x^2 + 6xy - 28y^2$   31. $72y^2$ $- 65yz + 7z^2$   33. $28x^4 - 23x^2 - 15$   35. $64x^2 + 144xy$ $+ 81y^2$   37. $\frac{1}{25}x^2 - \frac{4}{9}y^2$   39. $-40y^9 + 15y^8 + 45y^7 -$ $5y^6 + 40y^5 - 15y^4$   41. $\frac{1}{9}x^2 + \frac{1}{3}x - 2$

## Exercise Set 6–6, page 180

1. $650   3. $600   5. $1081.60   7. $933.12 9. $1071.23   11. $2339.72   13. $1126.49

# CHAPTER 7

## Answers for TRY THIS

**7–1**   1. $3x(x - 2)$   2. $4x^3(x^2 - 2)$   3. $p(1 + rt)$   4. $3y^2$ $(3y^2 - 5y + 1)$   5. $4p^2r(5p + 3)$   6. $3x^2y(2 - 7xy + y^2)$ 7. $(x + 4)(x + 5)$   8. $(y + 2)(5y + 2)$   9. $(p - q)(x + y)$ 10. $(y + 2)(y - 2)$   11. $(7x^2 + 5y^5)(7x^2 - 5y^2)$   12. $4y^4$ $(3 + 2y)(3 - 2y)$

**7–2**   1. Yes   2. Yes   3. No   4. Yes   5. No   6. No 7. No   8. No   9. $(x + 7)^2$   10. $(3y - 5)^2$   11. $(9y + 4x)^2$ 12. $(4x^2 - 5y^3)^2$   13. $-2(2a - 3b)^2$   14. $-3y^2$ $(2x^2 - 5y^3)^2$   15. $(x + 7)(x - 2)$   16. $(x - 7)(x - 3)$ 17. $(y - 2)(y + 1)$

**7–3**   1. $(3x + 2)(x + 1)$   2. $(2x + 3)(2x - 1)$   3. $2(4y - 1)$ $(3y - 5)$   4. $4(2x - 1)(2x + 3)$   5. $(pq + 4)(pq + 3)$ 6. $(2x^2y^3 + 5)(x^2y^3 - 4)$   7. $(3x + 8)(x - 7)$   8. $(4x + 1)$ $(x + 9)$

**7–4**   1. $(x + 6)(x - 4)$   2. $(x + 7)(x + 1)$   3. $(x + 14)$ $(x - 6)$   4. $(x + y - 6)(x - y - 10)$   5. 36   6. 9   7. 49 8. 121   9. $(x + 6)(x + 2)$   10. $(y + 4)(y - 8)$   11. $(x + \frac{3}{2})$ $(x - \frac{1}{2})$

**7—5** 1. $(x - 2)(x^2 + 2x + 4)$ 2. $(y - 3)(y^2 + 3y + 9)$
3. $(3x + y)(9x^2 - 3xy + y^2)$ 4. $(2y + z)(4y^2 - 2yz + z^2)$
5. $(2x^2 + 3y^2)(4x^4 - 6x^2y^2 + 9y^4)$

**7—6** 1. $2(1 + 4x^2)(1 + 2x)(1 - 2x)$ 2. $7(a + 1)(a^2 - a + 1)$
$(a - 1)(a^2 + a + 1)$ 3. $(3 + x)(4 + x)$ 4. $(c - d + t + 4)$
$(c - d - t - 4)$

**7—7** 1. $4, 2$ 2. $\frac{1}{2}, -3$ 3. $0, 2$ 4. $-5$ 5. $-\frac{3}{2}, \frac{3}{2}$

**7—8** 1. $8, -6$ 2. Length is 8 cm; width is 3 cm

## Exercise Set 7—1, page 188

1. $y(y - 5)$ 3. $2a(2a + 1)$ 5. $y^2(y + 9)$ 7. $3(y^2 - y - 3)$
9. $3x^2(2 - x^2)$ 11. $2a(2b - 3c + 6d)$ 13. $4xy(x - 3y)$
15. $x^2(x^4 + x^3 - x + 1)$ 17. $12x(2x^2 - 3x + 6)$ 19. $5$
$(2a^4 + 3a^2 - 5a - 6)$ 21. $\frac{1}{7}x(4x^5 - 6x^3 + x - 3)$
23. $(a + c)(b - 2)$ 25. $(x - 2)(2x + 13)$ 27. $2a^2(x - y)$
29. $(a + b)(c + d)$ 31. $(b^2 + 2)(b - 1)$ 33. $(y - 1)(y - 8)$
35. $(2y^2 + 5)(y^2 + 3)$ 37. $(xy - 3)(2 - x)$ 39. $(x + 4)$
$(x - 4)$ 41. $(3x + 5)(3x - 5)$ 43. $(2x + 5)(2x - 5)$
45. $6(x + y)(x - y)$ 47. $3(x^4 + y^4)(x^2 + y^2)(x + y)(x - y)$
49. $4x(y^2 + z^2)(y + z)(y - z)$ 51. $(\frac{1}{5} + x)(\frac{1}{5} - x)$
53. $(0.5 + y)(0.5 - y)$ 55. $(0.2x + 0.3y)(0.2x - 0.3y)$

## Exercise Set 7—2, page 191

1. $(y - 3)^2$ 3. $(x + 7)^2$ 5. $(x + 1)^2$ 7. $(a + 2)^2$
9. $(y - 6)^2$ 11. $y(y - 9)^2$ 13. $3(2a + 3)^2$ 15. $2(x - 10)^2$
17. $(1 - 4d)^2$ 19. $(5y - 8)^2$ 21. $(xy + 2)^2(xy - 2)^2$
23. $(4a - 3b)^2$ 25. $(3y^4 + 2)^2$ 27. $(\frac{1}{6}x^4 + \frac{2}{3})^2$
29. $(0.5x + 0.3)^2$ 31. $(x + 5)(x + 4)$ 33. $(y - 4)^2$
35. $(x - 9)(x + 3)$ 37. $(m - 7)(m + 4)$ 39. $(x + 9)(x + 5)$
41. $(y + 9)(y - 7)$ 43. $(t - 7)(t - 4)$ 45. $(x + 5)(x - 2)$
47. $(x + 2)(x + 3)$ 49. $(8 - y)(4 + y)$ 51. $(t + 5)(t + 3)$
53. $(x^2 + 16)(x^2 - 5)$ 55. $(x + \frac{4}{5})(x - \frac{1}{5})$

## Exercise Set 7—3, page 194

1. $(3b + 2)(b + 2)$ 3. $(3y - 2)(2y + 1)$ 5. $(6a + 5)(a - 2)$
7. $(3a + 4)(3a - 2)$ 9. $(3x + 2)(x - 6)$ 11. $(3x - 5)$
$(2x + 3)$ 13. $(3a - 4)(a - 2)$ 15. $(5y + 2)(7y + 4)$
17. $(5t - 3)(t + 1)$ 19. $4(2x + 1)(x - 4)$ 21. $x(3x + 1)$
$(x - 2)$ 23. $(24x + 1)(x - 2)$ 25. $(7x + 3)(3x + 4)$
27. $(5x + 4)(8x - 3)$ 29. $(4a - 3)(3a - 2)$ 31. $(2x - 3y)$
$(x + 2y)$ 33. $(2x - 3y)(4x + 3y)$ 35. $(7ab + 6)(ab + 1)$

## Exercise Set 7—4, page 197

1. $(c + 6)(c + 2)$ 3. $(t - 3)(t - 7)$ 5. $(y + 4)(y - 6)$
7. $(x - 4)(x - 10)$ 9. $(r + 14)(r - 2)$ 11. $(m + 5)(m - 3)$
13. $(p + 5)(p + 3)$ 15. $(t + 11)(t + 1)$ 17. $3(x - 1)$
$(x - 13)$ 19. $5(a + 6)(a - 14)$ 21. $(x + 6)(x + 1)$
23. $(x - \frac{1}{2})(x - \frac{5}{2})$ 25. $(x + 5.766)(x - 1.284)$

## Exercise Set 7—5, page 199

1. $(x + 2)(x^2 - 2x + 4)$ 3. $(y - 4)(y^2 + 4y + 16)$
5. $(w + 1)(w^2 - w + 1)$ 7. $(2a + 1)(4a^2 - 2a + 1)$
9. $(y - 2)(y^2 + 2y + 4)$ 11. $(2 - 3b)(4 + 6b + 9b^2)$

13. $(4y + 1)(16y^2 - 4y + 1)$ 15. $(2x + 3)(4x^2 - 6x + 9)$
17. $(a - b)(a^2 + ab + b^2)$ 19. $(a + \frac{1}{2})(a^2 - \frac{1}{2}a + \frac{1}{4})$
21. $(2x - 3y)(4x^2 + 6xy + 9y^2)$ 23. $r(s + 4)(s^2 - 4s + 16)$
25. $5(x - 2z)(x^2 + 2xz + 4z^2)$ 27. $(x + 0.1)(x^2 - 0.1x + 0.01)$ 29. $8(2x^2 - t^2)(4x^4 + 2x^2t^2 + t^4)$

## Exercise Set 7—6, page 201

1. $(x + 12)(x - 12)$ 3. $(2x + 3)(x + 4)$ 5. $3(x^2 + 2)(x^2 - 2)$
7. $(a + 5)^2$ 9. $2(x - 11)(x + 6)$ 11. $(3x + 5y)(3x - 5y)$
13. $(2c - d)^2$ 15. $(x^2 + 2)(2x - 7)$ 17. $(4x - 15)(x - 3)$
19. $(m^3 + 10)(m^3 - 2)$ 21. $(c - b)(a + d)$ 23. $(m + 1)$
$(m^2 - m + 1)(m - 1)(m^2 + m + 1)$ 25. $(x + y + 3)$
$(x - y + 3)$ 27. $(6y - 5)(6y + 7)$ 29. $(a^4 + b^4)(a^2 + b^2)$
$(a + b)(a - b)$ 31. $(2p + 3q)(4p^2 - 6pq + 9q^2)$
33. $(4p - 1)(16p^2 + 4p + 1)$ 35. $ab(a + 4b)(a - 4b)$
37. $(4xy - 3)(5xy - 2)$ 39. $2(x + 2)(x - 2)(x + 3)$

## Exercise Set 7—7, page 204

1. $-7, 4$ 3. $4$ 5. $6$ 7. $-5, -4$ 9. $0, -8$ 11. $-3, 3$
13. $-6, 6$ 15. $-5, -9$ 17. $-9, 7$ 19. $7, 4$ 21. $8, -4$
23. $-\frac{2}{3}, -2$ 25. $\frac{3}{4}, \frac{1}{2}$ 27. $0, 6$ 29. $-\frac{3}{4}, \frac{2}{3}$ 31. $-2, 1$
33. $\frac{1}{2}, 7$ 35. $-\frac{5}{7}, \frac{2}{3}$ 37. $0, \frac{1}{5}$ 39. $-\frac{9}{10}, \frac{9}{10}$

## Exercise Set 7—8, page 206

1. $\frac{7}{2}, -\frac{3}{2}$ 3. $-12, 11$ 5. Length is 12 cm; width is 5 cm
7. Length is 100 m; width is 75 m 9. 9 and 11 11. 3 cm
13. Height is 7 cm; base is 16 cm 15. 2 17. $-10, -8,$ and
$-6; 6, 8,$ and 10 19. 11, 12, and 13; $-2, -1,$ and 0

## CHAPTER 8

## Answers for TRY THIS

**8—1** 1. $\{(5, 4), (6, 4), (6, 5)\}$ 2. $\{(a, 1), (a, 2), (b, 1),$
$(b, 2), (c, 1), (c, 2)\}$ 3. $\{(x, x), (x, y), (x, z), (y, x), (y, y),$
$(y, z), (z, x), (z, y), (z, z)\}$ 4. $\{(3, 2), (4, 3), (4, 2), (5, 4),$
$(5, 3), (5, 2)\}$ 5. Domain: $\{a, b, c, d\}$; range: $\{1, 2\}$

**8—2** 1. Line through $(1, 3)$ and $(-2, -3)$ 2. All points
above, and including, parabola through $(-2, 3), (-1, 0),$
$(0, -1), (1, 0),$ and $(2, 3)$

**8—3** 1. a and b 4. Symmetric with respect to y-axis
5. Symmetric with respect to both axes

**8—4** 1. b 3. Yes 4. Yes 5. No 6. $(1, 0), (5, -2),$
$(-2, 5)$ 7. $x = y^2 + 4$ 8. Yes 9. No

**8—5** 1. Yes 2. No 3. Yes 4. a) 0 b) 2 c) $-4$
5. a) 2 b) $-10$ c) $-4$ d) $-\frac{13}{4}$ e) $3a - 4$ f) $3a - 7$
g) $3a - 1$ 6. a) 4 b) 9 c) $\frac{1}{16}$ d) $x^2 + 2x + 1$ 7. a) $-4$
b) $-7$ c) 3 d) $-\frac{7}{2}$ 8. a) 0 b) 6 c) 20 d) 20
9. a) $-\frac{1}{2}$ b) $\frac{1}{4}$ c) $\frac{1}{3}$ d) $-3$

**8—6** 1. $g^{-1}(x) = x - 2$ 2. $g^{-1}(x) = \frac{1}{3}(x - 2)$ 3. $f^{-1}(x) = $
$x^2 - 1$ 4. $579; -83,479$

**8–7** 1. Ray from (0, −1) through (2, 1); ray from (0, −1) through (−2, 1)   2. Ray from (0, 4) through (2, 6); ray from (0, 4) through (−2, 6)   3. Ray from (−3, 0) through (0, 3); ray from (−3, 0) through (−6, 3)   4. Ray from (1, 0) through (4, 3); ray from (1, 0) through (−2, 3)

**8–8** 1. Graph consists of segments from (−6, 0) to (−4, 6) to (−2, 0) to (0, 6) to (2, 0) to (4, 6) to (6, 0)   2. Graph consists of segments from (−6, 0) to (−4, 1) to (−2, 0) to (0, 1) to (2, 0) to (4, 1) to (6, 0)   3. Graph consists of segments from (−6, 0) to (−4, −1) to (−2, 0) to (−1, −1) to (2, 0) to (4, −1) to (6, 0)   4. Graph consists of segments from (−2, 0) to (−$\frac{3}{2}$, 2) to (−$\frac{1}{2}$, −2) to ($\frac{1}{2}$, 2) to ($\frac{3}{2}$, −2) to (2, 0)   5. Graph consists of segments from (−8, 0) to (−6, 2) to (−2, −2) to (2, 2), to (6, −2) to (8, 0)   6. Graph consists of segments from (−8, 0) to (−6, −2) to (−2, 2) to (2, −2) to (6, 2) to (8, 0)

**8–9** 1. f(3) = −9, f(0) = −3, f(−3) = 3; line through (0, −3) and (−3, 3)   2. f(−x) = (−x)⁴ + 2(−x)⁶ = x⁴ + 2x⁶ = f(x)   3. f(−x) = (−x)⁵ − 3(−x)³ = −x⁵ + 3x³, −f(x) = −(x⁵ − 3x³) = −x⁵ + 3x³ Since f(−x) = −f(x) for all x in the domain, f is odd.

### Exercise Set 8–1, page 217

1. {(−1, 0), (−1, 1), (−1, 2), (0, 1), (0, 2), (1, 2)}   3. {(−1, −1), (−1, 0), (−1, 1), (−1, 2), (0, 0), (0, 1), (0, 2), (1, 1), (1, 2), (2, 2)}   5. {(−1, −1), (0, 0), (1, 1), (2, 2)}   7. {(0, a), (0, b), (0, c), (2, a), (2, b), (2, c), (4, a), (4, b), (4, c), (5, a), (5, b), (5, c)}   9. {(x, 1), (x, 2), (y, 1), (y, 2), (z, 1), (z, 2)}   11. {(−1, −1), (−1, 0), (−1, 1), (−1, 2), (0, −1), (0, 0), (0, 1), (0, 2), (1, −1), (1, 0), (1, 1), (1, 2), (2, −1), (2, 0), (2, 1), (2, 2)}   13. Domain: {5, 6, 8}; range: {2, 4, 6}   15. Domain: {6, 7, 8}; range: {0, 5}   17. Domain: {8, 5}; range: {1}   19. Domain: {5}; range: {6}

### Exercise Set 8–2, page 219

1. Line through (0, 1) and (−1, −3)   3. All points above, and including, parabola through (−2, 6), (−1, 3), (0, 2), (1, 3), (2, 6)   5. Parabola through (6, 2), (3, 1), (2, 0), (3, −1), (6, −2)   7. Line through (3, 0) and (0, −8)   9. Line through (−4, 0) and (0, 3)   11. Horizontal line through (0, −2)   13. Vertical line through (3, 0)   15. Line through ($\frac{1}{2}$, 2), (1, 1), (2, $\frac{1}{2}$) and line through (−2, −$\frac{1}{2}$), (−1, −1), (−$\frac{1}{2}$, −2)

### Exercise Set 8–3, page 223

1. Yes   3. No   5. Yes   11. y-axis   13. Both axes   15. Neither axis   17. y-axis   19. Both axes   21. Neither axis

### Exercise Set 8–4, page 229

1. Yes   3. No   5. Yes   11. Yes   13. Yes   15. Yes   17. Yes   19. No   21. No   23. (1, 0), (6, 5), (−4, −2)   25. (−1, −1), (−4, −3)   27. x = 4y − 5   29. x = 3y² + 2   31. y² − 3x² = 3   33. y · x = 7   35. No   37. Yes   39. Yes   41. Yes   43. Yes   45. No

### Exercise Set 8–5, page 235

1. Yes   3. No   5. Yes   7. a) 1   b) −3   c) −6   d) 9   9. a) 0   b) 1   c) 57   d) 5t² + 4t   11. a) 15   b) 32   c) 20   d) 4   13. a) 5   b) −2   c) −4   d) 4|y| + 6y   15. a) 17   b) 6   c) 14   17. a) 3   b) −1   c) 24   19. a) 8   b) 8   c) 12

### Exercise Set 8–6, page 239

1. f⁻¹(x) = x + 1   3. f⁻¹(x) = x − 4   5. f⁻¹(x) = x − 8   7. f⁻¹(x) = $\frac{x − 5}{2}$   9. f⁻¹(x) = $\frac{x + 1}{3}$   11. f⁻¹(x) = 2(x − 2)   13. f⁻¹(x) = x² + 1   15. f⁻¹(x) = x² − 2   17. 3; −125   19. 12,053; −17,243

### Exercise Set 8–7, page 243

1. Ray from (0, 2) through (2, 4); ray from (0, 2) through (−2, 4)   3. Ray from (0, −2) through (2, 0); ray from (0, −2) through (−2, 0)   5. Ray from (0, 5) through (2, 7); ray from (0, 5) through (−2, 7)   7. Ray from (0, −4) through (4, 0); ray from (0, −4) through (−4, 0)   9. Ray from (0, $\frac{1}{2}$) through (3, $\frac{7}{2}$); ray from (0, $\frac{1}{2}$) through (−3, $\frac{7}{2}$)   11. Ray from (3, 0) through (6, 3); ray from (3, 0) through (0, 3)   13. Ray from (−2, 0) through (1, 3); ray from (−2, 0) through (−5, 3)   15. Ray from (4, 0) through (7, 3); ray from (4, 0) through (1, 3)   17. Ray from (−5, 0) through (−2, 3); ray from (−5, 0) through (−8, 3)   19. Ray from ($\frac{1}{2}$, 0) through ($\frac{7}{2}$, 3); ray from ($\frac{1}{2}$, 0) through (−$\frac{5}{2}$, 3)

### Exercise Set 8–8, page 247

1. Ray from (0, 0) through (2, 8); ray from (0, 0) through (−2, 8)   3. Ray from (0, 0) through (2, 10); ray from (0, 0) through (−2, 10)   5. Ray from (0, 0) through (4, 1); ray from (0, 0) through (−4, 1)   7. Ray from (0, 0) through (2, −6); ray from (0, 0) through (−2, −6)   9. Ray from (0, 0) through (4, −1); ray from (0, 0) through (−4, −1)   11. Graph consists of segments from (−4, 0) to (0, 12) to (2, −12) to (3, 0)   13. Graph consists of segments from (−4, 0) to (0, −8) to (2, 8) to (3, 0)   15. Graph consists of segments from (−4, 0) to (0, 16) to (2, −16) to (3, 0)   17. Graph consists of segments from (−4, 0) to (0, 2) to (2, −2) to (3, 0)   19. Graph consists of segments from (−4, 0) to (0, −2) to (2, 2) to (3, 0)   21. Ray from (0, 0) through (4, 8); ray from (0, 0) through (−4, 8)   23. Ray from (0, 0) through (4, 2); ray from (0, 0) through (−4, 2)   25. Graph consists of segments from (−$\frac{4}{3}$, 0) to (0, 4) to ($\frac{2}{3}$, −4) to (1, 0)   27. Graph consists of segments from (−8, 0) to (0, 4) to (4, −4) to (6, 0)   29. Graph consists of segments from (−$\frac{3}{2}$, 0) to (−1, −4) to (0, 4) to (2, 0)   31. Graph consists of segments from (−6, 0) to (−4, −4) to (0, 4) to (8, 0)

### Exercise Set 8–9, page 250

1. f(−5) = −8, f(−3) = −6, f(2) = −1; line through (3, 0) and (0, −3)   3. g(2) = 1, g(0) = −3, g(−4) = −11; line through (3, 3) and (0, −3)   5. h(−1) = 5, h(2) = −4, h(−3) = 11; line through (1, −1) and (0, 2)   7. f(6) = 4, f(2) = 2,

$f(-8) = -3$; line through $(2, 2)$ and $(-2, 0)$    9. $f(-x) = 2(-x)^4 + 4(-x)^2 = 2x^4 + 4x^2 = f(x)$    11. $f(-x) = |2(-x)| = |-2x| = |2x| = f(x)$    13. $f(-x) = 3(-x)^4 - 4(-x)^6 = 3x^4 - 4x^6 = f(x)$    15. $g(-x) = 4(-x)^3 - (-x) = -4x^3 + x$, $-g(x) = -(4x^3 - x) = -4x^3 + x$    17. $h(-x) = 2(-x) + 5(-x)^3 = -2x - 5x^3$, $-h(x) = -(2x + 5x^3) = -2x - 5x^3$    19. $f(-x) = 4(-x) = -4x$, $-f(x) = -(4x) = -4x$    21. $f(-x) = (-x)^5 + (-x)^3 + (-x) = -x^5 - x^3 - x$, $-f(x) = -(x^5 + x^3 + x) = -x^5 - x^3 - x$    23. a) Even  b) Even  c) Odd  d) Neither

## CHAPTER 9

### Answers for TRY THIS

**9–1**  1. $\dfrac{x^2 - 4}{5x + 20}$  2. $\dfrac{x^2 + 2xy + y^2}{x^2 - 9}$  3. $\dfrac{3x^2 + 2xy}{5x^2 + 4xy}$
4. $\dfrac{6x^3 + 4x^2 - 3xy - 2y}{9x^2 + 18x + 8}$  5. $\dfrac{5 - 2a}{b - a}$  6. $7x$  7. $2a + 3$
8. $\dfrac{3x + 2}{x + 2}$  9. $\dfrac{y + 2}{y - 1}$  10. $\dfrac{3(x - y)}{x + y}$  11. $a - b$  12. $\dfrac{x - 5}{x + 3}$
13. $\dfrac{1}{x + 7}$  14. $y^3 - 9$  15. $\dfrac{x + 5}{x - 5}$  16. $\dfrac{2ab(a + b)}{a - b}$

**9–2**  1. 90  2. 252  3. 72  4. $90a^3b^2$  5. $(x + 1)(x + 1)(x + 4)$  6. $5(x - 3)(x^2 + 10)$  7. $2(a + b)(a - b)$ or $2(a + b)(b - a)$  8. $(y + 4)(y + 4)(y + 3)$

**9–3**  1. $\dfrac{12 + y}{y}$  2. $3x + 1$  3. $\dfrac{a - b}{b + 2}$  4. $\dfrac{y + 12}{y^2 + y^2}$
5. $\dfrac{1 - b^2}{3}$  6. $\dfrac{2x^2 + 11}{x - 5}$  7. $\dfrac{3 + 7x}{4y}$  8. $\dfrac{11x^2}{x - y}$  9. $\dfrac{9x^2 + 28y}{21x}$
10. $\dfrac{34y^2 + 21y - 1}{3y(y - 1)(y + 1)}$  11. $\dfrac{x}{x - y}$  12. $\dfrac{a + 12}{a(a + 3)}$
13. $\dfrac{3y^2 + 12y + 3}{(y - 4)(y - 3)(y + 5)}$  14. $\dfrac{6x^2 - 2x - 3}{x^2(x + 1)}$

**9–4**  1. $\dfrac{7(2y + 1)}{2(7y - 1)}$  2. $\dfrac{x}{x + 1}$  3. $\dfrac{a^2b^2}{b^2 + ab + a^2}$  4. $\dfrac{b + a}{b - a}$
5. $\dfrac{1}{a(a + h)}$

**9–5**  1. $\dfrac{x^2}{2} + 8x + 3$  2. $5y^3 - 2y^2 + 6y$  3. $\dfrac{x^2}{2} + 5x + 8$
4. $x + 5$  5. $y^3 - 2y^2 + 5y - 10$  6. $y^2 - 8y - 24$, R $-66$
7. $x + 9$, R $x + 4$

**9–6**  1. $\dfrac{2}{3}$  2. No solution  3. 3

**9–7**  1. $R = \dfrac{E}{I}$  2. $R = \dfrac{r_1 r_2}{r_1 + r_2}$

**9–8**  1. 4  2. 35.5 km/h  3. $2\dfrac{2}{5}$ hours  4. Pipe A 32 hours; Pipe B 96 hours

**9–9**  1. $y = \dfrac{2}{5}x$  2. $y = 0.7x$  3. 175,000 tons  4. $y = \dfrac{0.6}{x}$  5. $7\dfrac{1}{2}$ hours

### Exercise Set 9–1, page 262

1. $\dfrac{y^2 + y - 6}{4y + 16}$  3. $\dfrac{z^2 + z - 2}{z^2 - 2z - 3}$  5. $\dfrac{x^2 - y^2}{4x^2 - y^2}$  7. $\dfrac{x^3 - 8}{x^3 + 1}$
9. $\dfrac{3x^2 + 3x}{3x^2 + 9x}$  11. $\dfrac{y^2 - 4}{y - 6}$  13. $\dfrac{t^2 - 6t + 9}{t^2 - t - 6}$
15. $\dfrac{4x^3 - 3x^2 - 4x + 3}{x^3 + 5x^2 - x - 5}$  17. $\dfrac{3y}{5}$  19. $a - 3$  21. $\dfrac{y - 3}{y + 3}$

23. $\dfrac{t + 4}{t - 4}$  25. $\dfrac{x + 8}{4(x - 1)}$  27. $x - 2$  29. $\dfrac{a^2 + ab + b^2}{a + b}$
31. $\dfrac{(x + 4)(x - 4)}{x(x + 3)}$  33. $\dfrac{y + 4}{2}$  35. $\dfrac{(x + 5)(2x + 3)}{7x}$  37. $c - 2$  39. $\dfrac{1}{x + y}$  41. 3  43. $\dfrac{(y - 3)(y + 2)}{y}$  45. $\dfrac{2a + 1}{a + 2}$
47. $\dfrac{(x + 4)(x + 2)}{3(x - 5)}$  49. $\dfrac{y(y^2 + 3)}{(y + 3)(y - 2)}$  51. $\dfrac{x^2 + 4x + 16}{(x + 4)^2}$

### Exercise Set 9–2, page 265

1. 140  3. 504  5. $24x^3$  7. $12x^2y$  9. $30a^3b^2$
11. $(a + b)(a - b)$  13. $6(y - 2)$ or $6(2 - y)$  15. $3(y + 3)(y - 3)$  17. $5(y - 3)(y - 3)$  19. $(a + 1)(a - 1)(a - 1)$  21. $(x + 2)(x - 2)$ or $(x + 2)(2 - x)$  23. $(x + 5)(x + 5)(x - 3)$  25. $(2r + 3)(r - 4)(3r - 1)$  27. $(2x + 1)(x - 3)(x - 1)$

### Exercise Set 9–3, page 270

1. $\dfrac{a + 8}{a}$  3. 2  5. $\dfrac{9x^2 + 5x + 10}{x^3}$  7. $\dfrac{3y + 5}{y - 2}$  9. $\dfrac{4}{y}$
11. $\dfrac{2y^2 + 2}{2y + 1}$  13. $a + b$  15. $\dfrac{14x}{3x - 4}$  17. $\dfrac{11}{x}$  19. $\dfrac{1}{x + 5}$
21. $\dfrac{2y^2 + 22}{(y + 4)(y - 5)}$  23. $\dfrac{x + y}{x - y}$  25. $\dfrac{3x - 4}{(x - 2)(x - 1)}$
27. $\dfrac{8x + 1}{(x + 1)(x - 1)}$  29. 0  31. $\dfrac{2x - 14}{15(x + 5)}$
33. $\dfrac{-a^2 + 7ab - b^2}{(a + b)(a - b)}$  35. $\dfrac{y}{(y - 2)(y - 3)}$
37. $\dfrac{2x^2 - 13x + 7}{(x + 3)(x - 1)(x - 3)}$  39. 0  41. $\dfrac{3}{x + 2}$
43. $\dfrac{-3x^2 - 3x - 4}{(x + 1)(x - 1)}$

### Exercise Set 9–4, page 273

1. $\dfrac{1 + 4x}{1 - 3x}$  3. $\dfrac{x^2 - 1}{x^2 + 1}$  5. $\dfrac{3y + 4x}{4y - 3x}$  7. $\dfrac{x + y}{x}$  9. $\dfrac{a^2(b - 3)}{b^2(a - 1)}$
11. $\dfrac{1}{a - b}$  13. $\dfrac{1 + x^2}{x}$  15. $\dfrac{y - 3}{y + 5}$  17. $\dfrac{1 + x}{1 - x}$  19. $\dfrac{3}{4}$
21. $\dfrac{6x - 2}{5x + 6}$

### Exercise Set 9–5, page 277

1. $6x^4 - 3x^2 + 8$  3. $-2a^2 + 4a - 3$  5. $y^3 - 2y^2 + 3y$
7. $-6x^5 + 3x^3 + 2x$  9. $1 - ab^2 - a^3b$  11. $-2pq + 3p - 4q$  13. $x + 7$  15. $a - 12$, R 32  17. $x + 2$, R 4  19. $y - 5$  21. $y^2 - 2y - 1$, R $-8$  23. $a^2 + 4a + 15$, R 72
25. $4x^2 - 6x + 9$  27. $x^2 + 6$  29. $x^3 + x^2 - 1$, R 1

### Exercise Set 9–6, page 280

1. $\dfrac{51}{2}$  3. $-2$  5. 144  7. $-5, -1$  9. 2  11. $\dfrac{17}{4}$  13. 11
15. No solution  17. 2  19. $\dfrac{3}{5}$  21. 5  23. $-145$
25. $-\dfrac{10}{3}$  27. $-3$  29. $-6, 5$

### Exercise Set 9–7, page 283

1. $d_1 = \dfrac{d_2 W_1}{W_2}$  3. $t = \dfrac{2S}{v_1 + v_2}$  5. $R_1 = \dfrac{RR_2}{R_2 - R}$  7. $s = \dfrac{Rg}{g - R}$

9. $r = \dfrac{2V - IR}{2I}$  11. $f = \dfrac{pq}{q+p}$  13. $r = \dfrac{nE - IR}{In}$  15. $H = m(t_1 - t_2)S$  17. $e = \dfrac{Er}{R+r}$  19. $a = \dfrac{S - Sr}{1 - r^n}$

**Exercise Set 9–8, page 287**

1. $\frac{35}{12}$  3. $-3, -2$  5. $\frac{7}{4}$  7. 7 km/h  9. Train A 46 km/h, Train B 58 km/h  11. 9 km/h  13. 2 km  15. $3\frac{3}{14}$ hours  17. $2\frac{2}{9}$ hours  19. $8\frac{4}{7}$ hours  21. 50 km/h and 75 km/h  23. $3\frac{3}{14}$ hours

**Exercise Set 9–9, page 292**

1. $y = 8x$  3. $y = -6x$  5. $y = 5x$  7. $y = \frac{15}{4}x$  9. $y = \frac{8}{5}x$  11. 6 amperes  13. 125,000  15. 532,500 tons  17. 40 kg  19. $y = \frac{60}{x}$  21. $y = \frac{12}{x}$  23. $y = \frac{36}{x}$  25. $y = \frac{9}{x}$  27. $y = \frac{0.32}{x}$  29. $\frac{2}{9}$ ampere  31. 160 cm³  33. $6\frac{2}{3}$ hours  35. $685\frac{5}{7}$ kg

# CHAPTER 10

## Answers for TRY THIS

**10–1**  1. $-9ab^2$  2. 1  3. $-\dfrac{2}{a^5b^6}$  4. $\dfrac{1}{(x^2+y^2)^3}$  5. $180a^{-5}$  6. $-20a^{-1}b^3$  7. $-4x^{-8}y^{-2}$  8. $\frac{2}{3}a^{-2}b^{-5}c^3$  9. $y^{-24}$  10. $512a^6b^{-12}$  11. $\dfrac{a^4}{b^4}$  12. $\dfrac{x^8y^{-12}}{81a^4}$  13. $4.6 \times 10^{11}$  14. $1.5 \times 10^8$  15. $1.235 \times 10^{-8}$  16. $1.7 \times 10^{-24}$  17. 789,300,000,000  18. 0.0000567  19. $7.462 \times 10^{-13}$  20. $5.6 \times 10^{-15}$  21. $2 \times 10^3$  22. $5.5 \times 10^2$

**10–2**  1. $3, -3$  2. $6, -6$  3. $11, -11$  4. 1  5. 6  6. $\frac{9}{10}$  7. 0.08  8. $-4$  9. $-7$  10. $-14$  11. $28 + x$  12. $\dfrac{y}{y+3}$  13. $|y|$  14. 24  15. $5|y|$  16. $|x+7|$  17. $|x-3|$  18. 0  19. $-2$  20. 6  21. $-\frac{7}{4}$  22. 2  23. $-2$  24. $-5$  25. $-1$  26. $|a|$  27. $y+7$  28. 5  29. $5|xy|$

**10–3**  1. $\sqrt{133}$  2. $\sqrt{x^2-4y^2}$  3. $\sqrt[4]{2821}$  4. $\sqrt[3]{8x^5+40x}$  5. $10\sqrt{3}$  6. $6y$  7. $(x+2)\sqrt{3}$  8. $2bc\sqrt{3ab}$  9. $2\sqrt[3]{2}$  10. $3xy^2$  11. $(a+b)\sqrt[3]{a+b}$  12. $3\sqrt{2}$  13. $6y\sqrt{7}$  14. $3x\sqrt[3]{4y}$  15. $7\sqrt{3ab}$  16. $2(y+5)\sqrt[3]{(y+5)^2}$  17. 12.6  18. 18.5  19. 6.7  20. 0.9

**10–4**  1. $\frac{5}{6}$  2. $\frac{10}{3}$  3. $\frac{3}{10}$  4. $\dfrac{2a\sqrt{a}}{b^2}$  5. $\dfrac{3x\sqrt[3]{2x^2}}{5}$  6. 5  7. $56\sqrt{xy}$  8. $5a$  9. $\frac{20}{7}$  10. $\dfrac{2ab}{3}$  11. $3\sqrt[3]{3}$  12. $6y\sqrt{6y}$

**10–5**  1. $13\sqrt{2}$  2. $10\sqrt[4]{5x} - \sqrt{7}$  3. $19\sqrt{5}$  4. $(3y+4)\sqrt[3]{y^2} + 2y^2$  5. $2\sqrt{x} - 1$

**10–6**  1. $5\sqrt{6} + 3\sqrt{14}$  2. $a\sqrt[3]{3} - \sqrt[3]{2a^2}$  3. $-4 - 9\sqrt{6}$  4. $-18 + 2\sqrt{6}$  5. $-3$  6. $29 - 12\sqrt{5}$  7. $58 + 12\sqrt{6}$

**10–7**  1. $\dfrac{\sqrt{6}}{3}$  2. $\dfrac{\sqrt{70}}{7}$  3. $\dfrac{\sqrt[3]{4}}{2}$  4. $\dfrac{2\sqrt{3ab}}{3|b|}$  5. $\dfrac{2x^2\sqrt{3xy}}{3y^2}$

6. $\dfrac{\sqrt[3]{28}}{2}$  7. $\dfrac{x\sqrt[3]{12x^2y^2}}{2y}$  8. $\dfrac{11}{\sqrt{66}}$  9. $\dfrac{7}{\sqrt[3]{196}}$  10. $\dfrac{\sqrt{3}+1}{\sqrt{3}+1}$  11. $\dfrac{\sqrt{2}-\sqrt{3}}{\sqrt{2}-\sqrt{3}}$  12. $-5(1+\sqrt{2})$  13. $\dfrac{4}{3\sqrt{2} - \sqrt{10} - 3\sqrt{6} + \sqrt{30}}$

**10–8**  1. $\sqrt[4]{y}$  2. $\sqrt{3a}$  3. $\sqrt[4]{16}$ or 2  4. $\sqrt[3]{125}$ or 5  5. $\sqrt[5]{a^3b^2c}$  6. $19^{1/3}$  7. $(abc)^{1/2}$  8. $\left(\dfrac{x^2y}{16}\right)^{1/5}$  9. $x\sqrt{x}$  10. 4  11. 32  12. $(7abc)^{4/3}$  13. $6^{7/5}$  14. $\dfrac{1}{5^{1/4}}$  15. $\dfrac{1}{(3xy)^{7/8}}$  16. $\sqrt{a}$  17. $x$  18. $\sqrt{2}$  19. $ab^2$  20. $xy^3$  21. $\sqrt[4]{63}$  22. $\sqrt[20]{(x+2)^9}$  23. $\sqrt[6]{x^4y^3z^5}$  24. $\sqrt[4]{ab}$

**10–9**  1. 100  2. No solution  3. 4  4. 5

**Exercise Set 10–1, page 301**

1. 1  3. $x^2 + y$  5. $\dfrac{3}{ab^2}$  7. $\dfrac{t^3}{rs^2}$  9. $\dfrac{1}{(x^3+y^3)^2}$  11. $-12a^{-2}b^2$  13. $a^{-2}b^{-1}$  15. $-31,104y^6z^{-8}$  17. $-8m^{-6}n^9$  19. $\dfrac{x^{12}y^6}{8}$  21. $\dfrac{27a^{-6}b^3}{c^6}$  23. $4.7 \times 10^{10}$  25. $8.63 \times 10^{17}$  27. $1.6 \times 10^{-8}$  29. $7 \times 10^{-11}$  31. 0.0004  33. 673,000,000  35. 0.0000000008923  37. $9.11 \times 10^{-28}$  39. $4.8 \times 10^{-10}$  41. $9.66 \times 10^{-5}$  43. $1.3338 \times 10^{-11}$  45. $2.5 \times 10^3$  47. $5 \times 10^{-4}$

**Exercise Set 10–2, page 307**

1. $4, -4$  3. $12, -12$  5. $20, -20$  7. $-\frac{7}{6}$  9. 17  11. $-\frac{4}{9}$  13. 0.3  15. $-0.07$  17. $p^2 + 4$  19. $\dfrac{x}{y+4}$  21. $4|x|$  23. $7|c|$  25. $|a+1|$  27. $|x-2|$  29. $|2x+7|$  31. 2  33. $-3$  35. $-6$  37. 0.7  39. 5  41. $-1$  43. $-\frac{2}{3}$  45. $|x|$  47. $5|a|$  49. 6  51. $|a+b|$

**Exercise Set 10–3, page 311**

1. $\sqrt{6}$  3. $\sqrt[3]{10}$  5. $\sqrt[4]{72}$  7. $\sqrt{30ab}$  9. $\sqrt[5]{18t^3}$  11. $\sqrt{x^2-a^2}$  13. $\sqrt[3]{0.06x^2}$  15. $\sqrt[4]{x^2-1}$  17. $\sqrt[5]{(x-2)^3}$  19. $\sqrt{\dfrac{6y}{5x}}$  21. $2\sqrt{2}$  23. $2\sqrt{6}$  25. $2\sqrt{10}$  27. $6x^2\sqrt{5}$  29. $3x^2\sqrt[3]{2x^2}$  31. $2x^2\sqrt[3]{10x^2}$  33. $2\sqrt[4]{2}$  35. $3cd\sqrt[4]{2d^2}$  37. $(x+y)\sqrt[3]{x+y}$  39. $(x+3)\sqrt{2}$  41. $3\sqrt{2}$  43. $3\sqrt{10}$  45. $4\sqrt{3}$  47. $3\sqrt[3]{2}$  49. $30\sqrt{3}$  51. $5bc^2\sqrt{2b}$  53. $2y^3\sqrt[3]{2}$  55. $(b+3)^2$  57. $4a^3b\sqrt{6ab}$  59. $2cd^2\sqrt[3]{6cd}$  61. 13.4  63. 14.0  65. 3.6  67. $-0.3$

**Exercise Set 10–4, page 315**

1. $\frac{5}{6}$  3. $\frac{4}{3}$  5. $\frac{7}{y}$  7. $\dfrac{5y\sqrt{y}}{x^2}$  9. $\dfrac{2x\sqrt[3]{x^2}}{3y}$  11. $\sqrt{7}$  13. 3  15. $y\sqrt{5y}$  17. $2\sqrt[3]{a^2b}$  19. $3\sqrt{xy}$  21. $\sqrt{x^2+xy+y^2}$  23. $6a\sqrt{6a}$  25. $4b\sqrt[3]{4b}$  27. $54a^3b\sqrt{2b}$  29. $2c\sqrt[3]{18cd}$

**Exercise Set 10–5, page 317**

1. $8\sqrt{3}$  3. $3\sqrt[3]{5}$  5. $13\sqrt[3]{y}$  7. $7\sqrt{2}$  9. $6\sqrt[3]{5}$  11. $23\sqrt{2}$  13. $21\sqrt{3}$  15. $38\sqrt{5}$  17. $122\sqrt{2}$  19. $9\sqrt[3]{2}$  21. $4\sqrt[3]{4}$  23. $29\sqrt{2}$  25. $(1+6a)\sqrt{5a}$  27. $(2-x)\sqrt[3]{3x}$  29. $10(a-1)\sqrt[3]{a}$  31. $3\sqrt{2y-2}$  33. $(x+3)\sqrt{x-1}$

### Exercise Set 10–6, page 319

1. $2\sqrt{6} - 18$   3. $\sqrt{6} - \sqrt{10}$   5. $2\sqrt{15} - 6\sqrt{3}$   7. $-6$
9. $3a\sqrt[3]{2}$   11. 1   13. $-12$   15. $a - b$   17. $1 + \sqrt{5}$   19. $7$
$+ 3\sqrt{3}$   21. $-6$   23. $a + \sqrt{3a} + \sqrt{2a} + \sqrt{6}$   25. $2\sqrt[3]{9} -$
$3\sqrt[3]{6} - 2\sqrt[3]{4}$   27. $7 + 4\sqrt{3}$   29. $21 - 6\sqrt{6}$

### Exercise Set 10–7, page 324

1. $\dfrac{\sqrt{30}}{5}$   3. $\dfrac{\sqrt{70}}{7}$   5. $\dfrac{2\sqrt{15}}{5}$   7. $\dfrac{2\sqrt[3]{6}}{3}$   9. $\dfrac{\sqrt[3]{75ac^2}}{5c}$

11. $\dfrac{y\sqrt[3]{9yx^2}}{3x^2}$   13. $\dfrac{\sqrt[3]{x^2y^2}}{xy}$   15. $\dfrac{7}{\sqrt{21}}$   17. $\dfrac{2}{\sqrt{6}}$   19. $\dfrac{52}{3\sqrt{91}}$

21. $\dfrac{7}{\sqrt[3]{98}}$   23. $\dfrac{7|x|}{\sqrt{21xy}}$   25. $\dfrac{5y^2}{x^3\sqrt{150x^2y^2}}$   27. $\dfrac{|ab|}{3\sqrt{ab}}$

29. $\dfrac{5(8 + \sqrt{6})}{58}$   31. $-2\sqrt{7}(\sqrt{5} + \sqrt{3})$

33. $\dfrac{\sqrt{15} + 20 - 6\sqrt{2} - 8\sqrt{30}}{77}$   35. $\dfrac{|x| - 2\sqrt{xy} + |y|}{|x| - |y|}$

37. $\dfrac{3\sqrt{6} + 4}{2}$   39. $\dfrac{-11}{4(\sqrt{3} - 5)}$   41. $\dfrac{-22}{\sqrt{6} + 5\sqrt{2} + 5\sqrt{3} + 25}$

43. $\dfrac{3}{\sqrt{10} + 2 + \sqrt{15} + \sqrt{6}}$   45. $\dfrac{7}{43\sqrt{2} + 66}$

### Exercise Set 10–8, page 329

1. $\sqrt[4]{x}$   3. 2   5. $\sqrt[5]{a^2b^2}$   7. $\sqrt[3]{a^2}$   9. 8   11. $20^{1/3}$
13. $17^{1/2}$   15. $(cd)^{1/4}$   17. $(xy^2z)^{1/5}$   19. $(3mn)^{3/2}$
21. $(8x^2y)^{5/7}$   23. $\dfrac{1}{x^{1/3}}$   25. $\dfrac{1}{(2rs)^{3/4}}$   27. $10^{2/3}$   29. $x^{2/3}$
31. $\sqrt[3]{a^2}$   33. $2y^2$   35. $2c^2d^3$   37. $\dfrac{m^2n^4}{2}$   39. $\sqrt[4]{r^2s}$
41. $\sqrt{2ts}$   43. $\sqrt[6]{x^5 - 4x^4 + 4x^3}$   45. $\sqrt[6]{a + b}$   47. $\sqrt[12]{a^8b^9}$

### Exercise Set 10–9, page 333

1. 2   3. 168   5. 3   7. 19   9. $\dfrac{80}{3}$   11. 4   13. $-27$
15. 397   17. No solution   19. $\dfrac{1}{64}$   21. $-6$   23. 5
25. $-\dfrac{1}{4}$   27. 3   29. 9   31. 7   33. $\dfrac{80}{9}$   35. $-1$   37. 6, 2

## CHAPTER 11

### Answers for TRY THIS

**11–1**   1. $i\sqrt{7}$   2. $-bi$   3. $4i\sqrt{10}$   4. $-18$   5. $-3\sqrt{3}$
6. $-3\sqrt{2}$   7. $7i$   8. $4 + 7i$   9. $-2 - i$   10. 0   11. $-i$
12. $-3 + 5i$   13. $-2 + 7i$   14. $-6 - 9i$

**11–2**   1. $x = -1$, $y = 2$   2. $-30$   3. $-100$   4. $25 + 45i$
5. $3 - 28i$   6. $-24 - 70i$   7. $6 - 3i$   8. $-9 + 5i$   9. $7i$
10. $-8$   11. 53   12. 10   13. $p^2 + q^2$   14. $2i$   15. $\dfrac{10}{17}$
$- \dfrac{11}{17}i$   16. $\dfrac{3}{25} - \dfrac{4}{25}i$

**11–3**   1. $(3i)^2 + 9 = 9i^2 + 9 = -9 + 9 = 0$; $(-3i)^2 + 9 =$
$9i^2 + 9 = -9 + 9 = 0$   2. $(1 + i)^2 - 2(1 + i) + 2 = 1 + 2i +$
$i^2 - 2 - 2i + 2 = 0$   3. $(1 - i)^2 + 2(1 - i) + 1 = 1 - 2i + i^2$
$+ 2 - 2i + 1 = 3 - 4i$; Therefore $(1 - i)$ is not a solution of
$x^2 + 2x + 1 = 0$.   4. $x^2 - 2ix - x + i - 1 = 0$   5. $x^3 -$
$2x^2 + x - 2 = 0$   6. $2 + 5i$   7. $(x + 2i)(x - 2i) = x^2 + 2ix$
$- 2ix - 4i^2 = x^2 + 4$   8. $(-1 + i)^2 = 1 - 2i + i^2 = 1 - 2i -$
$1 = -2i$; $1 - i$

**11–4**   2. 5   3. 13   4. $\sqrt{2}$

**11–5**   1. $\overline{(3 + 2i) + (4 - 5i)} = \overline{(7 - 3i)} = 7 + 3i$; $\overline{(3 + 2i)} +$
$\overline{(4 - 5i)} = (3 - 2i) + (4 + 5i) = 7 + 3i$   2. $\overline{(2 + 5i)(1 + 3i)} =$
$\overline{(-13 + 11i)} = -13 - 11i$; $\overline{(2 + 5i)} \circ \overline{(1 + 3i)} = (2 - 5i)$
$(1 - 3i) = -13 - 11i$   3. $\overline{z^3} = \overline{z \cdot z \cdot z} = \overline{z} \cdot \overline{z} \cdot \overline{z} = \overline{z}^3$
4. $5\overline{z}^3 + 4\overline{z}^2 - 2\overline{z} + 1$   5. $7\overline{z}^5 - 3\overline{z}^3 + 8\overline{z}^2 + \overline{z}$

### Exercise Set 11–1, page 344

1. $i\sqrt{2}$   3. $6i$   5. $-3i$   7. $8i\sqrt{2}$   9. $\dfrac{3}{4}i$   11. $-4i\sqrt{5}$
13. $92i$   15. $-4\sqrt{3}$   17. $-\sqrt{6}$   19. 6   21. $-3\sqrt{5}$
23. $-10$   25. $9i$   27. $-6i$   29. $8 - 2i$   31. $8 + i$   33. $9 -$
$5i$   35. $i$   37. $14i$   39. $-4 + 5i$   41. $-2 - 3i$   43. $-1 + i$

### Exercise Set 11–2, page 349

1. $x = -\dfrac{3}{2}$, $y = 7$   3. $x = -2$, $y = -8$   5. $x = 2$, $y = 3$
7. $-63$   9. $-81$   11. $-9$   13. $1 + 5i$   15. $18 + 14i$
17. $38 + 9i$   19. $2 - 46i$   21. $21 - 20i$   23. $-8 + 6i$
25. $-4 - 8i$   27. $6 + 5i$   29. $\sqrt{2} + \dfrac{1}{2}i$   31. $r + ti$   33. 25
35. 2   37. $\dfrac{5}{4}$   39. 4   41. $i$   43. $\dfrac{8}{5} + \dfrac{1}{5}i$   45. $-i$   47. $-\dfrac{37}{53}$
$- \dfrac{50}{53}i$   49. $\dfrac{1}{3} + \dfrac{2}{3}\sqrt{2}i$   51. $2 - 3i$   53. $\dfrac{1}{5} + \dfrac{2}{5}i$   55. $-i$
57. $\dfrac{1}{10} + \dfrac{2}{5}i$   59. $-\dfrac{4}{65} - \dfrac{7}{65}i$

### Exercise Set 11–3, page 354

1. Yes, yes   3. No, yes   5. Yes, yes   7. $x^2 + 25$   9. $x^2 -$
$2x + 2$   11. $x^2 - 4x + 13$   13. $x^2 - ix - 3x + 3i$   15. $x^3$
$- x^2 + 9x - 9$   17. $x^3 - 2ix^2 - 3x^2 + 5ix + x - 2i + 2$
19. $x^3 - 2ix^2 + x - 2i$   21. $\dfrac{2}{5} + \dfrac{6}{5}i$   23. $\dfrac{8}{5} - \dfrac{9}{5}i$   25. $2 - i$
27. $\dfrac{11}{25} + \dfrac{2}{25}i$   29. $(2x + i)(2x - i) = 4x^2 - 2ix + 2ix - i^2$
$= 4x^2 + 1$   31. $(2 + i)^2 = 4 + 4i + i^2 = 3 + 4i$, $-2 - i$

### Exercise Set 11–4, page 356

7. 5   9. 17   11. $\sqrt{10}$   13. 3   15. $\sqrt{c^2 + d^2}$

### Exercise Set 11–5, page 360

1. $\overline{z}^2 - 3\overline{z} + 5$   3. $3\overline{z}^5 - 4\overline{z}^2 + 3\overline{z} - 5$   5. $7\overline{z}^4 + 5\overline{z}^3 -$
$12\overline{z}$   7. $5\overline{z}^{10} - 7\overline{z}^8 + 13\overline{z}^2 - 4$   9. $7\overline{z}^{100} - 5\overline{z}^{89} + \overline{z}^2$

## CHAPTER 12

### Answers for TRY THIS

**12–1**   1. $\pm\sqrt{3}$   2. 0   3. $\pm\dfrac{2\sqrt{6}}{3}$   4. $\pm\dfrac{i\sqrt{2}}{2}$

**12–2**   1. 0, $\dfrac{3}{4}$   2. $\dfrac{3}{5}$, 1   3. 2 cm   4. A: 4 km/h, B: 3 km/h

**12–3**   1. $\dfrac{-1 \pm \sqrt{22}}{3}$   2. $\dfrac{1 \pm i\sqrt{7}}{4}$   3. 2, $-\dfrac{1}{3}$   4. 1.2, $-1.9$

**12–4**   1. Two real   2. One real   3. Two nonreal

**12–5**   1. Sum = 4, Product = $\dfrac{4}{3}$   2. Sum = $-\sqrt{2}$, Product
$= -4$   3. $4x^2 - 12x - 1 = 0$   4. $3x^2 + 7x - 20 = 0$   5. $x^2$
$- x - 56 = 0$   6. $x^2 - (m + n)x + mn = 0$   7. $x^2 + x - 72$
$= 0$   8. $x^2 - 6x + 7 = 0$   9. $4x^2 - 8x - 1 = 0$

**12–6** 1. $w_2 = \dfrac{w_1}{A^2}$  2. $r = \sqrt{\dfrac{V}{\pi h}}$  3. $s = \dfrac{R \pm \sqrt{R^2 + 4LC}}{2L}$

**12–7** 1. 6.25%  2. a) 4.33 s  b) 1.87 s  c) 44.9 m

**12–8** 1. $\pm 3, \pm 1$  2. 4  3. 4, 2, $-1$, $-3$  4. 125, $-8$

### Exercise Set 12–1, page 369

1. $\pm\sqrt{5}$  3. 0  5. $\pm\dfrac{\sqrt{6}}{2}$  7. $\pm\dfrac{\sqrt{15}}{3}$  9. $\pm\dfrac{1}{2}$  11. $\pm\dfrac{2}{5}i$

13. $\pm\dfrac{i\sqrt{3}}{3}$  15. $\pm i\sqrt{5}$  17. $\pm i\sqrt{7}$  19. $\pm\dfrac{3}{2}$  21. $\pm 7$  23. $\pm 8$

### Exercise Set 12–2, page 372

1. 0, 5  3. 0, $-2$  5. 0, $\dfrac{2}{3}$  7. 0, $-\dfrac{9}{14}$  9. 0, 5  11. 5, 1

13. 5, $-1$  15. $-5$, $-3$  17. $\dfrac{2}{3}$, $-\dfrac{1}{2}$  19. $-\dfrac{4}{3}$, $-\dfrac{1}{3}$  21. $-\dfrac{5}{3}$,

1  23. $-\dfrac{1}{4}$, $\dfrac{3}{2}$  25. 10, $-3$  27. $-2$, $-1$  29. 2 cm

31. Length is 6 m; width is 2m  33. Length is 24 m; width is 12 m  35. 4 m and 3 m  37. 24 m and 10 m  39. A: 15 km/h, B: 20 km/h

### Exercise Set 12–3, page 377

1. $-3 \pm \sqrt{5}$  3. 1, $-5$  5. 3, $-10$  7. 2, $-\dfrac{1}{2}$  9. $-1$, $-\dfrac{5}{3}$

11. $\dfrac{1 \pm i\sqrt{3}}{2}$  13. $-1 \pm 2i$  15. $1 \pm 2i$  17. $2 \pm 3i$

19. $\pm i\sqrt{5}$  21. $\dfrac{-3 \pm \sqrt{41}}{2}$  23. $\pm\dfrac{\sqrt{10}}{2}$  25. 0, $-1$

27. $\dfrac{-1 \pm 2i}{5}$  29. $\dfrac{3}{4}$, $-2$  31. $\dfrac{1 \pm 3i}{2}$  33. $\dfrac{3}{2}$, $\dfrac{2}{3}$  35. 1.3,

$-5.3$  37. 5.2, 0.8  39. 2.8, $-1.3$  41. $-0.3$, $-2.4$

### Exercise Set 12–4, page 380

1. One real  3. Two nonreal  5. Two real  7. One real
9. Two nonreal  11. Two real  13. Two real  15. One real

### Exercise Set 12–5, page 383

1. Sum = $-7$, Product = 8  3. Sum = 1, Product = 1
5. Sum = 2, Product = $-4$  7. Sum = 0, Product = $-25$

9. Sum = $-\dfrac{5}{9}$, Product = $\dfrac{4}{9}$  11. Sum = 54, Product = 0

13. $2x^2 + 10x + 1 = 0$  15. $x^2 - \sqrt{3}x + 8 = 0$  17. $x^2 + 2x - 99 = 0$  19. $x^2 - 14x + 49 = 0$  21. $25x^2 - 20x - 12 = 0$  23. $4x^2 - 2(c + d)x + cd = 0$  25. $x^2 + 4\sqrt{2}x + 6 = 0$  27. $x^2 + \pi x - 2\pi^2 = 0$  29. $x^2 - 7x + 12 = 0$  31. $4x^2 + 3x - 10 = 0$  33. $x^2 - 2x - 1 = 0$  35. $4x^2 - 8x + 1 = 0$  37. $mnx^2 - (m^2 - n^2)x - mn = 0$  39. $x^2 - 4x + 29 = 0$

### Exercise Set 12–6, page 385

1. $s = \dfrac{\sqrt{P}}{2}$  3. $r = \sqrt{\dfrac{Gm_1 m_2}{F}}$  5. $L = \dfrac{gT^2}{16\pi^2}$  7. $r = \sqrt{x^2 + y^2}$

9. $z = \sqrt{d^2 - x^2 - y^2}$  11. $t = \dfrac{v_0 \pm \sqrt{v_0^2 - 64h}}{32}$  13. $t = \sqrt{\dfrac{2S}{g}}$  15. $r = \dfrac{-\pi h + \sqrt{\pi^2 h^2 + 2\pi A}}{2\pi}$  17. $t = \dfrac{\pi \pm \sqrt{\pi^2 - 12k\sqrt{2}}}{2\sqrt{2}}$

### Exercise Set 12–7, page 388

1. 30%  3. 25%  5. 12.5%  7. 73.2%  9. a) 3.91 s
b) 1.91 s  c) 79.6 m  11. 8%  13. 11%

### Exercise Set 12–8, page 391

1. 81, 1  3. $\pm\sqrt{5}$  5. $-27$, 8  7. 16  9. 7, $-1$, 5, 1
11. 4, 1, 6, $-1$  13. $\pm\sqrt{2 + \sqrt{6}}$, $\pm\sqrt{2 - \sqrt{6}}$  15. $\dfrac{1}{3}$, $-\dfrac{1}{2}$
17. 2, $-1$  19. 28.5

## CHAPTER 13

### Answers for TRY THIS

**13–1** 1. a) Parabola through $(-1, 3)$, $(0, 0)$, $(1, 3)$  b) Upward  c) y-axis ($x = 0$)  d) $(0, 0)$  2. a) Parabola through $(-4, -4)$, $(0, 0)$, $(4, -4)$  b) Downward  c) y-axis ($x = 0$)  d) $(0, 0)$  3. a) Parabola through $(-1, 3)$, $(0, 0)$, $(1, 3)$  b) Parabola through $(1, 3)$, $(2, 0)$, $(3, 3)$  c) $(2, 0)$  d) $x = 2$  e) Upward  f) To the right  4. a) Parabola through $(-1, -3)$, $(0, 0)$, $(1, -3)$  b) Parabola through $(-3, -3)$, $(-2, 0)$, $(-1, -3)$  c) $(-2, 0)$  d) $x = -2$  e) Downward  f) To the left

**13–2** 1. a) Parabola through $(1, 7)$, $(2, 4)$, $(3, 7)$  b) $(2, 4)$  c) $x = 2$  d) Yes, 4  e) No  2. a) Parabola through $(-3, -4)$, $(-2, -1)$, $(-1, -4)$  b) $(-2, -1)$  c) $x = -2$  d) No  e) Yes, $-1$  3. a) $(5, 40)$  b) $x = 5$  c) Yes, 40  d) No  4. a) $(5, 0)$  b) $x = 5$  c) No  d) Yes, 0  5. a) $\left(-\dfrac{3}{4}, -6\right)$  b) $x = -\dfrac{3}{4}$  c) Yes, $-6$  d) No  6. a) $(-9, 3)$  b) $x = -9$  c) No  d) Yes, 3

**13–3** 1. a) $f(x) = (x - 2)^2 + 3$  b) $(2, 3)$, $x = 2$, min. = 3

2. a) $f(x) = -4\left(x - \dfrac{3}{2}\right)^2 + 4$  b) $\left(\dfrac{3}{2}, 4\right)$, $x = \dfrac{3}{2}$, max. = 4

3. 225  4. 25 m by 25 m

**13–4** 1. $(1 + \sqrt{6}, 0)$, $(1 - \sqrt{6}, 0)$  2. $(3, 0)$, $(-1, 0)$
3. $(-4, 0)$  4. None

**13–5** 1. $f(x) = x^2 - 2x + 1$  2. a) $f(x) = 0.625x^2 - 50x + 1150$  b) 510  3. a) Max. height is 12.4 m in 0.286 s  b) 1.876 s

**13–6** 1. $y = 7x^2$  2. $y = \dfrac{9}{x^2}$  3. $y = \dfrac{1}{2}xz$  4. $y = \dfrac{5xz^2}{w}$

5. 490 m  6. 1 ohm  7. Division by zero is undefined.

### Exercise Set 13–1, page 399

1. a) Parabola through $(-2, 4)$, $(0, 0)$, $(2, 4)$  b) $(0, 0)$  c) $x = 0$  3. a) Parabola through $(-1, -4)$, $(0, 0)$, $(1, -4)$  b) $(0, 0)$  c) $x = 0$  5. a) Parabola through $(1, 4)$, $(3, 0)$, $(5, 4)$  b) $(3, 0)$  c) $x = 3$  7. a) Parabola through $(2, 2)$, $(3, 0)$, $(4, 2)$  b) $(3, 0)$  c) $x = 3$  9. a) Parabola through $(-10, -2)$, $(-9, 0)$, $(-8, -2)$  b) $(-9, 0)$  c) $x = -9$  11. a) Parabola through $(0, 3)$, $(1, 0)$, $(2, 3)$  b) $(1, 0)$  c) $x = 1$  13. a) Parabola through $\left(-\dfrac{3}{2}, -2\right)$, $\left(-\dfrac{1}{2}, 0\right)$, $\left(\dfrac{1}{2}, -2\right)$  b) $\left(-\dfrac{1}{2}, 0\right)$  c) $x = -\dfrac{1}{2}$

### Exercise Set 13–2, page 402

1. a) Parabola through $(1, 5)$, $(3, 1)$, $(5, 5)$  b) $(3, 1)$  c) $x = 3$  d) min. = 1  3. a) Parabola through $(-3, 2)$, $(-1, -2)$,

(1, 2) b) (−1, −2) c) $x = -1$ d) min. = −2 5. a) Parabola through (0, −1), (1, −3), (2, −1) b) (1, −3) c) $x = 1$ d) min. = −3 7. a) Parabola through (−5, −2), (−4, 1), (−3, −2) b) (−4, 1) c) $x = -4$ d) max. = 1 9. a) (9, 5) b) $x = 9$ c) min. = 5 11. a) $(-\frac{1}{4}, -13)$ b) $x = -\frac{1}{4}$ c) min. = −13 13. a) (10, −20) b) $x = 10$ c) max. = −20 15. a) (−4.58, 65π) b) $x = -4.58$ c) min. = 65π

### Exercise Set 13−3, page 405

1. a) $f(x) = (x - 1)^2 - 4$ b) (1, 4), $x = 1$, min. = −4 3. a) $f(x) = -(x - 2)^2 + 10$ b) (2, 10), $x = 2$, max. = 10 5. a) $f(x) = (x + \frac{3}{2})^2 - \frac{49}{4}$ b) $(-\frac{3}{2}, -\frac{49}{4})$, $x = -\frac{3}{2}$, min. $= -\frac{49}{4}$ 7. a) $f(x) = (x - \frac{9}{2})^2 - \frac{81}{4}$ b) $(\frac{9}{2}, -\frac{81}{4})$, $x = \frac{9}{2}$, min. $= -\frac{81}{4}$ 9. a) $f(x) = 3(x - 4)^2 + 2$ b) (4, 2), $x = 4$, min. = 2 11. a) $f(x) = \frac{3}{4}(x + 6)^2 - 27$ b) (−6, −27), $x = -6$, min. = −27 13. a) $f(x) = -2(x - \frac{1}{2})^2 + \frac{3}{2}$ b) $(\frac{1}{2}, \frac{3}{2})$, $x = \frac{1}{2}$, max. $= \frac{3}{2}$ 15. 19 m by 19 m, 361 m$^2$ 17. 121, 11 and 11 19. −4, 2, and −2 21. $-\frac{25}{4}, \frac{5}{2}$ and $-\frac{5}{2}$ 23. Min. ≈ −6.9536605

### Exercise Set 13−4, page 408

1. $(2 + \sqrt{3}, 0), (2, -\sqrt{3}, 0)$ 3. (3, 0), (−1, 0) 5. None 7. None 9. $(-\frac{3}{2}, 0)$ 11. (62.758520, 0), (31.941480, 0)

### Exercise Set 13−5, page 412

1. $f(x) = 2x^2 + 3x - 1$ 3. $f(x) = -3x^2 + 13x - 5$ 5. a) $f(x) = -4x^2 + 40x + 2$ b) \$98 7. a) $f(x) = 0.05x^2 - 10.5x + 650$ b) 250 9. a) Max. height is 1102.5 m in 15 s b) 30 s

### Exercise Set 13−6, page 417

1. $y = 15x^2$ 3. $y = \frac{0.0015}{x^2}$ 5. $y = xz$ 7. $y = \frac{3}{10}xz^2$ 9. $y = \frac{1}{5}\frac{xz}{wp}$ 11. 180 m 13. 94.03 kg 15. 97

## CHAPTER 14

### Answers for TRY THIS

**14−1** 1. $\sqrt{149}$ 2. $6\sqrt{2}$ 3. $(\frac{3}{2}, -\frac{5}{2})$ 4. (9, −5)

**14−2** 1. 6 2. 10 3. $5\sqrt{2}$ 4. $(x - 5)^2 + (y + 2)^2 = 3$ 5. $(x + 2)^2 + (y + 6)^2 = 7$ 6. Circle with center (−1, 3), radius 2 7. (7, −2), $r = 8$

**14−3** 1. Vertices: (−3, 0), (3, 0), (0, 1), (0, −1); foci: $(-2\sqrt{2}, 0), (2\sqrt{2}, 0)$ 2. Vertices: (−3, 0), (3, 0), (0, 5), (0, −5); foci: (0, 4), (0, −4) 3. Vertices: $(-\sqrt{2}, 0), (\sqrt{2}, 0)$, (0, 2), (0, −2); foci: $(0, \sqrt{2}), (0, -\sqrt{2})$ 4. Center: (−3, 2); vertices: $(-\frac{16}{5}, 2), (-\frac{14}{5}, 2), (-3, \frac{7}{3}), (-3, \frac{5}{3})$; foci: $(-3, \frac{34}{15}), (-3, \frac{26}{15})$ 5. Center: (2, −3); vertices: $(\frac{5}{3}, -3), (\frac{7}{3}, -3), (2, -\frac{14}{5}), (2, -\frac{16}{5})$; foci: $(\frac{34}{15}, -3), (\frac{26}{15}, -3)$

**14−4** 1. Vertices: (−3, 0), (3, 0); foci: $(-\sqrt{13}, 0)$, $(\sqrt{13}, 0)$; asymptotes: $y = \frac{2}{3}x, y = -\frac{2}{3}x$ 2. Vertices: (−4, 0), (4, 0); foci: $(-4\sqrt{2}, 0), (4\sqrt{2}, 0)$; asymptotes: $y = x, y = -x$ 3. Vertices: (0, 5), (0, −5); foci: $(0, \sqrt{34})$, $(0, -\sqrt{34})$; asymptotes: $y = \frac{5}{3}x, y = -\frac{5}{3}x$ 4. Vertices: (0, 5), (0, −5); foci: $(0, 5\sqrt{2}), (0, -5\sqrt{2})$; asymptotes: $y = x, y = -x$ 5. Center: (1, −2); vertices: (−4, −2), (6, −2); foci: $(1 - \sqrt{29}, -2), (1 + \sqrt{29}, -2)$; asymptotes: $y + 2 = \frac{2}{5}(x - 1), y + 2 = -\frac{2}{5}(x - 1)$ 6. Center: (−1, 2); vertices: (−1, 5), (−1, −1); foci: (−1, 7), (−1, −3); asymptotes: $y - 2 = \frac{3}{4}(x + 1), y - 2 = -\frac{3}{4}(x + 1)$ 7. Hyperbola with x-axis and y-axis as asymptotes; one branch through (1, 3), $(\sqrt{3}, \sqrt{3})$, (3, 1); one branch through (−3, −1), $(-\sqrt{3}, -\sqrt{3})$, (−1, −3) 8. Hyperbola with x-axis and y-axis as asymptotes; one branch through $(-2, \frac{1}{2})$, (−1, 1), $(-\frac{1}{2}, 2)$; one branch through $(\frac{1}{2}, -2)$, (1, −1), $(2, -\frac{1}{2})$

**14−5** 1. Parabola through (−1, 2), (0, 0), (1, 2); vertex: (0, 0); focus: $(0, \frac{1}{8})$; directrix: $y = -\frac{1}{8}$ 2. Parabola through (4, 2), (0, 0), (−4, 2); vertex: (0, 0); focus: (0, 2); directrix: $y = -2$ 3. Parabola through (−2, −4), (0, 0), (2, −4); vertex: (0, 0); focus: $(0, -\frac{1}{4})$; directrix: $y = -\frac{1}{4}$ 4. Parabola through $(-\frac{3}{2}, 3)$, (0, 0), $(-\frac{3}{2}, -3)$; vertex: (0, 0); focus: $(-\frac{3}{2}, 0)$; directrix: $x = \frac{3}{2}$ 5. Parabola through (−3, 0), $(-1, -\frac{1}{2})$, (1, 0); vertex: $(-1, -\frac{1}{2})$; focus: $(-1, \frac{3}{2})$; directrix: $y = -\frac{5}{2}$ 6. Parabola through (−2, 3), (2, −1), (−2, −5); vertex: (2, −1); focus: (1, −1); directrix: $x = 3$

**14−6** 1. (4, 3), (−3, −4) 2. (4, 7), (−1, 2) 3. (−4, 4), (2, 1) 4. $(-\frac{5}{7}, \frac{22}{7})$, (1, −2) 5. 11 and 7 6. Length is 12 m; width is 5 m

**14−7** 1. (2, 3), (2, −3), (−2, 3), (−2, −3) 2. (3, 2), (−3, −2), (2, 3), (−2, −3) 3. Length is 2 cm; width is 1 cm

### Exercise Set 14−1, page 427

1. 5 3. $3\sqrt{2}$ 5. 5 7. 8 9. $\sqrt{a^2 + 64}$ 11. $\sqrt{a^2 + b^2}$ 13. $2\sqrt{a}$ 15. $(-\frac{1}{2}, -1)$ 17. $(-\frac{7}{2}, -\frac{15}{2})$ 19. (4, 4) 21. (a, 0)

### Exercise Set 14−2, page 431

1. $x^2 + y^2 = 49$ 3. $(x + 2)^2 + (y - 7)^2 = 5$ 5. Circle with center (−1, −3), radius 2 7. (8, −3), $r = 2\sqrt{10}$ 9. (0, 0), $r = \sqrt{2}$ 11. (5, 0), $r = \frac{1}{2}$ 13. (−4, 3), $r = 2\sqrt{10}$ 15. (4, −1), $r = 2$ 17. (2, 0), $r = 2$

### Exercise Set 14−3, page 435

1. Center: (0, 0); vertices: (−2, 0), (2, 0), (0, 1), (0, −1); foci: $(-\sqrt{3}, 0), (\sqrt{3}, 0)$ 3. Center: (1, 2); vertices: (−1, 2),

(3, 2), (1, 3), (1, 1); foci: $(1 - \sqrt{3}, 2)$, $(1 + \sqrt{3}, 2)$  5. Center: $(-3, 2)$; vertices: $(-8, 2)$, $(2, 2)$, $(-3, 6)$, $(-3, -2)$; foci: $(-6, 2)$, $(0, 2)$  7. Center: $(0, 0)$; vertices: $(-3, 0)$, $(3, 0)$, $(0, 4)$, $(0, -4)$; foci: $(0, \sqrt{7})$, $(0, -\sqrt{7})$  9. Center: $(-2, 1)$; vertices: $(-10, 1)$, $(6, 1)$, $(-2, 1 + 4\sqrt{3})$, $(-2, 1 - 4\sqrt{3})$; foci: $(-6, 1)$, $(2, 1)$  11. Center: $(0, 0)$; vertices: $(-\sqrt{3}, 0)$, $(\sqrt{3}, 0)$, $(0, \sqrt{2})$, $(0, -\sqrt{2})$; foci: $(-1, 0)$, $(1, 0)$  13. Center: $(0, 0)$; vertices: $(-\frac{1}{2}, 0)$, $(\frac{1}{2}, 0)$, $(0, \frac{1}{3})$, $(0, -\frac{1}{3})$; foci: $(\frac{\sqrt{5}}{6}, 0)$, $(-\frac{\sqrt{5}}{6}, 0)$  15. Center: $(2, -1)$; vertices: $(-1, -1)$, $(5, -1)$, $(2, 1)$, $(2, -3)$; foci: $(2 - \sqrt{5}, -1)$, $(2 + \sqrt{5}, -1)$  17. Center: $(1, 1)$; vertices: $(0, 1)$, $(2, 1)$, $(1, 3)$, $(1, -1)$; foci: $(1, 1 + \sqrt{3})$, $(1, 1 - \sqrt{3})$

## Exercise Set 14–4, page 440

1. Center: $(0, 0)$; vertices: $(3, 0)$, $(-3, 0)$; foci: $(\sqrt{10}, 0)$, $(-\sqrt{10}, 0)$; asymptotes: $y = \frac{1}{3}x$, $y = -\frac{1}{3}x$  3. Center: $(2, -5)$; vertices: $(5, -5)$, $(-1, -5)$; foci: $(2 + \sqrt{10}, -5)$, $(2 - \sqrt{10}, -5)$; asymptotes: $y + 5 = \frac{1}{3}(x - 2)$, $y + 5 = -\frac{1}{3}(x - 2)$  5. Center: $(-1, -3)$; vertices: $(-1, -1)$, $(-1, -5)$; foci: $(-1, -3 + 2\sqrt{5})$, $(-1, -3 - 2\sqrt{5})$; asymptotes: $y + 3 = \frac{1}{2}(x + 1)$, $y + 3 = -\frac{1}{2}(x + 1)$  7. Center: $(0, 0)$; vertices: $(2, 0)$, $(-2, 0)$; foci: $(\sqrt{5}, 0)$, $(-\sqrt{5}, 0)$; asymptotes: $y = \frac{1}{2}x$, $y = -\frac{1}{2}x$  9. Center: $(0, 0)$; vertices: $(\sqrt{2}, 0)$, $(-\sqrt{2}, 0)$; foci: $(2, 0)$, $(-2, 0)$; asymptotes: $y = x$, $y = -x$  11. Center: $(1, -2)$; vertices: $(2, -2)$, $(0, -2)$; foci: $(1 + \sqrt{2}, -2)$, $(1 - \sqrt{2}, -2)$; asymptotes: $y + 2 = x - 1$, $y + 2 = -(x - 1)$  13. Center: $(\frac{1}{3}, 3)$; vertices: $(\frac{4}{3}, 3)$, $(-\frac{2}{3}, 3)$; foci: $(\frac{1}{3} + \sqrt{37}, 3)$, $(\frac{1}{3} - \sqrt{37}, 3)$; asymptotes: $y - 3 = 6(x - \frac{1}{3})$, $y - 3 = -6(x - \frac{1}{3})$  15. Hyperbola with x-axis and y-axis as asymptotes; one branch through $(\frac{1}{2}, 2)$, $(1, 1)$, $(2, \frac{1}{2})$; one branch through $(-2, -\frac{1}{2})$, $(-1, -1)$, $(-\frac{1}{2}, -2)$  17. Hyperbola with x-axis and y-axis as asymptotes; one branch through $(-4, 2)$, $(-\sqrt{8}, \sqrt{8})$, $(-2, 4)$; one branch through $(4, -2)$, $(\sqrt{8}, -\sqrt{8})$, $(2, -4)$

## Exercise Set 14–5, page 444

1. Parabola through $(-4, 2)$, $(0, 0)$, $(4, 2)$; vertex: $(0, 0)$; focus: $(0, 2)$; directrix: $y = -2$  3. Parabola through $(-\frac{3}{2}, 3)$, $(0, 0)$, $(-\frac{3}{2}, -3)$; vertex: $(0, 0)$; focus: $(-\frac{3}{2}, 0)$; directrix: $x = \frac{3}{2}$  5. Parabola through $(-4, 4)$, $(0, 0)$, $(4, 4)$; vertex: $(0, 0)$; focus: $(0, 1)$; directrix: $y = -1$  7. Parabola through $(-1, 4)$, $(0, 0)$, $(1, 4)$; vertex: $(0, 0)$; focus: $(0, \frac{1}{16})$; directrix: $y = -\frac{1}{16}$  9. Parabola through $(-5, -\frac{1}{2})$, $(-2, 1)$, $(1, -\frac{1}{2})$; vertex: $(-2, 1)$; focus: $(-2, -\frac{1}{2})$; directrix: $y = \frac{5}{2}$  11. Parabola through $(-3, -5)$, $(0, 0)$, $(1, -5)$; vertex: $(-1, -3)$; focus: $(-1, -\frac{7}{2})$; directrix: $y = -\frac{5}{2}$  13. Parabola through $(-2, 2)$, $(0, -2)$, $(2, 2)$; vertex: $(0, -2)$; focus:

$(0, -\frac{7}{4})$; directrix: $y = -\frac{5}{2}$  15. Parabola through $(-4, 3)$, $(-2, -1)$, $(0, 3)$; vertex: $(-2, -1)$; focus: $(-2, -\frac{3}{4})$; directrix: $y = -\frac{5}{4}$  17. Parabola through $(8, 2)$, $(\frac{23}{4}, \frac{1}{2})$, $(8, -1)$; vertex: $(\frac{23}{4}, \frac{1}{2})$; focus: $(6, \frac{1}{2})$; directrix: $x = \frac{11}{2}$

## Exercise Set 14–6, page 447

1. $(-4, -3)$, $(3, 4)$  3. $(0, 2)$, $(3, 0)$  5. $(-2, 1)$  7. $(4, \frac{3}{2})$, $(3, 2)$  9. $(\frac{5 + \sqrt{70}}{3}, \frac{-1 + \sqrt{70}}{3})$, $(\frac{5 - \sqrt{70}}{3}, \frac{-1 - \sqrt{70}}{3})$  11. $(\frac{15 + \sqrt{561}}{8}, \frac{11 - 3\sqrt{561}}{8})$, $(\frac{15 - \sqrt{561}}{8}, \frac{11 + 3\sqrt{561}}{8})$  13. 9 and 5  15. Length is 8 cm; width is 6 cm  17. Length is 5 m; width is 4 m

## Exercise Set 14–7, page 450

1. $(-5, 0)$, $(4, 3)$, $(4, -3)$  3. $(3, 0)$, $(-3, 0)$  5. No real solution  7. $(\sqrt{2}, \sqrt{14})$, $(\sqrt{2}, -\sqrt{14})$, $(-\sqrt{2}, \sqrt{14})$, $(-\sqrt{2}, -\sqrt{14})$  9. $(1, 2)$, $(-1, -2)$, $(2, 1)$, $(-2, -1)$  11. $(3, 2)$, $(-3, -2)$  13. 13 and 12; −13 and −12  15. Length is $\sqrt{3}$ m; width is 1 m  17. 24 m and 16 m

## CHAPTER 15

### Answers for TRY THIS

**15–1**  1. a) Yes  b) No  c) Yes  2. a) Yes  b) Yes  c) No  d) No  3. a) No  b) No  c) No  d) Yes  4. a) Yes  b) No  5. a) No  b) Yes  c) No  6. $x^3 + 2x^2 - 5x - 6 = (x - 3)(x^2 + 5x + 10) + 24$

**15–2**  1. −1  2. 3  3. 0  4. No  5. No  6. a) Yes  b) $x^2 + 8x + 15$  c) $(x - 2)(x + 5)(x + 3)$

**15–3**  1. Q: $x^2 + 8x + 15$, R: 0  2. Q: $x^2 - 4x + 13$, R: −30  3. Q: $y^2 - y + 1$, R: 0  4. Q: $x^4 + x^3 + x^2 + x + 1$, R: 0  5. a) 73, 120  b) −37, 292  6. a) Yes  b) No  c) Yes

**15–4**  1. 5(multiplicity 2), −6(multiplicity 1)  2. −7(multiplicity 2), 3(multiplicity 1)  3. −2(multiplicity 3), 3(multiplicity 1), −3(multiplicity 1)  4. 4(multiplicity 2), 3(multiplicity 2)  5. 1(multiplicity 1), −1(multiplicity 1)  6. $x^3 - 6x^2 + 3x + 10$  7. $x^3 - (1 - 5i)x^2 - (2 + 5i)x - 10i$  8. $x^5 + 6x^4 + 12x^3 + 8x^2$  9. $x^4 + 2x^3 - 12x^2 + 14x - 5$  10. $6 + 2i$, $\sqrt{3} + i$  11. $24 - 5i$  12. $7 + 2i$, $3 - \sqrt{5}$  13. $x^4 - 6x^3 + 11x^2 - 10x + 2$  14. $x^3 - 2x^2 + 4x - 8$  15. $-i$, −2, 1

**15–5**  1. a) 1, −1, 3, −3  b) 1, −1, 2, −2  c) 1, −1, $\frac{1}{2}$, −$\frac{1}{2}$, 3, −3, $\frac{3}{2}$, −$\frac{3}{2}$  d) −3, $\frac{1}{2}$  e) $3 + \sqrt{10}$, $3 - \sqrt{10}$  2. a) 1, −1, 2, −2, 4, −4, 7, −7, 14, −14, 28, −28  b) 1, −1  c) 1, −1, 2, −2, 4, −4, 7, −7, 14, −14, 28, −28  d) All coefficients of P(x) are positive. When any positive number is substituted in P(x), we get a positive value, never 0.  e) −7  f) 2i, −2i  3. a) All coefficients of P(x) are positive  b) None  4. a) None  b) $\frac{-3 + i\sqrt{3}}{2}$, $\frac{-3 - i\sqrt{3}}{2}$  Since $x^2 + 3x + 3$ is quadratic, the quadratic formula can be used.

## Exercise Set 15–1, page 458

1. Yes, No, No  3. Yes, No, Yes, Yes  5. a) Yes  b) No
c) No  7. a) Yes  b) Yes  c) No  9. $x^3 + 6x^2 - x - 30 =$
$(x - 2)(x^2 + 8x + 15) + 0$  11. $x^3 + 6x^2 - x - 30 = (x - 3)$
$(x^2 + 9x + 26) + 48$  13. $x^3 - 8 = (x + 2)(x^2 - 2x + 4) +$
$(-16)$  15. $x^4 + 9x^2 + 20 = (x^2 + 4)(x^2 + 5) + 0$

## Exercise Set 15–2, page 461

1. 6  3. $-1$  5. $-12$  7. 0  9. $-5 - 24i$  11. $4 + 4i$
13. No  15. Yes  17. Yes  19. Yes, yes, yes, yes, no
21. a) Yes  b) $x^2 + 3x + 2$  c) $(x - 1)(x + 2)(x + 1)$
22. a) Yes  b) $x^2 + 3x - 4$)  c) $(x + 1)(x + 4)(x - 1)$

## Exercise Set 15–3, page 465

1. Q: $x^2 - 9x + 5$, R: $-7$  3. Q: $2x^3 + 13x^2 + 39x + 118$,
R: 342  5. Q: $x^2 - 4x + 8$, R: $-24$  7. Q: $x^2 - 3x + 9$,
R: 0  9. Q: $x^3 + x^2 + x + 1$, R: 0  11. Q: $2x^3 + x^2 +$
$\frac{7}{2}x + \frac{7}{4}$, R: $-\frac{1}{8}$  13. Q: $x^3 + 2x^2 + 4x + 8$, R: 0  15. Q:
$x^2 - ix + i + 1$, R: $4 + i$  17. $P(1) = 0$, $P(-2) = -60$,
$P(3) = 0$  19. $p(20) = 5,935,988$, $P(-3) = -772$  21. Yes,
no  23. No, no  25. Yes, yes, yes

## Exercise Set 15–4, page 470

1. $-3$(multiplicity 2), 1(multiplicity 1)  3. 3(multiplicity 2),
$-4$(multiplicity 3), 0(multiplicity 4)  5. 3(multiplicity 2),
2(multiplicity 2)  7. $x^3 - 6x^2 - x + 30$  9. $x^3 - 2x^2 + x$
$- 2$  11. $x^3 - 7x^2 + 17x - 15$  13. $x^3 - \sqrt{3}x^2 - 2x +$
$2\sqrt{3}$, No  15. $x^4 - 10x^3 + 25x^2$  17. $x^4 - 3x^3 - 7x^2 +$
$15x + 18$  19. $5 - i$, $2i$  21. $-3 - 4i$, $4 + \sqrt{5}$  23. $1 + i$
25. $x^3 - 4x^2 + 6x - 4$  27. $x^3 + 2x^2 + 9x + 18$  29. $x^4$
$- 6x^3 + 11x^2 - 10x + 2$  31. $x^4 + 4x^2 - 45$  33. i, 2, 3
35. $-2i$, 2, $-2$  37. $2 + i$, $2 - i$  39. $-1 + i\sqrt{3}$, $-1 - i\sqrt{3}$

## Exercise Set 15–5, page 474

1. $-3$, $\sqrt{2}$, $-\sqrt{2}$  3. 1, $-\frac{1}{5}$, $2i$, $-2i$  5. $-1$, $-2$, $3 + \sqrt{13}$,
$3 - \sqrt{13}$  7. 1, $-1$, $-3$  9. $-2$, $1 + i\sqrt{3}$, $1 - i\sqrt{3}$  11. $\frac{3}{4}$,
i, $-i$  13. 1, 2, $-2$, $2 + i$, $2 - i$  15. No rational
17. No rational  19. No rational

## CHAPTER 16

### Answers for TRY THIS

**16–1**  1. a) 1, 3, 9, $\frac{1}{3}$, $\frac{1}{9}$, $\frac{1}{27}$  2. Curve through $(-2, 9)$,
$(-1, 3)$, $(0, 1)$, $(1, \frac{1}{3})$, $(2, \frac{1}{9})$

**16–2**  1. Curve through $(\frac{1}{4}, -1)$, $(1, 0)$, $(4, 1)$, $(16, 2)$

2. 1  3. 0  4. 0  5. 1  6. $0 = \log_6 1$  7. $-3 = \log_{10} 0.001$
8. $0.25 = \log_{16} 2$  9. $T = \log_m p$  10. $2^5 = 32$  11. $10^3 =$
1000  12. $a^7 = Q$  13. $t^x = M$  14. 10,000  15. 3  16. 3
17. 4  18. 1  19. $-2$  20. $-2$  21. $\pi$  22. 97  23. M
24. 42

**16–3**  1. $\log_5 25 + \log_5 5$  2. $\log_b P + \log_b Q$  3. $\log_3$
(7.5)  4. $\log_a C \cdot A \cdot B \cdot I \cdot N$  5. $5 \log_7 4$  6. $\frac{1}{2} \log_a 5$
7. $\log_b P - \log_b Q$  8. $-\log_c 4$  9. $\frac{1}{2}[3 \log_a z - \log_a x$
$- \log_a y]$  10. $\log_a \frac{x^5 z^{1/4}}{y}$  11. 0.954  12. 0.1505

13. 0.1003  14. 0.176  15. 1.584

**16–4**  1. $2 \times 8 \approx 10^{0.3010} \times 10^{0.9031} \approx 10^{1.2041} \approx 16$
2. $\log_{10} (4 \times 2) = \log_{10} 4 + \log_{10} 2 \approx 0.6021 + 0.3010 \approx$
$0.9031$; $4 \times 2 \approx$ antilog$_{10}$ $0.9031 \approx 8$  3. $\log_{10} \frac{15}{3} =$
$\log_{10} 15 - \log_{10} 3 \approx 1.1761 - 0.4771 \approx 0.6990$; $\frac{15}{3} \approx$
antilog$_{10}$ $0.6990 \approx 5$  4. $\log_{10} \sqrt[3]{8} = \frac{1}{3} \log_{10} 8 \approx$
$\frac{1}{3}(0.9031) \approx 0.3010$; $\sqrt[3]{8} \approx$ antilog$_{10}$ $0.3010 \approx 2$
5. $\log_{10} 3^2 = 2 \log_{10} 3 \approx 2(0.4771) \approx 0.9542$; $3^2 \approx$ anti-
log$_{10}$ $0.9542 \approx 9$  6. 0.4969  7. 0.9996  8. 0.6021
9. 5.74  10. 1  11. 3.62  12. $0.4609 + 2$  13. 0.4609
$+ (-4)$  14. 4.8312  15. 5.9504  16. 1.6618  17. 8.7846
18. $8.8932 - 10$  19. $6.0453 - 10$  20. $7.8976 - 10$
21. 64,100  22. 64,100  23. 8560  24. 0.000425
25. 0.0159

**16–5**  1. 0.05340  2. 13.51

**16–6**  1. 3.6592  2. $8.3779 - 10$  3. 5956
4. 0.0002856

**16–7**  1. a) 2.9999  b) 3  2. 2

**16–8**  1. 7  2. 34 decibels  3. 60 decibels  4. 8.4
5. a) 68  b) 57.11

## Exercise Set 16–1, page 484

1. Curve through $(-2, \frac{1}{4})$, $(-1, \frac{1}{2})$, $(0, 1)$, $(1, 2)$, $(2, 4)$,
$(3, 9)$  3. Curve through $(-1, \frac{1}{5})$, $(0, 1)$, $(1, 5)$  5. Curve
through $(-1, 4)$, $(0, 1)$, $(1, \frac{1}{4})$  7. Curve through $(-2, 6.25)$,
$(-1, 2.5)$, $(0, 1)$, $(1, 0.4)$  9. Curve through $(-1, \frac{1}{4})$, $(0, \frac{1}{2})$,
$(1, 1)$, $(2, 2)$, $(3, 4)$  11. Curve through $(-3, \frac{1}{5})$, $(-2, 1)$,
$(-1, 5)$

## Exercise Set 16–2, page 489

1. Curve through $(\frac{1}{2}, -1)$, $(1, 0)$, $(4, 2)$, $(8, 3)$  3. Curve
through $(-\frac{1}{2}, -1)$, $(0, 0)$, $(1, 1)$, $(3, 2)$, $(7, 3)$  5. $3 =$
$\log_{10} 1000$  7. $-3 = \log_5 \frac{1}{125}$  9. $\frac{1}{3} = \log_8 2$  11. $0.3010$
$= \log_{10} 2$  13. $-b = \log_a c$  15. $3^t = 8$  17. $5^2 = 25$
19. $10^{-1} = 0.1$  21. $10^{0.845} = 7$  23. $b^N = M$  25. 9
27. 4  29. $\frac{1}{2}$  31. 2  33. 6  35. 2  37. $-1$  39. 0
41. 4  43. 9  45. $\sqrt{5}$  47. 56

## Exercise Set 16–3, page 494

1. $\log_2 32 + \log_2 8$  3. $\log_4 64 + \log_4 16$  5. $\log_c B +$
$\log_c x$  7. $\log_a (6 \cdot 70)$  9. $\log_c (k \cdot y)$  11. $3 \log_a x$
13. $\log_a 67 - \log_a 5$  15. $2 \log_a x + 3 \log_a y + \log_a z$
17. $\log_b x + 2 \log_b y - 3 \log_b z$  19. $\log_a \frac{\sqrt[3]{x^2} \sqrt{y}}{y}$
21. $\log_a \frac{2x^4}{y^3}$  23. $\log_a \frac{\sqrt{a}}{x}$  25. 0.602
27. 1.699  29. 1.778  31. $-0.088$  33. 1.954  35. $-0.602$

## Exercise Set 16–4, page 500

1. 0.3909  3. 0.7251  5. 0.5705  7. 0.0294  9. 7.34

11. 4.79   13. 5.72   15. 3.59   17. 3.90   19. 2.24
21. 2.5403   23. 1.7202   25. 2.9212   27. 3.5877
29. 7.1271 − 10   31. 9.8062 − 10   33. 9.2380 − 10
35. 5.6064 − 10   37. 2330   39. 18   41. 0.613
43. 0.00346   45. 25.2   47. 0.00973   49. 0.000613

### Exercise Set 16—5, page 502

1. 189.6   3. 272.4   5. 8.770   7. 3.846   9. 3.637
11. 0.2560

### Exercise Set 16—6, page 506

1. 1.6194   3. 0.4689   5. 2.8130   7. 9.1538 − 10
9. 7.6291 − 10   11. 9.2494 − 10   13. 2.7786   15. 43.15
17. 4.444   19. 1.082   21. 0.7185   23. 0.002587
25. 0.01589

### Exercise Set 16—7, page 508

1. 3   3. 3.3223   5. $\frac{5}{2}$   7. −3, −1   9. 1.4036
11. 2.7093   13. 3.6064   15. 10   17. $\frac{1}{3}$   19. 5   21. 1,
$10^9$   23. $\pm 2\sqrt{6}$

### Exercise Set 16—8, page 512

1. 11.9   3. 65 decibels   5. 140 decibels   7. 6.7   9. $10^5$
times $I_o$   11. a) 82   b) 67.99   13. 9 months   15. 4.2

# CHAPTER 17

## Answers for TRY THIS

**17—1**   1. a) 1, 3, 5   b) 67   2. 2, 4, 8, 16   3. −1, 4, −9,
16   4. Answers may vary, 2n   5. Answers may vary, n
6. Answers may vary, $n^3$   7. Answers may vary, $\frac{x^n}{n}$
8. Answers may vary, $2^{n-1}$

**17—2**   1. 2 + 4 + 8 + 16 + 25 + 36   2. −2 + 4 + (−6) + 8 +
(−10)   3. $x + x^2 + x^3 + x^4 + \ldots + x^n$   4. Answers may
vary, $\sum\limits_{k=1}^{5} 2k$   5. Answers may vary, $\sum\limits_{k=1}^{n} k^3$   6. Answers may
vary, $\sum\limits_{k=1}^{6} \frac{x^k}{k}$   7. Answers may vary, $\sum\limits_{k=2}^{n} k$

**17—3**   1. $a_1 = 2$, d = 1   2. $a_1 = 1$, d = 3   3. $a_1 = 19$, d =
−5   4. $a_1 = 10$, d = 10   5. $a_1 = 5$, d = $\frac{1}{4}$   6. $a_1 = 10$, d =
$-\frac{1}{2}$   7. 50   8. 75th   9. 17   10. 13   11. $a_1 = 7$, d = 12;
7, 19, 31, 43, . . .
**17—4**   1. 20,100   2. 225   3. 455   4. 120
**17—5**   1. 5   2. −3   3. $-\frac{1}{4}$   4. 256   5. −9375
6. $476.41
**17—6**   1. 11,718   2. $\frac{341}{256}$   3. 363
**17—7**   1. a) 1, $\frac{1}{2}$, $\frac{3}{4}$, $\frac{5}{8}$, $\frac{11}{16}$   b) $\frac{2}{3}$   2. No   3. No   4. Yes
5. $\frac{3}{2}$   6. $\frac{16}{5}$   7. $\frac{5}{11}$   8. $\frac{59}{11}$

### Exercise Set 17—1, page 521

1. 4, 7, 10, 13; 31; 46   3. $\frac{1}{2}$, $\frac{2}{3}$, $\frac{3}{4}$, $\frac{4}{5}$; $\frac{10}{11}$; $\frac{15}{16}$   5. 0, 1, 4,
9; 81; 196   7. 2, $2\frac{1}{2}$, $3\frac{1}{3}$, $4\frac{1}{4}$; $10\frac{1}{10}$; $15\frac{1}{15}$   9. 1, $-\frac{1}{2}$, $\frac{1}{4}$,
$-\frac{1}{8}$; $-\frac{1}{512}$; 16,384   11. Answers may vary; 2n − 1
13. Answers may vary, $\frac{n+1}{n+2}$   15. Answers may vary, $3^{n/2}$
17. Answers may vary, −(3n − 2)

### Exercise Set 17—2, page 523

1. $\frac{1}{2} + \frac{1}{4} + \frac{1}{6} + \frac{1}{8} + \frac{1}{10}$   3. $2^0 + 2^1 + 2^2 + 2^3 + 2^4 + 2^5$
5. log 7 + log 8 + log 9 + log 10   7. $1^3 + 2^3 + 3^3 + 4^3 + 5^3$
9. Answers may vary, $\sum\limits_{k=1}^{6} \frac{k}{k+1}$   11. Answers may vary,
$\sum\limits_{k=1}^{6} (-1)^k 2^k$   13. Answers may vary, $\sum\limits_{k=1}^{6} 2^{k-1}$   15. Answers
may vary, $\sum\limits_{k=1}^{7} -k$   17. Answers may vary, $\sum\limits_{k=4}^{n} k$   19. Answers may vary, $\sum\limits_{k=2}^{n} (-1)^k k^2$

### Exercise Set 17—3, page 526

1. $a_1 = 2$, d = 5   3. $a_1 = 7$, d = −4   5. $a_1 = \frac{3}{2}$, d = $\frac{3}{4}$
7. 46   9. −41   11. 27th   13. 102 nd   15. 101   17. 5
19. 28   21. 8, 5, 2, −1, −4

### Exercise Set 17—4, page 530

1. 670   3. 375   5. 2550   7. 990   9. 432   11. 855
13. 465

### Exercise Set 17—5, page 533

1. 2   3. $-\frac{1}{3}$   5. −1   7. $\frac{1}{x}$   9. 243   11. 1250
13. $933.12   15. 678.4, 590.208, 513.48096, 446.72843

### Exercise Set 17—6, page 535

1. 762   3. 1275   3. $\frac{547}{18}$   5. $\frac{1-x^8}{1-x}$   9. $\frac{63}{32}$   11. 21,844

### Exercise Set 17—7, page 539

1. 2, No   3. $\frac{1}{3}$, Yes   5. 0.1, Yes   7. $-\frac{1}{5}$, Yes   9. 8
11. $\frac{125}{9}$   13. 2   15. $\frac{160}{9}$   17. $\frac{7}{9}$   19. $\frac{7}{33}$   21. $\frac{170}{33}$

# CHAPTER 18

## Answers for TRY THIS

**18—1**   1. $(-\frac{63}{29}, -\frac{114}{29})$   2. (−2, −5)   3. (1, 2)
4. (2, −1)
**18—2**   1. (−1, 2, 3)
**18—3**   1. −5   2. −5   3. $\frac{79}{2}$   4. −9   5. (3, −1)
6. $(\frac{28}{11}, -\frac{10}{11})$
**18—4**   1. −6   2. 93   3. 4   4. (1, 3, −2)
**18—5**   1. 3 X 2   2. 2 X 2   3. 3 X 3   4. 1 X 2   5. 2 X 1

6. $1 \times 1$  7. a) $\begin{bmatrix} -2 & -6 \\ 13 & 0 \end{bmatrix}$  b) $\begin{bmatrix} -2 & -6 \\ 13 & 0 \end{bmatrix}$  8. a) $\begin{bmatrix} 4 & -3 \\ 5 & 8 \end{bmatrix}$

b) $\begin{bmatrix} 4 & -3 \\ 5 & 8 \end{bmatrix}$  9. $\begin{bmatrix} -1 & 4 & -7 \\ -2 & -4 & 8 \end{bmatrix}$  10. $\begin{bmatrix} -6 & 6 \\ 1 & -4 \\ -7 & 5 \end{bmatrix}$

11. $\begin{bmatrix} -2 & 1 & -5 \\ -6 & -4 & 3 \end{bmatrix}$  12. a) $\begin{bmatrix} -6 & 6 \\ 1 & -4 \\ -7 & 5 \end{bmatrix}$  b) $\begin{bmatrix} 6 & -6 \\ -1 & 4 \\ 7 & -5 \end{bmatrix}$

**18-6**  1. $\begin{bmatrix} 5 & -10 & 5x \\ 20 & 5y & 5 \\ 0 & -25 & 5x^2 \end{bmatrix}$  2. $\begin{bmatrix} t & -t & 4t & tx \\ ty & 3t & -2t & ty \\ t & 4t & -5t & t^2 \end{bmatrix}$  3. $[-13]$

4. $[-2x + y]$  5. $\begin{bmatrix} 12 \\ 13 \\ 5 \\ 16 \end{bmatrix}$  6. $\begin{bmatrix} 12 & 6 \\ 13 & 19 \\ 5 & -17 \\ 16 & -10 \end{bmatrix}$

## Exercise Set 18-1, page 546
1. $(\frac{3}{2}, \frac{5}{2})$  3. $(\frac{1}{2}, \frac{3}{2})$  5. $(3, -2)$  7. $(-3, 0)$

## Exercise Set 18-2, page 548
1. $(-1, 2, -2)$  3. $(\frac{3}{2}, -4, 3)$  5. $(1, -3, 3)$

## Exercise Set 18-3, page 551
1. 3  3. 36  5. −10.3  7. 0  9. $(-\frac{25}{2}, -\frac{11}{2})$  11. $(2, 0)$
13. $(-4, -5)$  15. $(0.9232208, -0.8334688)$

## Exercise Set 18-4, page 554
1. −10  3. −3  5. 93  7. $(\frac{3}{2}, \frac{13}{14}, \frac{33}{14})$  9. $(2, -1, 4)$
11. $(1, 2, 3)$

## Exercise Set 18-5, page 558
1. $2 \times 2$  3. $2 \times 3$  5. $\begin{bmatrix} -2 & -3 \\ 6 & -4 \end{bmatrix}$  7. $\begin{bmatrix} 4 & 4 \\ 0 & 0 \end{bmatrix}$
9. $\begin{bmatrix} -5 & 0 & 11 \\ 3 & 2 & 0 \end{bmatrix}$  11. $\begin{bmatrix} 0 & -2 & 3 \\ 1 & -1 & 2 \\ 1 & -5 & 5 \end{bmatrix}$  13. $\begin{bmatrix} 1 & 2 \\ 4 & -3 \end{bmatrix}$
15. $\begin{bmatrix} 1 & -1 \\ -1 & 1 \end{bmatrix}$  17. $\begin{bmatrix} 4 & 7 \\ 2 & -2 \end{bmatrix}$  19. $\begin{bmatrix} 2 & 2 \\ -2 & -2 \end{bmatrix}$  21. $\begin{bmatrix} 3 & -7 & 7 \\ 0 & 0 & 3 \\ 0 & 0 & 6 \end{bmatrix}$
23. $\begin{bmatrix} -1 & -6 & 3 \\ -13 & 2 & 2 \end{bmatrix}$  25. $\begin{bmatrix} -1 & -1 \\ -1 & -1 \end{bmatrix}$  27. $\begin{bmatrix} -1 & -3 \\ -2 & -6 \end{bmatrix}$
29. $\begin{bmatrix} 0 & 2 \\ 2 & 0 \end{bmatrix}$  31. $\begin{bmatrix} -3 & 7 & -7 \\ 0 & 0 & -3 \\ 0 & 0 & -6 \end{bmatrix}$  33. $\begin{bmatrix} 1 & 6 & -3 \\ 13 & -2 & -2 \end{bmatrix}$
35. $\begin{bmatrix} -3 & -3 \\ 1 & 1 \end{bmatrix}$

## Exercise Set 18-6, page 561
1. $\begin{bmatrix} -2 & -4 \\ -8 & -6 \end{bmatrix}$  3. $\begin{bmatrix} 14 & -14 \\ -14 & 14 \end{bmatrix}$  5. $\begin{bmatrix} t & 3t \\ 2t & 6t \end{bmatrix}$  7. $\begin{bmatrix} 2 & -9 & -6 \\ 3 & -3 & -4 \\ -2 & 2 & -1 \end{bmatrix}$
9. $[-22]$  11. $[-36]$  13. $\begin{bmatrix} 1 & 3 \\ -6 & 17 \end{bmatrix}$  15. $\begin{bmatrix} 0 & 0 \\ 0 & 0 \end{bmatrix}$
17. $[-14 \quad -11 \quad -3]$  19. $[-13 \quad -1 \quad -4]$  21. $\begin{bmatrix} 3 & 3 \\ -1 & -1 \end{bmatrix}$
23. $\begin{bmatrix} -5 & 4 & 3 \\ 5 & -9 & 4 \\ 7 & -18 & 17 \end{bmatrix}$  25. $\begin{bmatrix} -7 \\ -18 \end{bmatrix}$  27. Not possible

# CHAPTER 19

## Answers for TRY THIS
**19-1**  1. 6, 27  2. 40  3. 120  4. 120  5. 6  6. 120
7. 720  8. 24  9. 720  10. 40,320  11. 362,880  12. 24
13. 18!  14. $10 \cdot 9!$  15. $20 \cdot 19!$  16. $11 \cdot 10 \cdot 9 \cdot 8!$
17. $17 \cdot 16 \cdot 15 \cdot 14 \cdot 13 \cdot 12!$

**19-2**  1. 210  2. 5040  3. 56  4. 55,440  5. 95,040
6. 151,200  7. 2880  8. $26^5$  9. a) 2652  b) 2704

**19-3**  1. a) 1  b) 4  c) 6  d) 4  e) 1  2. 45  3. 45  4. 21
5. 21  6. 792  7. 6160  8. $\binom{9}{0} + \binom{9}{1} + \binom{9}{2} + \ldots + \binom{9}{9}$ or 512

**19-4**  1. $-1512x^5$  2. $8064y^{10}$  3. $x^{10} - 5x^8 + 10x^6 - 10x^4 + 5x^2 - 1$  4. $16x^4 + 32\frac{x^3}{y} + 24\frac{x^2}{y^2} + 8\frac{x}{y^3} + \frac{1}{y^4}$
5. $2^{50}$  6. $2^9$ or 512

**19-5**  1. $\frac{1}{2}$  2. a) $\frac{1}{13}$  b) $\frac{1}{4}$  c) $\frac{1}{2}$  d) $\frac{2}{13}$  3. $\frac{6}{11}$
4. $\frac{11}{850}$  5. $\frac{15}{91}$  6. $\frac{6}{13}$  7. $\frac{1}{6}$

## Exercise Set 19-1, page 570
1. 24, 256  3. 720  5. 336  7. 720  9. 24  11. 5040
13. 720  15. 40,320  17. 120  19. 1  21. $9 \cdot 8!$  23. $a \cdot (a - 1)!$  25. $27 \cdot 26 \cdot 25 \cdot 24 \cdot 23 \cdot 22!$

## Exercise Set 19-2, page 573
1. 24  3. 604,800  5. 380  7. 336  9. 120, 60  11. 360
13. 1296, 360  15. 11,880  17. 648, 180  19. 648, 180

## Exercise Set 19-3, page 576
1. 126  3. 1225  5. 495  7. $\frac{n(n - 1)(n - 2)}{6}$  9. 8855
11. 72  13. 28, 56  15. 1200  17. $\binom{58}{6} \cdot \binom{42}{4}$
19. 4512

## Exercise Set 19-4, page 581
1. $15a^4b^2$  3. $-745{,}472a^3$  5. $1120x^{12}y^2$
7. $-1{,}959{,}552u^5v^{10}$  9. $m^5 + 5m^4n + 10m^3n^2 + 10m^2n^3 + 5mn^4 + n^5$  11. $x^{10} - 15x^8y + 90x^6y^2 - 270x^4y^3 + 405x^2y^4 - 243y^5$  13. $x^{-8} + 4x^{-4} + 6 + 4x^4 + x^8$  15. $\binom{n}{0} - \binom{n}{1} + \binom{n}{2} - \binom{n}{3} + \ldots + \binom{n}{n}(-1)^n$  17. $140\sqrt{2}$  19. $-7 - 4i\sqrt{2}$  21. 128  23. $2^{26}$

## Exercise Set 19-5, page 586
1. $\frac{1}{4}$  3. $\frac{1}{13}$  5. $\frac{1}{2}$  7. $\frac{2}{13}$  9. $\frac{2}{7}$  11. 0  13. $\frac{11}{4165}$
15. $\frac{60}{143}$  17. $\frac{5}{36}$  19. $\frac{1}{36}$  21. $\frac{245}{1938}$